INSTRUCTOR'S MANAGEMENT SYSTEM FOR

PHYSICS

SIXTH EDITION

PHYSICS

SIXTH EDITION

Paul E. Tippens

Paul Zitzewitz

Graig Kramer

Glencoe
McGraw-Hill

New York, New York   Columbus, Ohio   Woodland Hills, California   Peoria, Illinois

Cover photo: Richard Magna/Fundamental Photographs

Physics, Sixth Edition   ISBN 0-07-820340-6
Activities Manual   ISBN 0-07-820341-4
Instructor's Management System   ISBN 0-07-820342-2

Glencoe/McGraw-Hill

A Division of The **McGraw·Hill** *Companies*

Instructor's Management System for Physics, Sixth Edition

Send all inquiries to:
Glencoe/McGraw-Hill
8787 Orion Place
Columbus, OH 43240

ISBN 0-07-820342-2

1 2 3 4 5 6 7 8 9   055   06 05 04 03 02 01 00

Contents

Preface

The *Instructor's Management System for Physics,* Sixth Edition, contains five important resources. Unit A is the Solutions Manual; all answers to textbook problems are given in the Solutions Manual. Unit B contains Instructor Notes for the Laboratory Experiments in the Activities Manual. Unit C provides a technical overview of the Internet. Unit D provides information about Tech Prep, and Unit E contains the transparency masters.

Unit A provides worked-out solutions to the problems that appear at the end of the text chapters. For *Physics,* Sixth Edition, all chapter-ending problems were revised or reorganized, or are new to this edition. Chapter-ending problems are arranged by chapter section; these are followed by Challenge Problems and Critical Thinking Questions. The problems grouped according to chapter sections are usually one-step problems that basically involve substitution into formulas. The Challenge Problems can be assigned whenever instructors expect students to do more than basic numerical substitution into given formulas. Critical Thinking Questions may be assigned at the instructor's discretion. This three-layered approach allows instructors to assign problems based on the abilities of their students. All solutions also appear on the CD-ROM included with this book. Care has been taken to include all necessary steps to allow the instructor to see at a glance which problems are most appropriate for assignment. The answers are boxed for quick identification, and horizontal lines separate the problems from one another. In general, answers assume three significant digits for all input information.

Answers to odd-numbered problems are also given in the textbook. Even-numbered answers can be obtained only from this book. The same broad coverage is provided for both even and odd problems, allowing flexibility in making assignments. An asterisk identifies problems that may involve more than a single concept or that may be of moderate difficulty.

The author strongly favors providing the students with answers to all problems—not just the odd-numbered problems. Some students may work for hours searching for an answer, not knowing that they have arrived at the answer all along. Others may arrive at a quick solution, only to find out much later that the problem was more complicated than they had originally thought. Students need immediate reinforcement in their learning. Once the students attempted the problems, some instructors who used the last edition found it useful to copy portions of the Solutions Manual as an instructional aid. We have made life a little easier for instructors using *Physics,* Sixth Edition. The solutions are also included on the CD-ROM. You can use your computer with individual students to discuss any given problem. If you wish, you can also transfer the chapter-by-chapter Word files to your personal computer or laptop. In this way you can even use an in-class computer projection system to discuss the solution of any given text problem. All answers have been triple-checked for accuracy.

Unit B provides Instructor Notes for the laboratory experiments in the companion *Activities Manual for Physics,* Sixth Edition. The laboratory activities present a learner-centered, classroom-tested, flexible laboratory program that emphasizes the processes

of science, the concepts of physics, and the attitudinal objectives of students. Students experience the principles of physics in action using the laboratory as the setting. They also work in a cooperative learning situation as a lab team to collect data and discuss observations for analysis.

The skills of communicating experimental results to others through a laboratory report are developed as the student uses the report sheets that accompany each experiment. All experiments give definite results if the student uses reasonable care. On the other hand, the student is not expected to achieve precise solutions to difficult laboratory problems. Simple apparatus required for experiments is common to nearly all physics laboratories.

The notes for the instructor included in Unit B contain science process skills, alternative materials, teaching suggestions, troubleshooting, and sample observations and data. Suggestions for modifying apparatus to suit individual laboratory situations are provided in many investigations. Complete answers and sample data are given for determining the degree of precision to expect in student analysis of data. Sample graphs are provided for all data that students are required to plot.

Unit C provides suggestions for integrating the Internet into the classroom. *Physics*, Sixth Edition, includes a hundred Internet sites that are designed to enhance student learning and classroom discussion. Exactly how this is accomplished is up to the instructor. For example, for a gifted student, the Internet can be used as a research medium for exploring specific areas of physics.

Tech Prep is the subject of Unit D. It provides an overview of the goals of Tech Prep for the student who is following this type of program. It also provides a general introduction to Tech Prep, along with competencies for physics and suggested readings.

Unit E contains transparency masters that the instructor may use in the classroom. These transparencies are intended to be used with selected sections of the text. The text section references are listed on the opening pages of Unit E and are also printed at the foot of each transparency master.

The CD-ROM is a new feature to the *Instructor's Management System*. It contains Unit A—all textbook solutions. It also includes chapter-by-chapter PowerPoint presentations and a Windows-based test bank.

The author welcomes your comments, corrections, and suggestions for improvement of the sixth edition of *Physics* and the supporting materials.

Paul E. Tippens

Solutions Manual

UNIT

A

Chapter 2. Technical Mathematics

Signed Numbers

2-1. +7	2-8. -17	2-15. +2	2-22. +12
2-2. +4	2-9. +6	2-16. -2	2-23. +8
2-3. +2	2-10. -32	2-17. -4	2-24. -4
2-4. -2	2-11. -36	2-18. -3	2-25. 0
2-5. -10	2-12. +24	2-19. +2	2-26. +220
2-6. -33	2-13. 48	2-20. -4	2-27. +32
2-7. -5	2-14. +144	2-21. -3	2-28. -32

2-29. (a) -6^0C; (b) -17^0C; (c) 36^0C

2-30. $\Delta L = 2\ mm[(-30^0C) - (-5^0C)] = 2\ mm(-25) = -50\ mm$; Decrease in length.

Algebra Review

2-31. $x = (2) + (-3) + (-2) = -3$; $x = -3$

2-32. $x = (2) - (-3) - (-2) = +7$; $x = +7$

2-33. $x = (-3\_ + (-2\_ - (+2) = -7$; $x = -7$

2-34. $x = -3[(2) - (-2)] = -3(2 + 2) = -12$; $x = -12$

2-35. $x = \dfrac{b-c}{a} = \dfrac{-3-(-2)}{2} = \dfrac{-3+2}{2} = -\dfrac{1}{2}$; $x = -\dfrac{1}{2}$

2-36. $x = \dfrac{2+(-3)}{-2} = \dfrac{2-3}{-2}$; $x = +\dfrac{1}{2}$

2-37. $x = (-3)^2 - (-2)^2 = 9 - 4 = 5$; $x = 5$

2-38. $x = \dfrac{-b}{ac} = \dfrac{-(-3)}{(2)(-2)} = \dfrac{3}{-4}$; $x = -\dfrac{3}{4}$

2-39. $x = \dfrac{2}{(-3)(-2)}[2-(-2)] = \dfrac{1}{3}(4)$; $x = \dfrac{4}{3}$

2-40. $x = (2)^2 + (-3)^2 + (-2)^2$; $x = 17$

2-41. $x = \sqrt{a^2 + b^2 + c^2} = \sqrt{17}$

2-42. $x = (2)(-3)[(-2) - (+2)]^2$; $x -6(-4)^2 = -96$

2-43. Solve for x: $2ax - b = c$; $2ax = b + c$; $x = \dfrac{b+c}{2a} = \dfrac{-3-2}{2(2)}$; $x = -\dfrac{5}{4}$

2-44. $ax + bx = 4c$; $(a+b)x = 4c$; $x = \dfrac{4c}{a+b} = \dfrac{4(-2)}{2+(-3)}$; $x = +8$

2-45. $3ax = \dfrac{2ab}{c}$; $3cx = 2b$; $x = \dfrac{2b}{3c} = \dfrac{2(-3)}{3(-2)}$; $x = +1$

2-46. $\dfrac{4ac}{b} = \dfrac{2x}{b} - 16$; $4ac = 2x - 16b$; $x = \dfrac{4ac+16b}{2} = \dfrac{4(2)(-2)+16(-3)}{2}$; $x = -32$

2-47. $5m - 16 = 3m - 4$
$5m - 3m = -4 + 16$
$2m = 12$; $m = 6$

2-48. $3p = 7p - 16$
$3p - 7p = -16$
$-4p = -16$; $p = +4$

2-49. $4m = 2(m-4)$
$4m = 2m - 8$
$2m = -8$; $m = -4$

2-50. $3(m-6) = 6$
$3m - 18 = 6$
$3m = 24$; $m = +8$

2-51. $\dfrac{x}{3} = (4)(3) = 12$; $x = 36$

2-52. $\dfrac{p}{3} = \dfrac{2}{6} = \dfrac{1}{3}$; $p = 1$

2-53. $\dfrac{96}{x} = 48$; $x = \dfrac{96}{48} = 2$

2-54. $14 = 2(b-7)$; $14 = 2b - 14$; $b = 14$

2-55. $R^2 = (4)^2 + (3)^2 = 16 + 9$
$R^2 = \sqrt{25}$ $R = 5$

2-56. $\dfrac{1}{2} = \dfrac{1}{p} + \dfrac{1}{6}$; $\dfrac{6p}{2} = \dfrac{6p}{p} + \dfrac{6p}{6}$
$3p = 6 + p$; $p = 3$

2-57. $V = IR$; $R = \dfrac{V}{I}$

2-58. $PV = nRT$; $T = \dfrac{PV}{nR}$

2-59. $F = ma$; $a = \dfrac{F}{m}$

2-60. $s = vt + d$; $d = s - vt$

2-61. $F = \dfrac{mv^2}{R}$; $FR = mv^2$; $R = \dfrac{mv^2}{F}$

2-62. $s = \frac{1}{2}at^2$; $2s = at^2$; $a = \dfrac{2s}{t^2}$

2-63. $2as = v_f^2 - v_0^2$; $a = \dfrac{v_f^2 - v_0^2}{2s}$

2-64. $C = \dfrac{Q^2}{2V}$; $V = \dfrac{Q^2}{2C}$

2-65. $\dfrac{1}{R_1} + \dfrac{1}{R_2} = \dfrac{1}{R}$; $R_2R + R_1R = R_1R_2$;
$(R_1 + R_2)R = R_1R_2$; $R = \dfrac{R_1R_2}{R_1 + R_2}$

2-66. $mv = Ft$; $\dfrac{mv}{F} = t$
$t = \dfrac{mv}{F}$

2-67. $mv_2 - mv_1 = Ft$; $mv_2 = Ft + mv_1$
$v_2 = \dfrac{Ft + mv_1}{m}$

2-68. $\dfrac{PV_1}{T_1} = \dfrac{P_2V_2}{T_2}$; $PV_1T_2 = P_2V_2T_1$
$T_2 = \dfrac{P_2V_2T_1}{PV_1}$

2-69. $v = v_0 + at$; $v - v_0 = at$
$a = \dfrac{v - v_0}{t}$

2-70. $c^2 = a^2 + b^2$; $b^2 = c^2 - a^2$
$b = \sqrt{c^2 - a^2}$

Exponents and Radicals

2-71. 2^{12}	2-72. $3^5 2^3$	2-73. x^{10}
2-74. x^5	2-75. $1/a$	2-76. a/b^2
2-77. $1/2^2$	2-78. a^2/b^2	2-79. $2x^5$
2-80. $1/a^2 b^2$	2-81. m^6	2-82. c^4/n^6
2-83. 64×10^6	2-84. $(1/36) \times 10^4$	2-85. 4
2-86. 3	2-87. x^3	2-88. a^2b^3
2-89. 2×10^2	2-90. 2×10^{-9}	2-91. $2a^2$
2-92. $x + 2$		

Scientific Notation

2-93. 4.00×10^4	2-94. 6.70×10^1	2-95. 4.80×10^2
2-96. 4.97×10^5	2-97. 2.10×10^{-3}	2-98. 7.89×10^{-1}
2-99. 8.70×10^{-2}	2-100. 9.67×10^{-4}	2-101. 4,000,000

2-102. 4670	2-103. 37.0	2-104. 140,000
2-105. 0.0367	2-106. 0.400	2-107. 0.006
2-108. 0.0000417	2-109. 8.00×10^6	2-110. 7.40×10^4
2-111. 8.00×10^2	2-112. 1.80×10^{-8}	2-113. 2.68×10^9
2-114. 7.40×10^{-3}	2-115. 1.60×10^{-5}	2-116. 2.70×10^{19}
2-117. 1.80×10^{-3}	2-118. 2.40×10^1	2-119. 2.00×10^6
2-120. 2.00×10^{-3}	2-121. 2.00×10^{-9}	2-122. 5.71×10^{-1}
2-123. 2.30×10^5	2-124. 6.40×10^2	2-125. 2.40×10^3
2-126. 5.60×10^{-5}	2-127. -6.90×10^{-2}	2-128. -3.30×10^{-3}
2-129. 6.00×10^{-4}	2-130. 6.40×10^6	2-131. -8.00×10^6
2-132. -4.00×10^{-2}		

Graphs

2-133. Graph of speed vs. time: When t = 4.5 s, v = 144 ft/s; When v = 100 m/s, t = 3.1 s.

2-134. Graph of advance of screw vs. turns: When screw advances 2.75 in., N = 88 turns.

2-135. Graph of wavelength vs. frequency: 350 kHz → 857 m; 800 kHz → 375 m.

2-136. Electric Power vs. Electric Current: 3.20 A → 10.4 W; 8.0 A → 64.8 W.

Geometry

2-137. 90^0, 180^0, 270^0, and 45^0

2-138.

A = 50^0 Rule 2;   B = 40^0 Rule 2.

2-139. A = 17^0, B = 35^0, C = 38^0,

B = 70^0,   C = 42^0 Rule 2

2-140. A = 50^0 Rule 3;   B = 130^0;

Right Triangle Trigonometry

2-141. 0.921	2-147. 19.3	2-153. 684	2-159. 54.2^0	2-165. 36.9^0
2-142. 0.669	2-148. 143	2-154. 346	2-160. 6.37^0	2-166. 76.0^0
2-143. 1.66	2-149. 267	2-155. 803	2-161. 50.2^0	2-167. 31.2^0
2-144. 0.559	2-150. 32.4	2-156. 266	2-162. 27.1^0	
2-145. 0.875	2-151. 235	2-157. 2191	2-163. 76.8^0	
2-146. 0.268	2-152. 2425	2-158. 1620	2-164. 6.37^0	

Solve triangles for unknown sides and angles

2-168. $\tan \theta = 18/35$, $\theta = 35.8^0$; $R = \sqrt{18^2 + 25^2}$ $R = 30.8$ ft

2-169. $\tan \phi = 600/400$, $\phi = 56.3^0$; $R = \sqrt{40^2 + 80^2}$ $R = 721$ m.

2-170. $y = 650 \sin 21^0 = 233$ m; $x = 650 \cos 21^0 = 607$ m.

2-171. $\sin \phi = 200/500$, $\phi = 23.6^0$; $500^2 = x^2 + 200^2$, $x = 458$ km.

2-172. $\sin \theta = 210/400$, $\theta = 31.7^0$. $500^2 = m^2 + 200^2$, $m = 340$ m.

2-173. $x = 260 \cos 51^0 = 164$ in.; $y = 260 \sin 51^0 = 202$ in.

2-174. $\tan \theta = 40/80$, $\theta = 26.6^0$; $R = \sqrt{40^2 + 80^2}$ $R = 89.4$ lb

2-175. $\phi = 180^0 - 120^0 = 60^0$; $y = 300 \sin 60^0 = 260$ m; $x = 300 \cos 60^0 = 150$ m, left

PROBLEMS

2-176. 30.21 – 0.59 in. = 29.62 in.

2-177. $\Delta T = T_f - T_0 = -15^0C - (29^0C)$; $\Delta T = -44\ C^0$.

2-178. $T_f - T_0 = -34^0C$; $T_f - 20^0C = -34^0C$; $T_f = -14^0C$

2-179. Six pieces @ 4.75 in. = 6(4.75 in.) = 28.5 in.; Five cuts @ 1/16 = 5/16 = 0.3125 in.

Original length = 28.5 in. + 0.3125 in. = 28.8 in.

2-180. $V = \pi r^2 h$; Solve for h: $h = \dfrac{V}{\pi r^2}$

2-181. $F = \dfrac{Gm_1m_2}{R^2} = \dfrac{(6.67 \times 10^{-11})(4 \times 10^{-8})(3 \times 10^{-7})}{(4 \times 10^{-2})^2}$; $F = 5.00 \times 10^{-22}$

2-182. Solve for x and evaluate: a = 2, b = -2, c = 3, and d = -1

$xb + cd = a(x + 2) \rightarrow xb + cd = ax + 2a \rightarrow xb - ax = 2a - cd \rightarrow (b - a)x = 2a - cd$

$x = \dfrac{2a - cd}{b - a}$; $x = \dfrac{2a - cd}{b - a} = \dfrac{2(2) - (3)(-1)}{(-2) - (2)} = \dfrac{7}{-4}$; $x = -\dfrac{7}{4}$

2-183. $c^2 = b^2 + a^2$ $b = \sqrt{c^2 - a^2}$; $b = \sqrt{50^2 + 20^2} = 53.9$ $b = 53.9$

2-184. $F = \dfrac{Gm_1m_2}{R^2} = \dfrac{(6.67 \times 10^{-11})(4 \times 10^{-8})(3 \times 10^{-7})}{(4 \times 10^{-2})^2}$; $F = 5.00 \times 10^{-22}$

2-185. $L = L_0 + \alpha L_0(t - t_0)$; $L = 21.41$ cm $+ (2 \times 10^{-3}/C^0)(21.41$ cm $)(100^0C - 20^0C)$; $L = 24.84$ cm.

2-186. Construct graph of $y = 2x$ and verify that $x = 3.5$ when $y = 7$ (from the graph).

2-187. (a) $A + 60^0 = 90^0$; $A = 30^0$. $A + C = 90^0$. $C = 60^0$. $B = 60^0$ by rule 2.

(b) $D + 30^0 = 90^0$; $D = 60^0$. $A = 60^0$ (alt. int. angles); $B = 30^0$; $C = 120^0$.

4

Critical Thinking Problems

2-188. A = (-8) - (-4) = -4;   B = (-6) + (14) = 8;   C = A - B = (-4) - (8) = -12;   C = -12 cm.

B - A = (8) - (-4) = +12. There is a difference of <u>24 cm</u> between B - A and A - B.

2-189. $T = 2\pi\sqrt{\dfrac{L}{g}}$ → $T^2 = 4\pi^2\dfrac{L}{g}$ → $L = \dfrac{gT^2}{4\pi^2}$

Let L = 4L₀; Since $\sqrt{4} = 2$, the period will be doubled when the length is quadrupled.

Let $g_m = g_e/6$. Then, T would be changed by a factor of $\sqrt{\dfrac{1}{1/6}} = \sqrt{6} = 2.45$

Thus, the period T on the moon would be 2(2.45) or 4.90 s.

2-190. (a) Area = LW = $(3.45 \times 10^{-4}$ m$)(9.77 \times 10^{-5}$ m$)$;   Area = 3.37×10^{-8} m².

Perimeter (P) = 2L + 2W = 2(L + W); P = $2(3.45 \times 10^{-4} + 9.77 \times 10^{-5}) = 8.85 \times 10^{-4}$ m.

(b) L = L₀/2 and W = 2W₀: A = (L₀/2)(2W₀) = L₀W₀; No change in area.

P - P₀ = [2(L₀/2) + 2(2W₀)] - [2L₀ + 2W₀] = 2W₀ - L₀

$\Delta P = 2(9.77 \times 10^{-5}) - 3.45 \times 10^{-4}$ $\Delta P = -1.50 \times 10^{-4}$ m.

The area doesn't change, but the perimeter decreases by 0.150 mm.

2-191. Graph shows when T = 420 K, P = 560 lb/in.²; when T = 600 K, P = 798 lb/in.²

2-192. Graph shows when V = 26 V, I = 377 mA; when V = 48 V, I = 696 mA.

Chapter 3. Technical Measurement and Vectors

Unit Conversions

3-1. A soccer field is 100 m long and 60 m across. What are the length and width of the field in feet?

$(100 \text{ m})\left(\dfrac{100 \text{ cm}}{1 \text{ m}}\right)\left(\dfrac{1 \text{ in.}}{2.54 \text{ cm}}\right)\left(\dfrac{1 \text{ ft}}{12 \text{ in.}}\right) = 328 \text{ ft}$ L = 328 ft

$(60 \text{ m})\left(\dfrac{100 \text{ cm}}{1 \text{ m}}\right)\left(\dfrac{1 \text{ in.}}{2.54 \text{ cm}}\right)\left(\dfrac{1 \text{ ft}}{12 \text{ in.}}\right) = 197 \text{ ft}$ W = 197 ft

3-2. A wrench has a handle 8 in. long. What is the length of the handle in centimeters?

$(8 \text{ in.})\left(\dfrac{2.54 \text{ cm}}{1 \text{ in.}}\right) = 20.3 \text{ cm}$ L = 20.3 cm

3-3. A 19-in. computer monitor has a viewable area that measures 18 in. diagonally. Express this distance in meters.

$(18 \text{ in.})\left(\dfrac{2.54 \text{ cm}}{1 \text{ in.}}\right)\left(\dfrac{1 \text{ m}}{100 \text{ cm}}\right) = 0.457 \text{ m}$ L = 0.457 m

3-4. The length of a notebook is 234.5 mm and the width is 158.4 mm. Express the surface area in square meters.

$Area = (234.5 \text{ mm})(158.4 \text{ mm})\left(\dfrac{1 \text{ m}}{1000 \text{ mm}}\right)\left(\dfrac{1 \text{ m}}{1000 \text{ mm}}\right) = 0.037$ A = 0.0371 m²

3-5. A cube has 5 in. on a side. What is the volume of the cube in SI units and in fundamental USCS units?

$V = (5 \text{ in.})^3 = (125 \text{ in.}^3)\left(\dfrac{2.54 \text{ cm}}{1 \text{ in.}}\right)^3\left(\dfrac{1 \text{ m}}{100 \text{ cm}}\right)^3 = 0.00205 \text{ m}^3$ V = 0.00205 m³

$V = (125 \text{ in.}^3)\left(\dfrac{1 \text{ ft}}{12 \text{ in.}}\right)^3 = 0.0723 \text{ ft}^3$ V = 0.0723 ft³

3-6. The speed limit on an interstate highway is posted at 75 mi/h. (a) What is this speed in kilometers per hour? (b) In feet per second?

(a) $75 \dfrac{\text{mi}}{\text{h}} \left(\dfrac{1.609 \text{ km}}{1 \text{ mi}} \right) = \boxed{121 \text{ km/h}}$

(b) $75 \dfrac{\text{mi}}{\text{h}} \left(\dfrac{1 \text{ h}}{3600 \text{ s}} \right) \left(\dfrac{5280 \text{ ft}}{1 \text{ mi}} \right) = \boxed{110 \text{ ft/s}}$

3-7. A Nissan engine has a piston displacement (volume) of 1600 cm³ and a bore diameter of 84 mm. Express these measurements in cubic inches and inches.   Ans. 97.6 in.³, 3.31 in.

(a) $(1600 \text{ cm}^3)\left(\dfrac{1 \text{ in.}}{2.54 \text{ cm}} \right)^3 = \boxed{97.6 \text{ in.}^3}$

(b) $84 \text{ mm} = \left(\dfrac{1 \text{ in.}}{25.4 \text{ mm}} \right) = \boxed{3.31 \text{ in.}}$

3-8. An electrician must install an underground cable from the highway to a home located 1.20 mi into the woods. How many feet of cable will be needed?

$1.2 \text{ mi} \left(\dfrac{5280 \text{ ft}}{1 \text{ mi}} \right) = 6340 \text{ ft}$ $\boxed{L = 6340 \text{ ft}}$

3-9. One U.S. gallon is a volume equivalent to 231 in.³. How many gallons are needed to fill a tank that is 18 in. long, 16 in. wide, and 12 in. high?   Ans. 15.0 gal.

$V = (18 \text{ in.})(16 \text{ in.})(12 \text{ in.}) = 3456 \text{ in.}^3$

$V = (3456 \text{ in.}^3)\left(\dfrac{1 \text{ gal}}{231 \text{ in.}^3} \right) = 15.0 \text{ gal}$ $\boxed{V = 15.0 \text{ gal}}$

3-10. The density of brass is 8.89 g/cm³. What is the density in kg/m³?

$\left(8.89 \dfrac{\text{g}}{\text{cm}^3} \right)\left(\dfrac{1 \text{ kg}}{1000 \text{ g}} \right)\left(\dfrac{100 \text{ cm}}{1 \text{ m}} \right)^3 = 8890 \dfrac{\text{kg}}{\text{m}^3}$ $\boxed{\rho = 8890 \text{ kg/m}^3}$

Addition of Vectors by Graphical Methods

3-11. A woman walks 4 km east and then 8 km north. (a) Use the polygon method to find her resultant displacement. (b) Verify the result by the parallelogram method.

Let 1 cm = 1 km; Then: $\boxed{R = 8.94 \text{ km}, \theta = 63.4^0}$

3-12. A land-rover, on the surface of Mars, moves a distance of 38 m at an angle of 180^0. It then turns and moves a distance of 66 m at an angle of 270^0. What is the displacement from the starting position?

Choose a scale, e.g., 1 cm = 10 m

Draw each vector to scale as shown.

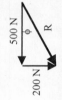

Measure R = 7.62 cm or   R = 76.2 m

Measure angle $\phi = 60.1^0$ S of W

$\theta = 180^0 + 60.1^0 = 240.1^0$ $\boxed{R = 76.2 \text{ m, } 240.1^0}$

3-13. A surveyor starts at the southeast corner of a lot and charts the following displacements:

A = 600 m, N; B = 400 m, W; C = 200 m, S; and D = 100 m, E.   What is the net displacement from the starting point?

Choose a scale, 1 cm = 100 m

Draw each vector tail to tip until all are drawn.

Construct resultant from origin to finish.

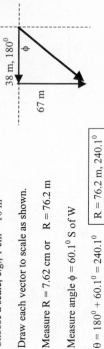

$\boxed{R = 500 \text{ m, } \phi = 53.1^0 \text{ N of E or } \theta = 126.9^0.}$

3-14. A downward force of 200 N acts simultaneously with a 500-N force directed to the left. Use the polygon method to find the resultant force.

Chose scale, measure: $\boxed{R = 539 \text{ N, } \phi = 21.8^0 \text{ S. of E.}}$

3-15. The following three forces act simultaneously on the same object. A = 300 N, 30^0 N of E; B = 600 N, 270^0; and C = 100 N due east. Find the resultant force using the polygon method.   *Choose a scale, draw and measure:*

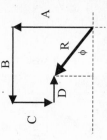

$\boxed{R = 576 \text{ N, } \phi = 51.4^0 \text{ S of E}}$

3-16. A boat travels west a distance of 200 m, then north for 400 m, and finally 100 m at 30° S of E. What is the net displacement? (*Set* 1 cm = 100 N)

Draw and measure: $R = 368$ N, $\theta = 108.0^{0}$

3-17. Two ropes A and B are attached to a mooring hook so that an angle of 60° exists between the two ropes. The tension in rope A is 80 lb and the tension in rope B is 120 lb. Use the parallelogram method to find the resultant force on the hook.

Draw and measure: $R = 174$ lb

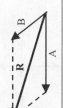

3-18. Two forces A and B act on the same object producing a resultant force of 50 lb at 36.9° N of W. The force A = 40 lb due west. Find the magnitude and direction of force B.

Draw R = 50 lb, 36.9° N of W first, then draw 40 lb, W.

$\mathbf{F} = 30$ lb, 90^{0}

Trigonometry and Vectors

3-19. Find the x and y-components of: (a) a displacement of 200 km, at 34°. (b) a velocity of 40 km/h, at 120°; and (c) A force of 50 N at 330°.

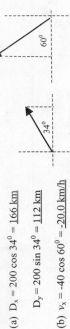

(a) $D_x = 200 \cos 34^0 = \underline{166\ km}$

$D_y = 200 \sin 34^0 = \underline{112\ km}$

(b) $v_x = -40 \cos 60^0 = \underline{-20.0\ km/h}$

$v_y = 40 \sin 60^0 = \underline{+34.6\ km/h}$

(c) $F_x = 50 \cos 30^0 = \underline{43.3\ N};$ $F_y = - 50 \sin 30^0 = \underline{-25.0\ N}$

3-20. A sled is pulled with a force of 540 N at an angle of 40° with the horizontal. What are the horizontal and vertical components of this force?

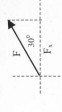

$F_x = 540 \cos 40^0 = \boxed{414\ N}$ $F_y = 540 \sin 40^0 = \boxed{347\ N}$

3-21. The hammer in Fig. 3-25 applies a force of 260 N at an angle of 15° with the vertical. What is the upward component of the force on the nail?

$F = 260$ lb, $\phi = 75^0$; $F_{xy} = 260 \sin 75^0$ $\boxed{F_y = 251\ N.}$

3-22. A jogger runs 2.0 mi west and then 6.0 mi north. Find the magnitude and direction of the resultant displacement.

$R = \sqrt{(2)^2 + (6)^2} = \boxed{6.32\ mi}$ $\tan\phi = \dfrac{6}{2};$ $\boxed{\phi = 71.6^0\ N\ of\ W}$

3-23. A river flows south with a velocity of 20 km/h. A boat has a maximum speed of 50 km/h. In the river, at maximum throttle, the boat heads due west. What is the resultant speed and direction of the boat?

$R = \sqrt{(50)^2 + (20)^2} = 53.9$ km / h;

$\tan\phi = \dfrac{20}{50};$ $\phi = 21.8^0$ S of W $\boxed{R = 53.9\ km/h, 21.8^0\ S}$

3-24. A rope, making an angle of 30° with the horizontal, drags a crate along the floor. What must be the tension in the rope, if a horizontal force of 40 lb is required to drag the crate?

$F_x = F \cos 30^0;$ $F = \dfrac{F_x}{\cos 30^0} = \dfrac{40\ lb}{\cos 30^0};$ $\boxed{F = 46.2\ N}$

*3-25. An vertical lift of 80 N is needed to lift a window. A long pole is used to lift the window. What force must be exerted along the pole if it makes an angle of 34° with the wall?

$$F_y = F\sin 30°; \quad F = \frac{F_y}{\sin 34°} = \frac{40\text{ lb}}{\sin 34°}; \qquad \boxed{F = 96.5\text{ N}}$$

*3-26. The resultant of two forces A and B is 400 N at 210°. If force A is 200 N at 270°, what are the magnitude and direction of force B? $(\phi = 210 - 180 - 30°)$

$$B = -400\text{ N}\cos 30° = -346\text{ N}: \qquad \boxed{B = 346\text{ N}, 180°}$$

The Component Method of Vector Addition

3-27. Find the resultant of the following perpendicular forces: (a) 400 N, 0°; (b) 820 N, 270°, and (b) 500 N, 90°.   *Draw each vector, then find* **R**:

$$A_x = +400\text{ N}; \quad B_x = 0; \quad C_x = 0: \qquad R_x = +400\text{ N}$$

$$A_y = 0; \quad B_y = -820\text{ N}; \quad C_y = +500\text{ N}; \qquad R_y = 0 - 820\text{ N} + 500\text{ N} = -320\text{ N}$$

$$R = \sqrt{(400)^2 + (-320)^2}; \quad \tan\phi = \frac{-320}{400}; \qquad \boxed{R = 512\text{ N}, 38.7°\text{ S of E}}$$

3-28. Four ropes, all at right angles to each other, pull on a ring. The forces are A = 40 lb, E; B = 80 lb, N; C = 70 lb, W; and D = 20 lb, S. Find the resultant force on the ring.

$$A_x = +40\text{ lb}; \quad B_x = 0; \quad C_x = -70\text{ lb} \quad D_x = 0:$$

$$R_x = +40\text{ lb} - 70\text{ lb} = -30\text{ lb}$$

$$A_y = 0; \quad B_y = +80\text{ lb}; \quad C_y = 0; \quad D_y = -20\text{ lb};$$

$$R_y = 0 + 80\text{ lb} - 20\text{ lb} = +60\text{ lb}$$

$$R = \sqrt{(-30)^2 + (60)^2}; \quad \tan\phi = \frac{60}{-30}; \qquad \boxed{R = 67.1\text{ N}, 116.6°}$$

---

*3-29. Two forces act on the car in Fig. 3-26. Force A is 120 N, west and force B is 200 N at 60° N of W. What are the magnitude and direction of the resultant force on the car?

$$A_x = -120; \quad B_x = -(200\text{ N})\cos 60° = -100\text{ N}$$

$$R_x = -120\text{ N} - 100\text{ N}; \quad R_x = -220\text{ N}$$

$$A_y = 0, \quad B_y = 200\sin 60° = +173\text{ N}; \quad R_y = 0 + 173\text{ N} = 173\text{ N};$$

$$\text{Thus, } R_x = -222\text{ N}, \quad R_y = +173\text{ N} \quad \text{and} \quad R = \sqrt{(-222)^2 + (173)^2} = 280\text{ N}$$

Resultant direction: $\tan\phi = \dfrac{173}{-210}$; $\phi = 38.2°$ N of W

*3-30. Suppose the direction of force B in Problem 3-29 is reversed (+180°) and other parameters are unchanged. What is the new resultant? (This result is the vector difference A − B).

The vector **B** *will now be 60° S of E instead of N of E.*

$$A_x = -120; \quad B_x = +(200\text{ N})\cos 60° = +100\text{ N}$$

$$R_x = -120\text{ N} + 100\text{ N}; \quad R_x = -20\text{ N}$$

$$A_y = 0; \quad B_y = -200\sin 60° = -173\text{ N}; \quad R_y = 0 - 173\text{ N} = -173\text{ N};$$

$$\text{Thus, } R_x = -20\text{ N}, \quad R_y = -173\text{ N} \quad \text{and} \quad R = \sqrt{(-20)^2 + (173)^2} = 174\text{ N}$$

Resultant direction: $\tan\phi = \dfrac{-173}{-20}$; $\phi = 83.4°$ S of W

*3-31. Determine the resultant force on the bolt in Fig. 3-27.   ($A_x = 0$)

$$B_x = -40\cos 20° = -37.6\text{ lb}; \quad B_x = -50\cos 60° = -25.0\text{ lb}$$

$$R_x = 0 - 37.6\text{ lb} - 25.0\text{ lb}; \quad R_x = -62.6\text{ lb}$$

$$A_y = +60\text{ lb}; \quad B_y = 40\sin 20° = 13.7\text{ lb}; \quad C_y = 50\sin 60 = -43.3\text{ lb};$$

$$R_y = 60\text{ lb} - 13.7\text{ lb} - 43.3\text{ lb}; \quad R_y = +30.4\text{ lb}$$

$$R = \sqrt{(-62.6)^2 + (30.4)^2} = 69.6\text{ lb}; \quad \tan\phi = \frac{30.4}{-62.6}; \quad \phi = 25.9°\text{ N of W}$$

3-35. A cable is attached to the end of a beam. What pull at an angle of 40° with the horizontal is needed to produce an effective horizontal force of 200 N?

P cos 40° = 200 N; $\boxed{P = 261 \text{ N}}$

3-36. A fishing dock runs north and south. What must be the speed of a boat heading at an angle of 40° E of N if its velocity component along the dock is to be 30 km/h?

v cos 40° = 30 km/h; $\boxed{v = 39.2 \text{ km/h}}$

3-37. Find the resultant **R = A + B** for the following pairs of forces: **A** = (520 N, south); **B** = 269 N, west; (b) **A** = 18 m/s, north; **B** = 15 m/s, west.

(a) $R = \sqrt{(-269)^2 + (520)^2} = 585$ N

$\tan\phi = \dfrac{520}{-295}$; $\boxed{R = 585 \text{ N}, \; \phi = 62.6° \text{ S of W}}$

(b) $R = \sqrt{(-15)^2 + (18)^2}$; $\tan\phi = \dfrac{18}{-15}$;

$\boxed{R = 23.4 \text{ N}, \; 50.2° \text{ N of W}}$

3-38. Determine the vector difference (**A – B**) for the pairs of forces in Problem 3-37.

Change **B** *into the vector* –**B**, *then ADD*:

(a) $R = \sqrt{(269)^2 + (520)^2} = 585$ N

$\tan\phi = \dfrac{520}{295}$; $\boxed{R = 585 \text{ N}, \; 62.6° \text{ S of E}}$

(b) $R = \sqrt{(15)^2 + (18)^2}$; $\tan\phi = \dfrac{18}{15}$;

$\boxed{R = 23.4 \text{ N}, \; 50.2° \text{ N of E}}$

3-39. A traffic light is attached to the midpoint of a rope so that each segment makes an angle of 10° with the horizontal. The tension in each rope segment is 200 N. If the resultant force at the midpoint is zero, what must be the weight of the traffic light?

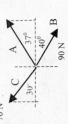

$R_x = \Sigma F_x = 0$;   T sin 10° + T sin 10° – W = 0;

2(200) sin 10° = W; $\boxed{W = 69.5 \text{ N}}$

---

*3-32. Determine the resultant of the following forces by the component method of vector addition: **A** = (200 N, 30°); **B** = (300 N, 330°); and **C** = (400 N, 250°).

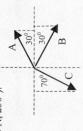

$A_x = 200 \cos 30° = 173$ N; $B_x = 300 \cos 30° = 260$ N

$C_x = -400 \cos 70° = -137$ N; $R_x = \Sigma F_x = 296$ N

$A_y = 200 \sin 30° = 100$ N; $B_y = 300 \sin 30° = -150$ N

$C_y = -400 \sin 70° = -376$ N; $R_y = \Sigma F_y = -430$ N

$R = \sqrt{(296)^2 + (-430)^2} = 519$ N; $\tan\phi = \dfrac{-426}{296}$; $\phi = 55.2° \text{ S of E}$

*3-33. Three boats exert forces on a mooring hook as shown in Fig. 3-28. Find the resultant of these three forces.

$A_x = 420 \cos 60° = +210$ N; $C_x = -500 \cos 40° = -383$ N

$B_x = 0$; $R_x = 210 \text{ N} + 0 - 383 \text{ N}$; $R_x = \underline{-173 \text{ N}}$

$A_y = 420 \sin 60° = 364$ N; $B_y = 150$;

$C_y = 500 \sin 40° = 321$ N $R_y = \Sigma F_y = \underline{835 \text{ N}}$;

$R = \sqrt{(-173)^2 + (835)^2}$; $\tan\phi = \dfrac{835}{-173}$; $\boxed{R = 853 \text{ N}, \; 78.3° \text{ N of W}}$

Supplementary Problems

3-34. Find the horizontal and vertical components of the following vectors: **A** = (400 N, 37°); **B** = 90 m, 320°); and **C** = (70 km/h, 150°).

$A_x = 400 \cos 37° = \underline{319 \text{ N}}$; $A_y = 400 \sin 37° = \underline{241 \text{ N}}$

$B_x = 90 \cos 40° = 68.9$ N; $B_y = 90 \sin 40° = \underline{57.9}$

$C_x = -70 \cos 30° = \underline{-60.6 \text{ N}}$; $C_y = 70 \sin 30° = \underline{25.0 \text{ N}}$

Critical Thinking Questions

3-44. Consider three vectors: A = 100 m, 0°; B = 400 m, 270°; and C = 200 m, 30°. Choose an appropriate scale and show graphically that the order in which these vectors is added does not matter, i.e., A + B + C = C + B + A. Is this also true for subtracting vectors? Show graphically how A – C differs from C – A.

A + B + C   C + B + A   A – C   C – A

3-45. Two forces A = 30 N and B = 90 N can act on an object in any direction desired. What is the maximum resultant force? What is the minimum resultant force? Can the resultant force be zero?

Maximum resultant force occurs when A and B are in same direction.

A + B = 30 N + 90 N = <u>120 N</u>

Minimum resultant force occurs when A and B are in opposite directions.

B - A = 90 N – 30 N = <u>60 N</u>

<u>*No combination gives R = 0.*</u>

*3-46. Consider two forces A = 40 N and B = 80 N. What must be the angle between these two forces in order to produce a resultant force of 60 N?

Since R = C = 60 N is smaller than 80 N, the angle θ between A and B must be > 90°. Applying the law of cosines to the triangle, we can find ϕ and then θ.

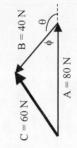

---

*3-40. Determine the resultant of the forces shown in Fig. 3-29.

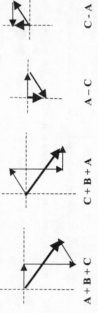

$R_x = 420 N - 200 \cos 70^0 - 410 \cos 53^0 = 105$ lb

$R_y = 0 + 200 \sin 70^0 - 410 \sin 70^0 = -139.5$ lb

$R = \sqrt{R_x^2 + R_y^2}$ $\boxed{R = 175 \text{ lb};\ \theta = 306.9^0}$

*3-41. Determine the resultant of the forces shown in Fig. 3-30.

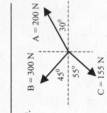

$R_x = 200 \cos 30^0 - 300 \cos 45^0 - 155 \cos 55^0 = 128$ N

$R_y = 0 + 200 \sin 70^0 - 410 \sin 70^0 = -185$ N;

$R = \sqrt{R_x^2 + R_y^2}$ $\boxed{R = 225 \text{ N};\ \theta = 124.6^0}$

*3-42. A 200-N block rests on a 30° inclined plane. If the weight of the block acts vertically downward, what are the components of the weight down the plane and perpendicular to the plane? *Choose x-axis along plane and y-axis perpendicular.*

$W_x = 200 \sin 30^0$;   <u>$W_3 = 173$ N, down the plane.</u>

$W_y = 200 \sin 60^0$;   <u>$W_x = 100$ N, normal to the plane.</u>

*3-43. Find the resultant of the following three displacements: A = 220 m, 60°; B = 125 m, 210°; and C = 175 m, 340°.

$A_x = 220 \cos 60^0 = 110$ m; $A_y = 220 \sin 60^0 = 190.5$ m

$B_x = 125 \cos 210^0 = -108$ m; $B_y = 125 \sin 210^0 = -62.5$ m

$C_x = 175 \cos 340^0 = 164.4$ m; $C_y = 175 \sin 340^0 = -59.9$ m

$R_x = 110 m - 108 m + 164.4 m$; $R_y = 190.5 m - 62.5 m - 59.9 m$;

$R_x = 166.4 m$; $R_y = 68.1 m$ $R = \sqrt{(166.4)^2 + (68.1)^2} = 180$ m

$\tan \theta = \dfrac{68.1}{166.4}$; $\theta = 22.3^0$; $\boxed{R = 180 \text{ m},\ \theta = 22.3^0}$

$C^2 = A^2 + B^2 - 2AB \, Cos \, \phi$; $(60)^2 = (80)^2 + (40)^2 - 2(80)(40) \, Cos \, \phi$; $\phi = 46.6^0$.

The angle between the direction of A and the direction of B is $\theta = 180^0 - \phi$; $\boxed{\theta = 133.4^0.}$

*3-47. What third force **F** must be added to the following two forces so that the resultant force is zero: **A** = 120 N, 110° and **B** = 60 N, 200°?

Components of A: $A_x = 120 \, Cos \, 110^0 = -41.0$ N; $A_y = 120 \, Sin \, 110^0 = 113$ N

Components of B: $B_x = 60 \, Cos \, 200^0 = -56.4$ N; $B_y = 60 \, Sin \, 200^0 = -20.5$ N

$R_x = 0$; $R_x = A_x + B_x + F_x = 0$; $R_x = -41.0 \, N -56.4 \, N + F_x = 0$;   Or $F_x = +97.4$ N

$R_y = 0$; $R_y = A_y + B_y + F_y = 0$; $R_y = 113 \, N - 20.5 \, N + F_y = 0$;   Or $F_y = -92.2$ N

$F = \sqrt{(97.4)^2 + (-92.2)^2} = 131$ N $tan \, \phi = \dfrac{-92.2}{97.4}$; $\phi = -43.3^0$;   And $\theta = 360^0 - 43.4^0$

$\boxed{F = 134 \, N, \theta = 316.6^0}$

Thus, the force F has a magnitude and direction of: $\boxed{F = 134 \, N, \theta = 316.6^0}$

*3-48. An airplane needs a resultant heading of due west. The speed of the plane is 600 km/h in still air. If the wind has a speed of 40 km/h and blows in a direction of 30° S of W, what direction should the aircraft be pointed and what will be its speed relative to the ground?

A = 600 km/h, R, φ, 30°, B = 40 km/h

From the diagram, $R_x = R$, $R_y = 0$, So that $A_y + B_y = 0$.

$A_y = 600 \, sin \, \phi$; $B_y = -40 \, sin \, 30^0 = -20$ km/h

$600 \, sin \, \phi - 20 = 0$; $600 \, sin \, \phi = 20$

$sin \, \phi = \dfrac{20}{600}$; $\phi = 1.91^0$ N of W (direction aircraft should be pointed)

Noting that $R = R_x$ and that $A_x + B_x = R_x$, we need only find sum of x-components.

$A_x = -600 \, cos \, 1.91^0 = 599.7$ km/h; $B_x = 40 \, Cos \, 30^0 = -34.6$ km/h

$R = -599.7$ km/h -34.6 km/h; $R = -634$ km/h.   Thus, the speed of the plane relative to the ground is 634 km/h, 0°; and the plane must be pointed in a direction of 1.91° N of W.

*3-49. What are the magnitude F and direction θ of the force needed to pull the car of Fig. 3-31 directly east with a resultant force of 400 lb?

F, E, φ, 20°, A = 200 lb

$R_x = 400$ lb and $R_y = 0$; $R_x = A_x + F_x = 400$ lb

$200 \, Cos \, 20^0 + F_x = 400$ lb

$F_x = 400 \, lb - 200 \, Cos \, 20^0 = 212$ lb

$R_y = 0 = A_y + F_y$; $A_y = -200 \, sin \, 20^0 = -68.4$ lb

$F_y = -A_y = +68.4$ lb;   So, $F_x = 212$ lb and $F_y = +68.4$ lb

$F = \sqrt{(212)^2 + (68.4)^2}$; $tan \, \theta = \dfrac{68.4}{212}$;

$\boxed{R = 223 \, lb, 17.9^0 \, N \, of \, E}$

Chapter 4. Translational Equilibrium and Friction.

Note: For all of the problems at the end of this chapter, the rigid booms or struts are considered to be of negligible weight. All forces are considered to be concurrent forces.

Free-body Diagrams

4-1. Draw a free-body diagram for the arrangements shown in Fig. 4-18. Isolate a point where the important forces are acting, and represent each force as a vector. Determine the reference angle and label components.

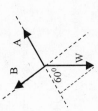

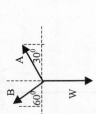

(a) Free-body Diagram   (b) Free-body with rotation of axes to simplify work.

4-2. Study each force acting at the end of the light strut in Fig. 4-19. Draw the appropriate free-body diagram.

There is no particular advantage to rotating axes.
Components should also be labeled on diagram.

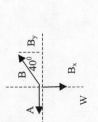

Solution of Equilibrium Problems:

4-3. Three identical bricks are strung together with cords and hung from a scale that reads a total of 24 N. What is the tension in the cord that supports the lowest brick? What is the tension in the cord between the middle brick and the top brick?

Each brick must weight 8 N. The lowest cord supports only one brick, whereas the middle cord supports two bricks.   Ans. 8 N, 16 N.

4-4. A single chain supports a pulley whose weight is 40 N. Two identical 80-N weights are then connected with a cord that passes over the pulley. What is the tension in the supporting chain? What is the tension in each cord?

Each cord supports 80 N but chain supports everything.

$T = 2(80\ N) + 40\ N = 200\ N.$ $T = 200\ N$

*4-5. If the weight of the block in Fig. 4-18a is 80 N, what are the tensions in ropes A and B?

$B_y - W = 0;\quad B \sin 40^0 - 80\ N = 0;\quad B = 124.4\ N$

$B_x - A = 0;\quad B \cos 40^0 = A;\quad A = (124.4\ N)\cos 40^0$

$A = 95.3\ N;\quad B = 124\ N.$

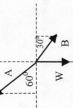

*4-6. If rope B in Fig. 4-18a will break for tensions greater than 200 lb, what is the maximum weight W that can be supported?

$\Sigma F_y = 0;\quad B_y - W = 0;\quad W = B \sin 40^0;\quad B = 200\ N$

$W = (200\ N)\sin 40^0;$ $W = 129\ lb$

*4-7. If W = 600 N in Fig. 4-18b, what is the force exerted by the rope on the end of the boom A in Fig. 4-18b? What is the tension in rope B?

$\Sigma F_x = 0;\quad A - W_x = 0;\quad A = W_x = W \cos 60^0$

$A = (600\ N)\cos 60^0 = 300\ N$

$\Sigma F_y = 0;\quad B - W_y = 0;\quad B = W_y = W \sin 60^0$

$B = (600\ N)\sin 60^0 = 520\ N$

$A = 300\ N;\quad B = 520\ N$

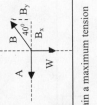

*4-8. If the rope B in Fig. 4-18a will break if its tension exceeds 400 N, what is the maximum weight W?

$\Sigma F_y = B_y - W = 0$; $B_y = W$

$B \sin 40° = 400$ N ; $\boxed{B = 622 \text{ N}}$ $\Sigma F_x = 0$

$B_x - A = 0$; $B \cos 40° = A$; $A = (622 \text{ N}) \cos 40°$ $\boxed{A = 477 \text{ N.}}$

*4-9. What is the maximum weight W for Fig. 4-18b if the rope can sustain a maximum tension of only 800 N? (Set B = 800 N).

Draw diagram, then rotate x-y axes as shown to right.

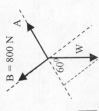

$\Sigma F_y = 0$; $800 \text{ N} - W \sin 60° = 0$; $\boxed{W = 924 \text{ N.}}$

The compression in the boom is $A = 924 \cos 60°$ $\boxed{A = 462 \text{ N.}}$

*4-10. A 70-N block rests on a 35° inclined plane. Determine the normal force and find the friction force that keeps the block from sliding. (Rotate axes as shown.)

$\Sigma F_x = \mathcal{N} - W_x = 0$; $\mathcal{N} = W_x = (70 \text{ N}) \cos 30°$; $\boxed{\mathcal{N} = 60.6 \text{ N}}$

$\Sigma F_x = \mathcal{F} - W_y = 0$; $\mathcal{F} = W_y = (70 \text{ N}) \sin 30°$; $\boxed{\mathcal{F} = 35.0 \text{ N.}}$

*4-11. A wire is stretched between two poles 10 m apart. A sign is attached to the midpoint of the line causing it to sag vertically a distance of 50 cm. If the tension in each line segment is 2000 N, what is the weight of the sign? (h = 0.50 m)

$\tan \phi = (0.5/5)$ or $\phi = 5.71°$; $2(2000 \text{ N}) \sin \phi = W$

$W = 4000 \sin 5.71$; $\boxed{W = 398 \text{ N.}}$

*4-12. An 80-N traffic light is supported at the midpoint of a 30-m length of cable between two poles. Find the tension in each cable segment if the cable sags a vertical distance of 1 m.

Solution to 4-12 (Cont.):

$h = 1$ m; $Tan \phi = (1/15)$; $\phi = 3.81°$

$T \sin \phi + T \sin \phi = 80$ N; $2T \sin 3.81° = 80$ N

$T = \dfrac{80 \text{ N}}{2 \sin 3.81°} = 601$ N; $\boxed{T = 601 \text{ N}}$

*4-13. The ends of three 8-ft studs are nailed together forming a tripod with an apex that is 6ft above the ground. What is the compression in each of these studs if a 100-lb weight is hung from the apex?

Three upward components F_y hold up the 100 lb weight:

$3 F_y = 100$ lb; $F_y = 33.3$ lb $\sin \phi = (6/8)$; $\phi = 48.9°$

$F \sin 48.9° = 33.3$ lb; $F = \dfrac{33.3 \text{ lb}}{\sin 48.9°} = 44.4$ lb $\boxed{F = 44.4 \text{ lb, compression}}$

*4-14. A 20-N picture is hung from a nail as in Fig. 4-20, so that the supporting cords make an angle of 60°. What is the tension of each cord segment?

According to Newton's third law, the force of frame on nail (20 N) is the same as the force of the nail on the rope (20 N, up).

$\Sigma F_y = 0$; $20 \text{ N} = T_y + T_y$; $2T_y = 20 \text{ N}$; $T_y = 10 \text{ N}$

$T_y = T \sin 60°$;   So $T \sin 60° = 10 \text{ N}$,   and $\boxed{T = 11.5 \text{ N.}}$

Friction

4-15. A horizontal force of 40 N will just start an empty 600-N sled moving across packed snow. After motion is begun, only 10 N is needed to keep motion at constant speed. Find the coefficients of static and kinetic friction.

$\mu_s = \dfrac{40 \text{ N}}{600 \text{ N}} = 0.0667$ $\mu_k = \dfrac{10 \text{ N}}{600 \text{ N}} = 0.0167$

$\boxed{\mu_s = 0.0667; \quad \mu_k = 0.016}$

4-16. Suppose 200-N of supplies are added to the sled in Problem 4-13. What new force is needed to drag the sled at constant speed?

$\mathcal{N}$ = 200 N + 600 N = 800 N; $\mathscr{F}_k$ = $\mu_k \mathcal{N}$ = (0.0167)(800 N); $\boxed{\mathscr{F}_k = 13.3 \text{ N}}$

4-17. Assume surfaces where μ_s = 0.7 and μ_k = 0.4. What horizontal force is needed to just start a 50-N block moving along a wooden floor? What force will move it at constant speed?

$\mathscr{F}_s$ = $\mu_s \mathcal{N}$ = (0.7)(50 N) $\boxed{35 \text{ N}}$; $\mathscr{F}_k$ = $\mu_s \mathcal{N}$ = (0.4)(50 N) = $\boxed{20 \text{ N}}$

4-18. A dockworker finds that a horizontal force of 60 lb is needed to drag a 150-lb crate across the deck at constant speed. What is the coefficient of kinetic friction?

$\mu_k = \dfrac{F}{N}$; $\mu_k = \dfrac{60 \text{ lb}}{150 \text{ lb}}$ = 0.400 $\boxed{\mu_k = 0.400}$

4-19. The dockworker in Problem 4-18 finds that a smaller crate of similar material can be dragged at constant speed with a horizontal force of only 40 lb. What is the weight of this crate?

$\mathscr{F}_k$ = $\mu_k \mathcal{N}$ = (0.4)W = 40 lb; W = (40 lb/0.4) = 100 lb; W = 100 lb.

4-20. A steel block weighing 240 N rests on level steel beam. What horizontal force will move the block at constant speed if the coefficient of kinetic friction is 0.12?

$\mathscr{F}_k$ = $\mu_s \mathcal{N}$ = (0.12)(240 N); $\boxed{\mathscr{F}_k = 28.8 \text{ N.}}$

4-21. A 60-N toolbox is dragged horizontally at constant speed by a rope making an angle of 35^0 with the floor. The tension in the rope is 40 N. Determine the magnitude of the friction force and the normal force.

ΣF_x = T cos 35^0 - $\mathcal{F}$ = 0; $\mathcal{F}$ = (40 N) cos 35^0 = 32.8 N

ΣF_y = $\mathcal{N}$ + T_y - W = 0; $\mathcal{N}$ = W - T_y = 60 N - T sin 35^0

$\mathcal{N}$ = 60 N - (40 N) sin 35^0; $\boxed{\mathcal{N} = 37.1 \text{ N}}$ $\boxed{\mathscr{F}_k = 32.8 \text{ N}}$

4-22. What is the coefficient of kinetic friction for the example in Problem 4-21?

$\mu_k = \dfrac{\mathcal{F}}{\mathcal{N}} = \dfrac{32.8 \text{ N}}{37.1 \text{ N}}$; $\boxed{\mu_k = 0.884}$

4-23. The coefficient of static friction for wood on wood is 0.7. What is the maximum angle for an inclined wooden plane if a wooden block is to remain at rest on the plane?

Maximum angle occurs when tan θ = μ_s; μ_s = tan θ = 0.7; $\boxed{\theta = 35.0^0}$

4-24. A roof is sloped at an angle of 40^0. What is the maximum coefficient of static friction between the sole of the shoe and the roof to prevent slipping?

Tan θ = μ_k; μ_k = Tan 40^0 = 0.839; $\boxed{\mu_k = 0.839}$

*4-25. A 200 N sled is pushed along a horizontal surface at constant speed with a 50-N force that makes an angle of 28^0 below the horizontal. What is the coefficient of kinetic friction?

ΣF_x = T cos 28^0 - $\mathcal{F}_k$ = 0; $\mathcal{F}_k$ = (50 N) cos 28^0 = 44.1 N

ΣF_y = $\mathcal{N}$ - T_y - W = 0; $\mathcal{N}$ = W + T_y = 200 N + T sin 28^0

$\mathcal{N}$ = 200 N + (50 N) sin 35^0; $\mathcal{N}$ = 223 N

$\mu_k = \dfrac{\mathcal{F}}{\mathcal{N}} = \dfrac{44.1 \text{ N}}{223 \text{ N}}$ $\boxed{\mu_k = 0.198}$

*4-26. What is the normal force on the block in Fig. 4-21? What is the component of the weight acting down the plane?

ΣF_y = $\mathcal{N}$ - W cos 43^0 = 0; $\mathcal{N}$ = (60N) cod 43^0 = 43.9 N

W_x = (60 N) sin 35^0. $\boxed{W_x = 40.9 \text{ N}}$

*4-27. What push **P** directed up the plane will cause the block in Fig. 4-21 to move up the plane with constant speed? [*From Problem 4-25:* $\mathcal{N}$ = 43.9 N and W_x = 40.9 N] *down plane.*

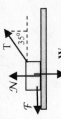

$\mathcal{F}_k$ = $\mu_k \mathcal{N}$ = (0.3)(43.9 N); $\mathcal{F}_k$ = 13.2 N

$\Sigma F_x = P - \mathcal{F}_k - W_x = 0$; $P = \mathcal{F}_k + W_x$; $P = 13.2\ N + 40.9\ N$; $\boxed{P = 54.1\ N}$

*4-28. If the block in Fig. 4-21 is released, it will overcome static friction and slide rapidly down the plane. What push **P** directed up the incline will retard the downward motion until the block moves at constant speed? (*Note that $\mathcal{F}$ is up the plane now.*)

Magnitudes of $\mathcal{F}$, W_x, and $\mathcal{N}$ are same as Prob. 4-27.

$\Sigma F_x = P + \mathcal{F}_k - W_x = 0$; $P = W_x - \mathcal{F}_k$; $P = 40.9\ N - 13.2\ N$

$\boxed{P = 27.7\ N \quad directed\ UP\ the\ inclined\ plane}$

Supplementary Problems

*4-29. Determine the tension in rope A and the compression B in the strut for Fig. 4-22.

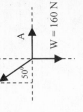

$\Sigma F_y = 0$; $\quad B_y - 400\ N = 0$; $\quad B = \dfrac{400\ N}{\sin 60^0} = 462\ N$

$\Sigma F_x = 0$; $\quad B_x - A = 0$; $\quad A = B \cos 60^0$

$A = (462\ N) \cos 60^0$; $\quad \boxed{A = 231\ N \quad and \quad B = 462\ N}$

*4-30. If the breaking strength of cable A in Fig. 4-23 is 200 N, what is the maximum weight that can be supported by this apparatus?

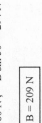

$\Sigma F_y = 0$; $\quad A_y - W = 0$; $\quad W = (200\ N) \sin 40^0 = 129\ N$

The maximum weight that can be supported is $\boxed{129\ N.}$

*4-31. What is the minimum push P parallel to a 37^0 inclined plane if a 90-N wagon is to be rolled up the plane at constant speed? Ignore friction.

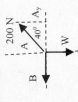

$\Sigma F_x = 0$; $\quad P - W_x = 0$; $\quad P = (90\ N) \sin 37^0$

$\boxed{P = 54.2\ N}$

4-32. A horizontal force of only 8 lb moves a cake of ice with constant speed across a floor (μ_k = 0.1). What is the weight of the ice?

$\mathcal{F}_k = \mu_k \mathcal{N} = (0.3)\ W$; $\quad \mathcal{F}_k = 8\ lb$; $\quad (0.1)W = 8\ lb$; $\quad \boxed{W = 80\ lb.}$

*4-33. Find the tension in ropes A and B for the arrangement shown in Fig. 4-24a.

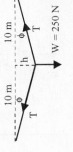

$\Sigma F_x = B - W_x = 0$; $\quad B = W_x = (340\ N) \cos 30^0$; $\quad B = 294\ N$

$\Sigma F_y = A - W_y = 0$; $\quad A = W_y = (340\ N) \sin 30^0$; $\quad A = 170\ N$

$\boxed{A = 170\ N; \quad B = 294\ N}$

*4-34. Find the tension in ropes A and B in Fig. 4-24b.

$\Sigma F_y = B_y - 160\ N = 0$; $\quad B_y = 160\ N$; $\quad B \sin 50^0 = 294\ N$

$B = \dfrac{160\ N}{\sin 50^0}$; $\quad \boxed{B = 209\ N}$

$\Sigma F_x = A - B_x = 0$; $\quad A = B_x = (209\ N) \cos 50^0$; $\quad \boxed{A = 134\ N}$

*4-35. A cable is stretched horizontally across the top of two vertical poles 20 m apart. A 250-N sign suspended from the midpoint causes the rope to sag a vertical distance of 1.2 m.

What is the tension in each cable segment?

$h = 1.2\ m$; $\quad \tan \phi = \dfrac{1.2}{10}$; $\quad \phi = 6.84^0$

$2T \sin 6.84^0 = 250\ N$; $\quad \boxed{T = 1050\ N}$

*4-36. Assume the cable in Problem 4-35 has a breaking strength of 1200 N. What is the maximum weight that can be supported at the midpoint?

$2T \sin 6.84^0 = 250\ N$; $\quad 2(1200\ N) \sin 6.84^0 = W$; $\quad \boxed{W = 289\ N}$

Critical Thinking Questions

4-41. Study the structure drawn in Fig. 4-27 and analyze the forces acting at the point where the rope is attached to the light poles. What is the direction of the forces acting ON the ends of the poles? What is the direction of the forces exerted BY the poles at that point? Draw the appropriate free-body diagram. *Imagine that the poles are bolted together at their upper ends, then visualize the forces ON that bolt and BY that bolt.*

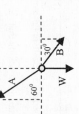

Forces ON Bolt at Ends (Action Forces):

The force **W** is exerted ON the bolt BY the weight. The force **B** is exerted ON bolt BY right pole. The force **A** is exerted ON bolt BY the middle pole. To understand these directions, imagine that the poles snap, then what would be the resulting motion?

Forces BY Bolt at Ends (Reaction Forces):

The force $\mathbf{W_r}$ is exerted BY the bolt ON the weight. The force $\mathbf{B_r}$ is exerted ON bolt BY right pole. The force $\mathbf{A_r}$ is exerted BY bolt ON the middle pole. Do not confuse action forces with the reaction forces.

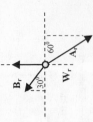

*4-42. Determine the forces acting ON the ends of the poles in Fig 3-27 if W = 500 N.

$\Sigma F_x = B_x - A_x = 0$; $B \cos 30^0 = A \cos 60^0$; $B = 0.577 A$

$\Sigma F_y = A \sin 60^0 - B \sin 30^0 - 500$ N $= 0$; $0.866 A - 0.5 B = 500$ N

Substituting $B = 0.577 A$: $0.866 A - (0.5)(0.577 A) = 500$ N

Solving for A, we obtain: A = 866 N; and B = 0.577 A = 0.577(866) or B = 500 N

Thus the forces are : [A = 866 N; B = 500 N]

Can you explain why B = W? Would this be true for any weight W?

Try another value, for example W = 800 N and solve again for B.

---

*4-37. Find the tension in the cable and the compression in the light boom for Fig. 4-25a.

$\Sigma F_y = A_y - 26$ lb $= 0$; $A_y = 26$ lb; $A \sin 37^0 = 26$ lb

$A = \dfrac{26 \text{ lb}}{\sin 37^0}$; [A = 43.2 lb]

$\Sigma F_x = B - A_x = 0$; $B = A_x = (43.2 \text{ lb}) \cos 37^0$; [B = 34.5 lb]

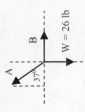

*4-38. Find the tension in the cable and the compression in the light boom for Fig. 4-25b.

First recognize that $\phi = 90^0 - 42^0 = 48^0$, Then W = 68 lb

$\Sigma F_y = B_y - 68$ lb $= 0$; $B_y = 68$ lb; $B \sin 48^0 = 68$ lb

$B = \dfrac{68 \text{ lb}}{\sin 48^0}$; [A = 915 lb]

$\Sigma F_x = B_x - A = 0$; $A = B_x = (91.5 \text{ lb}) \cos 48^0$; [B = 61.2 lb]

*4-39. Determine the tension in the ropes A and B for Fig. 4-26a.

$\Sigma F_x = B_x - A = 0$; $B \cos 30^0 = A \cos 45^0$; $B = 0.816 A$

$\Sigma F_y = A \sin 45^0 - B \sin 30^0 - 420$ N $= 0$; $0.707 A - 0.5 B = 420$ N

Substituting B = 0.816A: $0.707 A - (0.5)(0.816 A) = 420$ N

Solving for A, we obtain: A = 1406 N; and B = 0.816A = 0.816(1406) or B = 1148 N

Thus the tensions are : [A = 1410 N; B = 1150 N]

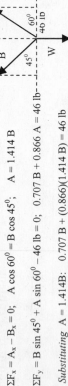

*4-40. Find the forces in the light boards of Fig. 4-26b and state whether the boards are under tension or compression. (*Note:* $\theta_A = 90^0 - 30^0 = 60^0$)

$\Sigma F_x = A_x - B_x = 0$; $A \cos 60^0 = B \cos 45^0$; $A = 1.414 B$

$\Sigma F_y = B \sin 45^0 + A \sin 60^0 - 46$ lb $= 0$; $0.707 B + 0.866 A = 46$ lb

Substituting A = 1.414B: $0.707 B + (0.866)(1.414 B) = 46$ lb

Solving for B: $B = 23.8$ lb; and $A = 1.414B = 01.414 (23.8$ lb$)$ or $A = 33.7$ lb

[A = 33.7 lb, tension; B = 23.8 lb, compression]

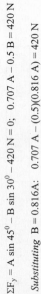

*4-43. A 2-N eraser is pressed against a vertical chalkboard with a horizontal push of 12 N. If $\mu_s = 0.25$, find the horizontal force required to start motion parallel to the floor. What if you want to start its motion upward or downward? Find the vertical forces required to just start motion up the board and then down the board. Ans. 3.00 N, up = 5 N, down = 1 N.

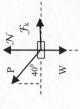

For horizontal motion, $P = \mathcal{F}_s = \mu_s \mathcal{N}$

$P = 0.25 \ (12 \ N);$ $\boxed{P = 3.00 \ N}$

For upward motion, $P - 2 \ N - \mathcal{F}_k = 0$

$P = 2 \ N + 3 \ N;$ $\boxed{P = 5.00 \ N}$

For down motion: $\ - P - \mathcal{F}_k - 2 \ N = 0$ $\boxed{P = 1.00 \ N}$

---

*4-44. It is determined experimentally that a 20-lb horizontal force will move a 60-lb lawn mower at constant speed. The handle of the mower makes an angle of 40° with the ground. What push along the handle will move the mower at constant speed? Is the normal force equal to the weight of the mower? What is the normal force?

$\mu_k = \dfrac{20 \ lb}{60 \ lb} = 0.333$ $\Sigma F_y = \mathcal{N} - P_y - W = 0;$ $W = 60 \ lb$ $\mathcal{F}_k = \mu_k \mathcal{N} = 0.333 \ \mathcal{N}$

$\mathcal{N} = P \sin 40^0 + 60 \ lb;$

$\Sigma F_y = P_x - \mathcal{F}_k = 0;$ $P \cos 40^0 - 0.333 \ \mathcal{N} = 0$

$P \cos 40^0 - 0.333 \ (P \sin 40^0 + 60 \ lb) = 0;$ $0.766 \ P = 0.214 \ P + 20 \ lb;$

$0.552 \ P = 20 \ lb;$ $P = \dfrac{20 \ lb}{0.552} = 36.2 \ lb;$ $\boxed{P = 36.2 \ lb}$

The normal force is: $\mathcal{N} = (36.2 \ lb) \sin 40^0 + 60 \ lb$ $\boxed{\mathcal{N} = 83.3 \ lb}$

---

*4-45. Suppose the lawn mower of Problem 4-44 is to be moved backward. What pull along the handle is required to move with constant speed? What is the normal force in this case? Discuss the differences between this example and the one in the previous problem.

$\mu_k = \dfrac{20 \ lb}{60 \ lb} = 0.333$ $\Sigma F_y = \mathcal{N} + P_y - W = 0;$ $W = 60 \ lb$ $\mathcal{F}_k = \mu_k \mathcal{N} = 0.333 \ \mathcal{N}$

$\mathcal{N} = 60 \ lb - P \sin 40^0;$

$\Sigma F_y = P_x - \mathcal{F}_k = 0;$ $P \cos 40^0 - 0.333 \ \mathcal{N} = 0$

$P \cos 40^0 - 0.333 \ (60 \ lb - P \sin 40^0) = 0;$ $0.766 \ P - 20 \ lb + 0.214 \ P = 0;$

$0.980 \ P = 20 \ lb;$ $P = \dfrac{20 \ lb}{0.980} = 20.4 \ lb;$ $\boxed{P = 20.4 \ lb}$

The normal force is: $\mathcal{N} = 60 \ lb - (20.4 \ lb) \sin 40^0$ $\boxed{\mathcal{N} = 46.9 \ lb}$

---

*4-46. A truck is removed from the mud by attaching a line between the truck and the tree. When the angles are as shown in Fig. 4-28, a force of 40 lb is exerted at the midpoint of the line. What force is exerted on the truck? $\phi = 20^0$

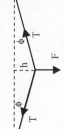

$T \sin 20^0 + T \sin 20^0 = 40 \ lb$ $2 \ T \sin 20^0 = 40 \ lb$

$\boxed{T = 58.5 \ lb}$

---

*4-47. Suppose a force of 900 N is required to move the truck in Fig. 4-28. What force is required at the midpoint of the line for the angles shown?

$2 \ T \sin 20^0 = F;$ $2(900 \ N) \sin 20^0 = F;$ $\boxed{F = 616 \ N}$

---

*4-48. A 70-N block of steel is at rest on a 40° incline. What is the static friction force directed up the plane? Is this necessarily the maximum force of static friction? What is the normal force?

$\mathcal{F} = (70 \ N) \sin 40^0$ $\boxed{\mathcal{F} = 45.0 \ N}$ $\mathcal{N} = (70 \ N) \cos 40^0$ $\boxed{\mathcal{N} = 53.6 \ N}$

**4-51. Find the tension in each cord of Fig. 4-30 if the suspended weight is 476 N.

Consider the knot at the bottom first since more information is given at that point.

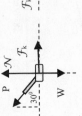

$C_y + C_y = 476$ N; 2C sin $60^0 = 476$ N

$$C = \frac{476 \text{ N}}{2\sin60^0} = 275 \text{ N}$$

$\Sigma F_y = A \sin 30^0 - (275 \text{ N}) \sin 60^0 = 0$

$A = 476$ N; $\Sigma F_x = A \cos 30^0 - C \cos 60^0 - B = 0$; $476 \cos 30^0 - 275 \cos 60^0 - B = 0$

$B = 412$ N $- 137$ N $= 275$ N; Thus: $\boxed{A = 476 \text{ N}, B = 275 \text{ N}, C = 275 \text{ N}}$

*4-52. Find the force required to pull a 40-N sled horizontally at constant speed by exerting a pull along a pole that makes a 30^0 angle with the ground ($\mu_k = 0.4$). Now find the force required if you push along the pole at the same angle. What is the major factor that changes in these cases?

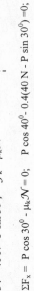

(a) $\Sigma F_y = \mathcal{N} + P_y - W = 0$; $W = 40$ N

$\mathcal{N} = 40$ N $- P \sin 30^0$; $\mathcal{F}_k = \mu_k \mathcal{N}$

$\Sigma F_x = P \cos 30^0 - \mu_k \mathcal{N} = 0$; $P \cos 40^0 - 0.4(40$ N $- P \sin 30^0) = 0$;

$0.866 P - 16$ N $+ 0.200 P = 0$; $\boxed{P = 15.0 \text{ N}}$

(b) $\Sigma F_y = \mathcal{N} - P_y - W = 0$; $\mathcal{N} = 40$ N $+ P \sin 30^0$; $\mathcal{F}_k = \mu_k \mathcal{N}$

$\Sigma F_x = P \cos 30^0 - \mu_k \mathcal{N} = 0$; $P \cos 40^0 - 0.4(40$ N $+ P \sin 30^0) = 0$;

$0.866 P - 16$ N $- 0.200 P = 0$; $\boxed{P = 24.0 \text{ N}}$ *Normal force is greater!*

---

*4-49. Determine the compression in the center strut B and the tension in the rope A for the situation described by Fig. 4-29. Distinguish clearly the difference between the compression force in the strut and the force indicated on your free-body diagram.

$\Sigma F_x = B_x - A_x = 0$; B cos $50^0 = A \cos 20^0$; $B = 1.46$ A

$\Sigma F_y = B \sin 50^0 - A \sin 20^0 - 500$ N $= 0$; $0.766 B - 0.342 A = 500$ N

Substituting $B = 1.46$ A: $0.766 (1.46 A) - (0.342 A) = 500$ N

Solving for A, we obtain: $A = 644$ N; and $B = 1.46 A = 1.46 (644)$ or $B = 940$ N

Thus the tensions are : $\boxed{A = 644 \text{ N}; \quad B = 940 \text{ N}}$

*4-50. What <u>horizontal</u> push P is required to just prevent a 200 N block from slipping down a 60^0 inclined plane where $\mu_s = 0.4$? Why does it take a lesser force if **P** acts <u>parallel</u> to the plane? Is the friction force greater, less, or the same for these two cases?

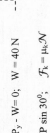

(a) $\Sigma F_y = \mathcal{N} - W_y - P_y = 0$; $W_y = (200$ N$) \cos 60^0 = 100$ N

$P_y = P \sin 60^0 = 0.866$ P; $\mathcal{N} = 100$ N $+ 0.866$ P

$\mathcal{F} = \mu \mathcal{N} = 0.4(100$ N $+ 0.866$ P$)$; $\mathcal{F} = 40$ N $+ 0.346$ P

$\Sigma F_x = P_x - W_x + \mathcal{F} = 0$;   P cos $60^0 - (200$ N$) \sin 60^0 + (40$ N $+ 0.346$ P$) = 0$

$0.5 P - 173.2$ N $+ 40$ N $+ 0.346 P = 0$ *Solving for P gives:* $\boxed{P = 157 \text{ N}}$

(b) *If* **P** *were parallel to the plane, the normal force would be LESS, and therefore the friction force would be reduced. Since the friction force is directed UP the plane, it is actually helping to prevent slipping. You might think at first that the push* **P** *(to stop downward slipping) would then need to be GREATER than before, due to the lesser friction force. However, only half of the push is effective when exerted horizontally. If the force* **P** *were directed up the incline, a force of only 133 N is required. You should verify this value by reworking the problem.*

Chapter 5. Torque and Rotational Equilibrium

Unit Conversions

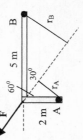

5-1. Draw and label the moment arm of the force F about an axis at point A in Fig. 5-11a. What is the magnitude of the moment arm?

Moment arms are drawn perpendicular to action line:

$$r_A = (2 \text{ ft}) \sin 25^0 \qquad r_A = 0.845 \text{ ft}$$

5-2. Find the moment arm about axis B in Fig. 5-11a. (*See figure above.*)

$$r_B = (3 \text{ ft}) \sin 25^0 \qquad r_B = 1.27 \text{ ft}$$

5-3. Determine the moment arm if the axis of rotation is at point A in Fig. 5-11b. What is the magnitude of the moment arm?

$$r_B = (2 \text{ m}) \sin 60^0 \qquad r_B = 1.73 \text{ m}$$

5-4. Find the moment arm about axis B in Fig. 5-11b.

$$r_B = (5 \text{ m}) \sin 30^0 \qquad r_B = 2.50 \text{ m}$$

Torque

5-5. If the force F in Fig. 5-11a is equal to 80 lb, what is the resultant torque about axis A neglecting the weight of the rod? What is the resultant torque about axis B?

Counterclockwise torques are positive, so that τ_A is - and τ_B is +.

(a) $\tau_A = (80 \text{ lb})(0.845 \text{ ft}) = \boxed{-67.6 \text{ lb ft}}$ (b) $\tau_B = (80 \text{ lb})(1.27 \text{ ft}) = \boxed{+101 \text{ lb ft}}$

5-6. The force F in Fig. 5-11b is 400 N and the angle iron is of negligible weight. What is the resultant torque about axis A and about axis B?

Counterclockwise torques are positive, so that τ_A is + and τ_B is -.

(a) $\tau_A = (400 \text{ N})(1.732 \text{ m}) = \boxed{+693 \text{ N m}}$;   (b) $\tau_B = (400 \text{ N})(2.50 \text{ m}) = \boxed{-1000 \text{ N m}}$

**4-53. Two weights are hung over two frictionless pulleys as shown in Fig. 4-31. What weight W will cause the 300-lb block to just start moving to the right? Assume $\mu_s = 0.3$. Note:

The pulleys merely change the direction of the applied forces.

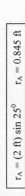

$$\Sigma F_y = \mathcal{N} + (40 \text{ lb}) \sin 45^0 + W \sin 30^0 - 300 \text{ lb} = 0$$

$$\mathcal{N} = 300 \text{ lb} - 28.3 \text{ lb} - 0.5 \ W; \qquad \mathcal{F} = \mu_s \mathcal{N}$$

$$\Sigma F_x = W \cos 30^0 - \mu_s \mathcal{N} - (40 \text{ lb}) \cos 45^0 = 0$$

$$0.866 \ W - 0.3(272 \text{ lb} - 0.5 \ W) - 28.3 \text{ lb} = 0; \qquad \boxed{W = 108 \text{ lb}}$$

**4-54. Find the maximum weight that can be hung at point O in Fig. 4-32 without upsetting the equilibrium. Assume that $\mu_s = 0.3$ between the block and table.

We first find $\mathcal{F}_{max}$ for the block

$$\mathcal{F} = \mu_s \mathcal{N} = 0.3 \ (200 \text{ lb}) = 60 \text{ lb}$$

Now set $A = \mathcal{F} = 60 \text{ lb}$ and solve for W:

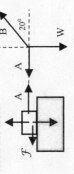

$$\Sigma F_x = B \cos 20^0 - A = 0; \qquad B \cos 20^0 = 60 \text{ lb}; \qquad B = 63.9 \text{ lb}$$

$$\Sigma F_y = B \sin 20^0 - W = 0; \qquad W = B \sin 20^0 = (63.9 \text{ lb}) \sin 20^0; \qquad \boxed{W = 21.8 \text{ lb}}$$

5-7. A leather belt is wrapped around a pulley 20 cm in diameter. A force of 60 N is applied to the belt. What is the torque at the center of the shaft?

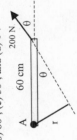

$r = \frac{1}{2}D = \boxed{10 \text{ cm}}$; $\quad \tau = (60 \text{ N})(0.10 \text{ m}) = \boxed{+6.00 \text{ N m}}$

5-8. The light rod in Fig. 5-12 is 60 cm long and pivoted about point A. Find the magnitude and sign of the torque due to the 200 N force if θ is (a) 90°, (b) 60°, (c) 30°, and (d) 0°.

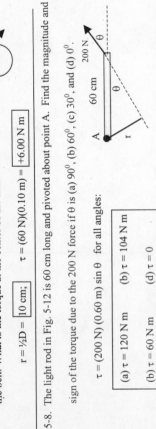

$\tau = (200 \text{ N})(0.60 \text{ m}) \sin\theta$ for all angles:

(a) $\tau = 120$ N m   (b) $\tau = 104$ N m

(b) $\tau = 60$ N m   (d) $\tau = 0$

5-9. A person who weighs 650 N rides a bicycle. The pedals move in a circle of radius 40 cm. If the entire weight acts on each downward moving pedal, what is the maximum torque?

$\tau = (650 \text{ N})(0.40 \text{ m})$ $\boxed{\tau = 260 \text{ N m}}$

5-10. A single belt is wrapped around two pulleys. The drive pulley has a diameter of 10 cm, and the output pulley has a diameter of 20 cm. If the top belt tension is essentially 50 N at the edge of each pulley, what are the input and output torques?

Input torque = (50 N)(0.10 m) $\boxed{5 \text{ N m}}$

Output torque = (50 N)(0.20 m) $\boxed{10 \text{ N m}}$

Resultant Torque

5-11. What is the resultant torque about point A in Fig. 5-13? Neglect weight of bar.

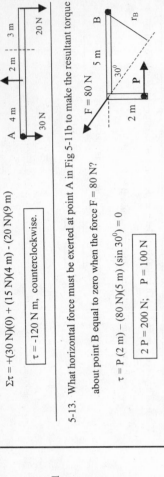

$\Sigma\tau = +(30 \text{ N})(6 \text{ m}) - (15 \text{ N})(2 \text{ m}) - (20 \text{ N})(3 \text{ m})$

$\boxed{\tau = 90.0 \text{ N m, CCW}}$

5-12. Find the resultant torque in Fig. 5-13, if the axis is moved to the left end of the bar.

$\Sigma\tau = +(30 \text{ N})(0) + (15 \text{ N})(4 \text{ m}) - (20 \text{ N})(9 \text{ m})$

$\boxed{\tau = -120 \text{ N m, counterclockwise.}}$

5-13. What horizontal force must be exerted at point A in Fig 5-11b to make the resultant torque about point B equal to zero when the force F = 80 N?

$\tau = P (2 \text{ m}) - (80 \text{ N})(5 \text{ m}) (\sin 30^0) = 0$

$\boxed{2 \, P = 200 \text{ N}; \quad P = 100 \text{ N}}$

5-14. Two wheels of diameters 60 cm and 20 cm are fastened together and turn on the same axis as in Fig. 5-14. What is the resultant torque about a central axis for the shown weights?

$r_1 = \frac{1}{2}(60 \text{ cm}) = 0.30 \text{ m} ; \; r_2 = \frac{1}{2}(30 \text{ cm}) = 0.15 \text{ m}$

$\tau = (200 \text{ N})(0.30 \text{ m}) - (150 \text{ N})(0.15 \text{ m}) = 37.5 \text{ N m};$ $\boxed{\tau = 37.5 \text{ N m, ccw}}$

5-15. Suppose you remove the 150-N weight from the small wheel in Fig. 5-14. What new weight can you hang to produce zero resultant torque?

$\tau = (200 \text{ N})(0.30 \text{ m}) - W (0.15 \text{ m}) = 0;$ $\boxed{W = 400 \text{ N}}$

5-16. Determine the resultant torque about the corner A for Fig. 5-15.

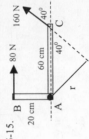

$\Sigma\tau = +(160 \text{ N})(0.60 \text{ m}) \sin 40^0 - (80 \text{ N})(0.20 \text{ m})$

$\Sigma\tau = 61.7 \text{ N m} - 16.0 \text{ N m} = 45.7 \text{ N m}$

$\boxed{\tau_R = 45.7 \text{ N m}}$

5-17. Find the resultant torque about point C in Fig. 5-15.

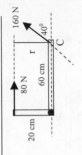

$\Sigma\tau = - (80 \text{ N})(0.20 \text{ m}) = \boxed{-16 \text{ N m}}$

*5-18. Find the resultant torque about axis B in Fig. 5-15.

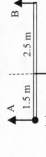
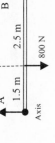

$F_x = 160 \cos 40^0$; $F_y = 160 \sin 40^0$

$\Sigma\tau = -(123 \text{ N})(0.2 \text{ m}) + (103 \text{ N})(0.6 \text{ m}) = \boxed{37.2 \text{ N m}}$

Equilibrium

5-19. A uniform meter stick is balanced at its midpoint with a single support. A 60-N weight is suspended at the 30 cm mark. At what point must a 40-N weight be hung to balance the system?   *(The 60-N weight is 20 cm from the axis)*

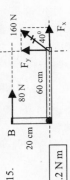

$\Sigma\tau = 0$; $(60 \text{ N})(20 \text{ cm}) - (40 \text{ N})x = 0$

$40 x = 1200 \text{ N cm}$ or $x = 30 \text{ cm}$:   *The weight must be hung at the 80-cm mark.*

5-20. Weights of 10 N, 20 N, and 30 N are placed on a meterstick at the 20 cm, 40 cm, and 60 cm marks, respectively. The meterstick is balanced by a single support at its midpoint. At what point may a 5-N weight be attached to produce equilibrium?

$\Sigma\tau = (10 \text{ N})(30 \text{ cm}) + (20 \text{ N})(10 \text{ cm})$

$\qquad\qquad -(30 \text{ N})(10 \text{ cm}) - (5 \text{ N})x = 0$

$5 x = (300 + 200 - 300)$ or $x = 40 \text{ cm}$

The 5-N weight must be placed at the 90-cm mark

5-21. An 8-m board of negligible weight is supported at a point 2 m from the right end where a 50-N weight is attached. What downward force must be exerted at the left end to produce equilibrium?

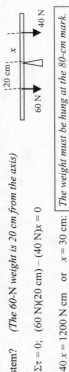

$\Sigma\tau = 0$: $F(6 \text{ m}) - (50 \text{ N})(2 \text{ m}) = 0$

$6 F = 100 \text{ N m}$ or $\boxed{F = 16.7 \text{ N}}$

5-22. A 4-m pole is supported at each end by hunters carrying an 800-N deer which is hung at a point 1.5 m from the left end. What are the upward forces required by each hunter?

$\Sigma\tau = A(0) - (800 \text{ N})(1.5 \text{ m}) + B(4.0 \text{ m}) = 0$

$4B = 1200 \text{ N}$ or $B = 300 \text{ N}$

$\Sigma F_y = A + B - 800 \text{ lb} = 0$; $\boxed{A = 500 \text{ N}}$

5-23. Assume that the bar in Fig. 5-16 is of negligible weight. Find the forces F and A provided the system is in equilibrium.

$\Sigma\tau = (80 \text{ N})(1.20 \text{ m}) - F(0.90 \text{ m}) = 0$; $F = 107 \text{ N}$

$\Sigma F_y = F - A - 80 \text{ N} = 0$; $A = 107 \text{ N} - 80 \text{ N} = 26.7 \text{ N}$

$\boxed{F = 107 \text{ N}, \quad A = 26.7 \text{ N}}$

5-24. For equilibrium, what are the forces F_1 and F_2 in Fig. 5-17? (Neglect weight of bar.)

$\Sigma\tau = (90 \text{ lb})(5 \text{ ft}) - F_2(4 \text{ ft}) - (20 \text{ lb})(5 \text{ ft}) = 0$;

$\boxed{F_2 = 87.5 \text{ lb}}$ $\Sigma F_y = F_1 - F_2 - 20 \text{ lb} - 90 \text{ lb} = 0$

$F_1 = F_2 + 110 \text{ lb} = 87.5 \text{ lb} + 110 \text{ lb}$, $\boxed{F_1 = 198 \text{ lb}}$

5-25. Consider the light bar supported as shown in Fig. 5-18. What are the forces exerted by the supports A and B?

$\Sigma\tau_A = B(11 \text{ m}) - (60 \text{ N})(3 \text{ m}) - (40 \text{ N})(9 \text{ m}) = 0$;

$\boxed{B = 49.1 \text{ N}}$ $\Sigma F_y = A + B - 40 \text{ N} - 60 \text{ N} = 0$

$A = 100 \text{ N} - B = 100 \text{ N} - 49.1 \text{ N}$; $\boxed{B = 50.9 \text{ N}}$

5-26. A V-belt is wrapped around a pulley 16 in. in diameter. If a resultant torque of 4 lb ft is required, what force must be applied along the belt?

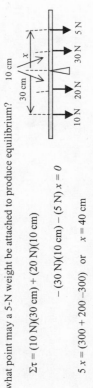
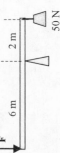

$R = \tfrac{1}{2}(16 \text{ in.}) = 8 \text{ in.}$ $R = (8/12 \text{ ft}) = 0.667 \text{ ft}$

$\tau = F(0.667 \text{ ft}) = 4 \text{ lb ft}$; $\boxed{F = 6.00 \text{ lb}}$

Center of Gravity

5-31. A uniform 6-m bar has a length of 6 m and weighs 30 N. A 50-N weight is hung from the left end and a 20-N force is hung at the right end. How far from the left end will a single upward force produce equilibrium?

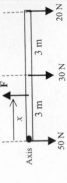

$\Sigma F_y = F - 50\ N - 30\ N - 20\ N = 0$; F = 100 N

$\Sigma \tau = F x - (30\ N)(3\ m) - (20\ N)(6\ m) = 0$

$(100\ N) x = 210\ N\cdot m$; $\boxed{x = 2.10\ m}$

5-32. A 40-N sphere and a 12-N sphere are connected by a light rod 200 mm in length. How far from the middle of the 40-N sphere is the center of gravity?

$\Sigma F_y = F - 40\ N - 12\ N = 0$; F = 52 N

$\Sigma \tau = F x - (40\ N)(0) - (12\ N)(0.20\ m) = 0$

$(52\ N) x = 2.40\ N\cdot m$; x = 0.0462 m or $\boxed{x = 46.2\ mm}$

5-33. Weights of 2, 5, 8, and 10 N are hung from a 10-m light rod at distances of 2, 4, 6, and 8 m from the left end. How far from the left end is the center of gravity?

$\Sigma F_y = F - 10\ N - 8\ N - 5\ N - 2\ N = 0$; F = 25 N

$Fx - (2\ N)(2\ m) - (5\ N)(4\ m) - (8\ N)(6\ m) - (10\ N)(8\ m) = 0$

$(25\ N) x = 152\ N\cdot m$; $\boxed{x = 6.08\ m}$

5-34. Compute the center of gravity of sledgehammer if the metal head weighs 12 lb and the 32-in. supporting handle weighs 2 lb. Assume that the handle is of uniform construction and weight.

$\Sigma F_y = F - 2\ lb - 12\ lb = 0$; F = 14 lb

$Fx - (12\ lb)(0) - (2\ lb)(16\ in.) = 0$; $Fx = 32$ lb in.

$(14\ lb) x = 32\ lb\ in.$; $\boxed{x = 2.29\ in.\ from\ head.}$

5-27. A bridge whose total weight is 4500 N is 20 m long and supported at each end. Find the forces exerted at each end when a 1600-N tractor is located 8 m from the left end.

$\Sigma \tau_A = B (20\ m) - (1600\ N)(8\ m) - (4500\ N)(10\ m) = 0$; $\Sigma F_y = A + B - 1600\ N - 4500\ N = 0$

$\boxed{B = 2890\ N}$

$A = 6100\ N - B = 6100\ N - 2890\ N$; $\boxed{A = 3210\ N}$

5-28. A 10-ft platform weighing 40 lb is supported at each end by stepladders. A 180-lb painter is located 4 ft from the right end. Find the forces exerted by the supports.

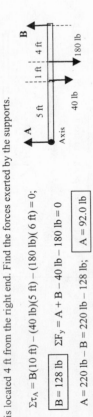

$\Sigma \tau_A = B(10\ ft) - (40\ lb)(5\ ft) - (180\ lb)(6\ ft) = 0$;

$\boxed{B = 128\ lb}$ $\Sigma F_y = A + B - 40\ lb - 180\ lb = 0$

$A = 220\ lb - B = 220\ lb - 128\ lb$; $\boxed{A = 92.0\ lb}$

*5-29. A horizontal, 6-m boom weighing 400 N is hinged at the wall as shown in Fig. 5-19. A cable is attached at a point 4.5 m away from the wall, and a 1200-N weight is attached to the right end. What is the tension in the cable?

$\phi = 90^0 - 37^0 = 53^0$; $T_y = T \sin 53^0$

$\Sigma \tau_A = (T \sin 53^0)(4.5\ m) - (400\ N)(3\ m) - (1200\ N)(6\ m) = 0$;

$3.59\ T = 1200\ N + 7200\ N$; $\boxed{T = 2340\ N}$

*5-30. What are the horizontal and vertical components of the force exerted by the wall on the boom? What is the magnitude and direction of this force?

$\Sigma F_x = H - T_x = 0$; $H - T \cos 53^0 = 0$; $H = (2340\ N) \cos 53^0$; H = 1408 N

$\Sigma F_y = V + T \sin 53^0 - 400\ N - 1200\ N = 0$; $V = 1600\ N - (2340\ N) \sin 53^0 = -269\ N$

Thus, the components are:

$\boxed{H = 1408\ N}$ and $V = -269$ N. The resultant of these is:

$R = \sqrt{H^2 + V^2} = 1434\ N$; $\tan\phi = \dfrac{-269}{1408}$ $\phi = 10.8^0$ S of E

$\boxed{R = 1434\ N,\ 349.2^0}$

Additional Problems

5-35. What is the resultant torque about the hinge in Fig. 5-20? Neglect weight of the curved bar.

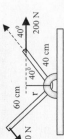

τ = (80 N)(0.6 m) – (200 N)(0.4 m) sin 40°

= 48.0 N·m – 51.4 N·m; $\boxed{\tau = -3.42 \text{ N m}}$

5-36. What horizontal force applied to the left end of the bar in Fig. 5-20 will produce rotational equilibrium?

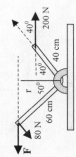

From Prob. 5-33: τ = - 3.42 N m.

Thus, if $\Sigma\tau = 0$, *then torque of* +3.42 N m *must be added.*

F (0.6 m) cos 40° = +3.45 N m; $\boxed{F = 7.45 \text{ N}}$

5-37. Weights of 100, 200, and 500 lb are placed on a light board resting on two supports as shown in Fig. 5-21. What are the forces exerted by the supports?

$\Sigma\tau$ = (100 lb)(4 ft) + B(16 ft)

– (200 lb)(6 ft) – (500 lb)(12 ft) = 0;   B = 425 lb

ΣF_y = A + B – 100 lb – 200 lb – 500 lb = 0

A = 800 lb – B = 800 lb – 425 lb;   A = 375 lb

The forces exerted by the supports are : $\boxed{A = 375 \text{ N and } B = 425 \text{ N}}$

5-38. An 8-m steel metal beam weighs 2400 N and is supported 3 m from the right end. If a 9000-N weight is placed on the right end, what force must be exerted at the left end to balance the system?

$\Sigma\tau_A$ = A (5 m) + (2400 N)(1 m) – (9000 N)(3 m) = 0;

$\boxed{A = 4920 \text{ N}}$ ΣF_y = A + B – 2400 N – 9000 N = 0

B = 11,400 N – A = 11,400 N – 4920 N; $\boxed{A = 6480 \text{ N}}$

***5-39.** Find the resultant torque about point A in Fig. 5-22.*

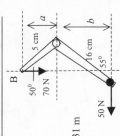

$\Sigma\tau$ = (70 N)(0.05 m) sin 50° – (50 N)(0.16 m) sin 55°

$\Sigma\tau$ = 2.68 N m – 6.55 N m = –3.87 N m

$\boxed{\Sigma\tau = -3.87 \text{ N m}}$

***5-40.** Find the resultant torque about point B in Fig. 5-22.*

$\Sigma\tau$ = (70 N)(0) – (50 N)(a + b) ;   *First find a and b.*

a = (0.05 m) cos 50° = 0.0231 m; b = (0.16 m) sin 55° = 0.131 m

$\Sigma\tau$ = – (50 N)(0.0231 m + 0.131 m) = –8.16 N m

$\boxed{\Sigma\tau = -8.16 \text{ N m}}$

Critical Thinking Questions

***5-41.** A 30-lb box and a 50-lb box are on opposite ends of a 16-ft board supported only at its midpoint. How far from the left end should a 40-lb box be placed to produce equilibrium? Would the result be different if the board weighed 90 lb? Why, or why not?*

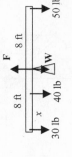

$\Sigma\tau$ = (30 lb)(8 ft) + (40 lb)(x) – (50 lb)(8 ft) = 0;

$\boxed{x = 4.00 \text{ ft}}$ *Note that the weight acting at the center of the board does NOT contribute to torque about the center, and therefore, the balance point is not affected, regardless of the weight.*

5-42. On a lab bench you have a small rock, a 4-N meterstick and a single knife-edge support. Explain how you can use these three items to find the weight of the small rock.

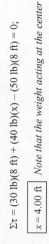

Measure distances a and b; determine F and then calculate the weight W from equilibrium methods.

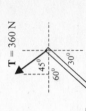

*5-46. For the conditions set in Problem 5-45, what are the horizontal and vertical components of the force exerted by the floor hinge on the base of the boom?

$\Sigma F_x = H - 1169\ N = 0$;   or $H = 1169\ N$

$\Sigma F_y = V - 100\ N - 400\ N = 0$;   or $V = 500\ N$

$$\boxed{H = 1169\ N \quad \text{and} \quad V = 500\ N}$$

**5-47. What is the tension in the cable for Fig. 5-25? The weight of the boom is 300 N but its length is unknown. (*Select axis at wall, L cancels.*)

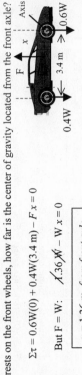

$\Sigma \tau = TL \sin 75^0 - (300N)\dfrac{L}{2}\sin 30^0 - 546\,L\,\sin 30^0 = 0$

$T \sin 75^0 = 75.0\ N + 273\ N$; $\boxed{T = 360\ N}$

**5-48. What are the magnitude and direction of the force exerted by the wall on the boom in Fig. 5-25? Again assume that the weight of the board is 300 N.

Refer to the figure and data given in Problem 5-7 and recall that $T = 360\ N$.

$\Sigma F_x = H - (360\ N)\cos 45^0 = 0$; $H = 255\ N$

$\Sigma F_y = V + (360\ N)\sin 45^0 - 300\ N - 546\ N = 0$; $V = 591\ N$

$$\boxed{H = 255\ N \quad \text{and} \quad V = 591\ N}$$

*5-49. A car has a distance of 3.4 m between front and rear axles. If 60 percent of the weight rests on the front wheels, how far is the center of gravity located from the front axle?

$\Sigma \tau = 0.6W(0) + 0.4W(3.4\ m) - F\,x = 0$

But F = W: $1.36\ \cancel{W} - \cancel{W}\,x = 0$

$$\boxed{x = 1.36\ m\ \text{from front axle}}$$

---

*5-43. Find the forces F₁, F₂, and F₃ such that the system drawn in Fig. 5-23 is in equilibrium.

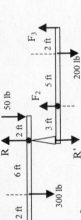

Note action-reaction forces R and R'.

First, let's work with top board.

$\Sigma \tau$ *(about R)* $= 0$; *Force* **R** *is upward.*

$\Sigma \tau_R = (300\ lb)(6\ ft) - (50\ lb)(2\ ft) - F_1(8\ ft) = 0$

$F_1 = 213\ lb$ *Now,* $\Sigma F_y = 0$ *gives:* $213\ lb + R - 300\ lb - 50\ lb = 0$; $R = 138\ lb = R'$

Next we sum torques about F_2 *with* $R' = 138\ lb$ *directed in a downward direction:*

$\Sigma \tau_F = (138\ lb)(3\ ft) + F_3(7\ ft) - (200\ lb)(5\ ft) = 0$;   *From which:* $F_3 = 83.9\ lb$

$\Sigma F_y = 0 = F_2 + 83.9\ lb - 138\ lb - 200\ lb$; $F_2 = -254\ lb$

The three unknown forces are: $\boxed{F_1 = 213\ lb,\ F_2 = -254\ lb,\ F_3 = 83.9\ lb}$

*5-44. (a) What weight W will produce a tension of 400 N in the rope attached to the boom in Fig. 5-24?. (b) What would be the tension in the rope if W = 400 N? Neglect the weight of the boom in each case.

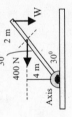

(a) $\Sigma \tau = (400\ N)(4\ m\ \sin 300) - W\,(6\ m)\cos 30^0 = 0$

$$\boxed{W = 154\ N}$$

(b) $\Sigma \tau = T(4\ m)\sin 30^0 - (400\ N)(6\ m)\cos 30^0 = 0$

$$\boxed{T = 600\ N}$$

*5-45. Suppose the boom in Fig. 5-24 has a weight of 100 N and the suspended weight W is equal to 40 N. What is the tension in the cord?

$\Sigma \tau = T(4\ m)\sin 300 - (400\ N)(6\ m)\cos 30^0 - (100\ N)(3\ m)\cos 30^0 = 0$

$$\boxed{T = 1169\ N}$$

Chapter 6. Uniform Acceleration

Problems:

Speed and Velocity

6-1. A car travels a distance of 86 km at an average speed of 8 m/s. How many hours were required for the trip?

$s = \bar{v}t$ $t = \dfrac{s}{\bar{v}} = \dfrac{86,000 \text{ m}}{8 \text{ m/s}} = 10,750 \text{ s} \left(\dfrac{1 \text{ h}}{3600 \text{ s}}\right)$ $\boxed{t = 2.99 \text{ h}}$

6-2. Sound travels at an average speed of 340 m/s. Lightning from a distant thundercloud is seen almost immediately. If the sound of thunder reaches the ear 3 s later, how far away is the storm?

$t = \dfrac{s}{t} = \dfrac{20 \text{ m}}{340 \text{ m/s}} = 0.0588 \text{ s}$ $\boxed{t = 58.8 \text{ ms}}$

6-3. A small rocket leaves its pad and travels a distance of 40 m vertically upward before returning to the earth five seconds after it was launched. What was the average velocity for the trip?

$\bar{v} = \dfrac{s}{t} = \dfrac{40 \text{ m} + 40 \text{ m}}{5 \text{ s}} = \dfrac{80 \text{ m}}{5 \text{ s}}$ $\boxed{v = 16.0 \text{ m/s}}$

6-4. A car travels along a U-shaped curve for a distance of 400 m in 30 s. Its final location, however is only 40 m from the starting position. What is the average speed and what is the magnitude of the average velocity?

D = 40 m

s = 400 m

Average speed: $\bar{v} = \dfrac{s}{t} = \dfrac{400 \text{ m}}{30 \text{ s}}$ $\boxed{v = 13.3 \text{ m/s}}$

Average velocity: $\bar{v} = \dfrac{D}{t} = \dfrac{40 \text{ m}}{30 \text{ s}}$ $\boxed{v = 1.33 \text{ m/s, E}}$

6-5. A woman walks for 4 min directly north with an average velocity of 6 km/h; then she walks eastward at 4 km/h for 10 min. What is her average speed for the trip?

$t_1 = 4 \text{ min} = 0.0667 \text{ h}$; $t_2 = 10 \text{ min} = 0.167 \text{ h}$

$s_1 = v_1 t_1 = (6 \text{ km/h})(0.0667 \text{ h}) = 0.400 \text{ km}$

$s_1 = v_2 t_2 = (4 \text{ km/h})(0.167 \text{ h}) = 0.667 \text{ km}$

$\bar{v} = \dfrac{s_1 + s_2}{t_1 + t_2} = \dfrac{0.4 \text{ km} + 0.667 \text{ km}}{0.0667 \text{ h} + 0.167 \text{ h}}$ $\boxed{v = 4.57 \text{ km/h}}$

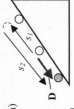

6-6. What is the average velocity for the entire trip described in Problem 6-5?

$D = \sqrt{(0.667 \text{ km})^2 + (0.400 \text{ km})^2}$; $\tan\theta = \dfrac{0.4 \text{ km}}{0.667 \text{ km}}$ $\boxed{D = 0.778 \text{ km}, 31.0^0}$

$v = \dfrac{0.778 \text{ km}}{0.0667 \text{ h} + 0.167 \text{ h}} = 3.33 \text{ km/h}$ $\boxed{v = 3.33 \text{ km/h}, 31.0^0}$

6-7. A car travels at an average speed of 60 mi/h for 3 h and 20 min. What was the distance?

$t = 3 \text{ h} + 0.333 \text{ h} = 3.33 \text{ h}$; $s = vt = (60 \text{ mi/h})(3.33 \text{ h})$; $\boxed{s = 200 \text{ mi}}$

6-8. How long will it take to travel 400 km if the average speed is 90 km/h?

$t = \dfrac{s}{t} = \dfrac{400 \text{ km}}{90 \text{ km/h}}$ $\boxed{t = 4.44 \text{ h}}$

*6-9. A marble rolls up an inclined ramp a distance of 5 m, then stops and returns to a point 5 m below its starting point. The entire trip took only 2 s. What was the average speed and what was the average velocity? $(s_1 = 5 \text{ m}, s_2 = -10 \text{ m})$

$speed = \dfrac{5 \text{ m} + 10 \text{ m}}{2 \text{ s}}$ $\boxed{v = 7.50 \text{ m/s}}$

$velocity = \dfrac{D}{t} = \dfrac{5 \text{ m} - 10 \text{ m}}{2 \text{ s}}$ $\boxed{v = -2.5 \text{ m/s, down plane.}}$

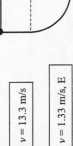

Uniform Acceleration

6-10. The tip of a robot arm is moving to the right at 8 m/s. Four seconds later, it is moving to the left at 2 m/s. What is the change in velocity and what is the acceleration?

$\Delta v = v_f - v_o = (-2 \text{ m/s}) - (8 \text{ m/s})$ $\boxed{\Delta v = -10 \text{ m/s}}$

$a = \dfrac{\Delta v}{t} = \dfrac{-10 \text{ m/s}}{4 \text{ s}}$ $\boxed{a = -2.50 \text{ m/s}^2}$

6-11. An arrow accelerates from zero to 40 m/s in the 0.5 s it is in contact with the bow string. What is the average acceleration?

$a = \dfrac{v_f - v_o}{t} = \dfrac{40 \text{ m/s} - 0}{0.5 \text{ s}}$ $\boxed{a = 80.0 \text{ m/s}^2}$

6-12. A car traveling initially at 50 km/h accelerates at a rate of 4 m/s² for 3 s. What is the final speed?

$v_o = 50 \text{ km/h} = 13.9 \text{ m/s};$ $v_f = v_o + at$

$v_f = (13.9 \text{ m/s}) + (4 \text{ m/s}^2)(3 \text{ s}) = 25.9 \text{ m/s};$ $\boxed{v_f = 25.9 \text{ m/s}}$

6-13. A truck traveling at 60 mi/h brakes to a stop in 180 ft. What was the average acceleration and stopping time?

$v_o = 60 \text{ mi/h} = 88.0 \text{ ft/s}$ $2as = v_f^2 - v_o^2$

$a = \dfrac{v_f^2 - v_o^2}{2s} = \dfrac{0 - (88.0 \text{ ft/s})^2}{2(180 \text{ ft})}$ $\boxed{a = -21.5 \text{ ft/s}^2}$

$x = \left(\dfrac{v_o + v_f}{2}\right) t;$ $t = \dfrac{2x}{v_0 + v_f} = \left(\dfrac{2(180 \text{ ft})}{88.0 \text{ ft/s} + 0}\right)$ $\boxed{t = 4.09 \text{ s}}$

6-14. An arresting device on a carrier deck stops an airplane in 1.5 s. The average acceleration was 49 m/s². What was the stopping distance? What was the initial speed?

$v_f = v_o + at;$ $0 = v_o + (-49 \text{ m/s}^2)(1.5 \text{ s});$ $\boxed{v_o = 73.5 \text{ m/s}}$

$s = v_f t - \tfrac{1}{2}at^2;$ $s = (0)(1.5 \text{ s}) - \tfrac{1}{2}(-49 \text{ m/s}^2)(1.5 \text{ s})^2;$ $\boxed{s = 55.1 \text{ m}}$

6-15. In a braking test, a car traveling at 60 km/h is stopped in a time of 3 s. What was the acceleration and stopping distance? ($v_o = 60 \text{ km/h} = 16.7 \text{ m/s}$)

$v_f = v_o + at;$ $(0) = (16.7 \text{ m/s}) + a (3 \text{ s});$ $\boxed{a = -5.56 \text{ m/s}^2}$

$s = \dfrac{v_o + v_f}{2} t = \left(\dfrac{16.6 \text{ m/s} + 0}{2}\right)(3 \text{ s});$ $\boxed{s = 25.0 \text{ m}}$

6-16. A bullet leaves a 28-in. rifle barrel at 2700 ft/s. What was its acceleration and time in the barrel?   (s = 28 in. = 2.33 ft)

$2as = v_o^2 - v_f^2;$ $a = \dfrac{v_f^2 - v_o^2}{2s} = \dfrac{(2700 \text{ ft/s})^2 - 0}{2(2.33 \text{ ft})};$ $\boxed{a = 1.56 \times 10^6 \text{ m/s}^2}$

$s = \dfrac{v_o + v_f}{2} t;$ $t = \dfrac{2s}{v_o + v_f} = \dfrac{2(2.33 \text{ ft})}{0 + 2700 \text{ ft/s}};$ $\boxed{t = 1.73 \text{ ms}}$

6-17. The ball in Fig. 6-13 is given an initial velocity of 16 m/s at the bottom of an inclined plane. Two seconds later it is still moving up the plane, but with a velocity of only 4 m/s. What is the acceleration?

$v_f = v_o + at;$ $a = \dfrac{v_f - v_o}{t} = \dfrac{4 \text{ m/s} - (16 \text{ m/s})}{2 \text{ s}};$ $\boxed{a = -6.00 \text{ m/s}^2}$

*6-18. For Problem 6-17, what is the maximum displacement from the bottom and what is the velocity 4 s after leaving the bottom? (*Maximum displacement occurs when $v_f = 0$*)

$2as = v_o^2 - v_f^2;$ $s = \dfrac{v_f^2 - v_o^2}{2a} = \dfrac{0 - (16 \text{ m/s})^2}{2(-6 \text{ m/s}^2)};$ $\boxed{s = +21.3 \text{ m}}$

$v_f = v_o + at = 16 \text{ m/s} = (-6 \text{ m/s}^2)(4 \text{ s});$ $\boxed{v_f = -8.00 \text{ m/s, down plane}}$

6-19. A monorail train traveling at 80 km/h must be stopped in a distance of 40 m. What average acceleration is required and what is the stopping time? (v_o = 80 km/h = 22.2 m/s)

$2as = v_o^2 - v_f^2$; $\quad a = \dfrac{v_f^2 - v_o^2}{2s} = \dfrac{0 - (22.2 \text{ m/s})^2}{2(40 \text{ m})}$; $\quad$ [a = -6.17 m/s²]

$s = \dfrac{v_o + v_f}{2}t$; $\quad t = \dfrac{2s}{v_o + v_f} = \dfrac{2(40 \text{ m})}{22.2 \text{ m/s} + 0}$; $\quad$ [t = 3.60 s]

Gravity and Free-Falling Bodies

6-20. A ball is dropped from rest and falls for 5 s. What are its position and velocity?

$s = v_o t + \tfrac{1}{2}at^2$; $\quad s = (0)(5 \text{ s}) + \tfrac{1}{2}(-9.8 \text{ m/s}^2)(5 \text{ s})^2$; $\quad$ [s = -122.5 m]

$v_f = v_o + at = 0 + (-9.8 \text{ m/s}^2)(5 \text{ s})$; $\quad$ [v = -49.0 m/s]

6-21. A rock is dropped from rest. When will its displacement be 18 m below the point of release? What is its velocity at that time?

$s = v_o t + \tfrac{1}{2}at^2$; $\quad (-18 \text{ m}) = (0)(t) + \tfrac{1}{2}(-9.8 \text{ m/s}^2)t^2$; $\quad$ [t = 1.92 s]

$v_f = v_o + at = 0 + (-9.8 \text{ m/s}^2)(1.92 \text{ s})$; $\quad$ [v_f = -18.8 m/s]

6-22. A woman drops a weight from the top of a bridge while a friend below measures the time to strike the water below. What is the height of the bridge if the time is 3 s?

$s = v_o t + \tfrac{1}{2}at^2 = (0) + \tfrac{1}{2}(-9.8 \text{ m/s}^2)(3 \text{ s})^2$; $\quad$ [s = -44.1 m]

6-23. A brick is given an initial downward velocity of 6 m/s. What is its final velocity after falling a distance of 40 m?

$2as = v_o^2 - v_f^2$; $\quad v_f = \sqrt{v_o^2 + 2as} = \sqrt{(-6 \text{ m/s})^2 + 2(-9.8 \text{ m/s}^2)(-40 \text{ m})}$;

$v = \pm28.6$ m/s; $\quad$ *Since velocity is downward,* $\quad$ [v = -28.6 m/s]

6-24. A projectile is thrown vertically upward and returns to its starting position in 5 s. What was its initial velocity and how high did it rise?

$s = v_o t + \tfrac{1}{2}at^2$; $\quad 0 = v_o(5 \text{ s}) + \tfrac{1}{2}(-9.8 \text{ m/s}^2)(5 \text{ s})^2$; $\quad$ [v_o = 24.5 m/s]

$2as = v_o^2 - v_f^2$; $\quad s = \dfrac{0 - (24.5 \text{ m/s})^2}{2(-9.8 \text{ m/s}^2)}$; $\quad$ [s = 30.6 m]

6-25. An arrow is shot vertically upward with an initial velocity of 80 ft/s. What is its maximum height? *(At maximum height, v_f = 0; $a = g = -32$ ft/s²)*

$2as = v_o^2 - v_f^2$; $\quad s = \dfrac{v_f^2 - v_o^2}{2a} = \dfrac{0 - (80 \text{ ft/s})^2}{2(-32 \text{ ft/s}^2)}$; $\quad$ [s = 100 ft]

6-26. In Problem 6-25, what are the position and velocity of the arrow after 2 s and after 6 s?

$s = v_o t + \tfrac{1}{2}at^2 = (80 \text{ ft/s})(2 \text{ s}) + \tfrac{1}{2}(-32 \text{ ft/s}^2)(2 \text{ s})^2$; $\quad$ [s = 96 ft]

$v_f = v_o + at = (80 \text{ ft/s}) + (-32 \text{ ft/s}^2)(2 \text{ s})$; $\quad$ [v_f = 16 ft/s]

$s = v_o t + \tfrac{1}{2}at^2 = (80 \text{ ft/s})(6 \text{ s}) + \tfrac{1}{2}(-32 \text{ ft/s}^2)(6 \text{ s})^2$; $\quad$ [s = -96 ft]

$v_f = v_o + at = (80 \text{ ft/s}) + (-32 \text{ ft/s}^2)(6 \text{ s})$; $\quad$ [v_f = -112 ft/s]

6-27. A hammer is thrown vertically upward to the top of a roof 16 m high. What minimum initial velocity was required?

$2as = v_o^2 - v_f^2$; $\quad v_o = \sqrt{v_f^2 - 2as} = \sqrt{(0)^2 - 2(-9.8 \text{ m/s}^2)(16 \text{ m})}$; $\quad$ [v_o = 17.7 m/s]

Horizontal Projection

6-28. A baseball leaves a bat with a horizontal velocity of 20 m/s. In a time of 0.25 s, how far will it have traveled horizontally and how far has it fallen vertically?

$x = v_{ox} t = (20 \text{ m/s})(2.5 \text{ s})$; $\quad$ [x = 50.0 m]

$y = v_{oy} + \tfrac{1}{2}gt^2 = (0)(2.5 \text{ s}) + \tfrac{1}{2}(-9.8 \text{ m/s}^2)(0.25 \text{ s})^2$; $\quad$ [y = -0.306 m]

6-29. An airplane traveling at 70 m/s drops a box of supplies. What horizontal distance will the box travel before striking the ground 340 m below?

First we find the time to fall: $y = \cancel{v_{oy}t}^{0} + \frac{1}{2}gt^2$ $t = \sqrt{\frac{2y}{g}} = \sqrt{\frac{2(-340 \text{ m})}{-9.8 \text{ m/s}^2}}$

$t = 8.33 \text{ s}$; $x = v_{ox}t = (70 \text{ m/s})(8.33 \text{ s})$; $x = 583 \text{ m}$

6-30. At a lumber mill, logs are discharged horizontally at 15 m/s from a greased chute that is 20 m above a mill pond. How far do the logs travel horizontally?

$y = \frac{1}{2}gt^2$; $t = \sqrt{\frac{2y}{g}} = \sqrt{\frac{2(-20 \text{ m})}{-9.8 \text{ m/s}^2}}$; $t = 2.02 \text{ s}$

$x = v_{ox}t = (15 \text{ m/s})(8.33 \text{ s})$; $x = 30.3 \text{ m}$

6-31. A steel ball rolls off the edge of a table top 4 ft above the floor. If it strikes the floor 5 ft from the base of the table, what was its initial horizontal speed?

First find time to drop 4 ft: $t = \sqrt{\frac{2y}{g}} = \sqrt{\frac{2(-4 \text{ ft})}{-32 \text{ ft/s}^2}}$; $t = 0.500 \text{ s}$

$x = v_{ox}t$; $v_{ox} = \frac{x}{t} = \frac{5 \text{ ft}}{0.5 \text{ s}}$; $v_{ox} = 10.0 \text{ ft/s}$

6-32. A bullet leaves the barrel of a weapon with an initial horizontal velocity of 400 m/s. Find the horizontal and vertical displacements after 3 s.

$x = v_{ox}t = (400 \text{ m/s})(3 \text{ s})$; $x = 1200 \text{ m}$

$y = v_{oy}t + \frac{1}{2}gt^2 = (0)(3 \text{ s}) + \frac{1}{2}(-9.8 \text{ m/s}^2)(3 \text{ s})^2$; $y = -44.1 \text{ m}$

6-33. A projectile has an initial horizontal velocity of 40 m/s at the edge of a roof top. Find the horizontal and vertical components of its velocity after 3 s.

$v_x = v_{ox} = 40 \text{ m/s}$ $v_y = v_{oy}t + gt = 0 + (-9.8 \text{ m/s}^2)(3s)$; $v_y = -29.4 \text{ m/s}$

The More General Problem of Trajectories

6-34. A stone is given an initial velocity of 20 m/s at an angle of 58°. What are its horizontal and vertical displacements after 3 s?

$v_{ox} = (20 \text{ m/s}) \cos 58^0 = 10.6 \text{ m/s}$; $v_{oy} = (20 \text{ m/s}) \sin 58^0 = 17.0 \text{ m/s}$

$x = v_{ox}t = (10.6 \text{ m/s})(3 \text{ s})$; $x = 31.8 \text{ m}$

$y = v_{oy}t + \frac{1}{2}gt^2 = (17.0 \text{ m/s})(3 \text{ s}) + \frac{1}{2}(-9.8 \text{ m/s}^2)(3 \text{ s})^2$; $y = 6.78 \text{ m}$

6-35. A baseball leaves the bat with a velocity of 30 m/s at an angle of 30°. What are the horizontal and vertical components of its velocity after 3 s?

$v_{ox} = (30 \text{ m/s}) \cos 30^0 = 26.0 \text{ m/s}$; $v_{oy} = (30 \text{ m/s}) \sin 30^0 = 15.0 \text{ m/s}$

$v_x = v_{ox} = 26.0 \text{ m/s}$; $v_x = 26.0 \text{ m/s}$

$v_y = v_{oy} + gt = (15 \text{ m/s}) + (-9.8 \text{ m/s}^2)(3 \text{ s})$; $v_y = -14.4 \text{ m/s}$

6-36. For the baseball in Problem 6-35, what is the maximum height and what is the range?

y_{max} occurs when $v_y = 0$, or when: $v_y = v_{oy} + gt = 0$ and $t = -v_{oy}/g$

$t = \frac{-v_{oy}}{g} = \frac{-30\sin30^0}{-9.8 \text{ m/s}}$; $t = 1.53 \text{ s}$;   Now we find y_{max} using this time.

$y_{max} = v_{oy}t + \frac{1}{2}gt^2 = (15 \text{ m/s})(1.53 \text{ s}) + \frac{1}{2}(-9.8 \text{ m/s}^2)(1.53 \text{ s})^2$; $y_{max} = 11.5 \text{ m}$

The range will be reached when the time is $t' = 2(1.53 \text{ s})$ or $t' = 3.06 \text{ s}$, thus

$R = v_{ox}t' = (30 \text{ m/s}) \cos 30^0 (3.06 \text{ s})$; $R = 79.5 \text{ m}$

6-37. An arrow leaves the bow with an initial velocity of 120 ft/s at an angle of 37° with the horizontal. What are the horizontal and vertical components of its displacement two seconds later?

$v_{ox} = (120 \text{ ft/s}) \cos 37^0 = 104 \text{ ft}$; $v_{oy} = (120 \text{ ft/s}) \sin 30^0 = 60.0 \text{ ft/s}$

6-37. (Cont.) *The components of the initial velocity are:* $v_{ox} = 104$ ft/s; $v_{oy} = 60.0$ ft/s.

$x = v_{ox}t = (104 \text{ ft/s})(2 \text{ s})$; $\boxed{x = 208 \text{ ft}}$

$y = v_{oy}t + \frac{1}{2}gt^2 = (60.0 \text{ m/s})(2 \text{ s}) + \frac{1}{2}(-32 \text{ ft/s}^2)(2 \text{ s})^2$; $\boxed{y = 56.0 \text{ ft}}$

*6-38. In Problem 6-37, what are the magnitude and direction of arrow's velocity after 2 s?

$v_x = v_{ox} = 104$ ft/s; $\boxed{v_x = 104 \text{ ft/s}}$

$v_y = v_{oy} + gt = (60 \text{ m/s}) + (-32 \text{ ft/s}^2)(2 \text{ s})$; $\boxed{v_y = -4.00 \text{ ft/s}}$

*6-39. A golf ball in Fig. 6-14 leaves the tee with a velocity of 40 m/s at 65°. If it lands on a green located 10 m higher than the tee, what was the time of flight, and what was the horizontal distance to the tee?

$v_{ox} = (40 \text{ m/s}) \cos 65^0 = 16.9$ m/s; $v_{oy} = (40 \text{ m/s}) \sin 65^0 = 36.25$ m/s;

$y = v_{oy}t + \frac{1}{2}gt^2$: $10 \text{ ft} = (36.25 \text{ m/s})t + \frac{1}{2}(-9.8 \text{ m/s}^2)t^2$

Solving quadratic $(4.9t^2 - 36.25t + 10 = 0)$ *yields:* $t_1 = 0.287$ s *and* $t_2 = 7.11$ s

The first time is for y = +10 m on the way up, the second is y = +10 m on the way down.

Thus, the time from tee to green was: $\boxed{t = 7.11 \text{ s}}$

Horizontal distance to tee: $x = v_{ox}t = (16.9 \text{ m/s})(7.11 \text{ s})$; $\boxed{x = 120 \text{ m}}$

*6-40. A projectile leaves the ground with a velocity of 35 m/s at an angle of 32°. What is the maximum height attained?

$v_{ox} = (35 \text{ m/s}) \cos 32^0 = 29.7$ m/s; $v_{oy} = (35 \text{ m/s}) \sin 32^0 = 18.55$ m/s

y_{max} *occurs when* $v_y = 0$, *or when:* $v_y = v_{oy} + gt = 0$ *and* $t = -v_{oy}/g$

$t = \dfrac{-v_{oy}}{g} = \dfrac{-18.55^0}{-9.8 \text{ m/s}^2}$; $t = 1.89$ s; *Now we find* y_{max} *using this time.*

$y_{max} = v_{oy}t + \frac{1}{2}gt^2 = (18.55 \text{ m/s})(1.89 \text{ s}) + \frac{1}{2}(-9.8 \text{ m/s}^2)(1.89 \text{ s})^2$; $\boxed{y_{max} = 17.5 \text{ m}}$

---

*6-41. The projectile in Problem 6-40 rises and falls, striking a billboard at a point 8 m above the ground. What was the time of flight and how far did it travel horizontally?

$v_{ox} = (35 \text{ m/s}) \cos 32^0 = 29.7$ m/s; $v_{oy} = (35 \text{ m/s}) \sin 32^0 = 18.55$ m/s

$y = v_{oy}t + \frac{1}{2}gt^2$: $8 \text{ m} = (18.55 \text{ m/s})t + \frac{1}{2}(-9.8 \text{ m/s}^2)t^2$

Solving quadratic $(4.9t^2 - 18.55t + 8 = 0)$ *yields:* $t_1 = 0.497$ s *and* $t_2 = 3.36$ s

The first time is for y = +8 m on the way up, the second is y = +8 m on the way down.

Thus, the time from tee to green was: $\boxed{t = 3.29 \text{ s}}$

Horizontal distance to tee: $x = v_{ox}t = (29.7 \text{ m/s})(3.29 \text{ s})$; $\boxed{x = 97.7 \text{ m}}$

Additional Problems

6-42. A rocket travels in space at 60 m/s before it is given a sudden acceleration. If its velocity increases to 140 m/s in 8 s, what was its average acceleration and how far did it travel in this time?

$a = \dfrac{v_f - v_0}{t} = \dfrac{(140 \text{ m/s}) - (60 \text{ m/s})}{8 \text{ s}}$; $\boxed{a = 10 \text{ m/s}^2}$

$s = \dfrac{v_0 + v_f}{2}\, t = \left(\dfrac{140 \text{ m/s} + 60 \text{ m/s}}{2}\right)(8 \text{ s})$; $\boxed{t = 800 \text{ s}}$

6-43. A railroad car starts from rest and coasts freely down an incline. With an average acceleration of 4 ft/s², what will be the velocity after 5 s? What distance does it travel?

$v_f = v_0 + at = 0 + (4 \text{ ft/s}^2)(5 \text{ s})$; $\boxed{v_f = 20 \text{ ft/s}}$

$s = v_0t + \frac{1}{2}at^2 = 0 + \frac{1}{2}(4 \text{ ft/s}^2)(5 \text{ s})^2$; $\boxed{s = 50 \text{ ft}}$

*6-44. An object is projected horizontally at 20 m/s. At the same time, another object located 12 m down range is dropped from rest. When will they collide and how far are they located below the release point?

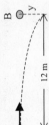

A: $v_{ox} = 20 \text{ m/s}$, $v_{oy} = 0$; **B:** $v_{ox} = v_{oy} = 0$

Ball B will have fallen the distance y at the same time t as ball A. Thus,

$x = v_{ox}t$ and $(20 \text{ m/s})t = 12 \text{ m}$; $\boxed{t = 0.600 \text{ s}}$

$y = \frac{1}{2}at^2 = \frac{1}{2}(-9.8 \text{ m/s}^2)(0.6 \text{ s})^2$; $\boxed{y = -1.76 \text{ m}}$

6-45. A truck moving at an initial velocity of 30 m/s is brought to a stop in 10 s. What was the acceleration of the car and what was the stopping distance?

$a = \dfrac{v_f - v_o}{t} = \dfrac{0 - 30 \text{ m/s}}{10 \text{ s}}$; $\boxed{a = -3.00 \text{ m/s}^2}$

$s = \dfrac{v_o + v_f}{2}t = \left(\dfrac{30 \text{ m/s} + 0}{2}\right)(10 \text{ s})$; $\boxed{s = 150 \text{ m}}$

6-46. A ball is thrown vertically upward with an initial velocity of 23 m/s. What are its position and velocity after 2s, after 4 s, and after 8 s?

Apply $s = v_o t + \frac{1}{2}at^2$ *and* $v_f = v_o + at$ *for time of 2, 4, and 8 s:*

(a) $s = (23 \text{ m/s})(2 \text{ s}) + \frac{1}{2}(-9.8 \text{ m/s}^2)(2 \text{ s})^2$; $\boxed{s = 26.4 \text{ m}}$

$v_f = (23 \text{ m/s}) + (-9.8 \text{ m/s}^2)(2 \text{ s})$; $\boxed{v_f = 3.40 \text{ m/s}}$

(b) $s = (23 \text{ m/s})(4 \text{ s}) + \frac{1}{2}(-9.8 \text{ m/s}^2)(4 \text{ s})^2$; $\boxed{s = 13.6 \text{ m}}$

$v_f = (23 \text{ m/s}) + (-9.8 \text{ m/s}^2)(4 \text{ s})$; $\boxed{v_f = -16.2 \text{ m/s}}$

(c) $s = (23 \text{ m/s})(8 \text{ s}) + \frac{1}{2}(-9.8 \text{ m/s}^2)(8 \text{ s})^2$; $\boxed{s = -130 \text{ m}}$

$v_f = (23 \text{ m/s}) + (-9.8 \text{ m/s}^2)(8 \text{ s})$; $\boxed{v_f = -55.4 \text{ m/s}}$

6-47. A stone is thrown vertically downward from the top of a bridge. Four seconds later it strikes the water below. If the final velocity was 60 m/s, what was the initial velocity of the stone and how high was the bridge?

$v_f = v_o + at$; $v_o = v_f - at = (-60 \text{ m/s}) - (-9.8 \text{ m/s}^2)(4 \text{ s})$; $\boxed{v_o = -20.8 \text{ m/s}}$

$s = v_o t + \frac{1}{2}at^2 = (-20.8 \text{ m/s})(4 \text{ s}) + \frac{1}{2}(-9.8 \text{ m/s}^2)(4 \text{ s})^2$; $\boxed{s = 162 \text{ m}}$

6-48. A ball is thrown vertically upward with an initial velocity of 80 ft/s. What are its position and velocity after (a) 1 s; (b) 3 s; and (c) 6 s?

Apply $s = v_o t + \frac{1}{2}at^2$ *and* $v_f = v_o + at$ *for time of 2, 4, and 8 s:*

(a) $s = (80 \text{ ft/s})(1 \text{ s}) + \frac{1}{2}(-32 \text{ ft/s}^2)(1 \text{ s})^2$; $\boxed{s = 64.0 \text{ ft}}$

$v_f = (80 \text{ ft/s}) + (-32 \text{ ft/s}^2)(2 \text{ s})$; $\boxed{v_f = 16.0 \text{ ft/s}}$

(b) $s = (80 \text{ ft/s})(3 \text{ s}) + \frac{1}{2}(-32 \text{ ft/s}^2)(3 \text{ s})^2$; $\boxed{s = 96.0 \text{ ft}}$

$v_f = (80 \text{ ft/s}) + (-32 \text{ ft/s}^2)(3 \text{ s})$; $\boxed{v_f = -16.0 \text{ ft/s}}$

(c) $s = (80 \text{ ft/s})(6 \text{ s}) + \frac{1}{2}(-32 \text{ ft/s}^2)(6 \text{ s})^2$; $\boxed{s = 64.0 \text{ ft}}$

$v_f = (80 \text{ ft/s}) + (-32 \text{ ft/s}^2)(6 \text{ s})$; $\boxed{v_f = -96.0 \text{ ft/s}}$

6-49. An aircraft flying horizontally at 500 mi/h releases a package. Four seconds later, the package strikes the ground below. What was the altitude of the plane?

$y = \frac{1}{2}gt^2 = \frac{1}{2}(-32 \text{ ft/s}^2)(4 \text{ s})^2$; $\boxed{y = -256 \text{ ft}}$

*6-50. In Problem 6-49, what was the horizontal range of the package and what are the components of its final velocity?

$v_o = 500 \text{ mi/h} = 733 \text{ ft/s}$; $v_x = v_{ox} = 733 \text{ ft/s}$; $v_{oy} = 0$; $t = 4 \text{ s}$

$x = v_x t = (733 \text{ ft/s})(4 \text{ s})$; $\boxed{x = 2930 \text{ ft}}$

$v_y = v_{oy} + at = 0 + (-32 \text{ ft/s}^2)(4 \text{ s})$; $\boxed{v_y = -128 \text{ ft/s};\ v_x = 733 \text{ m/s}}$

*6-51. A putting green is located 240 ft horizontally and 64 ft vertically from the tee. What must be the magnitude and direction of the initial velocity if a ball is to strike the green at this location after a time of 4 s?

$x = v_{ox}t$; $240 \text{ ft} = v_{ox}(4 \text{ s})$; $v_{ox} = 60 \text{ m/s}$

$s = v_0 t + \tfrac{1}{2}at^2$; $64 \text{ ft} = v_{oy}(4 \text{ s}) + \tfrac{1}{2}(-32 \text{ ft/s}^2)(4 \text{ s})^2$; $v_{oy} = 80 \text{ ft/s}$

$v = \sqrt{v_x^2 + v_y^2} = \sqrt{(60 \text{ ft/s})^2 + (80 \text{ ft/s})^2}$; $\tan\theta = \dfrac{80 \text{ ft/s}}{60 \text{ ft/s}}$; $\boxed{v = 100 \text{ ft/s}, \theta = 53.1^0}$

Critical Thinking Questions

6-52. A long strip of pavement is marked off in 100-m intervals. Students use stopwatches to record the times a car passes each mark. The following data is listed:

Distance, m	0	10 m	20 m	30 m	40 m	50 m
Time, s	0	2.1 s	4.3 s	6.4 s	8.4 s	10.5 s

Plot a graph with distance along the y-axis and time along the x-axis. What is the significance of the slope of this curve? What is the average speed of the car? At what instant in time is the distance equal to 34 m? What is the acceleration of the car?

Data taken directly from the graph (not drawn): **Ans.** *Slope is v,* 4.76 m/s, 7.14 s, 0.

6-53. An astronaut tests gravity on the moon by dropping a tool from a height of 5 m. The following data are recorded electronically.

Height, m	5.00 m	4.00 m	3.00 m	2.00 m	1.00 m	0 m
Time, s	0	1.11 s	1.56 s	1.92 s	2.21 s	2.47 s

6-53. (Cont.) Plot the graph of this data. Is it a straight line? What is the average speed for the entire fall? What is the acceleration? How would you compare this with gravity on earth?

Data taken directly from the graph (not drawn): **Ans.** *Slope is v,* 4.76 m/s, 7.14 s, 0.

*6-54. A car is traveling initially North at 20 m/s. After traveling a distance of 6 m, the car passes point A where its velocity is still northward but is reduced to 5 m/s. (a) What are the magnitude and direction of the acceleration of the car? (b) What time was required? (c) If the acceleration is held constant, what will be the velocity of the car when it returns to point A?

$v = 20 \text{ m/s}$ $\qquad$ $v = 5 \text{ m/s}$
$x = 0$ A $x = 6 \text{ m}$

(a) $v_o = 20 \text{ m/s}, v_f = 5 \text{ m/s}, x = 6 \text{ m}$

$2as = v_o^2 - v_f^2; a = \dfrac{v_f^2 - v_o^2}{2s} = \dfrac{(5 \text{ m/s})^2 - (20 \text{ m/s})^2}{2(6 \text{ m})}$; $\boxed{a = -31.2 \text{ m/s}^2}$

(b) $s = \dfrac{v_0 + v_f}{2}t$; $t = \dfrac{2s}{v_0 + v_f} = \dfrac{2(6 \text{ m})}{20 \text{ m/s} + 5 \text{ m/s}}$; $\boxed{t = 0.480 \text{ s}}$

(c) *Starts at A with* $v_o = + 5$ *m/s then returns to A with zero net displacement (s = 0):*

$2as = v_o^2 - v_f^2$; $0 = (5 \text{ m/s})^2 - v_f^2$; $v_f = \sqrt{(5 \text{ m/s})^2} = \pm 5 \text{ m/s}$; $\boxed{v_f = -5 \text{ m/s}}$

*6-55. A ball moving up an incline is initially located 6 m from the bottom of an incline and has a velocity of 4 m/s. Five seconds later, it is located 3 m from the bottom. Assuming constant acceleration, what was the average velocity? What is the meaning of a negative average velocity? What is the average acceleration and final velocity?

6 m   4 m/s
3 m
s = 0

$v_o = + 4 \text{ m/s}; s = -3 \text{ m}; t = 5 \text{ s}$ Find v_{avg}

$s = v_{avg} t$; $\bar{v} = \dfrac{-3 \text{ m}}{5 \text{ s}}$; $v_{avg} = -0.600 \text{ m/s}$

Negative average velocity means that the velocity was <u>down the plane most of the time</u>.

*6-55. (Cont.) $s = v_o t + \frac{1}{2}at^2$; $-3\,m = (4\,m/s)(5\,s) + \frac{1}{2}a(5\,s)^2$; $\boxed{a = -1.84\,m/s^2}$

$v_j = v_o + at = 4\,m/s + (-1.84\,m/s^2)(5\,s)$; $\boxed{v_j = -5.20\,m/s}$

*6-56. The acceleration due to gravity on a distant planet is determined to be one-fourth its value on the earth. Does this mean that a ball dropped from a height of 4 m above this planet will strike the ground in one-fourth the time? What are the times required on the planet and on earth?

The distance as a function of time is given by: $s = \frac{1}{2}at^2$ *so that*

one-fourth the acceleration should result in twice the drop time.

$t_e = \sqrt{\dfrac{2s}{g_e}} = \sqrt{\dfrac{2(4\,m)}{9.8\,m/s^2}}$ $\boxed{t_e = 0.904\,s}$

$t_p = \sqrt{\dfrac{2s}{g_p}} = \sqrt{\dfrac{2(4\,m)}{2.45\,m/s^2}}$ $\boxed{t_p = 1.81\,s}$

*6-57. Consider the two balls A and B shown in Fig. 6-15. Ball A has a constant acceleration of 4 m/s² directed to the right, and ball B has a constant acceleration of 2 m/s² directed to the left. Ball A is initially traveling to the left at 2 m/s, while ball B is traveling to the left initially at 5 m/s. Find the time t at which the balls collide. Also, assuming x = 0 at the initial position of ball A, what is their common displacement when they collide?

Equations of displacement for A and B:

$s = s_o + v_o t + \frac{1}{2}at^2$ *(watch signs)*

For A: $s_A = 0 + (-2\,m/s)t + \frac{1}{2}(+4\,m/s^2)t^2$

For B: $s_B = 18\,m + (-5\,m/s)t + \frac{1}{2}(-2\,m/s^2)t^2$;   *Next simplify and set $s_A = s_B$:*

$-2t + 2t^2 = 18 - 5t - t^2 \rightarrow 3t^2 + 3t - 18 = 0 \rightarrow$ $t_1 = -3\,s$, $\boxed{t_2 = +2\,s}$

Accept t = +2 s as meaningful answer, then substitute to find either s_A or s_B:

$s_A = -2(2\,s) + 2(2\,s)^2$; $\boxed{s = +4\,m}$

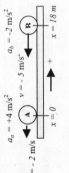

---

*6-58. Initially, a truck with a velocity of 40 ft/s is located a distance of 500 ft to the right of a car. If the car begins at rest and accelerates at 10 ft/s², when will it overtake the truck? How far is the point from the initial position of the car?

Equations of displacement for car and truck:

$s = s_o + v_o t + \frac{1}{2}at^2$ *(watch signs)*

For car: $s_C = 0 + \frac{1}{2}(+10\,ft/s^2)t^2$;   Truck: $s_T = 500\,ft + (40\,ft/s)t + 0$;

Set $s_C = s_T$: $5t^2 = 500 + 40t$ or $t^2 - 8t - 100 = 0$; $t_1 = -6.77\,s$; $\boxed{t_2 = +14.8\,s}$

Solve for either distance: $s_C = \frac{1}{2}(10\,ft/s^2)(14.8\,s)^2$; $\boxed{s = 1092\,ft}$

**6-59. A ball is dropped from rest at the top of a 100-m tall building. At the same instant a second ball is thrown upward from the base of the building with an initial velocity of 50 m/s. When will the two balls collide and at what distance above the street?

For A: $s_A = 100\,m + v_{0A}t + \frac{1}{2}gt^2 = 100\,m + 0 + \frac{1}{2}(-9.8\,m/s^2)t^2$

For B: $s_B = 0 + (50\,m/s)t + \frac{1}{2}(-9.8\,m/s^2)t^2$ *Set $s_A = s_B$*

$100 - 4.9\,t^2 = 50t - 4.9\,t^2$; $50t = 100$; $\boxed{t = 2.00\,s}$

Solve for s: $s_A = 100\,m - (4.9\,m/s^2)(2\,s)^2$; $\boxed{s = 80.4\,m}$

**6-60. A balloonist rising vertically with a velocity of 4 m/s releases a sandbag at the instant when the balloon is 16 m above the ground. Compute the position and velocity of the sandbag relative to the ground after 0.3 and 2 s. How many seconds after its release will it strike the ground?

The initial velocity of the bag is that of the balloon: $v_{oB} = +4\,m/s$

From ground: $s = s_{oB} + v_{oB}t + \frac{1}{2}gt^2$; $s = 18\,m + (4\,m/s)t + \frac{1}{2}(-9.8\,m/s^2)t^2$

$s = 18\,m + (4\,m/s)(0.3\,s) + \frac{1}{2}(-9.8\,m/s^2)(0.3\,s)^2$; $\boxed{s = 16.8\,m}$

**6-61. An arrow is shot upward with a velocity of 40 m/s. Three seconds later, another arrow is shot upward with a velocity of 60 m/s. At what time and position will they meet?

Let $t_1 = t$ be the time for first arrow, then $t_2 = t - 3$ for second arrow.

$s_1 = (40 \text{ m/s})t_1 + \tfrac{1}{2}(-9.8 \text{ m/s}^2)t_1^2$; $\quad s_1 = 40t - 4.9t^2$

$s_2 = (60 \text{ m/s})t_2 + \tfrac{1}{2}(-9.8 \text{ m/s}^2)t_2^2$; $\quad s_2 = 60(t-3) - 4.9(t-3)^2$

$s_1 = s_2$: $\quad 40t - 4.9t^2 = 60t - 180 - 4.9(t^2 - 6t + 9)$

The solution for t gives: $\boxed{t = 4.54 \text{ s}}$

Now find position: $\quad s_1 = s_2 = (40 \text{ m/s})(4.54 \text{ s}) - (4.9 \text{ m/s}^2)(4.54 \text{ s})^2$; $\quad \boxed{s = 80.6 \text{ m}}$

60 m/s

40 m/s

$s_1 = s_2$

**6-62. Someone wishes to strike a target, whose horizontal range is 12 km. What must be the velocity of an object projected at an angle of 35^0 if it is to strike the target? What is the time of flight?

$y = v_{oy}t + \tfrac{1}{2}gt^2 = 0$; $\quad (v_o \sin 35^0)t = (4.9 \text{ m/s}^2)t^2$ or $\quad t = \dfrac{0.574 v_o}{4.9}$; $\quad t = 0.117 v_o$

$R = v_{ox}t = 12$ km; $\quad (v_o \cos 35^0)t = 12{,}000$ m; $\quad t = \dfrac{14{,}649}{v_o}$ $\quad$ Set $t = t$

$\dfrac{0.574 v_o}{4.9} = \dfrac{14{,}649}{v_o}$; $\quad$ From which $\boxed{v_o = 354 \text{ m/s}}$ and $\boxed{t = 41.4 \text{ s}}$

**6-63. A wild boar charges directly toward a hunter with a constant speed of 60 ft/s. At the instant the boar is 100 yd away, the hunter fires an arrow at 30^0 with the ground. What must be the velocity of the arrow if it is to strike its target?

$y = 0 = (v_0 \sin 30^0)t + \tfrac{1}{2}(-32 \text{ ft/s}^2)t^2$; Solve for t

$t = \dfrac{0.5(2)v_o}{32} = 0.03125 v_o$; $\quad t = 0.03125 v_o$

$s_1 = (v_o \cos 30^0) t = (0.866 v_o)(0.03125 v_o)$; $\quad s_1 = 0.0271 v_o^2$

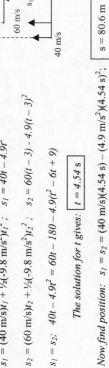

$v = -60$ ft/s

30^0

$s = 0$ $\quad s_1 = s_2$ $\quad s = 300$ ft

v_o

**6-63. (Cont.) $\quad s_1 = 0.0271 v_o^2$; $\quad t = 0.03125 v_o$

$v_B = -60$ ft/s; $\quad s_{oB} = 300$ ft

$s_2 = s_{oB} + v_{B}t = 300$ ft + (-60 ft/s)t $\qquad$ Now, set $s_1 = s_2$ and solve for v_o

$s_2 = 300 - 60 (0.03125\, v_o) = 300 - 1.875\, v_o$

$0.0271\, v_o^2 = 300 - 1.875\, v_o$ $\quad$ or $\quad v_o^2 + 69.2\, v_o - 11{,}070$

The quadratic solution gives: $\boxed{v_o = 76.2 \text{ ft/s}}$

30^0

$s = 0$ $\quad s_1 = s_2$ $\quad s = 300$ ft

v_o

Chapter 7. Newton's Second Law

Newton's Second Law

7-1. A 4-kg mass is acted on by a resultant force of (a) 4 N, (b) 8 N, and (c) 12 N. What are the resulting accelerations?

(a) $a = \frac{4N}{4\ kg} = \boxed{1\ m/s^2}$ (b) $a = \frac{8N}{4\ kg} = \boxed{2\ m/s^2}$ (c) $a = \frac{12N}{4\ kg} = \boxed{3\ m/s^2}$

7-2. A constant force of 20 N acts on a mass of (a) 2 kg, (b) 4 kg, and (c) 6 kg. What are the resulting accelerations?

(a) $a = \frac{20N}{2\ kg} = \boxed{10\ m/s^2}$ (b) $a = \frac{20N}{4\ kg} = \boxed{5\ m/s^2}$ (c) $a = \frac{20N}{6\ kg} = \boxed{3.33\ m/s^2}$

7-3. A constant force of 60 lb acts on each of three objects, producing accelerations of 4, 8, and 12 N. What are the masses?

$m = \frac{60\ lb}{4\ ft/s^2} = \boxed{15\ slugs}$ $m = \frac{60\ lb}{8\ ft/s^2} = \boxed{7.5\ slugs}$ $m = \frac{60\ lb}{12\ ft/s^2} = \boxed{5\ slugs}$

7-4. What resultant force is necessary to give a 4-kg hammer an acceleration of 6 m/s²?

$F = ma = (4\ kg)(6\ m/s^2)$; $\boxed{F = 24\ N}$

7-5. It is determined that a resultant force of 60 N will give a wagon an acceleration of 10 m/s². What force is required to give the wagon an acceleration of only 2 m/s²?

$m = \frac{60\ N}{10\ m/s^2} = 6\ slugs$; $F = ma = (6\ slugs)(2\ m/s^2)$; $\boxed{F = 12\ N}$

7-6. A 1000-kg car moving north at 100 km/h brakes to a stop in 50 m. What are the magnitude and direction of the force?   *Convert to SI units: 100 km/h = 27.8 m/s*

$2as = v_f^2 - v_o^2$; $a = \frac{v_f^2 - v_o^2}{2s} = \frac{(0)^2 - (27.8\ m/s)^2}{2(50\ m)}$; $a = 7.72\ m/s^2$

$F = ma = (1000\ kg)(7.72\ m/s^2)$; $\boxed{F = 772\ N,\ South.}$

66 Unit A   Solutions Manual

Copyright © by Glencoe/McGraw-Hill.

The Relationship Between Weight and Mass

7-7. What is the weight of a 4.8 kg mailbox? What is the mass of a 40-N tank?

$W = (4.8\ kg)(9.8\ m/s^2) = \boxed{47.0\ N}$; $m = \frac{40\ N}{9.8\ m/s^2} = \boxed{4.08\ kg}$

7-8. What is the mass of a 60-lb child? What is the weight of a 7-slug man?

$m = \frac{60\ lb}{32\ ft/s^2} = \boxed{1.88\ slugs}$; $W = (7\ slugs)(32\ ft/s^2) = \boxed{224\ lb}$

7-9. A woman weighs 180 lb on earth. When she walks on the moon, she weighs only 30 lb. What is the acceleration due to gravity on the moon and what is her mass on the moon? On the Earth?

Her mass is the same on the moon as it is on the earth, so we first find the constant mass:

$m_e = \frac{180\ lb}{32\ ft/s^2} = 5.625\ slugs$; $\boxed{m_m = m_e = 5.62\ slugs}$;

$W_m = m_m g_m$ $g_m = \frac{30\ lb}{5.625\ slugs}$; $\boxed{g_m = 5.33\ ft/s^2}$

7-10. What is the weight of a 70-kg astronaut on the surface of the earth. Compare the <u>resultant</u> force required to give him or her an acceleration of 4 m/s² on the earth with the resultant force required to give the same acceleration in space where gravity is negligible?

On earth: $W = (70\ kg)(9.8\ m/s^2) = \boxed{686\ N}$; $F_R = (70\ kg)(4\ m/s^2) = 280\ N$

Anywhere: $\boxed{F_R = 280\ N}$ *The mass doesn't change.*

7-11. Find the mass and the weight of a body if a resultant force of 16 N will give it an acceleration of 5 m/s².

$m = \frac{16\ N}{5.0\ m/s^2} = \boxed{3.20\ kg}$; $W = (3.20\ kg)(9.8\ m/s^2) = \boxed{31.4\ N}$

Chapter 7   Newton's Second Law   67

Copyright © by Glencoe/McGraw-Hill.

7-12. Find the mass and weight of a body if a resultant force of 200 lb causes its speed to increase from 20 ft/s to 60 ft/s in a time of 5 s.

$$a = \frac{60 \text{ ft/s} - 20 \text{ ft/s}}{5 \text{ s}} = 8 \text{ ft/s}^2; \quad m = \frac{200 \text{ lb}}{8 \text{ ft/s}^2}; \quad \boxed{25.0 \text{ slugs}}$$

$$W = mg = (25.0 \text{ slugs})(32 \text{ ft/s}^2); \quad \boxed{W = 800 \text{ lb}}$$

7-13. Find the mass and weight of a body if a resultant force of 400 N causes it to decrease its velocity by 4 m/s in 3 s.

$$a = \frac{\Delta v}{t} = \frac{-4 \text{ m/s}}{3 \text{ s}}; \quad a = -1.33 \text{ m/s}^2; \quad m = \frac{-400 \text{ N}}{-1.33 \text{ m/s}^2}; \quad \boxed{m = 300 \text{ kg}}$$

$$W = mg = (300 \text{ kg})(9.8 \text{ m/s}^2); \quad \boxed{W = 2940 \text{ N}}$$

Applications for Single-Body Problems:

7-14. What horizontal pull is required to drag a 6-kg sled with an acceleration of 4 m/s² if a friction force of 20 N opposes the motion?

$$P - 20 \text{ N} = (6 \text{ kg})(4 \text{ m/s}^2); \quad \boxed{P = 44.0 \text{ N}}$$

7-15. A 2500-lb automobile is speeding at 55 mi/h. What resultant force is required to stop the car in 200 ft on a level road. What must be the coefficient of kinetic friction? (55 mi/h = 80.7 m/s)

We first find the mass and then the acceleration.

$$m = \frac{2500 \text{ lb}}{32 \text{ ft/s}^2} = 78.1 \text{ slugs}; \quad \text{Now recall that: } 2as = v_f^2 - v_0^2$$

$$a = \frac{v_f^2 - v_0^2}{2s} = \frac{(0) - (80.7 \text{ ft/s})^2}{2(200 \text{ ft})}; \quad \text{and} \quad \boxed{a = -16.3 \text{ m/s}^2}$$

$$F = ma = (78.1 \text{ slugs})(-16.3 \text{ ft/s}^2); \quad \boxed{F = -1270 \text{ lb}}$$

$$F_k = \mu_k N; \quad \mu_k = \frac{1270 \text{ lb}}{2500 \text{ lb}}; \quad \boxed{\mu_k = 0.508}$$

7-16. A 10-kg mass is lifted upward by a light cable. What is the tension in the cable if the acceleration is (a) zero, (b) 6 m/s² upward, and (c) 6 m/s² downward?

Note that up is positive and that $W = (10 \text{ kg})(9.8 \text{ m/s}^2) = 98 \text{ N}$.

(a) $T - 98 \text{ N} = (10 \text{ kg})(0 \text{ m/s}^2)$ and $\boxed{T = 98 \text{ N}}$

(b) $T - 98 \text{ N} = (10 \text{ kg})(6 \text{ m/s}^2)$ and $T = 60 \text{ N} + 98 \text{ N}$ or $\boxed{T = 158 \text{ N}}$

(c) $T - 98 \text{ N} = (10 \text{ kg})(-6 \text{ m/s}^2)$ and $T = -60 \text{ N} + 98 \text{ N}$ or $\boxed{T = 38.0 \text{ N}}$

7-17. A 64-lb load hangs at the end of a rope. Find the acceleration of the load if the tension in the cable is (a) 64 lb, (b) 40 lb, and (c) 96 lb.

(a) $T - W = \frac{W}{g} a$; $\quad 64 \text{ lb} - 64 \text{ lb} = \left(\dfrac{64 \text{ lb}}{32 \text{ ft/s}^2}\right) a$; $\quad \boxed{a = 0}$

(b) $T - W = \frac{W}{g} a$; $\quad 40 \text{ lb} - 64 \text{ lb} = \left(\dfrac{64 \text{ lb}}{32 \text{ ft/s}^2}\right) a$; $\quad \boxed{a = -12.0 \text{ ft/s}^2}$

(b) $T - W = \frac{W}{g} a$; $\quad 96 \text{ lb} - 64 \text{ lb} = \left(\dfrac{64 \text{ lb}}{32 \text{ ft/s}^2}\right) a$; $\quad \boxed{a = 16.0 \text{ ft/s}^2}$

7-18. An 800-kg elevator is lifted vertically by a strong rope. Find the acceleration of the elevator if the rope tension is (a) 9000 N, (b) 7840 N, and (c) 2000 N.

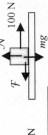

Newton's law for the problem is: $T - mg = ma$ *(up is positive)*

(a) $9000 \text{ N} - (800 \text{ kg})(9.8 \text{ m/s}^2) = (800 \text{ kg})a$; $\quad \boxed{a = 1.45 \text{ m/s}^2}$

(a) $7840 \text{ N} - (800 \text{ kg})(9.8 \text{ m/s}^2) = (800 \text{ kg})a$; $\quad \boxed{a = 0}$

(a) $2000 \text{ N} - (800 \text{ kg})(9.8 \text{ m/s}^2) = (800 \text{ kg})a$; $\quad \boxed{a = -7.30 \text{ m/s}^2}$

7-19. A horizontal force of 100 N pulls an 8-kg cabinet across a level floor. Find the acceleration of the cabinet if $\mu_k = 0.2$.

$$\mathcal{F} = \mu_k \mathcal{N} = \mu_k mg \qquad \mathcal{F} = 0.2(8 \text{ kg})(9.8 \text{ m/s}^2) = 15.7 \text{ N}$$

$$100 \text{ N} - \mathcal{F} = ma; \quad 100 \text{ N} - 15.7 \text{ N} = (8 \text{ kg}) a; \quad \boxed{a = 10.5 \text{ m/s}^2}$$

Applications for Multi-Body Problems

7-24. Assume zero friction in Fig. 7-11. What is the acceleration of the system? What is the tension T in the connecting cord?

Resultant force = total mass x acceleration

$80 \text{ N} = (2 \text{ kg} + 6 \text{ kg})a;$ $\boxed{a = 10 \text{ m/s}^2}$

To find T, apply F = ma to 6-kg block only: $80 \text{ N} - T = (6 \text{ kg})(10 \text{ m/s}^2);$ $\boxed{T = 20 \text{ N}}$

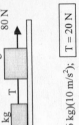

7-25. What force does block A exert on block B in Fig. 7-12?

$\Sigma F = m_T a;$ $45 \text{ N} = (15 \text{ kg}) a;$ $a = 3 \text{ m/s}^2$

Force ON B $= m_B a = (5 \text{ kg})(3 \text{ m/s}^2);$ $\boxed{F = 15 \text{ N}}$

*7-26. What are the acceleration of the system and the tension in the connecting cord for the arrangement shown in Fig. 7-13?

Assume zero friction and draw free-body diagrams.

For total system: $m_2 g = (m_1 + m_2)a$ ($m_1 g$ *is balanced by* $\mathcal{N}$)

$a = \dfrac{m_2 g}{m_1 + m_2} = \dfrac{(6 \text{ kg})(9.8 \text{ m/s}^2)}{4 \text{ kg} + 6 \text{ kg}};$ $\boxed{a = 5.88 \text{ m/s}^2}$

Now, to find T, consider only m_1

$\Sigma F = m_1 a$ $T = m_1 a = (4 \text{ kg})(5.88 \text{ m/s}^2);$ $\boxed{T = 23.5 \text{ N}}$

*7-27. If the coefficient of kinetic friction between the table and the 4 kg block is 0.2 in Fig. 7-13, what is the acceleration of the system. What is the tension in the cord?

$\Sigma F_y = 0;$ $\mathcal{N} = m_1 g;$ $\mathcal{F} = \mu_k \mathcal{N} = \mu_k m_1 g$

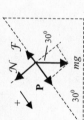

For total system: $m_2 g - \mu_k m_1 g = (m_1 + m_2)a$

$a = \dfrac{m_2 g - \mu_k m_1 g}{m_1 + m_2} = \dfrac{(6 \text{ kg})(9.8 \text{ m/s}^2) - (0.2)(4 \text{ kg})(9.8 \text{ m/s}^2)}{4 \text{ kg} + 6 \text{ kg}}$

7-20. In Fig. 7-10, an unknown mass slides down the 30° inclined plane. What is the acceleration in the absence of friction?

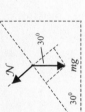

$\Sigma F_x = ma_x;$ $mg \sin 30^0 = ma;$ $a = g \sin 30^0$

$a = (9.8 \text{ m/s}^2) \sin 30^0 = \boxed{4.90 \text{ m/s}^2, \text{ down the plane}}$

7-21. Assume that $\mu_k = 0.2$ in Fig 7-10. What is the acceleration? Why did you not need to know the mass of the block?

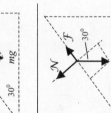

$\Sigma F_x = ma_x;$ $mg \sin 30^0 - \mu_k \mathcal{N} = ma;$ $\mathcal{N} = mg \cos 30^0$

$\cancel{m}g \sin 30^0 - \mu_k \cancel{m}g \cos 30^0 = \cancel{m}a;$ $a = g \sin 30^0 - \mu_k g \cos 30^0$

$a = (9.8 \text{ m/s}^2)(0.5) - 0.2(9.8 \text{ m/s}^2)(0.866);$ $\boxed{a = 3.20 \text{ m/s}^2, \text{ down the plane.}}$

*7-22. Assume that $m = 10$ kg and $\mu_k = 0.3$ in Fig. 7-10. What push P directed up and along the incline in Fig.7-10 will produce an acceleration of 4 m/s² also up the incline?

$\mathcal{F} = \mu_k \mathcal{N} = \mu_k mg \cos 30^0;$ $\mathcal{F} = 0.3(10 \text{ kg})(9.8 \text{ m/s}^2)\cos 30^0 = \underline{25.5 \text{ N}}$

$\Sigma F_x = ma;$ $P - \mathcal{F} - mg \sin 30^0 = ma$

$P - 25.5 \text{ N} - (10 \text{ kg})(9.8 \text{ m/s}^2)(0.5) = (10 \text{ kg})(4 \text{ m/s}^2)$

$P - 25.5 \text{ N} - 49.0 \text{ N} = 40 \text{ N};$ $\boxed{P = 114 \text{ N}}$

*7-23. What force P down the incline in Fig. 7-10 is required to cause the acceleration DOWN the plane to be 4 m/s²? Assume that $m = 10$ kg and $\mu_k = 0.3$.

See Prob. 7-22: $\mathcal{F}$ *is up the plane now. P is down plane (+).*

$\Sigma F_x = ma;$ $P - \mathcal{F} + mg \sin 30^0 = ma;$ *Still,* $\mathcal{F} = 25.5 \text{ N}$

$P - 25.5 \text{ N} + (10 \text{ kg})(9.8 \text{ m/s}^2)(0.5) = (10 \text{ kg})(4 \text{ m/s}^2)$

$P - 25.5 \text{ N} + 49.0 \text{ N} = 40 \text{ N};$ $\boxed{P = 16.5 \text{ N}}$

*7-27. (Cont.) $a = \dfrac{58.8 \text{ N} - 7.84 \text{ N}}{10 \text{ kg}}$ or $\boxed{a = 5.10 \text{ m/s}^2}$

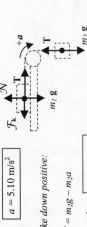

To find T, consider only m_2 and make down positive:

$\Sigma F_y = m_2 a$; $m_2 g - T = m_2 a$; $T = m_2 g - m_2 a$

$T = (6 \text{ kg})(9.8 \text{ m/s}^2) - (6 \text{ kg})(5.10 \text{ m/s}^2)$; $\boxed{T = 28.2 \text{ N}}$

*7-28. Assume that the masses $m_1 = 2$ kg and $m_2 = 8$ kg are connected by a cord that passes over a light frictionless pulley as in Fig. 7-14. What is the acceleration of the system and the tension in the cord?

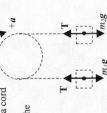

Resultant force = total mass of system x acceleration

$m_2 g - m_1 g = (m_1 + m_2)a$ $\qquad a = \dfrac{m_2 g - m_1 g}{m_1 + m_2}$

$a = \dfrac{(8 \text{ kg})(9.8 \text{ m/s}^2) - (2 \text{ kg})(9.8 \text{ m/s}^2)}{2 \text{ kg} + 8 \text{ kg}}$ $\qquad \boxed{a = 5.88 \text{ m/s}^2}$

Now look at m_1 alone:

$T - m_1 g = m_1 a$; $T = m_1(g + a) = (2 \text{ kg})(9.8 \text{ m/s}^2 + 5.88 \text{ m/s}^2)$; $\boxed{T = 31.4 \text{ N}}$

*7-29. The system described in Fig. 7-15 starts from rest. What is the acceleration assuming zero friction? (assume motion down plane)

$\Sigma F_x = m_T a$; $m_1 g \sin 32^0 - m_2 g = (m_1 + m_2)a$

$(10 \text{ kg})(9.8 \text{ m/s}^2)\sin 32^0 - (2 \text{ kg})(9.8 \text{ m/s}^2) = (10 \text{ kg} + 2 \text{ kg})a$

$a = \dfrac{51.9 \text{ N} - 19.6 \text{ N}}{12 \text{ kg}}$ $\qquad \boxed{a = 2.69 \text{ m/s}^2}$

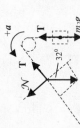

*7-30. What is the acceleration in Fig. 7-15 as the 10-kg block moves down the plane against friction ($\mu_k = 0.2$). Add friction force $\mathcal{F}$ up plane in figure for previous problem.

$m_1 g \sin 32^0 - m_2 g - \mathcal{F} = (m_1 + m_2)a$; $\quad \Sigma F_y = 0$; $\quad \mathcal{N} = m_1 g \cos 32^0$

---

*7-30. (Cont.) $m_1 g \sin 32^0 - m_2 g - \mathcal{F} = (m_1 + m_2)a$; $\quad \mathcal{F} = \mu_k \mathcal{N} = \mu_k m_1 g \cos 32^0$

$m_1 g \sin 32^0 - m_2 g - \mu_k m_1 g \cos 32^0 = (m_1 + m_2)a$; $\boxed{a = 1.31 \text{ m/s}^2}$

*7-31 What is the tension in the cord for Problem 7-30? Apply F = ma to mass m_2 only:

$T - m_2 g = m_2 a$; $\quad T = m_2(g + a) = (2 \text{ kg})(9.8 \text{ m/s}^2 + 1.31 \text{ m/s}^2)$; $\boxed{T = 22.2 \text{ N}}$

Supplementary Problems

7-32. A 2000-lb elevator is lifted vertically with an acceleration of 8 ft/s².

Find the minimum breaking strength of the cable pulling the elevator?

$\Sigma F_y = ma$; $\quad m = \dfrac{W}{g} = \dfrac{2000 \text{ lb}}{32 \text{ ft/s}^2}$; $\quad m = 62.5 \text{ slugs}$

$T - mg = ma$; $\quad T = m(g + a)$; $\quad T = (62.5 \text{ slugs})(32 \text{ ft/s}^2 + 8 \text{ ft/s}^2)$; $\boxed{T = 2500 \text{ lb}}$

7-33. A 200-lb worker stands on weighing scales in the elevator of Problem 7-32.

What is the reading of the scales as he is lifted at 8 m/s?

The scale reading will be equal to the normal force N on worker.

$\mathcal{N} - mg = ma$; $\quad \mathcal{N} = m(g + a)$; $\quad T = (62.5 \text{ slugs})(32 \text{ ft/s}^2 + 8 \text{ ft/s}^2)$; $\boxed{T = 2500 \text{ lb}}$

7-34. A 8-kg load is accelerated upward with a cord whose breaking strength is 200 N. What is the maximum acceleration?

$T_{max} - mg = ma$ $\qquad a = \dfrac{T_{max} - mg}{m} = \dfrac{200 \text{ N} - (8 \text{ kg})(9.8 \text{ m/s}^2)}{8 \text{ kg}}$

$\boxed{a = 15.2 \text{ m/s}^2}$

7-35. For rubber tires on a concrete road $\mu_k = 0.7$. What is the horizontal stopping distance for a 1600-kg truck traveling at 20 m/s? *The stopping distance is determined by the acceleration from a resultant friction force $\mathcal{F} = \mu_k \mathcal{N}$, where $\mathcal{N} = mg$:*

$$\mathcal{F} = -\mu_k mg = ma; \quad a = -\mu_k g = -(0.7)(9.8\ \text{m/s}^2); \quad a = -6.86\ \text{m/s}^2$$

Recall that: $2as = v_o^2 - v_f^2$; $s = \dfrac{v_f^2 - v_o^2}{2a} = \dfrac{0-(20\ \text{m/s})^2}{2(-6.86\ \text{m/s}^2)}$; $\boxed{s = 29.2\ \text{km}}$

*7-36. Suppose the 4 and 6-kg masses in Fig. 7-13 are switched so that the larger mass is on the table. What would be the acceleration and tension in the cord neglecting friction?

For total system: $m_2 g = (m_1 + m_2)$; $m_1 = 6$ kg; $m_2 = 4$ kg

$$a = \frac{m_2 g}{m_1 + m_2} = \frac{(4\ \text{kg})(9.8\ \text{m/s}^2)}{6\ \text{kg} + 4\ \text{kg}}; \quad \boxed{a = 3.92\ \text{m/s}^2}$$

$\Sigma F = m_1 a$ $\quad T = m_1 a = (6\ \text{kg})(5.88\ \text{m/s}^2)$; $\boxed{T = 23.5\ \text{N}}$

*7-37. Consider two masses A and B connected by a cord and hung over a single pulley. If mass A is twice that of mass B, what is the acceleration of the system?

$m_A = 2m_B$: *If the left mass B is m, the right mass A will be 2m.*

$2mg - mg = (2m + m)a$

$mg = 3ma$

$a = \dfrac{g}{3} = \dfrac{9.8\ \text{m/s}^2}{3}$; $\boxed{a = 3.27\ \text{m/s}^2}$

*7-38. A 5-kg mass rests on a 34^0 inclined plane where $\mu_k = 0.2$. What push up the incline, will cause the block to accelerate at 4 m/s²?

$\mathcal{F} = \mu_k \mathcal{N} = \mu_k mg \cos 34^0$; $\mathcal{F} = 0.2(5\ \text{kg})(9.8\ \text{m/s}^2)\cos 34^0 = \underline{8.12\ \text{N}}$

$\Sigma F_x = ma$; $P - \mathcal{F} - mg \sin 34^0 = ma$

$P - 8.12\ \text{N} - (5\ \text{kg})(9.8\ \text{m/s}^2) \sin 34^0 = (5\ \text{kg})(4\ \text{m/s}^2)$

$\boxed{P = 47.4\ \text{N}}$

---

*7-39. A 96-lb block rests on a table where $\mu_k = 0.4$. A cord tied to this block passes over a light frictionless pulley. What weight must be attached to the free end if the system is to accelerated at 4 ft/s²?

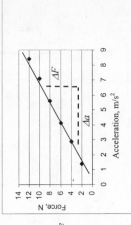

$\mathcal{F} = \mu_k \mathcal{N} = 0.2$ (96 lb); $\mathcal{F} = 19.2$ lb

$W - 19.2\ \text{lb} = \left(\dfrac{96\ \text{lb} + W}{32\ \text{ft/s}^2}\right)(4\ \text{ft/s}^2)$

$W - 19.2\ \text{lb} = 12\ \text{lb} + 0.125\ W$; $\boxed{W = 35.7\ \text{lb}}$

Critical Thinking Questions

7-40. In a laboratory experiment, the acceleration of a small car is measured by the separation of spots burned at regular intervals in a paraffin-coated tape. Larger and larger weights are transferred from the car to a hanger at the end of a tape that passes over a light frictionless pulley. In this manner, the mass of the entire system is kept constant. Since the car moves on a horizontal air track with negligible friction, the resultant force is equal to the weights at the end of the tape. The following data are recorded:

Weight, N	2	4	6	8	10	12
Acceleration, m/s²	1.4	2.9	4.1	5.6	7.1	8.4

Plot a graph of weight (force) versus acceleration. What is the mass?

this curve? What is the mass?

The slope is the change in Force over the change in acceleration, which is the mass of the system. Thus, the mass is found to be: $\boxed{m = 1.42\ \text{kg}}$

7-41. In the above experiment, a student places a constant weight of 4 N at the free end of the tape. Several runs are made, increasing the mass of the car each time by adding weights.

What happens to the acceleration as the mass of the system is increased? What should the value of the product of mass and acceleration be for each run? Is it necessary to include the mass of the constant 4 N weight in these experiments?

The acceleration increases with increasing mass. According to Newton's second law, the product of the total mass of the system and the acceleration must always be equal to the resultant force of 4 N for each run. It is necessary to add the mass of the 4-N weight to each of the runs because it is part of the total mass of the system.

7-42. An arrangement similar to that described by Fig. 7-13 is set up except that the masses are replaced. What is the acceleration of the system if the suspended mass is three times that of the mass on the table and $\mu_k = 0.3$.

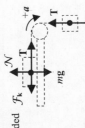

$\Sigma F_y = 0$; $\mathcal{N} = mg$; $\mathcal{F} = \mu_k \mathcal{N} = \mu_k mg$

For total system: $3mg - \mu_k mg = (3m + m)a$; $(3 - \mu_k)mg = 4ma$

$$a = \frac{(3 - \mu_k)g}{4} = \frac{(3 - 0.3)(9.8 \text{ m/s}^2)}{4} \qquad \boxed{a = 6.62 \text{ m/s}^2}$$

7-43. Three masses, 2 kg, 4 kg, and 6 kg, are connected (in order) by strings and hung from the ceiling with another string so that the largest mass is in the lowest position. What is the tension in each cord? If they are then detached from the ceiling, what must be the tension in the top string in order that the system accelerate upward at 4 m/s²? In the latter case what are the tensions in the strings that connect masses?

A 2 kg B 4 kg C 6 kg

The tension in each string is due only to the weights BELOW the string. Thus,

$T_C = (6 \text{ kg})(9.8 \text{ m/s}^2) = 58.8 \text{ N}$; $T_B = (6 \text{ kg} + 4 \text{ kg})(9.8 \text{ m/s}^2) = 98.0 \text{ N}$;

$$T_A = (6 \text{ kg} + 4 \text{ kg} + 2 \text{ kg})(9.8 \text{ m/s}^2) = \boxed{118 \text{ N}}$$

Now consider the upward acceleration of 4 m/s².

$\Sigma F_y = 0$; $T_A = (2 \text{ kg} + 4 \text{ kg} + 6 \text{ kg})(4 \text{ m/s}^2)$; $\boxed{T_A = 48 \text{ N}}$

$T_B = (4 \text{ kg} + 6 \text{ kg})(4 \text{ m/s}^2)$ $\boxed{40 \text{ N}}$; $T_C = (6 \text{ kg})(4 \text{ m/s}^2)$ $\boxed{24 \text{ N}}$

A 2 kg B 4 kg C 6 kg $a = +4 \text{ m/s}^2$

7-44. An 80-kg astronaut on a space walk pushes against a 200-kg solar panel that has become dislodged from a spacecraft. The force causes the panel to accelerate at 2 m/s². What acceleration does the astronaut receive? Do they continue to accelerate after the push?

The force on the solar panel F_p is equal and opposite that on the astronaut F_a.

$F_p = m_p a_p$; $F_a = m_a a_a$; *Thus,* $m_p a_p = -m_a a_a$; *solve for* a_a:

$$a_a = -\frac{m_p a_p}{m_a} = -\frac{(200 \text{ kg})(2 \text{ m/s}^2)}{80 \text{ kg}}; \qquad \boxed{a = -5 \text{ m/s}^2}$$

Acceleration exists only while a force is applied, once the force is removed, both astronaut and solar panel move in opposite directions at the speeds obtained when contact is broken.

7-45. A 400-lb sled slides down a hill ($\mu_k = 0.2$) inclined at an angle of 60°. What is the normal force on the sled? What is the force of kinetic friction? What is the resultant force down the hill? What is the acceleration? Is it necessary to know the weight of the sled to determine its acceleration?

$\Sigma F_y = 0$; $\mathcal{N} - W \cos 60^0 = 0$; $\mathcal{N} = (400 \text{ lb}) \cos 60^0 = \boxed{200 \text{ lb}}$;

$\mathcal{F} = \mu_k \mathcal{N} = (0.2)(200 \text{ lb})$; $\boxed{\mathcal{F} = 40 \text{ lb}}$

$\Sigma F_x = W \sin 60^0 - \mathcal{F} = (400 \text{ lb}) \sin 60^0 - 40 \text{ lb}$; $\boxed{F_R = 306 \text{ lb}}$

$\mathcal{N}$ $\mathcal{F}$ $+a$ 60° 60° $W = mg = 400 \text{ lb}$

7-45 (Cont.) Since $F_R = ma$; we note that: $W \sin 60^0 - \mu_k W = (W/g)a$; Thus, the weight divides out and it is not necessary for determining the resultant acceleration.

*7-46. Three masses, $m_1 = 10$ kg, $m_2 = 8$ kg, and $m_3 = 6$ kg, are connected as shown in Fig. 7-16. Neglecting friction, what is the acceleration of the system? What are the tensions in the cord on the left and in the cord on the right? Would the acceleration be the same if the middle mass m_2 were removed?

Total mass of system $= (10 + 8 + 6) = 24$ kg

Resultant Force on system $= m_1g - m_3g$

The normal force $\mathcal{N}$ balances m_2g: $\quad \Sigma F = m_T a$;

$m_1g - m_3g = (m_1 + m_2 + m_3)a$; $\quad (10 \text{ kg})(9.8 \text{ m/s}^2) - (6 \text{ kg})(9.8 \text{ m/s}^2) = (24 \text{ kg}) a$

$(24 \text{ kg})a = 98.0 \text{ N} - 58.8 \text{ N}$; $\quad \boxed{a = 1.63 \text{ m/s}^2}$; $\quad$ *The acceleration is not affected by m_2.*

To find T_A apply $\Sigma F = m_1 a$ to 10-kg mass: $\quad m_1g - T_A = m_1a$; $\quad T_A = m_1g - m_1a$

$T_A = m_1(g - a) = (10 \text{ kg})(9.8 \text{ m/s}^2 - 1.63 \text{ m/s}^2)$; $\quad \boxed{T_A = 81.7 \text{ N}}$

Now apply to 6-kg mass: $\quad T_B - m_3g = m_3a$; $\quad T_B = m_3g + m_3a$

$T_B = (6 \text{ kg})(9.8 \text{ m/s}^2 + 1.63 \text{ m/s}^2)$; $\quad \boxed{T_B = 68.6 \text{ N}}$

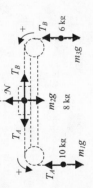

*7-47. Assume that $\mu_k = 0.3$ between the mass m_2 and the table in Fig. 7-16. The masses m_2 and m_3 are 8 and 6 kg, respectively. What mass m_1 is required to cause the system to accelerate to the left at 2 m/s²? ($\mathcal{F} = \mu_k m_2 g$ acts to right.)

Apply $\Sigma F = m_T a$ *to total system, left is positive.*

$m_1g - \mathcal{F} - m_3g = (m_1 + m_2 + m_3)a$; $\quad \mathcal{F} = \mu_k m_2 g = 0.3(8 \text{ kg})(9.8 \text{ m/s}^2)$; $\quad \mathcal{F} = 23.5 \text{ N}$

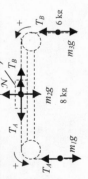

$m_1(9.8 \text{ m/s}^2) - 23.5 \text{ N} - (6 \text{ kg})(9.8 \text{ m/s}^2) = (m_1 + 14 \text{ kg})(2 \text{ m/s}^2)$

$9.8 m_1 - 23.5 \text{ kg} - 58.8 \text{ kg} = 2m_1 + 28 \text{ kg}$; $\quad \boxed{m_1 = 14.1 \text{ kg}}$

*7-48. A block of unknown mass is given a push up a 40^0 inclined plane and then released. It continues to move up the plane (+) at an acceleration of −9 m/s². What is the coefficient of kinetic friction?

Since block is moving up plane, $\mathcal{F}$ is directed down plane.

$\mathcal{F} = \mu_k \mathcal{N}$; $\quad \Sigma F_y = 0$; $\quad \mathcal{N} = mg \cos 40^0$; $\quad \mathcal{F} = \mu_k mg \cos 40^0$

$\Sigma F_x = ma$; $\quad -\mathcal{F} - mg \sin 40^0 = ma$; $\quad -\mu_k mg \cos 40^0 - mg \sin 40^0 = ma$

$a = -\mu_k g \cos 40^0 - g \sin 40^0$; $\quad -9 \text{ m/s}^2 = -\mu_k(9.8 \text{ m/s}^2) \cos 40^0 - (9.8 \text{ m/s}^2) \sin 40^0$

Solving for μ_k we obtain: $\quad \boxed{\mu_k = 0.360}$

*7-49. Block A in Fig. 7-17 has a weight of 64 lb. What must be the weight of block B if Block A moves up the plane with an acceleration of 6 ft/s². Neglect friction.

$\Sigma F_x = ma$: $\quad W_B - W_A \sin 60^0 = (m_A + m_B) a$

$W_B - W_A \sin 60^0 = \left(\dfrac{W_A + W_B}{g}\right) a$; $\quad \dfrac{a}{g} = \dfrac{6 \text{ ft/s}^2}{32 \text{ ft/s}^2} = 0.188$

$W_B - (64 \text{ lb})(0.866) = 0.188(64 \text{ lb} + W_B)$; $\quad \boxed{W_B = 83.0 \text{ lb}}$

$W_B - 55.4 \text{ lb} = 12.0 \text{ lb} + 0.188W_B$;

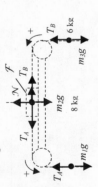

*7-50. The mass of block B in Fig. 7-17 is 4 kg. What must be the mass of block A if it is to move down the plane at an acceleration of 2 m/s²? Neglect friction.

$\Sigma F_x = ma$: $\quad m_Ag \sin 60^0 - m_Bg = (m_A + m_B) a$

$(9.8 \text{ m/s}^2)(0.866)m_A - (4 \text{ kg})(9.8 \text{ m/s}^2) = m_A(2 \text{ m/s}^2) + (4 \text{ kg})(2 \text{ m/s}^2)$

$8.49 m_A - 39.2 \text{ kg} = 2 m_A + 8 \text{ kg}$; $\quad \boxed{m_A = 7.28 \text{ kg}}$

Chapter 8. Work, Energy, and Power

Work

8-1. What is the work done by a force of 20 N acting through a parallel distance of 8 m? What force will do the same work through a distance of 4 m?

$$Work = (20 \text{ N})(8 \text{ m}) = \boxed{160 \text{ J}} \; ; \quad F(4 \text{ m}) = 160 \text{ J}; \quad \boxed{F = 40.0 \text{ N}}$$

8-2. A worker lifts a 40 lb weight through a height of 10 ft. How many meters can a 10-kg block be lifted by the same amount of work?

$$Work = (20 \text{ lb})(10 \text{ ft}) = 200 \text{ ft·lb}; \quad Work = 200 \text{ ft·lb}\left(\frac{1.356 \text{ J}}{1 \text{ ft·lb}}\right) = 271 \text{ J}$$

$$Work = Fs = mgs; \quad s = \frac{Work}{mg} = \frac{271 \text{ J}}{(10 \text{ kg})(9.8 \text{ m/s}^2)}; \quad \boxed{s = 2.77 \text{ m}}$$

8-3. A tugboat exerts a constant force of 4000 N on a ship, moving it a distance of 15 m. What work is done?

$$Work = (4000 \text{ N})(15 \text{ m}); \quad \boxed{Work = 60,000 \text{ J}}$$

8-4. A 5-kg hammer is lifted to a height of 3 m. What is the minimum required work?

$$Work = Fs = (5 \text{ kg})(9.8 \text{ m/s}^2)(3 \text{ m}); \quad \boxed{Work = 147 \text{ J}}$$

8-5. A push of 30 lb is applied along the handle of a lawn mower producing a horizontal displacement of 40 ft. If the handle makes an angle of 30^0 with the ground, what work was done by the 30-lb force?

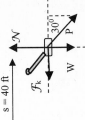

$$Work = (F \cos \theta)s = (30 \text{ lb}) \cos 30^0 (40 \text{ ft})$$

$$\boxed{Work = 1040 \text{ ft lb}}$$

---

*7-51. Assume that the masses A and B in Fig. 7-17 are 4 kg and 10 kg, respectively. The coefficient of kinetic friction is 0.3. Find the acceleration if (a) the system is initially moving up the plane, and (b) if the system is initially moving down the plane.

(a) *With upward initial motion, $\mathcal{F}$ is down the plane.*

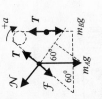

$$\mathcal{F} = \mu_k \mathcal{N}; \quad \Sigma F_y = 0; \quad \mathcal{N} = m_A g \cos 60^0; \quad \mathcal{F} = \mu_k m_A g \cos 60^0$$

Resultant force on entire system = total mass × acceleration

$$m_B g - m_A g \sin 60^0 - \mu_k m_A g \cos 60^0 = (m_A + m_B)a$$

$$(10 \text{ kg})(9.8 \text{ m/s}^2) - (4 \text{ kg})(9.8 \text{ m/s}^2)(0.866) - 0.3(10 \text{ kg})(9.8 \text{ m/s}^2)(0.5) = (14 \text{ kg})a$$

$$98 \text{ N} - 33.9 \text{ N} - 14.7 \text{ N} = (14 \text{ kg})a; \quad \text{or} \quad \boxed{a = 3.53 \text{ m/s}^2}$$

(b) *If initial motion is down the plane, then $\mathcal{F}$ is up the plane, but the resultant force is still down the plane. The block will side until it stops and then goes the other way.*

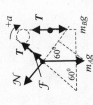

$$\Sigma F_x = ma; \quad m_B g - m_A g \sin 60^0 + \mu_k m_A g \cos 60^0 = (m_A + m_B)a$$

$$98 \text{ N} - 33.9 \text{ N} + 14.7 \text{ N} = (14 \text{ kg})a$$

$$\boxed{a = 5.63 \text{ m/s}^2} \quad \textit{The greater acceleration results from}$$

the fact that the friction force is increasing the resultant force instead of decreasing it as was the case in part (a).

8-6. The trunk in Fig. 8-10 is dragged a horizontal distance of 24 m by a rope that makes an angle θ with the floor. If the rope tension is 8 N, what works are done for the following angles: 0^0, 30^0, 60^0, 90^0?

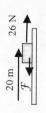

$Work = (F \cos \theta)s = (8\ \text{N}) \cos 0^0 (24\ \text{m}) = \boxed{192\ \text{J}}$

$Work = (8\ \text{N}) \cos 30^0 (24\ \text{m}) = \boxed{166\ \text{J}}$; $Work_{60} = \boxed{96\ \text{J}}$; $Work_{90} = \boxed{0\ \text{J}}$

8-7. A horizontal force pushes a 10-kg sled along a driveway for a distance of 40 m. If the coefficient of sliding friction is 0.2, what work is done by the friction force?

$Work = (F \cos \theta)s = (\mathcal{F})(\cos 180^0)s = -\mathcal{F}s$; but $\mathcal{F} = \mu_k \mathcal{N} = \mu_k mg$

$Work = \mu_k mg\, s = (0.2)(10\ \text{kg})(9.8\ \text{m/s}^2)(40\ \text{m})$; $\boxed{Work = -784\ \text{J}}$

*8-8. A sled is dragged a distance of 12.0 m by a rope under constant tension of 140 N. The task requires 1200 J of work. What angle does the rope make with the ground?

$Work = (F \cos \theta)s$; $\quad \cos \theta = \dfrac{Work}{Fs} = \dfrac{1200\ \text{J}}{(140\ \text{N})(12\ \text{m})}$

$\cos \theta = 0.714$; $\boxed{\theta = 44.4^0}$

Resultant Work

8-9. An average force of 40 N compresses a coiled spring a distance of 6 cm. What is the work done by the 40-N force? What work is done by the spring? What is the resultant work?

$Work_{40} = (40\ \text{N})(0.06\ \text{m}) = \boxed{2.40\ \text{J}}$, *(positive work)*

$Work_{sp} = (-40\ \text{N})(0.06\ \text{m}) = \boxed{-2.40\ \text{J}}$, *(negative work)*

$Resultant\ work = \Sigma(works) = 2.4\ \text{J} - 2.4\ \text{J} = \boxed{0\ \text{J}}$

Work is positive when force is with displacement, negative when against displacement.

8-10. A horizontal force of 20 N drags a small sled 42 m across the ice at constant speed. Find the work done by the pulling force and by the friction force. What is the resultant force?

$Work_{40} = (20\ \text{N})(24\ \text{m}) = \boxed{2.40\ \text{J}}$, *(positive work)*

$Work_{sp} = (-20\ \text{N})(24\ \text{m}) = \boxed{-2.40\ \text{J}}$, *(negative work)*

Resultant force and, hence, resultant work are zero.

*8-11. A 10-kg block is dragged 20 m by a parallel force of 26 N. If $\mu_k = 0.2$, what is the resultant work and what acceleration results?

$\mathcal{F} = \mu_k \mathcal{N} = \mu_k mg \qquad \mathcal{F} = 0.2(10\ \text{kg})(9.8\ \text{m/s}^2) = 19.6\ \text{N}$

$Work = F_R\, s = (P - \mathcal{F})s$; $\quad Work = (26\ \text{N} - 19.6\ \text{N})(20\ \text{m}) \qquad \boxed{Work = 128\ \text{J}}$

$F_R = (26\ \text{N} - 19.6) = 6.40\ \text{N}$; $\quad a = \dfrac{F}{m} = \dfrac{6.4\ \text{N}}{10\ \text{kg}}$; $\qquad \boxed{a = 0.640\ \text{m/s}^2}$

*8-12. A rope making an angle of 35^0 drags a 10-kg toolbox a horizontal distance of 20 m. The tension in the rope is 60 N and the constant friction force is 30 N. What work is done by friction? What is the resultant work?

$(Work)_{rope} = (60\ \text{N}) \cos 35^0 (20\ \text{m})$; $\quad \boxed{(Work)_r = 983\ \text{J}}$

$(Work)_f = (-30\ \text{N})(20\ \text{m}) = -600\ \text{J}$; $\quad \boxed{(Work)_f = -600\ \text{J}}$

$Resultant\ Work = \Sigma(works) = 983\ \text{J} - 600\ \text{J}$; $\quad \boxed{Resultant\ Work = 383\ \text{J}}$

Extra work can show that for this example, $\mu_k = 0.472$

*8-13. For the example described in Problem 8-12, what is the coefficient of friction between the toolbox and the floor? *(Refer to figure and information given in previous problem.)*

$\Sigma F_y = 0$; $\quad \mathcal{N} + (60\ \text{N}) \sin 35^0 - (10\ \text{kg})(9.8\ \text{m/s}^2) = 0$; and $\mathcal{N} = 63.6\ \text{N}$

$\mu_k = \dfrac{\mathcal{F}}{\mathcal{N}} = 0.472 \qquad \boxed{\mu_k = 0.472}$

*8-17. What is the resultant work when the 8-kg block slides from the top to the bottom of the incline in Fig. 8-11? Assume that $\mu_k = 0.4$.

The resultant work is the work of the resultant force:

$F_R = mg \sin 40^0 - \mathcal{F} = (78.4\text{ N})\sin 40^0 - 0.4(78.4\text{ N})\cos 40^0$

$F_R = 26.4\text{ N}; \quad Work = (26.4\text{ N})(18.67\text{ m}) = \boxed{492\text{ J}}$

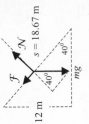

Work and Kinetic Energy

8-18. What is the kinetic energy of a 6-g bullet at the instant its speed is 190 m/s? What is the kinetic energy of a 1200-kg car traveling at 80 km/h? (80 km/h = 22.2 m/s)

$E_k = \frac{1}{2}mv^2 = \frac{1}{2}(0.006\text{ kg})(190\text{ m/s})^2; \quad \boxed{E_k = 217\text{ J}}$

$E_k = \frac{1}{2}mv^2 = \frac{1}{2}(1200\text{ kg})(22.2\text{ m/s})^2; \quad \boxed{E_k = 296\text{ kJ}}$

8-19. What is the kinetic energy of a 2400-lb automobile when its speed is 55 mi/h? What is the kinetic energy of a 9-lb ball when its speed is 40 ft/s? (55 mi/h = 80.7 ft/s)

$m_a = \dfrac{W}{g} = \dfrac{2400\text{ lb}}{32\text{ ft/s}^2} = 75.0\text{ slugs} \qquad m_b = \dfrac{9.00\text{ lb}}{32\text{ ft/s}^2} = 0.281\text{ slugs}$

$E_k = \frac{1}{2}mv^2 = \frac{1}{2}(75\text{ slugs})(80.7\text{ ft/s})^2; \quad \boxed{E_k = 244,000\text{ ft lb}}$

$E_k = \frac{1}{2}mv^2 = \frac{1}{2}(0.281\text{ slugs})(40\text{ ft/s})^2; \quad \boxed{E_k = 225\text{ ft lb}}$

8-20. What is the change in kinetic energy when a 50-g ball hits the pavement with a velocity of 16 m/s and rebounds with a velocity of 10 m/s?

Consider the upward direction as positive, then $v_o = -10$ m/s and $v_f = -16$ m/s.

$\Delta E_k = \frac{1}{2}mv_f^2 - \frac{1}{2}mv_o^2 = \frac{1}{2}(0.05\text{ kg})(10\text{ m/s})^2 - \frac{1}{2}(0.05\text{ kg})(-16\text{ m/s})^2$

$\Delta E_k = 2.50\text{ J} - 6.40\text{ J} = \boxed{-3.90\text{ J}}; \quad$ *The change represents a* **loss** *of kinetic energy.*

---

*8-14. A 40-kg sled is pulled horizontally for 500 m where $\mu_k = 0.2$. If the resultant work is 50 kJ, what was the parallel pulling force?

$\mathcal{F} = \mu_k \mathcal{N} = \mu_k mg = 0.2(40\text{ kg})(9.8\text{ m/s}^2); \quad \mathcal{F} = 78.4\text{ N}$

$(P - \mathcal{F})s = 50\text{ kJ}; \quad (P - 78.4\text{ N})(500\text{ m}) = 50,000\text{ J}; \quad \boxed{P = 178\text{ N}}$

*8-15. Assume that $m = 8$ kg in Fig. 8-11 and $\mu_k = 0$. What minimum work is required by the force P to reach the top of the inclined plane? What work is required to lift the 8 kg block vertically to the same height?

Minimum work is for $P = W \sin 40^0$ *with zero acceleration.*

$\sin\theta = \dfrac{12\text{ m}}{s}; \quad s = \dfrac{12\text{ m}}{\sin 40^0} = 18.67\text{ m}; \quad W = mg = 78.4\text{ N}$

$Work_P = P\,s = (W \sin 40^0)\,s = (78.4\text{ N}) \sin 40^0\,(18.67\text{ m}); \quad \boxed{Work_P = 941\text{ J}}$

$(Work)_V = W\,h = (78.4\text{ N})(12\text{ m}); \quad \boxed{(Work)_V = 941\text{ J}}$

*8-16. What is the minimum work by the force P to move the 8-kg block to the top of the incline if $\mu_k = 0.4$? Compare this with the work to lift it vertically to the same height.

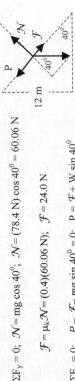

$\Sigma F_y = 0; \quad \mathcal{N} = mg \cos 40^0; \quad \mathcal{N} = (78.4\text{ N}) \cos 40^0 = 60.06\text{ N}$

$\mathcal{F} = \mu_k \mathcal{N} = (0.4)(60.06\text{ N}); \quad \mathcal{F} = 24.0\text{ N}$

$\Sigma F_x = 0; \quad P - \mathcal{F} - mg \sin 40^0 = 0; \quad P = \mathcal{F} + W \sin 40^0$

$P = 24.0\text{ N} + (78.4\text{ N}) \sin 40^0; \quad P = 74.4\text{ N}; \quad$ *Recall that* $s = 18.67\text{ m}$ *from Prob. 8-15.*

$Work_P = (74.4\text{ N})(18.67\text{ m}); \quad \boxed{Work_P = 1390\text{ J}}$

From Prob. 8-15, the work to lift vertically is: $\boxed{(Work)_V = 941\text{ J}}$

43

*8-21. A runaway, 400-kg wagon enters a cornfield with a velocity of 12 m/s and eventually comes to rest. What work was done on the wagon?

$Work = \tfrac{1}{2}mv_f^2 - \tfrac{1}{2}mv_o^2 = (0) - \tfrac{1}{2}(400 \text{ kg})(12 \text{ m/s})^2$; $\boxed{Work = -28.8 \text{ kJ}}$

*8-22. A 2400-lb car increases its speed from 30 mi/h to 60 mi/h? What resultant work was required? What is the equivalent work in joules?

$v_o = 30 \text{ mi/h} = 44 \text{ ft/s}$; $v_f = 60 \text{ mi/h} = 88 \text{ ft/s}$; $m = \dfrac{2400 \text{ lb}}{32 \text{ ft/s}^2} = 75.0 \text{ slugs}$

$Work = \tfrac{1}{2}mv_f^2 - \tfrac{1}{2}mv_o^2 = \tfrac{1}{2}(75 \text{ slugs})(88 \text{ ft/s})^2 - \tfrac{1}{2}(75 \text{ slugs})(44 \text{ ft/s})^2$;

$Work = \boxed{217,800 \text{ ft lb}}$; $Work = -217,800 \text{ ft lb}\left(\dfrac{1 \text{ J}}{0.7378 \text{ ft lb}}\right) = \boxed{295 \text{ kJ}}$

*8-23. A 0.6-kg hammer head is moving at 30 m/s just before striking the head of a spike. Find the initial kinetic energy. What work can be done by the hammer head?

$E_k = \tfrac{1}{2}mv^2 = \tfrac{1}{2}(0.6 \text{ kg})(30 \text{ m/s})^2$; $\boxed{E_k = 270 \text{ J}}$

$Work = \Delta E_k = 0 - 200 \text{ J}$; $\boxed{Work = -270 \text{ J}}$

*8-24. A 12-lb hammer moving at 80 ft/s strikes the head of a nail moving it into the wall a distance of ¼ in. What was the average stopping force?

$m = \dfrac{12 \text{ lb}}{32 \text{ ft/s}^2} = 0.375 \text{ slugs}$; $s = 0.250 \text{ in.} (1 \text{ ft/12 in.}) = 0.0203 \text{ ft}$; $v_o = 80 \text{ ft/s}$

$Fs = \tfrac{1}{2}mv_f^2 - \tfrac{1}{2}mv_o^2$; $F(0.0203 \text{ ft}) = 0 - \tfrac{1}{2}(0.375 \text{ slugs})(80 \text{ ft/s})^2$; $\boxed{F = 57,600 \text{ ft lb}}$

8-25. What average force is needed to increase the velocity of a 2-kg object from 5 m/s to 12 m/s over a distance of 8 m?

$Fs = \tfrac{1}{2}mv_f^2 - \tfrac{1}{2}mv_o^2$; $F(8 \text{ m}) = \tfrac{1}{2}(2 \text{ kg})(12 \text{ m/s})^2 - \tfrac{1}{2}(2 \text{ kg})(5 \text{ m/s})^2$; $\boxed{F = 14.9 \text{ N}}$

*8-26. Verify the answer to Problem 8-25 by applying Newton's second law of motion.

To apply $F = ma$, we need to find a: $\quad 2as = v_f^2 - v_o^2$

$a = \dfrac{v_f^2 - v_o^2}{2s} = \dfrac{(5 \text{ m/s})^2 - (12 \text{ m/s})^2}{2(8 \text{ m})}$; $\quad F = (2 \text{ kg})(-7.44 \text{ m/s}^2) = \boxed{-14.9 \text{ N}}$

*8-27. A 20-g projectile strikes a mud bank in Fig. 8-12, penetrating a distance of 6 cm before stopping. Find the stopping force F if the entrance velocity is 80 m/s.

$Fs = \tfrac{1}{2}mv_f^2 - \tfrac{1}{2}mv_o^2$; $\quad F(0.06 \text{ m}) = 0 - \tfrac{1}{2}(0.02 \text{ kg})(80 \text{ m/s})^2$

$\boxed{F = -1070 \text{ N}}$

*8-28. A 1500-kg car is moving along a level road at 60 km/h. What work is required to stop the car? If $\mu_k = 0.7$, what is the stopping distance? $\quad$ (60 km/h = 16.67 m/s)

$Work = \tfrac{1}{2}mv_f^2 - \tfrac{1}{2}mv_o^2$; $\quad Work = 0 - \tfrac{1}{2}(1500 \text{ kg})(16.67 \text{ m/s})^2$; $\boxed{Work = -208,300 \text{ J}}$

The work is done by friction: $\quad \mathcal{F} = \mu_k N = \mu_k mg \quad$ and $\quad (Work)_f = -(\mu_k mg)s$

$-(\mu_k mg)s = -208,300 \text{ J}$; $\quad s = \dfrac{-208,300 \text{ J}}{-0.7(1500 \text{ kg})(9.8 \text{ m/s}^2)}$; $\quad \boxed{s = 20.2 \text{ m}}$

Potential Energy

8-29. A 2-kg block rests on top of a table 80 cm from the floor. Find the potential energy of the book relative to (a) the floor, (b) the seat of a chair 40 cm from the floor, and (c) relative to the ceiling 3 m from the floor.

For $E_p = mgh$, the height h is measured from reference point:

For floor, h = 0.8 m; for seat, h = 0.4 m; for table, h = -2.2 m

(a) $E_p = (2 \text{ kg})(9.8 \text{ m/s}^2)(0.8 \text{ m}) = \boxed{15.7 \text{ J}}$

(b) $E_p = (2 \text{ kg})(9.8 \text{ m/s}^2)(0.4 \text{ m}) = \boxed{7.84 \text{ J}}$; (c) $E_p = (2 \text{ kg})(9.8 \text{ m/s}^2)(-2.2 \text{ m}) = \boxed{-43.1 \text{ J}}$

8-30. A 1.2 kg brick is held a distance of 2 m above a manhole. The bottom of the manhole is 3 m below the street. Relative to the street, what is the potential energy at each location? What is the change in potential energy?

$$E_p = (1.2 \text{ kg})(9.8 \text{ m/s}^2)(2 \text{ m}) = \boxed{23.5 \text{ J}} \text{ for held brick.}$$

$$E_p = (1.2 \text{ kg})(9.8 \text{ m/s}^2)(-3 \text{ m}) = \boxed{-35.3 \text{ J} \text{ for brick in hole}}$$

$$\Delta E_p = E_f - E_o = -35.3 \text{ J} - (23.5 \text{ J}); \quad \boxed{\Delta E_p = -58.8 \text{ J}}$$

8-31. At a particular instant a mortar shell has a velocity of 60 m/s. If its potential energy at that point is one-half of its kinetic energy, what is its height above the earth?

$E_k = \frac{1}{2}mv^2$ and $E_p = mgh$; At the instant in question, $E_p = \frac{1}{2}E_k$;

$$mgh = \frac{1}{2}\left(\frac{1}{2}mv^2\right) \quad \text{or} \quad 4gh = v^2 \quad \text{and} \quad h = \frac{v^2}{4g}$$

$$h = \frac{(60 \text{ m/s})^2}{4(9.8 \text{ m/s}^2)} \qquad \boxed{h = 91.8 \text{ m}}$$

*8-32. A 20-kg sled is pushed up a 34° slope to a vertical height of 140 m. A constant friction force of 50 N acts for the entire distance. What external work was required? What was the change in potential energy?

External work done by force P acting for distance s:

$\Sigma F_x = 0$: $P - mg \sin 34^0 - \mathcal{F} = 0$; $\mathcal{F} = 50 \text{ N}$, $m = 20 \text{ kg}$

$P = (5 \text{ kg})(9.8 \text{ m/s}^2) \sin 34^0 + 50 \text{ N}$; $\underline{P = 77.4 \text{ N}}$

$s = \dfrac{140 \text{ m}}{\sin 34^0} = 250 \text{ m}$; $(Work)_P = (77.4 \text{ N})(250 \text{ m})$; $\boxed{(Work)_P = 19,400 \text{ J}}$

$\Delta E_p = mgh = (5 \text{ kg})(9.8 \text{ m/s}^2)(140 \text{ m})$; $\boxed{\Delta E_p = 6860 \text{ J}}$

The difference: 19,400 J – 6860 J = 12,540 J is the work done against friction.

---

*8-33. An average force of 600 N is required to compress a coiled spring a distance of 4 cm. What work is done BY the spring? What is the change in potential energy of the compressed spring?

Work done BY spring is opposite to compressing force.

$Work = (-600 \text{ N})(0.04 \text{ m}) = -24.0 \text{ J}$ $\boxed{Work \text{ by spring} = -24.0 \text{ J}}$

Now, $E_p = 0$ initially, so that $\Delta E_p = -(Work)_{SP} = -(-24 \text{ J})$; $\boxed{\Delta E_p = +24.0 \text{ J}}$

Conservation of Energy (No Friction)

8-34. A 64-lb weight is lifted to a height of 10 ft and then released to fall freely. What is the potential energy, the kinetic energy and the total energy at (a) the highest point, (b) 3 ft above the ground, and (c) at the ground? ($W = 64 \text{ lb}$, $g = 32 \text{ ft/s}^2$)

(a) $E_p = Wh = (64 \text{ lb})(10 \text{ ft}) = 640 \text{ ft lb}$; $E_p = 640 \text{ ft lb}$

$E_k = \frac{1}{2}mv^2 = 0$ ($v_o = 0$); $E_T = E_p + E_k = 640 \text{ ft lb} + 0$

At 10 ft: $\boxed{E_p = 640 \text{ ft lb}; \quad E_k = 0; \quad \text{and} \quad E_T = 640 \text{ ft lb}}$

(b) $E_p = Wh = (64 \text{ lb})(3 \text{ ft}) = 192 \text{ ft lb}$; $E_p = 192 \text{ ft lb}$

$E_k = E_T - E_P$; $E_k = 640 \text{ ft lb} - 192 \text{ ft lb}$; $E_k = 448 \text{ ft lb}$

At 3 ft: $\boxed{E_P = 192 \text{ ft lb}; \quad E_k = 448 \text{ ft lb}; \quad \text{and} \quad E_T = 640 \text{ ft lb}}$

(c) At 0 ft $h = 0$ and E_T is same: $\boxed{E_P = 0 \text{ ft lb}; \quad E_k = 640 \text{ ft lb}; \quad \text{and} \quad E_T = 640 \text{ ft lb}}$

8-35. A 4-kg hammer is lifted to a height of 10 m and dropped. What are the potential and kinetic energies of the hammer when it has fallen to a point 4 m from the earth?

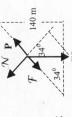

At 10 m: $E_k = 0$ and $E_p = mgh = (4 \text{ kg})(9.8 \text{ m/s}^2)(10 \text{ m})$; $E_T = 0 + 392 \text{ J} = \underline{392 \text{ J}}$

$E_p = mgh = (4 \text{ kg})(9.8 \text{ m/s}^2)(4 \text{ m})$; $E_p = 157 \text{ J}$; $E_k = E_T - E_P = 392 \text{ J} - 157 \text{ J}$

Thus at $h = 4 \text{ m}$: $\boxed{E_p = 157 \text{ J} \text{ and } E_k = 235 \text{ J}}$

*8-36. What will be the velocity of the hammer in Problem 8-35 just before striking the ground?

What is the velocity at the 4-m location?

At bottom, $E_p = 0$ and $E_T = 392$ J so that $E_k = 392$ J $- 0 = 392$ J;

$E_k = \frac{1}{2}mv^2 = 392$ J $v = \sqrt{\dfrac{2(392 \text{ J})}{4 \text{ kg}}}$ $\boxed{v = 14.0 \text{ m/s}}$

*8-37. What initial velocity must be given to a 5-kg mass if it is to rise to a height of 10 m?

What is the total energy at any point in its path?

In absence of friction, total energy at bottom must equal total energy at top:

$E_T = \frac{1}{2}mv_o^2 + 0 = 0 + mgh$; $v_o^2 = 2gh$

$v_o = \sqrt{2gh} = \sqrt{2(9.8 \text{ m/s}^2)(10 \text{ m})}$ $\boxed{v_o = 14.0 \text{ m/s}}$

At top: $E_T = 0 + mgh = (5 \text{ kg})(9.8 \text{ m/s}^2)(10 \text{ m})$; $\boxed{E_T = 490 \text{ J}}$

*8-38. A simple pendulum 1 m long has an 8-kg bob. How much work is needed to move the pendulum from its lowest point to a horizontal position? From energy considerations find the velocity of the bob as it swings through the lowest point.

A force F equal to the weight mg must act through a distance equal to length of string:

Work = mgh = (8 kg)(9.8 m/s²)(1 m); $\boxed{\text{Work} = 78.4 \text{ J}}$

The total energy at top (mgh) must be equal to total energy at bottom.($\frac{1}{2}mv^2$):

$mgh = \frac{1}{2}mv^2$ $v = \sqrt{2gh} = \sqrt{2(9.8 \text{ m/s}^2)(1 \text{ m})}$ $\boxed{v = 4.43 \text{ m/s}}$

*8-39. A ballistic pendulum is illustrated in Fig. 8-13. A 40-g ball is caught by a 500-g suspended mass. After impact, the two masses rise a vertical distance of 45 mm. Find the velocity of the combined masses just after impact.   *(See Figure next page)*

Total mass $M = 40$ g $+ 500$ g $= 540$ g; $M = 540$ g $= 0.540$ kg

---

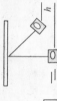

*8-39. (Cont.) Find v_o of total mass M such that M rises $h = 0.045$ m:

Energy conservation: $\frac{1}{2}Mv^2 + 0 = 0 + Mgh$;

$v = \sqrt{2gh} = \sqrt{2(9.8 \text{ m/s}^2)(0.045 \text{ m})}$ $\boxed{v = 0.939 \text{ m/s}}$

*8-40. A 100-lb sled slides from rest at the top of a 37⁰ inclined plane. The original height is 80 ft. In the absence of friction, what is the velocity of the sled when it reaches the bottom of the incline? *(Not dependent on either angle or weight.)*

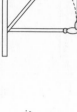

Energy conservation: $0 + mgh = \frac{1}{2}mv^2 + 0$;

$v = \sqrt{2gh} = \sqrt{2(32 \text{ ft/s}^2)(80 \text{ ft})}$ $\boxed{v = 71.6 \text{ ft/s}}$

*8-41. An 8-kg block in Fig. 8-14 has an initial downward velocity of 7 m/s. Neglecting friction, find the velocity when it reaches point B.

$\frac{1}{2}mv_o^2 + mgh_o = \frac{1}{2}mv_f^2 + mgh_f$

$v_o^2 + 2gh_o = v_f^2 + 0$; $v_f^2 = v_o^2 + 2gh_o$

$v_f = \sqrt{v_o^2 + 2gh_o} = \sqrt{(7 \text{ m/s})^2 + 2(9.8 \text{ m/s})(20 \text{ m})}$; $\boxed{v_f = 21.0 \text{ m/s}}$

*8-42. What is the velocity of the 8-kg block at point C in Problem 8-41? *(Note $h_f \neq 0$ this time)*

$\frac{1}{2}mv_o^2 + mgh_o = \frac{1}{2}mv_f^2 + mgh_f$; $v_o^2 + 2gh_o = v_f^2 + 2gh_f$; $v_f^2 = v_o^2 + 2gh_o - 2gh_f$

$v_f = \sqrt{v_o^2 + 2g(h_o - h_f)} = \sqrt{(7 \text{ m/s})^2 + 2(9.8 \text{ m/s}^2)(20 \text{ m} - 8 \text{ m})}$; $\boxed{v_f = 16.9 \text{ m/s}}$

*8-43. An 80-lb girl sits in a swing of negligible weight. If she is given an initial velocity of 20 ft/s, to what height will she rise?

Energy conservation: $0 + mgh = \frac{1}{2}mv^2 + 0$;

$h = \dfrac{v^2}{2g} = \dfrac{(20 \text{ ft/s})}{2(32 \text{ ft/s}^2)}$ $\boxed{h = 6.25 \text{ ft}}$

Energy and Friction Forces

*8-44. A 60-kg sled slides to the bottom of a 25° slope of length 30 m. A 100-N friction force acts for the entire distance. What is the total energy at the top of the slope and at the bottom? What is the velocity of the sled at the bottom?

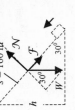

$h = (20\ \text{m})\sin 25^0 = 8.45\ \text{m};$ At top: $E_P = mgh;\ E_k = 0$

$E_T = E_P + E_k = mgh + 0;\quad E_T = (60\ \text{kg})(9.8\ \text{m/s}^2)(8.45\ \text{m})$

Total energy at top. $\boxed{E_T = 4969\ \text{J}}$ *Cons. of E:* $E_T(top) = E_{kf}(bottom) + Losses$

$Loss = (Work)_F = Fs;\quad Loss = (100\ \text{N})(30\ \text{m}) = 3000\ \text{J}$

Cons. of E: $4960\ \text{J} = \tfrac{1}{2}(60\ \text{kg})v^2 + 3000\ \text{J};$ *From which:* $\boxed{v = 8.10\ \text{m/s}}$

*8-45. A 500-g block is released from the top of a 30° incline and slides 160 cm to the bottom. What is the total energy at the bottom? A constant friction force of 0.9 N acts the entire distance. What is the velocity at the bottom? What work is done by friction? What is the total energy at the top?

$W = mg = (0.5\ \text{kg})(9.8\ \text{m/s}^2) = 4.90\ \text{N};$

$h = (1.60\ \text{m})\sin 30^0 = 0.800\ \text{m};\quad E_T = E_P + E_k$

$E_T = Wh + 0;\quad E_T = (4.90\ \text{N})(0.80\ \text{m});\quad \boxed{E_T = 3.92\ \text{J}}$

$(Work)_F = Fs = (-0.900\ \text{N})(1.60\ \text{m});\quad \boxed{(Work)_F = -1.44\ \text{J}}$ *(negative work)*

Total energy at top = total energy at bottom + work done against friction

$3.92\ \text{J} = \tfrac{1}{2}mv^2 + |Fs|;\quad 3.92\ \text{J} = \tfrac{1}{2}(0.5\ \text{kg})\,v^2 + 1.44\ \text{J}$

Solving for v, we obtain: $\boxed{v = 3.15\ \text{m/s}}$

Note that the work done BY friction is negative, but when applying conservation of energy we use the work AGAINST friction (+1.44 J) to account for the LOSS

---

*8-46. What initial velocity must be given to the 500-g block in Problem 8-45 if it is to just reach the top of the same slope? *(See previous problem)*

From Prob. 8-43: $F = 0.9\ \text{N},\ h = 0.8\ \text{m},\ W = 4.90\ \text{N}$

$\tfrac{1}{2}mv_o^2 = Wh_f + Fs = 3.92\ \text{J} + 1.44\ \text{J};\quad \tfrac{1}{2}mv_o^2 = 5.36\ \text{J}$

$v_o = \sqrt{\dfrac{2(5.36\ \text{J})}{m}} = \sqrt{\dfrac{2(5.36\ \text{J})}{0.500\ \text{kg}}}\quad \boxed{v_o = 4.63\ \text{m/s}}$

*8-47. A 64-lb cart starts up a 37° incline with an initial velocity of 60 ft/s. If it comes to rest after a moving a distance of 70 ft, how much energy was lost to friction?

$W = 64\ \text{lb};\quad m = (64/32) = 2\ \text{slugs};\quad h = 70\sin 37^0 = 42.1\ \text{m}$

$\tfrac{1}{2}mv_o^2 = Wh_f + Loss;\quad Loss = \tfrac{1}{2}mv_o^2 - Wh_f$

$Loss = \tfrac{1}{2}(2\ \text{slugs})(60\ \text{ft/s})^2 - (64\ \text{lb})(42.1\ \text{ft})$

$Loss = 3600\ \text{ft lb} - 2240\ \text{ft lb};\quad \boxed{Loss = 904\ \text{ft lb}}$

*8-48. A 0.4-kg ball drops a vertical distance of 40 m and rebounds to a height of 16 m. How much energy was lost in collision with the floor?   *Conservation of energy.*

$mgh_o = mgh_f + Loss;\quad Loss = mgh_o - mgh_f = mg(h_o - h_f)$

$Loss = (0.4\ \text{kg})(9.8\ \text{m/s}^2)(40\ \text{m} - 16\ \text{m});\quad \boxed{Loss = 94.1\ \text{J}}$

*8-49. A 4-kg sled is given an initial velocity of 10 m/s at the top of a 34° slope. If $\mu_k = 0.2$, how far must the sled travel until its velocity reaches 30 m/s?

$mgh_o + \tfrac{1}{2}mv_o^2 = 0 + \tfrac{1}{2}mv_f^2 + Fs$ *and* $h_o = s\sin 34^0$

$mg(s\sin 34^0) - Fs = \tfrac{1}{2}mv_f^2 - \tfrac{1}{2}mv_o^2;\quad F = \mu_k\, mg\cos 34^0$

$\cancel{m}g(s\sin 34^0) - (\mu_k\cancel{m}g\cos 34^0)s = \tfrac{1}{2}\cancel{m}v_f^2 - \tfrac{1}{2}\cancel{m}v_o^2$

8-53. A 40-kg mass is lifted through a distance of 20 m in a time of 3 s. Find average power.

$$P = \frac{Fs}{t} = \frac{mgs}{t}; \quad P = \frac{(40\ kg)(9.8\ m/s^2)(20\ m)}{3\ s}; \quad \boxed{P = 2610\ W}$$

8-54. A 300-kg elevator is lifted vertical distance of 100 m in 2 min. What is the output power?

$$P = \frac{Fs}{t} = \frac{mgs}{t}; \quad P = \frac{(300\ kg)(9.8\ m/s^2)(100\ m)}{120\ s}; \quad \boxed{P = 2.45\ kW}$$

8-55. A 90 kW engine is used to lift a 1200-kg load. What is the average velocity of the lift?

$$P = \frac{Fs}{t} = F\bar{v}; \quad \bar{v} = \frac{P}{F} = \frac{P}{mg} = \frac{90,000\ W}{(1200\ kg)(9.8\ m/s^2)}; \quad \boxed{v = 7.65\ m/s}$$

8-56. To what height can a 400 W engine lift a 100-kg mass in 3 s?

$$P = \frac{Fs}{t} = \frac{mgh}{t}; \quad h = \frac{Pt}{mg} = \frac{(400\ W)(3\ s)}{(100\ kg)(9.8\ m/s^2)}; \quad \boxed{h = 0.122\ m}$$

8-57. An 800-N student runs up a flight of stairs rising 6 m in 8 s. What is the average power?

$$P = \frac{Fs}{t} = \frac{Wh}{r}; \quad P = \frac{(800\ N)(6\ m)}{8\ s}; \quad P = 600\ W$$

*8-58. A speedboat must develop a 120 hp in order to move at a constant speed of 15 ft/s through the water. What is the average resistive force due to the water? $P = F\bar{v}$;

$$P = (120\ hp)\left(\frac{550\ ft\ lb/s}{1\ hp}\right) = 66,000\ ft\ lb/s; \quad P = F\bar{v}$$

$$F = \frac{P}{v} = \frac{66,000\ ft\ lb/s}{15\ ft/s}; \quad \boxed{F = 4400\ lb}$$

---

*8-49. (Cont.) $(g\sin 34^0 - \mu_k g\cos 34^0)s = \frac{1}{2}v_f^2 - \frac{1}{2}v_0$; $\quad s = \frac{v_f^2 - v_0^2}{2g(\sin 34^0 - \mu_k\cos 34^0)}$;

$$s = \frac{(30\ m/s)^2 - (10\ m/s)^2}{2(9.8\ m/s^2)(\sin 34^0 - 0.2\cos 34^0)}; \quad \boxed{s = 104\ m}$$

*8-50. Assume in Fig. 8-14 that the sliding mass is 6-kg and that 300 J of energy is lost doing work against friction. What is the velocity when the mass reaches point C?

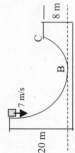

$$\frac{1}{2}mv_0^2 + mgh_o = \frac{1}{2}mv_c^2 + mgh_f + 300\ J$$

$$\frac{1}{2}mv_c^2 = \frac{1}{2}mv_0^2 + mgh_o - mgh_c - 300\ J$$

$$v_c^2 = v_0^2 + 2g(h_o - h_c) - \frac{2(300\ J)}{m}$$

$$v_0 = \sqrt{(7\ m/s)^2 + 2(9.8\ m/s^2)(20\ m - 8\ m) - \frac{2(300\ J)}{6\ kg}}$$

$$\boxed{v_c = 13.6\ m/s}$$

*8-51. A bus slams on brakes to avoid an accident. The tread marks of the tires are 80 feet long. If $\mu_k = 0.7$, what was the speed before applying brakes?

$$\mathcal{F} = \mu_k mg; \quad Work = \mathcal{F}s = \mu_k mgs$$

$$Work = \Delta E_k; \quad -\mu_k mgs = \frac{1}{2}mv_f^2 - \frac{1}{2}mv_0^2$$

$$v_0 = \sqrt{2\mu_k gs} = \sqrt{2(0.7)(32\ ft/s^2)(80\ ft)}$$

$$\boxed{v_0 = 59.9\ ft/s}$$

Power

8-52. A power-station conveyor belt lifts 500 tons of ore to a height of 90 ft in one hour. What average horsepower is required? ($W = 500\ tons = 1 \times 10^6\ lb$; $1\ hp = 550\ ft\ lb/s$)

$$Power = \frac{Work}{t} = \frac{Wh}{t}; \quad P = \frac{(1 \times 10^6\ lb)(90\ ft)}{3600\ s}; \quad P = 25,000\ ft\ lb/s = \boxed{45.5\ hp}$$

*8-63. A roller coaster boasts a maximum height of 100 ft. What is the maximum speed in miles per hour when it reaches its lowest point?   (*Conservation of Energy*)

$mgh + 0 = 0 + \frac{1}{2}mv^2$; $v = \sqrt{2gh} = \sqrt{2(32 \text{ ft/s}^2)(100 \text{ ft})}$; $\boxed{v = 80.0 \text{ ft/s}}$ (54.4 mph)

*8-64. A 20-N force drags an 8-kg block a horizontal distance of 40 m by a rope at an angle of 37° with the horizontal. Assume $\mu_k = 0.2$ and that the time required is one minute. What resultant work is done?

Resultant work = work of the resultant force

$F_R = (20 \text{ N})\cos 37° - \mathcal{F}$ $\mathcal{F} = \mu_k \mathcal{N}$ $\Sigma F_y = 0$

$\mathcal{N} + 20 \sin 37° - (8 \text{ kg})(9.8 \text{ m/s}^2) = 0$; $\mathcal{N} = 66.4$ N; $\mathcal{F} = 0.2(66.4 \text{ N}) = 13.3$ N

$F_R = 20 \cos 37° - 13.3 \text{ N} = 2.70$ N; $Work = F_R S = (2.70 \text{ N})(40 \text{ m})$; $\boxed{Work = 108 \text{ J}}$

*8-65. What is the velocity of the block in Problem 8-64 at the end of the trip? What <u>resultant</u> power was expended? (*Assume block starts from rest, then apply work-energy theorem.*)

$Work = \frac{1}{2}mv_f^2 - \frac{1}{2}mv_o^2$; $108 \text{ J} = \frac{1}{2}(8 \text{ kg})v^2 + 0$; $v = \sqrt{\dfrac{2(108 \text{ J})}{8 \text{ kg}}}$; $\boxed{v = 5.20 \text{ m/s}}$

$P = \dfrac{Work}{t} = \dfrac{108 \text{ J}}{60 \text{ s}}$ $\boxed{P = 1.80 \text{ W}}$

*8-66. A 70-kg skier slides down a 30 m slope that makes an angle of 28° with the horizontal. What is the velocity of the skier at the bottom of the slope? Assume that $\mu_k = 0.2$.

$mgh_o + \frac{1}{2}mv_o^2 = 0 + \frac{1}{2}mv_f^2 + \mathcal{F}s$ and $h_o = s \sin 28°$

$mg(s \sin 28°) - \mathcal{F}s = \frac{1}{2}mv_f^2 - \frac{1}{2}mv_o^2$; $\mathcal{F} = \mu_k \, mg \cos 28°$

$mg(s \sin 28°) - (\mu_k mg \cos 28°)s = \frac{1}{2}mv_f^2$

Supplementary Problems

*8-59. A worker lifts a 20-kg bucket from a well at constant speed and does 8 kJ of work. How deep is the well?

$Work = Fs$; $s = \dfrac{Work}{mg} = \dfrac{8000 \text{ J}}{(20 \text{ kg})(9.8 \text{ m/s}^2)}$; $\boxed{s = 40.8 \text{ m}}$

*8-60. A horizontal force of 200 N pushes an 800-N crate horizontally for a distance of 6 m at constant speed. What work is done by the 200-N force. What is the resultant work?

$Work = Fs = (200 \text{ N})(6 \text{ m})$; $Work = 1200$ J

Speed is constant, so $F_R = 0$, and $\boxed{Resultant \ work = 0 \text{ J}}$

*8-61. A 10-kg mass is lifted to a height of 20 m, and released. What is the total energy of the system? What is the velocity of the mass when it is located 5 m from the floor?

In absence of friction, total energy is constant, so that: $E_T(Top) = E_T(5 \text{ m})$

$E_T = mgh + 0 = (10 \text{ kg})(9.8 \text{ m/s}^2)(20 \text{ m})$; $\boxed{E_T = 1960 \text{ J}}$

When $h = 5$ m, $(10 \text{ kg})(9.8 \text{ m/s}^2)(5 \text{ m}) + \frac{1}{2}(10 \text{ kg})v_f^2 = 1960 \text{ J}$

$490 \text{ J} + (5 \text{ kg})v_f^2 = 1960 \text{ J}$; $\boxed{v_f = 17.1 \text{ m/s}}$

*8-62. A crate is lifted at a constant speed of 5 m/s by an engine whose output power is 4 kW. What is the mass of the crate?

$P = \bar{F}v = mgv$; $m = \dfrac{P}{gv} = \dfrac{4000 \text{ W}}{(9.8 \text{ m/s}^2)(5 \text{ m/s})}$; $\boxed{m = 81.6 \text{ kg}}$

*8-66. (Cont.) $(g \sin 28^0 - \mu_k g \cos 28^0)s = \frac{1}{2}v_f^2$; $v_f^2 = 2gs(\sin 28^0 - \mu_k \cos 28^0)$

$$v_f = \sqrt{2(9.8 \text{ m/s}^2)(30 \text{ m})(\sin 28^0 - 0.2\cos 28^0)} \quad \boxed{v_f = 13.1 \text{ m/s}}$$

*8-67. A 0.3 mg flea can jump to a height of about 3 cm. What must be the takeoff speed? Do you really need to know the mass of the flea?

$$\tfrac{1}{2}mv_o^2 = mgh \; ; \quad v_o = \sqrt{2gh} = \sqrt{2(9.8 \text{ m/s}^2)(0.03 \text{ m})} \; ;$$

$$\boxed{v = 0.767 \text{ m/s} \; ; \quad \textit{The mass is not needed.}}$$

*8-68. A roller coaster goes through a low point and barely makes the next hill 15 m higher. What is the minimum speed at the bottom of the loop?

$$\tfrac{1}{2}mv_o^2 = mgh \; ; \quad v_o = \sqrt{2gh} = \sqrt{2(9.8 \text{ m/s}^2)(15 \text{ m})} \quad \boxed{v = 17.1 \text{ m/s}}$$

*8-69. The hammer of a pile driver weighs 800 lb and falls a distance of 16 ft before striking the pile. The impact drives the pile 6 in. deeper into the ground. What was the average force driving the pile? $m = W/g = (800/32) = 25.0$ slugs; $s = 6$ in. $= 0.5$ ft

The work done by the pile driver Fs is determine from the change in kinetic energy, so we need to find the velocity of the driver just before striking the stake:

$$\tfrac{1}{2}mv_f^2 = mgh_o \; ; \quad v_f = \sqrt{2gh_o} = \sqrt{2(32 \text{ ft/s}^2)(16 \text{ ft})} \; ; \quad v = 32.0 \text{ ft/s}$$

Work to stop driver = change in kinetic energy of driver

$$Fs = \tfrac{1}{2}mv_f^2 - \tfrac{1}{2}mv_o^2 \; ; \quad F = -\frac{mv_o^2}{2s} = -\frac{(25 \text{ slugs})(32 \text{ ft/s})^2}{2(0.5 \text{ ft})} \quad \boxed{F = -25,600 \text{ lb}}$$

Critical Thinking Questions

*8-70. An inclined board is used to unload boxes of nails from the back of a truck. The height of the truck bed is 60 cm and the board is 1.2 m in length. Assume that $\mu_k = 0.4$ and the boxes are given an initial push to start sliding. What is their speed when they reach the ground below. What initial speed would they need at the bottom in order to slide back into the truck bed? In the absence of friction would these two questions have the same answer?   [$h = 0.6$ m ; $s = 1.2$ m ; $\sin \theta = 0.6/1.2$; $\theta = 30^0$]

(a) $(Work)_f = \mathcal{F}s = \mu_k \mathcal{N} = \mu_k \, mg \cos 30^0 s$

$mgh = \tfrac{1}{2}mv^2 + \mu_k \, mg \cos 30^0 s$; $2gh = v^2 + 2\mu_k gs \cos 30^0$

$v^2 = 2gh - 2g\mu_k s \cos 30^0 = 2(9.8 \text{ m/s}^2)(0.6 \text{ m}) - 2(9.8 \text{ m/s}^2)(0.4)(1.2 \text{ m})(0.866)$

$v^2 = 11.76 - 8.15 = 3.61 \text{ m}^2/\text{s}^2$; $v = \sqrt{3.61 \text{ m}^2/\text{s}^2}$; $\boxed{v = 1.90 \text{ m/s}}$

(b) *Going up the plane, the initial speed must provide the energy to overcome the friction force which would now be directed DOWN the plane.*

$\tfrac{1}{2}mv^2 = mgh + \mu_k mg \cos 30^0 s$ (*Note the difference in this equation from that above.*)

$v^2 = 2gh + 2\mu_k gs \cos 30^0 = (2)(9.8)(0.6) + 2(0.4)(9.8)(1.2)(0.866)$

$v^2 = 11.76 + 8.15 = 19.9 \text{ m}^2/\text{s}^2$; $v = \sqrt{19.9 \text{ m}^2/\text{s}^2}$; $\boxed{v = 4.46 \text{ m/s}}$

In the downhill case, the initial potential energy was lost to friction and what little remained appeared in the form of a small velocity at the bottom. In the uphill case, the initial kinetic energy (high velocity) was used to gain the height h, but more energy was needed to overcome friction. In the absence of friction, height is transferred into velocity going down, and velocity is transferred to height going up. Thus, absent friction, the same velocities would be found for each of the above cases. (v = 3.43 m/s)

Chapter 8   Work, Energy, and Power   **99**

*8-71. A 96-lb safe is pushed with negligible friction up a 30° incline for a distance of 12 ft.

What is the increase in potential energy? Would the same change in potential energy occur if a 10-lb friction force opposed the motion up the incline? Why? Would the same work be required? [$h = 12 \sin 30^0 = 6.00$ ft]

(a) $E_p = Wh = (96 \text{ lb})(6 \text{ ft})$ $\boxed{E_p = 576 \text{ ft lb}}$

(b) *E_p is a function only of weight and height, so the same change in potential energy occurs regard less of friction or the path taken.*

(c) *With a 10-lb friction force, a work of (10 lb)(12 ft) = 120 ft lb is needed in addition to the work of 576 ft lb just to lift the weight. The total work is 696 ft lb.*

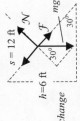

$s = 12$ ft

$h = 6$ ft

**8-72. A 2-kg ball is suspended from a 3-m cable attached to a spike in the wall. The ball is pulled out, so that the cable makes an angle of 70° with the wall, and then released. If 10 J of energy are lost during the collision with the wall, what is the maximum angle between the cable and the wall after the first rebound?

$y_o = (3 \text{ m}) \cos 70^0 = 1.026 \text{ m}$

$h_o = 3 \text{ m} - 1.026 \text{ m}; \quad h_o = 1.974 \text{ m}$

$mgh_o = mgh_f + 10 \text{ J}; \quad mgh_f = mgh_o - 10 \text{ J}$

$h_f = 1.974 \text{ m} - \dfrac{10 \text{ J}}{(2 \text{ kg})(9.8 \text{ m/s}^2)}; \quad h_f = 1.464 \text{ m}; \quad y_f = 3 \text{ m} - 1.464 \text{ m} = 1.536 \text{ m}$

$\cos\theta = \dfrac{y_f}{L} = \dfrac{1.536 \text{ m}}{3.00 \text{ m}}; \quad \boxed{\theta = 59.2^0}$

**8-73. A 3-kg ball dropped from a height of 12 m has a velocity of 10 m/s just before hitting the ground. What is the average retarding force due to the air? If the ball rebounds from the surface with a speed of 8 m/s, what energy was lost on impact? How high will it rebound if the average air resistance is the same as before?

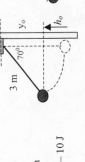

8 m/s   12 m h_f 10 m/s

First apply E conservation to the falling portion of the problem:

$mgh_o = \frac{1}{2}mv^2 + \mathcal{F}s$; $\mathcal{F}s = mgh_o - \frac{1}{2}mv^2$

$\mathcal{F}(12 \text{ m}) = (3 \text{ kg})(9.8 \text{ m/s}^2)(12 \text{ m}) - \frac{1}{2}(3 \text{ kg})(10 \text{ m/s})^2;$ $\boxed{\mathcal{F} = 16.9 \text{ N}}$

The loss or work done on impact equals the change in E_k: $Loss = Work = \frac{1}{2}mv^2 - \frac{1}{2}mv_o^2$

$Work = \frac{1}{2}(3 \text{ kg})(8 \text{ m/s})^2 - \frac{1}{2}(3 \text{ kg})(10 \text{ m/s})^2;$ $Work = -54 \text{ J};$ $\boxed{Impact \ loss = 54 \text{ J}}$

To find rebound height, apply conservation of energy with losses to air and to impact: $mgh_o = mgh_f + (\mathcal{F}s)_{Air} + Impact \ loss;$ $(s = 12 \text{ m} + h_f)$

$(3 \text{ kg})(9.8 \text{ m/s}^2)(12 \text{ m}) = (3\text{kg})(9.8 \text{ m/s}^2)h_f + (16.9 \text{ N})(12 \text{ m} + h_f) + 54 \text{ J}$

$353 \text{ J} = (29.4 \text{ N})h_f + 203 \text{ J} + (16.9 \text{ N})h_f + 54 \text{ J};$ $\boxed{h_f = 2.07 \text{ m}}$

*8-74. Consider a roller coaster where the first hill is 34 m high? If the coaster losses only 8% of its energy between the first two hills, what is the maximum height possible for the second hill?

$mgh_o = mgh_f + 0.08 \, mgh_o;$ $h_f = (1 - 0.08)h_o = 0.92 \ (34 \text{ m})$ $\boxed{h_f = 31.3 \text{ m}}$

*8-75. A 4-kg block is compressed against a spring at the bottom the inclined plane in Fig. 8-15. If it is then

A force of 4000 N was required to compress the spring a distance of 6 cm. If it is then

released and the coefficient of friction is 0.4, how far up the incline will the block move?

Work to compress spring $= (4000 \text{ N})(0.06 \text{ m}) = 240 \text{ J} = E_p$

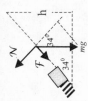

$E_p(\text{spring}) = mgh + \mathcal{F}s;$ $\mathcal{F}s = \mu_k mg \cos 30^0$

$\mathcal{F}s = (0.4)(4 \text{ kg})(9.8 \text{ m/s}^2)(0.866) s = (13.6 \text{ N}) s$ $h = s \sin 30^0 = 0.5 s$

$240 \text{ J} = (4 \text{ kg})(9.8 \text{ m/s}^2)h + (13.6 \text{ N}) s$

$240 \text{ J} = (4 \text{ kg})(9.8 \text{ m/s}^2)(2 s) + (13.6 \text{ N}) s;$ $\boxed{s = 2.61 \text{ m}}$

Chapter 9. Impulse and Momentum

9-1. A 0.5-kg wrench is dropped from a height of 10 m. What is its momentum just before it

strikes the floor? *(First find the velocity from conservation of energy.)*

$mgh = \tfrac{1}{2}mv^2;$ $v = \sqrt{2gh} = \sqrt{2(9.8 \text{ m/s}^2)(10 \text{ m})}$ $v = 14.0 \text{ m/s}$

$p = mv = (0.5 \text{ kg})(14 \text{ m/s});$ $\boxed{p = 7.00 \text{ kg m/s}}$

9-2. Compute the momentum and kinetic energy of a 2400-lb car moving north at 55 mi/h.

$m = \dfrac{W}{g} = \dfrac{2400 \text{ lb}}{32 \text{ ft/s}^2};$ $m = 75 \text{ slugs};$ $v = 55 \text{ mi/h} = 80.7 \text{ ft/s}$

$p = mv = (75 \text{ slugs})(80.7 \text{ ft/s});$ $\boxed{p = 6050 \text{ slug ft/s}}$

$K = \tfrac{1}{2}mv^2 = \tfrac{1}{2}(75 \text{ slugs})(80.66 \text{ ft/s})^2;$ $\boxed{K = 244{,}000 \text{ ft lb}}$

9-3. A 2500-kg truck traveling at 40 km/h strikes a brick wall and comes to a stop in 0.2 s. (a)

What is the change in momentum? (b) What is the impulse? (c) What is the average force

on the wall during the crash? *Take + to be toward the wall.* (40 km/h = 11.1 m/s)

$\Delta p = mv_f - mv_o = 0 - (2500 \text{ kg})(11.1 \text{ m/s});$ $\boxed{\Delta p = -27{,}800 \text{ kg m/s}}$

$Impulse = \Delta p;$ $\boxed{F\,t = -27{,}800 \text{ kg m/s}}$

Force ON truck: $F = \dfrac{-27{,}800}{0.2 \text{ s}};$ $F = -139{,}000 \text{ N}$

Force on wall is opposite, so $\boxed{F = + 139{,}000 \text{ N}}$

9-4. What is the momentum of a 3-kg bullet moving at 600 m/s in a direction 30^0 above the

horizontal? What are the horizontal and vertical components of this momentum?

$p = mv = (3 \text{ kg})(600 \text{ m/s});$ $\boxed{p = 1800 \text{ kg m/s, } 30^0}$

$p_x = 1800 \cos 30^0$ and $p_y = 1800 \sin 30^0;$ $\boxed{p_x = 1560 \text{ kg m/s}; \quad p_y = 900 \text{ kg m/s}}$

$(E_p)_{Beginning} = (E_k)_{Ground}$; $mgh_o = \frac{1}{2}mv_o^2$;

$v_o = \sqrt{2gh_o} = \sqrt{2(9.8 \text{ m/s}^2)(12 \text{ m})}$ $v_o = -15.3$ m/s

$\frac{1}{2}mv_f^2 = mgh_f$; $v_f = \sqrt{2(9.8 \text{ m/s}^2)(10 \text{ m})}$ $v_f = +14$ m/s

$F\Delta t = mv_f - mv_o$; $F(0.01 \text{ s}) = (0.4 \text{ kg})(14 \text{ m/s}) - (0.4 \text{ kg})(-15.3 \text{ m/s})$; $\boxed{F = 1170 \text{ N}}$

*9-9. A cue stick strikes an eight-ball with an average force of 80 N over a time of 12 ms. If the mass of the ball is 200 g, what will be its velocity?

$F\Delta t = mv_f - mv_o$;   (80 N)(0.012 s) = (0.2 kg)v_f– 0; $\boxed{v = 4.80 \text{ m/s}}$

9-10. A golfer hits a 46 g golf ball with an initial velocity of 50 m/s at 30^0.   What are the x- and y-components of the momentum imparted to the ball?

$v_x = (50) \cos 30^0 = 43.3$ m/s ; $v_y = (50) \sin 30^0 = 25.0$ m/s

$p_x = (0.046 \text{ kg})(43.3 \text{ m/s})$; $p_y = (0.046 \text{ kg})(25 \text{ m/s})$ $\boxed{p_x = 1.99 \text{ kg m/s}; p_y = 1.15 \text{ m/s}}$

**9-11. The face of the club in Problem 9-10 is in contact with the ball for 1.5 ms. What are the horizontal and vertical components of the average force on the ball?

We need to treat horizontal and vertical impulses and momenta separately:

From previous problem: $p_o = 0$, $p_f = 1.99$ kg m/s, $p_{fy} = 1.15$ kg m/s

$F_x \Delta t = p_{fx} - p_{ox} = 1.99$ kg m/s; $F_x = \dfrac{1.99 \text{ kg m/s}}{0.0015 \text{ s}}$; $\boxed{F_x = 1330 \text{ N}}$

$F_x \Delta t = p_{fx} - p_{ox} = 1.15$ kg m/s; $F_y = \dfrac{1.15 \text{ kg m/s}}{0.0015 \text{ s}}$; $\boxed{F_y = 767 \text{ N}}$

---

*9-5. A 0.2-kg baseball traveling to the left at 20 m/s is driven in the opposite direction at 35 m/s when it is hit by a bat. The average force on the ball is 6400 N. How long was it in contact with the bat? (*Impulse = change in momentum.*)

$F\Delta t = mv_f - mv_o = (0.2 \text{ kg})(35 \text{ m/s}) - (0.2 \text{ kg})(-20 \text{ m/s})$

(6400 N) $\Delta t = 11$ kg m/s; $\Delta t = 1.72$ ms

*9-6. A bat exerts an average force of 248 lb on a 0.6-lb ball for 0.01 s. The incoming velocity of the ball was 44 ft/s. If it leaves in the opposite direction what is its velocity?

Choose positive + as direction away from the bat, making incoming ball velocity negative:

$F\Delta t = mv_f - mv_o$; $F\Delta t = mv_f - mv_o$; $m = \dfrac{0.6 \text{ lb}}{32 \text{ ft/s}^2} = 0.01875$ slugs

(240 lb)(0.01 s) = (0.01875 slugs)v_f - (0.01875 slugs)(-44 ft/s)

0.01875 $v_f = 2.4$ lb s – 0.825; $\boxed{v_f = 84.0 \text{ ft/s}}$

*9-7. A 500-g ball travels from left to right at 20 m/s. A bat drives the ball in the opposite direction with a velocity of 36 m/s. The time of contact was 0.003 s. What was the average force on the ball?   (*m = 0.5 kg*, $v_o = +20$ m/s, $v_f = -36$ m/s, $\Delta t = 0.003$ s)

$F\Delta t = mv_f - mv_o$;   F(0.003 s) = (0.5 kg)(-36 m/s) – (0.5 kg)(20 m/s)

$F = \dfrac{-18 \text{ kg m/s} - 10 \text{ kg m/s}}{0.003 \text{ s}}$; $\boxed{F = 9330 \text{ N}}$

*9-8. A 400-g rubber ball is dropped a vertical distance of 12 m onto the pavement. It is in contact with the pavement for 0.01 s and rebounds to a height of 10 m. What is the total change in momentum? What average force is exerted on the ball?

To apply the impulse-momentum theorem, we need to first find the velocities

just before and just after impact with the ground.

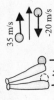

Conservation of Momentum

9-12. A spring is tightly compressed between a 6-kg block and a 2-kg block and then tied with a string. When the string breaks, the 2-kg block moves to the right with a velocity of 9 m/s. What is the velocity of the 6-kg block?

Total momentum is zero before and after the event.

$0 + 0 = m_1v_1 + m_2v_2$; $v_1 = \frac{-m_2v_2}{m_1} = \frac{-(2 \text{ kg})(9 \text{ m/s})}{(6 \text{ kg})}$; $\boxed{v_1 = -3.00 \text{ m/s}}$

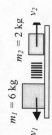

$m_1 = 6 \text{ kg}$ $m_2 = 2 \text{ kg}$ v_1 v_2

9-13. Two masses, one three times that of the other, are compressed against a spring and then tied together on a frictionless surface as shown in Fig. 9-8. The connecting string breaks and sends the smaller mass to the left with a velocity of 10 m/s. What was the velocity of the larger mass?

Momentum zero before and after: $0 + 0 = m_1v_1 + m_2v_2$

$v_2 = \frac{-m_1v_1}{m_2} = \frac{-m(10 \text{ m/s})}{(3m)}$; $\boxed{v_1 = -3.33 \text{ m/s}}$

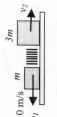

10 m/s v_1 m $3m$ v_2

9-14. A 70-kg person standing on a frictionless surface throws a football forward with a velocity of 12 m/s. If the person moves backward at 34 cm/s, what was the mass of the football?

Momentum zero before and after: $0 + 0 = m_1v_1 + m_2v_2$

$m_2 = \frac{-m_1v_1}{v_2} = \frac{-(70 \text{ kg})(0.34 \text{ m/s})}{(-12 \text{ m/s})}$; $\boxed{m_2 = 1.98 \text{ m/s}}$

9-15. A 20-kg child is at rest in a wagon. The child jumps forward at 2 m/s, sending the wagon backward at 12 m/s. What is the mass of the wagon?

$0 = m_1v_1 + m_2v_2$; $m_1 = \frac{-m_2v_2}{v_1} = \frac{-(20 \text{ kg})(2 \text{ m/s})}{(-12 \text{ m/s})}$; $\boxed{m_1 = -3.33 \text{ kg}}$

9-16. Two children, weighing 80 and 50 lb, are at rest on roller skates. The larger child pushes so that the smaller moves away at 6 mi/h. What is the velocity of the larger child?

$0 = m_1v_1 + m_2v_2$; $v_1 = \frac{-m_2v_2}{m_1} = \frac{-(50 \text{ lb})(6 \text{ ft/s})}{(80 \text{ lb})}$; $\boxed{v_1 = -3.75 \text{ ft/s}}$

(Here were able to use the weight because it is proportional to the mass)

9-17. A 60-g firecracker explodes, sending a 45-g piece to the left and another to the right with a velocity of 40 m/s. What is the velocity of the 45-g piece?

The two pieces add to 60 g: $m_1 + m_2 = 60$ g. Thus, $m_1 = 45$ g, $m_2 = 15$ g

$0 = m_1v_1 + m_2v_2$; $v_1 = \frac{-m_2v_2}{m_1} = \frac{-(15 \text{ g})(40 \text{ m/s})}{(45 \text{ g})}$; $\boxed{v_1 = -13.3 \text{ m/s}}$

*9-18. A 24-g bullet is fired with a muzzle velocity of 900 m/s from a 5-kg rifle. Find the recoil velocity of the rifle and the ratio of the kinetic energy of the bullet to that of the rifle?

$0 = m_1v_1 + m_2v_2$; $v_1 = \frac{-m_2v_2}{m_1} = \frac{-(24 \text{ g})(900 \text{ m/s})}{(5000 \text{ g})}$; $\boxed{v_1 = -4.32 \text{ m/s}}$

$\frac{E_{kb}}{E_{kr}} = \frac{\frac{1}{2}m_bv_b^2}{\frac{1}{2}m_rv_r^2} = \frac{(24 \text{ g})(900 \text{ m/s})^2}{(5000 \text{ g})(4.32 \text{ m/s})^2}$; $\boxed{\text{Ratio} = 208}$

*9-19. A 6-kg bowling ball collides head on with a 1.8-kg pin. The pin moves forward at 3 m/s and the ball slows to 1.6 m/s. What was the initial velocity of the bowling ball?

$m_bu_b + 0 = m_bv_b + m_pv_p$; $(6 \text{ kg})u_b = (6 \text{ kg})(1.6 \text{ m/s}) + (1.8 \text{ kg})(3 \text{ m/s})$; $\boxed{u_b = 2.50 \text{ m/s}}$

$6u_b = 9.6 \text{ m/s} + 5.4 \text{ m/s}$;

*9-20. A 60-kg man on a lake of ice catches a 2-kg ball. The ball and man each move at 8 cm/s after the ball is caught. What was the velocity of the ball before it was caught? What energy was lost in the process? (A completely inelastic collision: $v_c = v_m = v_b = 8$ cm/s)

$m_b u_b + m_m u_m = (m_b + m_m)v_c$; $(2 \text{ kg})u_b + 0 = (2 \text{ kg} + 60 \text{ kg})(0.08 \text{ m/s})$

$2u_b = 4.96 \text{ m/s}$; $\boxed{u_b = 2.48 \text{ m/s}}$

$\frac{1}{2}m_b u_b^2 + 0 = (m_b + m_m)v_c^2$; $\frac{1}{2}(2 \text{ kg})(2.48 \text{ m/s})^2 = \frac{1}{2}(62 \text{ kg})(0.08 \text{ m/s})^2 + \text{Loss}$

$\text{Loss} = 6.15 \text{ J} - 0.198 \text{ J}$; $\boxed{\text{Loss} = 5.95 \text{ J}}$

*9-21. A 200-g rock traveling south at 10 m/s strikes a 3-kg block initially at rest. (a) If the two stick together on collision, what will be their common velocity? (b) What energy was lost in the collision?

$m_r u_r + m_b u_b = (m_r + m_b)v_c$; $(0.2 \text{ kg})(10 \text{ m/s}) + 0 = (0.2 \text{ kg} + 3 \text{ kg})v_c$

$2 \text{ m/s} = 3.2 v_c$; $\boxed{v_c = 0.625 \text{ m/s}}$

$\frac{1}{2}m_r u_r^2 + 0 = (m_r + m_b)v_c^2$; $\frac{1}{2}(0.2 \text{ kg})(10 \text{ m/s})^2 = \frac{1}{2}(3.2 \text{ kg})(0.625 \text{ m/s})^2 + \text{Loss}$

$\text{Loss} = 10.0 \text{ J} - 0.625 \text{ J}$; $\boxed{\text{Loss} = 9.38 \text{ J}}$

Elastic and Inelastic Collisions

9-22. A car traveling at 8 m/s crashes into a car of identical mass stopped at a traffic light. What is the velocity of the wreckage immediately after the crash, assuming the cars stick together? ($u_1 = 8.00 \text{ m/s}$; $u_2 = 0$, $m_1 = m_2 = m$)

$mu_1 + mu_2^{\,0} = (m + m)v_c$; $mu_1 = 2mv_c$

$v_c = \dfrac{u_1}{2} = \dfrac{8 \text{ m/s}}{2}$; $\boxed{v_c = 4.00 \text{ m/s}}$

9-23. A 2000-kg truck traveling at 10 m/s crashes into a 1200-kg car initially at rest. What is the common velocity after the collision if they stick together? What is the loss in energy?

$m_1 u_1 + m_2 u_2 = (m_1 + m_2)v_c$; $(2000 \text{ kg})(10 \text{ m/s}) + 0 = (2000 \text{ kg} + 1200 \text{ kg})v_c$

$20{,}000 \text{ m/s} = 3200 v_c$; $\boxed{v_c = 6.25 \text{ m/s}}$

$\frac{1}{2}m_1 u_1^2 + 0 = (m_1 + m_2)v_c^2$; $\frac{1}{2}(2000 \text{ kg})(10 \text{ m/s})^2 = \frac{1}{2}(3200 \text{ kg})(6.25 \text{ m/s})^2 + \text{Loss}$

$\text{Loss} = 100{,}000 \text{ J} - 62{,}500 \text{ J}$; $\boxed{\text{Loss} = 37{,}500 \text{ J}}$

9-24. A 30-kg child stands on a frictionless surface. The father throws a 0.8-kg football with a velocity of 15 m/s. What velocity will the child have after catching the football?

$m_1 v_1 + m_2 v_2$; $(0.8 \text{ kg})(15 \text{ m/s}) = (30 \text{ kg} + 0.8 \text{ kg})v_c$

$(30.8 \text{ kg})v_c = 12 \text{ m/s}$; $\boxed{v_c = 0.390 \text{ m/s}}$

*9-25. A 20-g object traveling to the left at 8 m/s collides head on with a 10-g object traveling to the right at 5 m/s. What is their combined velocity after impact?

$m_1 u_1 + m_2 u_2 = (m_1 + m_2)v_c$; $(20 \text{ g})(-8 \text{ m/s}) + (10 \text{ g})(5 \text{ m/s}) = (20 \text{ g} + 10 \text{ g})v_c$

$-110 \text{ m/s} = 30 v_c$; $\boxed{v_c = -3.67 \text{ m/s, to left}}$

*9-26. Find the percent loss of energy for the collision in Problem 9-25.

Conservation of Energy: $\frac{1}{2}m_1 u_1^2 + \frac{1}{2}m_2 u_2^2 = \frac{1}{2}(m_1 + m_2)v_c^2 + \text{Loss}$

$\frac{1}{2}(20 \text{ g})(-8 \text{ m/s})^2 + \frac{1}{2}(10 \text{ g})(5 \text{ m/s})^2 = \frac{1}{2}(30 \text{ g})(-3.67 \text{ m/s})^2 + \text{Loss}$

$765 \text{ J} = 202 \text{ J} + \text{Loss}$; $\text{Loss} = 563 \text{ J}$; $\%\text{Loss} = \dfrac{563 \text{ J}}{765 \text{ J}} = \boxed{73.6\%}$

Chapter 9   Impulse and Momentum 109

108 Unit A   Solutions Manual

Copyright © by Glencoe/McGraw-Hill.

*9-27. A 2-kg block of clay is tied to the end of a string as shown in Fig. 9-9. A 500-g steel ball embeds itself into the clay causing both to rise to a height of 20 cm. Find the entrance velocity of the ball?

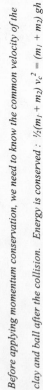

Before applying momentum conservation, we need to know the common velocity of the clay and ball after the collision. Energy is conserved: $\frac{1}{2}(m_1 + m_2)v_c^2 = (m_1 + m_2)gh$;

$$v_c = \sqrt{2gh} = \sqrt{2(9.8 \text{ m/s}^2)(0.20 \text{ m})} \; ; \qquad v_c = 1.98 \text{ m/s}$$

$$m_1u_1 + 0 = (m_1 + m_2)v_c \; ; \qquad (0.5 \text{ kg}) u_1 = (0.5 \text{ kg} + 2 \text{ kg})(1.98 \text{ m/s})$$

$$(0.5 \text{ kg})u_1 = 4.95 \text{ m/s}; \qquad \boxed{u_1 = 9.90 \text{ m/s}}$$

*9-28. In Problem 9-27, suppose the 500-g ball passes entirely through the clay and emerges with a velocity of 10 m/s. what must be the new entrance velocity if the block is to rise to the same height of 20 cm?

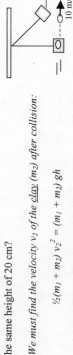

We must find the velocity v_2 of the clay (m_2) after collision:

$$\frac{1}{2}(m_1 + m_2) v_2^2 = (m_1 + m_2) gh$$

$$v_c = \sqrt{2gh} = \sqrt{2(9.8 \text{ m/s}^2)(0.20 \text{ m})} \; ; \qquad v_2 = 1.98 \text{ m/s};$$

Momentum is conserved: $m_1u_1 + 0 = m_1v_1 + m_2v_2$;

$$(0.5 \text{ kg})u_1 = (0.5 \text{ kg})(10 \text{ m/s}) + (2 \text{ kg})(1.98 \text{ m/s}); \qquad \boxed{u_1 = 17.9 \text{ m/s}}$$

*9-29. A 9-g bullet is embedded into a 2.0 kg ballistic pendulum (see Fig. 8-13). What was the initial velocity of the bullet if the combined masses rise to a height of 9 cm?

$$\frac{1}{2}(m_1 + m_2) v_c^2 = (m_1 + m_2) gh \; ;$$

$$v_c = \sqrt{2gh} = \sqrt{2(9.8 \text{ m/s}^2)(0.09 \text{ m})} \; ; \qquad v_c = 1.33 \text{ m/s}$$

$$m_1u_1 + 0 = (m_1 + m_2)v_c \; ; \qquad (0.009 \text{ kg}) u_1 = (0.009 \text{ kg} + 2 \text{ kg})(1.33 \text{ m/s})$$

$$(0.009 \text{ kg})u_1 = 2.68 \text{ m/s}; \qquad \boxed{u_1 = 297 \text{ m/s}}$$

---

*9-30. A billiard ball moving to the left at 30 cm/s collides head on with another ball moving to the right at 20 cm/s. The masses of the balls are identical. If the collision is perfectly elastic, what is the velocity of each ball after impact? *(Consider right as +.)*   *Given:* $m_1 = m_2 = m$, $v_1 = -30$ cm/s, $v_2 = 0$

Momentum: $m_1u_1 + m_2u_2 = m_1v_1 + m_2v_2$; $\cancel{m}(-30 \text{ cm/s}) + 0 = \cancel{m}v_1 + \cancel{m}v_2$; $v_1 + v_2 = (-30 \text{ cm/s}) + (20 \text{ cm/s})$; $\underline{v_1 + v_2 = -10 \text{ cm/s}}$

Energy (e = 1): $v_2 - v_1 = u_1 - u_2 = (-30 \text{ cm/s}) - (20 \text{ cm/s})$; $\underline{v_2 - v_1 = -50 \text{ cm/s}}$

From second equation: $v_2 = v_1 - 50 \text{ cm/s}$; *Substituting this for v_2, we obtain:*

$v_1 + (v_1 - 50 \text{ cm/s}) = -10 \text{ cm/s}$;   *and* $\boxed{v_1 = 20 \text{ cm/s, to right}}$

And, $v_2 = v_1 - 50 \text{ cm/s} = (20 \text{ cm/s}) - 50 \text{ cm/s}$; $\boxed{v_2 = -30 \text{ cm/s, to left}}$

9-31. The coefficient of restitution for steel is 0.90. If a steel ball is dropped from a height of 7 m, how high will it rebound?

$$e = \sqrt{\frac{h_2}{h_1}} \; ; \qquad e^2 = \frac{h_2}{h_1} \; ; \qquad h_2 = h_1e^2 = (7 \text{ m})(0.9)^2 \; ; \qquad \boxed{h_2 = 5.67 \text{ m}}$$

*9-32. What is the time between the first contact with the surface and the second contact for Problem 9-31?   *(We need to know v_o to rise to 5.67 m, then find t.)*

$$\frac{1}{2}mv_0^2 = mgh; \quad v_0 = \sqrt{2gh} = \sqrt{2(9.8 \text{ m/s}^2)(5.67 \text{ m})}; \qquad v_o = 10.54 \text{ m/s}$$

$$s = \frac{v_0 + v_f}{2}t; \quad t = \frac{2s}{v_o + 0} = \frac{2(5.67 \text{ m})}{10.54 \text{ m/s}};$$

$$t = 1.07 \text{ s}; \qquad T = 2t; \qquad \boxed{T = 2.15 \text{ s}}$$

*9-33. A ball dropped from rest onto a fixed horizontal plate rebounds to a height that is 81 percent of its original height. What is the coefficient of restitution? What is the required velocity on the first impact to cause the ball to rebound to a height of 8 m.

$$e = \sqrt{\frac{h_2}{h_1}} = \sqrt{0.81}; \quad \boxed{e = 0.900}$$

$$e = \frac{v_2 - v_1}{u_1 - u_2}; \quad v_2 = u_2 = 0; \quad e = \frac{-v_1}{u_1}; \quad u_1 = \frac{-v_1}{e} = \frac{-v_1}{(0.9)}; \quad u_1 = -1.11v_1$$

$$\tfrac{1}{2}mv_1^2 = mgh; \quad v_1 = \sqrt{2gh} = \sqrt{2(9.8 \text{ m/s}^2)(8 \text{ m})}; \quad \boxed{v_1 = -12.5 \text{ m/s}}$$

$$u_1 = -1.11v_1; \quad u_1 = -1.11(-12.5 \text{ m/s}); \quad \boxed{u_1 = 13.9 \text{ m/s}}$$

*9-34. A 300-g block moving north at 50 cm/s collides with a 200-g block moving south at 100 cm/s. If the collision is completely inelastic, what is their common velocity after sticking together? What is the loss in energy? *(Consider north as positive)*

Momentum: $m_1u_1 + m_2u_2 = m_1v_1 + m_2v_2$; $\quad v_1 = v_2 = v_c$ *for inelastic collision*

$$(300 \text{ g})(50 \text{ cm/s}) + (200 \text{ g})(-100 \text{ cm/s}) = (300 \text{ g} + 200 \text{ g})v_c$$

$$15,000 \text{ g cm/s} - 20,000 \text{ g cm/s} = (500 \text{ g})v_c; \quad \boxed{v_c = -10 \text{ cm/s, south}}$$

(Note: When working with energy, it is necessary to use kg for the mass unit.)

Conservation of Energy: $\tfrac{1}{2}m_1u_1^2 + \tfrac{1}{2}m_2u_2^2 = \tfrac{1}{2}(m_1 + m_2)v_c^2 + Loss$

$$\tfrac{1}{2}(0.3 \text{ kg})(-8 \text{ m/s})^2 + \tfrac{1}{2}(0.2 \text{ kg})(5 \text{ m/s})^2 = \tfrac{1}{2}(0.3 \text{ kg} + 0.2 \text{ kg})(-3.67 \text{ m/s})^2 + Loss$$

Solving for "loss", we obtain: $\boxed{Loss = 0.135 \text{ J}}$

**9-35. Suppose the collision in Prob. 9-34 is perfectly elastic. Find the velocities after impact.

$$m_1u_1 + m_2u_2 = m_1v_1 + m_2v_2; \quad m_1 = 300 \text{ g}, m_2 = 200 \text{ g}, u_1 = 50 \text{ cm/s}, u_2 = -100 \text{ cm/s}$$

$$(300 \text{ g})(50 \text{ cm/s}) + (200 \text{ g})(-100 \text{ cm/s}) = (300 \text{ g})v_1 + (200 \text{ g})v_2$$

Dividing each term by 100 g: $\quad \underline{3v_1 + 2v_2 = -50 \text{ cm/s}}$

Energy (e = 1): $v_2 - v_1 = u_1 - u_2 = (50 \text{ cm/s}) - (-100 \text{ cm/s})$; $\quad v_2 - v_1 = 150 \text{ cm/s}$

Substitute $v_2 = v_1 + 150$ cm/s *into the earlier equation and solve for v_1*:

$$3v_1 + 2(v_1 + 150 \text{ cm/s}) = -50 \text{ cm/s}; \quad \boxed{v_1 = -80 \text{ cm/s, to left}}$$

$$v_2 - (-80 \text{ cm/s}) = 150 \text{ cm/s}; \quad \boxed{v_2 = 70 \text{ cm/s, to right}}$$

**9-36. A 5-lb and a 12-lb object approach each other with equal velocities of 25 ft/s. What will be their velocities after impact if the collision is (a) completely inelastic or (b) perfectly elastic? *Since weight is proportional to mass, we will use the weights instead.*

Momentum: $W_1u_1 + W_2u_2 = W_1v_1 + W_2v_2$; $\quad v_1 = v_2 = v_c$ *for inelastic collision*

$$(5 \text{ lb})(25 \text{ ft/s}) + (12 \text{ lb})(-25 \text{ ft/s}) = (5 \text{ lb} + 12 \text{ lb})v_c; \quad \boxed{v_c = -10.3 \text{ ft/s}}$$

Elastic case: $(5 \text{ lb})(25 \text{ ft/s}) + (12 \text{ lb})(-25 \text{ ft/s}) = (5 \text{ lb})v_1 + (12 \text{ lb})v_2$;

Dividing each term by 5 lb: $\quad \underline{v_1 + 2.4v_2 = -35 \text{ ft/s}}$

Energy (e = 1): $v_2 - v_1 = u_1 - u_2 = (25 \text{ ft/s}) - (-25 \text{ ft/s})$; $\quad \underline{v_2 - v_1 = 50 \text{ ft/s}}$

Substitute $v_1 = v_2 - 50$ ft/s *into the earlier equation and solve for v_1*:

$$(v_2 - 50 \text{ ft/s}) + 2.4v_2 = -35 \text{ ft/s}; \quad \boxed{v_2 = 4.41 \text{ ft/s}}$$

$$v_1 = v_2 - 50 \text{ ft/s} = 4.41 \text{ ft/s} - 50 \text{ ft/s}; \quad \boxed{v_1 = -45.6 \text{ ft/s}}$$

Supplementary Problems

9-37. An average force of 4000 N acts on a 400-g piece of metal causing it to move from rest to a velocity of 30 m/s. What was the time of contact for this force?

$$F\,\Delta t = mv_f - mv_o = (0.4 \text{ kg})(30 \text{ m/s}) - 0;$$

$$(4000 \text{ N})\Delta t = 12 \text{ kg m/s}; \quad \boxed{\Delta t = 3.00 \text{ ms}}$$

*9-38. A 600-g object whose velocity is initially 12 m/s, collides with a wall and rebounds with half of its original kinetic energy. What impulse was applied by the wall?

$\frac{1}{2}mv_0^2 = 2(\frac{1}{2}mv_f^2)$; $v_f = \sqrt{\frac{v_0^2}{2}} = \sqrt{\frac{(12 \text{ m/s})^2}{2}}$; $v_f = -8.49$ m/s

$F\Delta t = mv_f - mv_o = (0.6 \text{ kg})(-2.45 \text{ m/s}) - (0.6 \text{ kg})(12 \text{ m/s})$; $\boxed{F\Delta t = -12.3 \text{ N m}}$

*9-39. A 10-kg block at rest on a horizontal surface is struck by a 20-g bullet moving at 200 m/s. The bullet passes entirely through the block and exits with a velocity of 10 m/s. What is the velocity of the block?

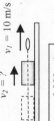

$v_2 = ?$ $v_1 = 10$ m/s

$m_1u_1 + 0 = m_1v_1 + m_2v_2$; $m_1 = 0.02$ kg

$(0.02 \text{ kg})(200 \text{ m/s}) = (0.02 \text{ kg})(10 \text{ m/s}) + (10 \text{ kg})v_2$; $\boxed{v_2 = 0.380 \text{ m/s}}$

9-40. In Problem 9-39, how much kinetic energy was lost?

Conservation of Energy: $\frac{1}{2}m_1u_1^2 + 0 = m_1v_1^2 + m_2v_2^2 + Loss$

$\frac{1}{2}(0.2 \text{ kg})(200 \text{ m/s})^2 = \frac{1}{2}(0.2 \text{ kg})(10 \text{ m/s})^2 + \frac{1}{2}(10 \text{ kg})(0.380 \text{ m/s})^2 + Loss$

Solving for "loss", we obtain: $\boxed{Loss = 3990 \text{ J}}$

*9-41. A 60-g body having an initial velocity of 100 cm/s to the right collides with a 150-g body moving to the left at 30 cm/s. The coefficient of restitution is 0.8. What are the velocities after impact. What percent of the energy is lost in collision?

$m_1u_1 + m_2u_2 = m_1v_1 + m_2v_2$; $m_1 = 60$ g, $m_2 = 150$ g, $u_1 = 100$ cm/s, $u_2 = -30$ cm/s

$(60 \text{ g})(100 \text{ cm/s}) + (150 \text{ g})(-30 \text{ cm/s}) = (60 \text{ g})v_1 + (150 \text{ g})v_2$

Divide each term by 60 g and simplify: $v_1 + 2.5 v_2 = 25$ cm/s

$v_2 - v_1 = e(u_1 - u_2)$; $v_2 - v_1 = 0.8[100 \text{ cm/s} - (-30 \text{ cm/s})]$; $v_2 - v_1 = 104$ cm/s

Solve for v_1: $v_1 = v_2 - 104$ cm/s;   Now substitute to find v_2.

*9-41. (Cont.) $(v_2 - 104 \text{ cm/s}) + 2.5 v_2 = 25$ cm/s; $\boxed{v_2 = 36.9 \text{ cm/s, to right}}$

$v_1 = v_2 - 104$ cm/s = (36.9 cm/s) - 104 cm/s; $\boxed{v_1 = -67.1 \text{ cm/s, to left}}$

Conservation of Energy: $\frac{1}{2}m_1u_1^2 + \frac{1}{2}m_2u_2^2 = m_1v_1^2 + m_2v_2^2 + Loss$

For energy we must use SI units with mass in "kg" and velocity in "m/s."

$E_{ok} = \frac{1}{2}(0.06 \text{ kg})(1 \text{ m/s})^2 + \frac{1}{2}(0.15 \text{ kg})(-0.3 \text{ m/s})^2$; $E_{ok} = 0.03675$ J

$E_{fk} = \frac{1}{2}(0.06 \text{ kg})(-0.671 \text{ m/s})^2 + \frac{1}{2}(0.15 \text{ kg})(0.369 \text{ m/s})^2$; $E_{fk} = 0.0237$ J

$\%Loss = 100\left(\frac{E_{ok} - E_{fk}}{E_{ok}}\right) = 100\left(\frac{0.03675 \text{ J} - 0.0237 \text{ J}}{0.03675 \text{ J}}\right)$ $\boxed{\%Loss = 35.5\%}$

*9-42. The block in Fig. 9-6 weighs 6 lb. How high will it rise if a 0.4-lb projectile with an initial velocity of 90 ft/s embeds itself into the block?

Momentum is conserved: $m_1u_1 + 0 = m_1v_1 + m_2v_2$; $m \propto W$

$(0.4 \text{ lb})(90 \text{ ft/s}) = (0.4 \text{ kg} + 6 \text{ lb})v_c$ $v_c = 5.625$ ft/s

Now, we can find h using conservation of energy and the common initial velocity v_c:

$\frac{1}{2}(m_1 + m_2) v_c^2 = (m_1 + m_2) gh$;   The mass divides out.

$h = \frac{v_0^2}{2g} = \frac{(5.625 \text{ ft/s})^2}{2(32 \text{ ft/s}^2)}$; $h = 0.494$ ft; $\boxed{h = 5.93 \text{ in.}}$

*9-43. A single railroad car moving north at 10 m/s strikes two identical, coupled cars initially moving south at 2 m/s. If all three couple together after colliding, what is their common velocity? $m_1 = m_2 = m_3 = m$; $u_1 = 10$ m/s; $u_2 = u_3 = -2$ m/s; $v_1 = v_2 = v_3 = v_c$

Momentum is conserved: $\cancel{m}u_1 + \cancel{m}(u_2 + u_3) = (3\cancel{m})v_c$ (Mass divides out.)

$10 \text{ m/s} - 2 \text{ m/s} - 2 \text{ m/s} = 3 v_c$; $\boxed{v_c = 2.00 \text{ m/s, north}}$

*9-44. An atomic particle of mass 2.00 x 10⁶... An atomic particle of mass 2.00×10^{-27} kg moves with a velocity of 4.00×10^6 and collides head on with a particle of mass 1.20×10^{-27} kg initially at rest. Assuming a perfectly elastic collision, what is the velocity of the incident particle after the collision?

$m_1u_1 + 0 = m_1v_1 + m_2v_2$; $m_1 = 2 \times 10^{-27}$ kg, $m_2 = 1.2 \times 10^{-27}$ kg, $u_1 = 4 \times 10^6$ m/s

$(2 \times 10^{-27}$ kg$)(4 \times 10^6$ m/s$) = (2 \times 10^{-27}$ kg$)v_1 + (1.2 \times 10^{-27}$ kg $)v_2$

Dividing each term by 2×10^{-27} kg: $\boxed{v_1 + 0.6 v_2 = 4 \times 10^6 \text{ m/s}}$

Energy (e = 1): $v_2 - v_1 = u_1 - u_2 = 4 \times 10^6$ m/s $- 0$; $v_2 - v_1 = 4 \times 10^6$ m/s

Substitute $v_2 = (v_1 + 4 \times 10^6$ m/s$)$ *into the earlier equation and solve for* v_1:

$v_1 + 0.6 (v_1 + 4 \times 10^6$ m/s$) = 4 \times 10^6$ m/s; $\boxed{v_1 = 1.00 \times 10^6 \text{ m/s}}$

*9-45. A bat strikes a 400-g softball moving horizontally to the left at 20 m/s. It leaves the bat with a velocity of 60 m/s at an angle of 30⁰ with the horizontal. What are the horizontal and vertical components of the impulse imparted to the ball?

First find components of velocity: $v_{1x} = -20$ m/s; $v_{1y} = 0$

$v_{2x} = (60 \cos 30^0) = 52.0$ m/s; $v_{2y} = (60 \sin 30^0) = 30$ m/s

$F_x \Delta t = J = mv_{2x} - mv_{1x}$; $J_x = (0.4$ kg$)(52.0$ m/s$) - (0.4$ kg$)(-20$ m/s$)$; $\boxed{J_x = 28.8 \text{ N s}}$

$F_y \Delta t = J = mv_{2y} - mv_{1y}$; $J_y = (0.4$ kg$)(30$ m/s$) - 0$; $\boxed{J_y = 12.0 \text{ N s}}$

*9-46. If the bat in Problem 9-45 was in contact with the ball for 5 ms, what was the magnitude of the average force on the softball?

$F_x = \dfrac{28.8 \text{ N s}}{0.005 \text{ s}} = 5760$ N; $F_y = \dfrac{12.0 \text{ N s}}{0.005 \text{ s}} = 2400$ N

$F = \sqrt{F_x^2 + F_y^2} = \sqrt{(5760 \text{ N})^2 + (2400 \text{ N})^2}$; $\boxed{F = 6240 \text{ N}}$

*9-47. A cart A has a mass of 300 g and moves on a frictionless air track at 1.4 m/s when it hits a second cart B at rest. The collision is perfectly elastic and the 300-g cart's velocity is reduced to 0.620 m/s after the collision. What was the mass of the other cart and what was its velocity after the collision? $m_1 = 300$ g; $u_1 = 1.4$ m/s; $v_1 = 0.620$ m/s

$m_1u_1 + 0 = m_1v_1 + m_2v_2$;   *Elastic collision:* $v_2 - v_1 = u_1 - u_2 = (1.4$ m/s$) - 0$

$(300$ g$)(1.4$ m/s$) = (300$ g$)(0.620$ m/s$) + m_2v_2$

$m_2v_2 = 234$ g m/s;   *Elastic collision:* $v_2 - v_1 = u_1 - u_2 = 1.4$ m/s;

$v_2 = v_1 + 1.4$ m/s $= 0.620$ m/s $+ 1.4$ m/s; $\boxed{v_2 = 2.02 \text{ m/s}}$

$m_2v_2 = 234$ g m/s; $m_2 = \dfrac{234 \text{ g m/s}}{2.02 \text{ m/s}}$ $\boxed{m_2 = 116 \text{ g}}$

*9-48. In the collision in Fig. 9-10, assume that the collision of the two masses is completely inelastic. What is the common velocity after the collision and what is the ratio of the final kinetic energy to the initial kinetic energy?

$m_1u_1 + 0 = (m_1 + m_2)v_c$; $u_1 = 15$ m/s

$(1$ kg$)(15$ m/s$) + 0 = (1$ kg $+ 2$ kg$)v_c$ $\boxed{v_c = 5.00 \text{ m/s}}$

$\dfrac{E_{k2}}{E_{k1}} = \dfrac{½(m_1 + m_2)v_c^2}{½m_1u_1^2} = \dfrac{(3 \text{ kg})(5 \text{ m/s})^2}{(1 \text{ kg})(15 \text{ m/s})^2}$; $\boxed{Ratio = 0.333}$

15 m/s

1 kg   2 kg

*9-49. Assume the collision in Problem 9-48 is perfectly elastic. What is the velocity of each mass after the collision?

Elastic: $m_1u_1 + 0 = m_1v_1 + m_2v_2$ *and* $v_2 - v_1 = u_1 - u_2$

$(1$ kg$)(15$ m/s$) = (1$ kg$)v_1 + (2$ kg$)v_2$; $v_1 + 2v_2 = 15$ m/s ; $v_1 = 15$ m/s $- 2 v_2$

$v_2 - v_1 = u_1 - u_2 = (15$ m/s$) - 0$; $v_2 = 15$ m/s $+ v_1$

$v_2 = 15$ m/s $+ (15$ m/s $- 2v_2)$; $v_2 = 10$ m/s ; $v_1 = 15$ m/s $- 2(10$ m/s$) = -5$ m/s

$\boxed{v_1 = -5 \text{ m/s} \quad \text{and} \quad v_2 = 10 \text{ m/s}}$

*9-50. A 2-kg mass moves to right at 2 m/s and collides with a 6-kg mass moving to the left at 4 m/s. If the collision is completely inelastic, what is their common velocity after colliding, and how much energy is lost in the collision?

Momentum: $m_1u_1 + m_2u_2 = m_1v_1 + m_2v_2$; $v_1 = v_2 = v_c$ for inelastic collision

$(2\text{ kg})(2\text{ m/s}) + (6\text{ kg})(-4\text{ m/s}) = (2\text{ kg} + 6\text{ kg})v_c$

$4\text{ kg m/s} - 24\text{ kg m/s} = (8\text{ kg})v_c$; $\boxed{v_c = -2.50\text{ m/s}}$

Conservation of Energy: $\frac{1}{2}m_1u_1^2 + \frac{1}{2}m_2u_2^2 = \frac{1}{2}(m_1 + m_2)v_c^2 + Loss$

$\frac{1}{2}(2\text{ kg})(2\text{ m/s})^2 + \frac{1}{2}(6\text{ kg})(-4\text{ m/s})^2 = \frac{1}{2}(2\text{ kg} + 6\text{ kg})(-2.50\text{ m/s})^2 + Loss$

Solving for "loss", we obtain: $\boxed{Loss = 27.0\text{ J}}$

**9-51. In Problem 9-50, assume the collision is perfectly elastic. What are the velocities after the collision?

$m_1u_1 + m_2u_2 = m_1v_1 + m_2v_2$; $m_1 = 2\text{ kg}, m_2 = 6\text{ kg}, u_1 = 2\text{ m/s}, u_2 = -4\text{ m/s}$

$(2\text{ kg})(2\text{ m/s}) + (6\text{ kg})(-4\text{ m/s}) = (2\text{ kg})v_1 + 6\text{ kg})v_2$

Dividing each term by 2 kg: $v_1 + 3\ v_2 = -10\text{ m/s}$

Energy ($e=1$): $v_2 - v_1 = u_1 - u_2 = (2\text{ m/s}) - (-4\text{ m/s})$; $v_2 - v_1 = 6\text{ m/s}$

Substitute $v_2 = v_1 + 6\text{ m/s}$ into the earlier equation and solve for v_1:

$v_1 + 3(v_1 + 6\text{ m/s}) = -10\text{ m/s}$; $\boxed{v_1 = -7.00\text{ m/s}}$

$v_2 - (-7.00\text{ m/s}) = 6\text{ m/s}$; $\boxed{v_2 = -1.00\text{ m/s}}$

Critical Thinking Questions

*9-52. An astronaut in orbit outside a capsule uses a revolver to control motion. The astronaut with gear weighs 200 lb on the earth. If the revolver fires 0.05-lb bullets at 2700 ft/s, and 10 shots are fired, what is the final velocity of the astronaut? Compare the final kinetic energy of the ten bullets with that of the astronaut. Why is the difference so great?

$0 + 0 = W_a v_a + W_b v_b$; $v_a = \frac{-W_b v_b}{W_a} = \frac{-(0.05\text{ lb})(2700\text{ ft/s})}{200\text{ lb}}$; $v_a = -0.675\text{ ft/s}$

Each shot changes v_a by -0.675 ft/s: $v_f = 10(0.675\text{ m/s})$; $\boxed{v_f = -6.75\text{ ft/s}}$

We need masses: $m_b = \frac{0.05\text{ lb}}{32\text{ ft/s}^2} = 0.00156\text{ slugs}$; $m_b = \frac{200\text{ lb}}{32\text{ ft/s}^2} = 6.25\text{ slugs}$

$E_{kb} = 10\ (\frac{1}{2}mv_b^2) = (5)(0.00156\text{ slugs})(2700\text{ ft/s})^2$; $\boxed{E_{kb} = 56{,}950\text{ ft lb}}$

$E_{ka} = \frac{1}{2}m_a v_a^2 = \frac{1}{2}(6.25\text{ slugs})(6.75\text{ ft/s})^2$; $\boxed{E_{ka} = 142\text{ ft}\cdot\text{lb}}$

The kinetic energy of the bullets is much larger because when finding the kinetic energy, one must deal with the square of velocity. The speeds dominate.

9-53. In applying conservation of momentum for colliding objects to find final velocities, could we use the weight of the objects instead of the mass? Why, or why not? Verify your answer by applying it to one of the examples in the text.

Since weight is proportional to mass: W = mg, and since mass appears in every term involving conservation of momentum, the weight can be used instead of the mass to calculate either velocities or weights of colliding objects. For example, see Prob. 9-36.

$m_1u_1 + m_2u_2 = m_1v_1 + m_2v_2$

$\frac{W_1}{g}u_1 + \frac{W_2}{g}u_2 = \frac{W_1}{g}v_1 + \frac{W_2}{g}v_2$

$W_1u_1 + W_2u_2 = W_1v_1 + W_2v_2$

*9-56. (Cont.)   (2 kg)(-2.50 m/s) - (2 kg)(2 m/s) = -[(6 kg)(-2.50 m/s) - (6 kg)(-4 m/s)]

- 9 kg m/s = - 9 kg m/s; *It works for inelastic collisions.*

Prob. 9-51: Same test: $m_1v_1 - m_1u_1 = -(m_2v_2 - m_2u_2)$; $v_1 = -7$ m/s; $v_2 = -1$ m/s

(2 kg)(-7 m/s) - (2 kg)(2 m/s) = -[(6 kg)(-1 m/s) - (6 kg)(-4 m/s)]

- 18 kg m/s = - 18 kg m/s; *It also works for elastic collisions.*

9-57. Two toy cars of masses m and $3m$ approach each other, each traveling at 5 m/s. If they couple together, what is their common speed afterward? What are the velocities of each car if the collision is perfectly elastic?   ($m_1 = m$, $m_2 = 3m$, $u_1 = 5$ m/s, $u_2 = -5$ m/s)

$m_1u_1 + m_2u_2 = (m_1 + m_2) v_c$; $m(5$ m/s$) + 3m(-5$ m/s$) = (m + 3m) v_c$ *For inelastic case*

-10 m/s $= 4 v_{ci}$; $\boxed{v_c = -2.50 \text{ m/s}}$

$m_1u_1 + m_2u_2 = m_1v_1 + m_2v_2$; $m(5$ m/s$) + 3m(-5$ m/s$) = mv_1 + 3mv_2$ Now for elastic: $v_2 - v_1 = u_1 - u_2$

$\underline{v_1 + 3v_2 = -10 \text{ m/s}}$; $v_2 - v_1 = 5$ m/s $- (-5$ m/s$) = 10$ m/s; $\underline{v_1 = v_2 - 10 \text{ m/s}}$

$(v_2 - 10$ m/s$) + 3 v_2 = -10$ m/s; $\boxed{v_2 = 0}$

$v_1 = (0) - 10$ m/s $= - 10$ m/s; $\boxed{v_1 = -10 \text{ m/s}}$

9-58. An 8-g bullet is fired horizontally at two blocks resting on a frictionless surface. The first block has a mass of 1-kg and the second has a mass of 2-kg. The bullet passes completely through the first block and lodges into the second. After the collisions, the 1-kg block moves with a velocity of 1 m/s and the 2-kg block moves with 2 m/s. What is the velocity of the bullet before and after emerging from the first block?

--*Observe the figure on the next page* --

9-54. A 20-g bullet, moving at 200 m/s, strikes a 10-kg wooden block and passes entirely through it, emerging with a velocity of 10 m/s. What is the velocity of the block after impact?   How much energy was lost?

$m_1u_1 + 0 = m_1v_1 + m_2v_2$

$(0.020$ kg$)(200$ m/s$) = (0.020$ kg$)(10$ m/s$) + (10$kg$)v_2$; $\boxed{v_2 = 0.380 \text{ m/s}}$

Conservation of Energy: $\frac{1}{2}m_1u_1^2 + 0 = \frac{1}{2}(m_1 + m_2)v_c^2 + Loss$

$\frac{1}{2}(0.02$ kg$)(200$ m/s$)^2 = \frac{1}{2}(10.02$ kg$)(0.38$ m/s$)^2 + Loss$ $\boxed{Loss = 399 \text{ J}}$

*9-55. A 0.30-kg baseball moving horizontally at 40 m/s is struck by a bat. The ball is in contact with the bat for a time of 5 ms, and it leaves with a velocity of 60 m/s at an angle of 30^0, what are the horizontal and vertical components of the average force acting on the bat?

First find components of velocity: $v_{1x} = -20$ m/s; $v_{1y} = 0$

$v_{2x} = (60 \cos 30^0) = 52.0$ m/s; $v_{2y} = (60 \sin 30^0) = 30$ m/s

$F_x \Delta t = mv_{2x} - mv_{1x} = (0.3$ kg$)(52.0$ m/s$) - (0.3$ kg$)(-40$ m/s$)$;

$F_x(0.005$ s$) = 27.6$ N s ; $\boxed{F_x = 5520 \text{ N}}$

$F_y \Delta t = mv_{2y} - mv_{1y} = (0.3$ kg$)(30$ m/s$) - 0$; $F_y(0.005$ s$) = 9.00$ N s ; $\boxed{F_y = 1800 \text{ N}}$

*9-56. When two masses collide they produce equal but opposite impulses. The masses do not change in the collision, so the change in momentum of one should be the negative of the change for the other. Is this true whether the collision is elastic or inelastic. Verify your answer by using the data in Problems 9-50 and 9-51.

Momentum is conserved whether energy is lost in collision or not. Therefore, equal but opposite impulses should always produce equal and opposite changes in momentum.

Prob. 9-50: The test is whether: $m_1v_1 - m_1u_1 = -(m_2u_2 - m_2v_2)$; $v_1 = v_2 = -2.5$ m/s

Centripetal Acceleration

10-1. A ball is attached to the end of a 1.5 m string and it swings in a circle with a constant speed of 8 m/s. What is the centripetal acceleration?

$$a_c = \frac{v^2}{R} = \frac{(8 \text{ m/s})^2}{1.5 \text{ m}} \qquad \boxed{a_c = 42.7 \text{ m/s}^2}$$

10-2. What are the period and frequency of rotation for the ball in Problem 10-1?

$$v = 2\pi f R; \quad v = \frac{2\pi R}{T}, \quad T = \frac{2\pi R}{v} = \frac{2\pi(1.5 \text{ m})}{8 \text{ m/s}}; \quad \boxed{T = 1.18 \text{ s}}$$

$$f = \frac{1}{T} = \frac{1}{1.18 \text{ s}}; \quad \boxed{f = 0.849 \text{ rev/s}}$$

10-3. A drive pulley 6-cm in diameter is set to rotate at 9 rev/s. What is the centripetal acceleration of a point on the edge of the pulley? What would be the linear speed of a belt around the pulley? [R = (0.06 m/2) = 0.03 m]

$$a_c = 4\pi^2 f^2 R = 4\pi^2 (9 \text{ rev/s})^2 (0.03 \text{ m}); \quad \boxed{a_c = 95.9 \text{ m/s}^2}$$

$$v = 2\pi f R = 2\pi(9 \text{ rev/s})(0.03 \text{ m}); \quad \boxed{v = 1.70 \text{ m/s}}$$

10-4. An object revolves in a circle of diameter 3 m at a frequency of 6 rev/s. What is the period of revolution, the linear speed, and the centripetal acceleration? [R = (3 m/2) = 1.5 m]

$$T = \frac{1}{f} = \frac{1}{6 \text{ rev/s}}; \quad \boxed{T = 0.167 \text{ s}};$$

$$v = 2\pi f R = 2\pi(6 \text{ rev/s})(1.5 \text{ m}); \quad \boxed{v = 56.5 \text{ m/s}}$$

$$a_c = \frac{v^2}{R} = \frac{(56.5 \text{ m/s})^2}{(1.5 \text{ m})}; \quad \boxed{a_c = 2130 \text{ m/s}^2}$$

---

*9-58. (Cont.)

Total momentum at start = total momentum at finish

$$(0.008 \text{ kg}) v_1 = (1 \text{ kg})(1 \text{ m/s}) + (2.008 \text{ kg})(2 \text{ m/s}); \quad \boxed{v_1 = 627 \text{ m/s}}$$

To find velocity emerging from 1-kg mass, we apply conservation to first block only:

$$(0.008 \text{ kg})(627 \text{ m/s}) = (0.008 \text{ kg})v_e + (1 \text{ kg})(1 \text{ m/s}); \quad \boxed{v_e = 502 \text{ m/s}}$$

*9-59. A 1-kg mass A is attached to a support by a cord of length 80 cm, and it is held horizontally as in Fig. 9-11. After release it swings downward striking the 2-kg mass B which is at rest on a frictionless tabletop. Assuming that the collision is perfectly elastic what are the velocities of each mass immediately after impact?

First find u_A from energy of fall: $\frac{1}{2}mv^2 = mgh$

$$v = \sqrt{2gh} = \sqrt{2(9.8 \text{ m/s}^2)(0.8 \text{ m})}; \quad v = 3.96 \text{ m/s}$$

$$m_A u_A + 0 = m_A v_A + m_B v_B: \quad m_A = 1 \text{ kg}; \quad u_A = 3.96 \text{ m/s}$$

$$(1 \text{ kg})(3.96 \text{ m/s}) = (1 \text{ kg})v_A + (2 \text{ kg}) v_B$$

$$\underline{v_A + 2\, v_B = 3.96 \text{ m/s}}; \quad \text{Elastic:} \quad v_B - v_A = u_A - u_B = 3.96 \text{ m/s} - 0$$

$$\underline{v_B - v_A = 3.96 \text{ m/s}}; \quad v_A = v_B - 3.96 \text{ m/s}; \quad \text{Substitute for } v_A \text{ in the other equation.}$$

$$(v_B - 3.96 \text{ m/s}) + 2\, v_B = 3.96 \text{ m/s}; \quad \text{From which:} \quad \boxed{v_B = 2.64 \text{ m/s}}$$

$$v_A = v_B - 3.96 \text{ m/s} = 2.64 \text{ m/s} - 3.96 \text{ m/s}; \quad \boxed{v_A = -1.32 \text{ m/s}}$$

10-5. A car moves around a curve 50 m in radius and undergoes a centripetal acceleration of 2 m/s². What is its constant speed?

$$a = \frac{v^2}{R}; \quad v = \sqrt{aR} = \sqrt{(2 \text{ m/s}^2)(50 \text{ m})}; \quad \boxed{v = 10.0 \text{ m/s}}$$

10-6. A 1500-kg car moves at a constant speed of 22 m/s along a circular track. The centripetal acceleration is 6 m/s². What is the radius of the track and the centripetal force on the car?

$$a = \frac{v^2}{R}; \quad R = \frac{v^2}{a} = \frac{(22 \text{ m/s})^2}{6 \text{ m/s}^2}; \quad \boxed{R = 80.7 \text{ m}}$$

$$F = \frac{mv^2}{R} = \frac{(1500 \text{ kg})(22 \text{ m/s})^2}{(80.7 \text{ m})}; \quad \boxed{F_c = 9000 \text{ N}}$$

10-7. An airplane dives along a curved path of radius R and velocity v. The centripetal acceleration is 20 m/s². If both the velocity and the radius are doubled, what will be the new acceleration?

$$a_1 = \frac{v^2}{R}; \quad a_2 = \frac{(2v)^2}{2R} = \frac{4v^2}{2R}; \quad a_2 = \frac{2v^2}{R};$$

$$a_2 = 2a_1 = 2(20 \text{ m/s}^2); \quad \boxed{a = 40 \text{ m/s}^2}$$

Centripetal Force

10-8. A 20-kg child riding a loop-the-loop at the Fair moves at 16 m/s through a track of radius 16 m. What is the resultant force on the child?

$$F = \frac{mv^2}{R} = \frac{(20 \text{ kg})(16 \text{ m/s})^2}{16 \text{ m}}; \quad \boxed{F_c = 320 \text{ N}}$$

10-9. A 3-kg rock, attached to a 2-m cord, swings in a horizontal circle so that it makes one revolution in 0.3 s. What is the centripetal force on the rock? Is there an outward force on the rock?

$$F_c = 4\pi^2 f^2 mR = 4\pi^2 \left(\frac{1}{0.3 \text{ s}}\right)^2 (3 \text{ kg})(2 \text{ m}); \quad \boxed{F_c = 2630 \text{ N, No}}$$

10-10. An 8-lb object swings in horizontal circle with a speed of 95 ft/s. What is the radius of the path, if the centripetal force is 2000 lb?

$$m = \frac{8 \text{ lb}}{32 \text{ ft/s}^2} = 0.25 \text{ slug}; \quad F_c = \frac{mv^2}{R}$$

$$R = \frac{mv^2}{F_c} = \frac{(0.25 \text{ slug})(95 \text{ ft/s})^2}{2000 \text{ lb}}; \quad \boxed{R = 1.13 \text{ ft}}$$

*10-11. Two 8-kg masses are attached to the end of a tin rod 400 mm long. The rod is supported in the middle and whirled in a circle. The rod can support a maximum tension of only 800 N. What is the maximum frequency of revolution? [R = (400 mm/2) = 200 mm]

$$F_c = \frac{mv^2}{R}; \quad v = \sqrt{\frac{F_c R}{m}} = \sqrt{\frac{(800 \text{ N})(0.20 \text{ m})}{8 \text{ kg}}}; \quad v = 4.47 \text{ m/s}$$

$$v = 2\pi fR; \quad f = \frac{v}{2\pi R} = \frac{4.47 \text{ m/s}}{2\pi(0.20 \text{ m})}; \quad \boxed{f = 3.56 \text{ rev/s}}$$

*10-12. A 500-g damp shirt rotates against the wall of a washer at 300 rpm. The diameter of the rotating drum is 70 cm. What is the magnitude and direction of the resultant force on the shirt? [R = (70 cm/2) = 35 cm; f = 300 rpm(60 s/min) = 1800 rev/s]

$$F_c = 4\pi^2 f^2 mR = 4\pi^2 (1800 \text{ rev/s})^2 (0.5 \text{ kg})(0.35 \text{ m});$$

$$\boxed{F_c = 2.24 \times 10^7 \text{ N, toward the center}}$$

10-13. A 70-kg runner rounds a track of radius 25 m at a speed of 8.8 m/s. What is the central force causing the runner to turn and what exerts the force?

$$F_c = \frac{mv^2}{R} = \frac{(70 \text{ kg})(8.8 \text{ m/s})^2}{25 \text{ m}}; \qquad \boxed{F_c = 217 \text{ N, friction}}$$

10-14. In Olympic bobsled competition, a team takes a turn of radius 24 ft at a speed of 60 mi/h.

What is the acceleration? How many g's do passengers experience? (60 mi/h = 88 ft/s)

$$a_c = \frac{v^2}{R} = \frac{(88 \text{ ft/s})^2}{24 \text{ ft}}; \qquad \boxed{a_c = 323 \text{ ft/s}^2 \quad or \quad 10.1 \text{ g's}}$$

Flat Curves and Banked Curves

10-15. On a rainy day the coefficient of static friction between tires and the roadway is only 0.4.

What is the maximum speed at which a car can negotiate a turn of radius 80 m?

$$\frac{mv^2}{R} = \mu_s mg; \qquad v_c = \sqrt{\mu_s gR} = \sqrt{(0.4)(9.8 \text{ m/s}^2)(80 \text{ m})};$$

$$\boxed{v_c = 17.7 \text{ m/s} \quad or \quad 63.8 \text{ km/h}}$$

10-16. A bus negotiates a turn of radius 400 ft while traveling at a speed of 60 mi/h. If slipping just begins at this speed, what is the coefficient of static friction between the tires and the road? (60 mi/h = 88 ft/s)

$$\frac{mv^2}{R} = \mu_s mg; \qquad \mu_s = \frac{v^2}{gR} = \frac{(88 \text{ ft/s})^2}{(32 \text{ ft/s}^2)(400 \text{ ft})}; \qquad \boxed{\mu_s = 0.605}$$

10-17. Find the coefficient of static friction necessary to sustain motion at 20 m/s around a turn of radius 84 m.

$$\frac{mv^2}{R} = \mu_s mg; \qquad \mu_s = \frac{v^2}{gR} = \frac{(20 \text{ m/s})^2}{(9.8 \text{ m/s}^2)(84 \text{ m})}; \qquad \boxed{\mu_s = 0.486}$$

---

*10-18. A 20-kg child sits 3 m from the center of a rotating platform. If $\mu_s = 0.4$, what is the maximum number of revolutions per minute that can be achieved without slipping?

(Slipping occurs when the centripetal force equals the maximum force of static friction.)

$$F_c = 4\pi^2 f^2 mR = \mu_s mg; \qquad f = \sqrt{\frac{\mu_s g}{4\pi^2 R}} = \sqrt{\frac{(0.4)(9.8 \text{ m/s}^2)}{4\pi^2 (3 \text{ m})}};$$

$$f = 0.182 \text{ rev/s} \text{ (60 s/min)}; \qquad \boxed{f = 10.9 \text{ rpm}}$$

*10-19. A platform rotates freely at 100 rpm. If the coefficient of static friction is 0.5, how far from the center of the platform can a bolt be placed to without slipping?

$$f = 100 \text{ rev/min} (1 \text{ min}/60 \text{ s}) = 1.67 \text{ rev/s}; \quad \mu_s = 0.5; \quad R = ?$$

$$F_c = 4\pi^2 f^2 mR = \mu_s mg; \qquad R = \sqrt{\frac{\mu_s g}{4\pi^2 f^2}} = \sqrt{\frac{(0.5)(9.8 \text{ m/s}^2)}{4\pi^2 (1.67 \text{ rev/s})^2}}; \qquad R = 21.1 \text{ cm}$$

10-20. Find the required banking angle to negotiate the curve of Prob.10-15 without slipping.

$$\tan\theta = \frac{v^2}{gR} = \frac{(17.7 \text{ m/s})^2}{(9.8 \text{ m/s}^2)(80 \text{ m})}; \qquad \boxed{\theta = 21.8^0}$$

10-21. Find the required banking angle for Problem 10-16 to prevent slipping?

$$\tan\theta = \frac{v^2}{gR} = \frac{(88 \text{ ft/s})^2}{(32 \text{ ft/s}^2)(400 \text{ ft})}; \qquad \boxed{\theta = 31.2^0}$$

10-22. The optimum banking angle for a curve of radius 20 m is found to be 28^0. For what speed was this angle designed?

$$\tan\theta = \frac{v^2}{gR}; \qquad v = \sqrt{gR\tan\theta} = \sqrt{(9.8 \text{ m/s}^2)(20 \text{ m})\tan 28^0}; \qquad \boxed{v = 10.3 \text{ m/s}}$$

10-27. Each of the flyweights in Fig. 10-16 has a mass of 2 kg. The length L = 40 cm and the shaft rotates at 80 rpm. What is the tension in each arm? What is the angle θ? What is the height h?

80 rpm = 1.33 rev/s; $\quad T\sin\theta = F_c = mv^2/R$

$\sin\theta = \dfrac{R}{L} = \dfrac{R}{0.4\text{ m}}$; $\quad T\left(\dfrac{R}{0.4\text{ m}}\right) = 4\pi^2 f^2 mR$

$T = (0.4\text{ m})(4\pi^2)(1.33\text{ rev/s})^2(2\text{ kg})$; $\quad \boxed{T = 56.1\text{ N}}$

$T\cos\theta = mg$; $\quad \cos\theta = \dfrac{mg}{T} = \dfrac{(2\text{ kg})(9.8\text{ m/s}^2)}{56.1\text{ N}}$; $\quad \boxed{\theta = 69.6^0}$

$h = L\cos\theta = (0.4\text{ m})\cos 69.6^0$; $\quad h = 0.14\text{ m}$ or $\boxed{h = 14.0\text{ cm}}$

10-28. In Fig. 10-16, assume that L = 6 in., each flyweight is 1.5 lb, and the shaft is rotating at 100 rpm. What is the tension in each arm? What is the angle θ? What is the distance h?

100 rpm = 1.67 rev/s; $\quad T\sin\theta = F_c = mv^2/R$

$m = \dfrac{1.5\text{ lb}}{32\text{ ft/s}} = 0.0469\text{ slug}$; $\quad L = 6\text{ in.} = 0.50\text{ ft}$

$\sin\theta = \dfrac{R}{L} = \dfrac{R}{0.5\text{ ft}}$; $\quad T\left(\dfrac{R}{0.5\text{ ft}}\right) = 4\pi^2 f^2 mR$

$T = (0.5\text{ ft})(4\pi^2)(1.67\text{ rev/s})^2(0.0469\text{ slug})$; $\quad \boxed{T = 2.75\text{ lb}}$

$T\cos\theta = mg$; $\quad \cos\theta = \dfrac{mg}{T} = \dfrac{(0.0469\text{ slug})(32\text{ ft/s}^2)}{2.57\text{ lb}}$; $\quad \boxed{\theta = 54.3^0}$

$h = \text{L}\cos\theta = (0.5\text{ ft})\cos 54.3^0$; $\quad \boxed{h = 0.292\text{ ft}}$

---

*10-23. A curve in a road 9 m wide has a radius of 96 m. How much higher than the inside edge should the outside edge be for an automobile to travel at the optimum speed of 40 km/h? What is the height h?

$v = 40\text{ km/h} = 11.1\text{ m/s}$; $\quad h = (9\text{ m})\sin\theta$; $\quad \tan\theta = \dfrac{v^2}{gR}$

$\tan\theta = \dfrac{v^2}{gR} = \dfrac{(11.1\text{ m/s})^2}{(9.8\text{ m/s}^2)(96\text{ m})}$; $\quad \theta = 7.48^0$; $\quad h = (9\text{ m})\sin 7.48^0$; $\quad \boxed{h = 1.17\text{ m}}$

The Conical Pendulum

10-24. A conical pendulum swings in a horizontal circle of radius 30 cm. What angle does the supporting cord make with the vertical when the linear speed of the mass is 12 m/s?

$\tan\theta = \dfrac{v^2}{gR} = \dfrac{(12\text{ m/s})^2}{(9.8\text{ m/s}^2)(0.30\text{ m})}$; $\quad \boxed{\theta = 88.8^0}$

10-25. What is the linear speed of the flyweights in Fig. 10-16 if L = 20 cm and θ = 60°? What is the frequency of revolution?

$L = 20\text{ cm} = 0.20\text{ m}$; $\quad R = L\sin\theta = (0.2\text{ m})\sin 60^0$; $\quad R = 0.173\text{ m}$

$\tan\theta = \dfrac{v^2}{gR}$; $\quad v = \sqrt{gR\tan\theta} = \sqrt{(9.8\text{ m/s}^2)(0.173\text{ m})(\tan 60^0)}$; $\quad \boxed{v = 1.71\text{ m/s}}$

$v = 2\pi fR$; $\quad f = \dfrac{v}{2\pi R} = \dfrac{1.71\text{ m/s}}{2\pi(0.173\text{ m})}$; $\quad \boxed{f = 1.58\text{ rev/s}}$

10-26. The length of the L in Fig. 10-16 is 60 cm. What velocity is required to cause the flyweights to move to an angle of 30° with the vertical?

$R = L\sin\theta = (60\text{ cm})\sin 30^0$; $\quad R = 30\text{ cm} = 0.30\text{ m}$

$\tan\theta = \dfrac{v^2}{gR}$; $\quad v = \sqrt{gR\tan\theta} = \sqrt{(9.8\text{ m/s}^2)(0.30\text{ m})\tan 30^0}$; $\quad \boxed{v = 1.30\text{ m/s}}$

10-29. Consider the rotating swings in Fig. 10-17. The length $L = 10$ m and the distance $a = 3$ m. What must be the linear velocity of the seat if the rope is to make an angle of 30^0 with the vertical?

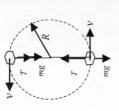

$[L = 10$ m; $a = 3$ m, $\theta = 30^0]$

$b = L \sin \theta = (10$ m$) \sin 30^0 = 5$ m; $R = a + b = 7$ m;

$\tan \theta = \dfrac{v^2}{gR}$; $v = \sqrt{gR \tan \theta}$

$v = \sqrt{(9.8 \text{ m/s}^2)(7 \text{ m}) \tan 30^0}$

$\boxed{v = 6.73 \text{ m/s}}$

10-30. What must be the frequency of revolution for the swing in Fig. 10-17 if the angle θ is to be equal to 25^0?

$b = L \sin 28^0 = (10$ m$) \sin 28^0$, $b = 4.695$ m; $R = a + b = 7.695$ m;

$\tan \theta = \dfrac{v^2}{gR}$; $v = \sqrt{gR \tan \theta}$; $v = \sqrt{(9.8 \text{ m/s}^2)(7.695 \text{ m}) \tan 28^0}$; $v = 6.33$ m/s

$v = 2\pi fR$; $f = \dfrac{v}{2\pi R} = \dfrac{6.33 \text{ m/s}}{2\pi(7.695 \text{ m})}$; $\boxed{f = 0.131 \text{ rev/s or } 7.86 \text{ rpm}}$

Motion in a Vertical Circle

10-31. A rock rests on the bottom of a bucket moving in a vertical circle of radius 70 cm. What is the least speed the bucket must have as it rounds the top of the circle if it is to remain in the bucket?

[Resultant force to center = mv^2/R]

$\cancel{T}^{\,0} + mg = \dfrac{mv^2}{R}$; Critical speed v_c is when $T = 0$

$v_c = \sqrt{gR} = \sqrt{(9.8 \text{ m/s}^2)(0.7 \text{ m})}$; $\boxed{v_c = 6.86 \text{ m/s}}$

10-32. A 1.2-kg rock is tied to the end of a 90-cm length of string. The rock is then whirled in a vertical circle at a constant speed. What is the critical velocity at the top of the path if the string is not to become slack?

$\cancel{T}^{\,0} + mg = \dfrac{mv^2}{R}$; Critical speed v_c is when $T = 0$

$v_c = \sqrt{gR} = \sqrt{(9.8 \text{ m/s}^2)(0.7 \text{ m})}$; $\boxed{v_c = 2.97 \text{ m/s}}$

*10-33. Assume that the rock of Problem 10-32 moves in a vertical circle at a constant speed of 8 m/s? What are the tensions in the rope at the top and bottom of the circle.

At Top: $T + mg = \dfrac{mv^2}{R}$ and $T = \dfrac{mv^2}{R} - mg$

$T = \dfrac{(1.2 \text{ kg})(8 \text{ m/s})^2}{(0.9 \text{ m})} - (1.2 \text{ kg})(9.8 \text{ m/s}^2)$; $\boxed{T = 73.6 \text{ N}}$

At Bottom: $T - mg = \dfrac{mv^2}{R}$ and $T = \dfrac{mv^2}{R} + mg$

$T = \dfrac{(1.2 \text{ kg})(8 \text{ m/s})^2}{(0.9 \text{ m})} + (1.2 \text{ kg})(9.8 \text{ m/s}^2)$; $\boxed{T = 97.1 \text{ N}}$

*10-34. A test pilot in Fig. 10-18 goes into a dive at 620 ft/s and pulls out in a curve of radius 2800 ft. If the pilot weighs 160 lb, what acceleration will be experienced at the lowest point? What is the force exerted by the seat on the pilot?

$W = 160$ lb; $m = 160$ lb/32 ft/s$^2 = 5$ slugs; $v = 620$ ft/s;

$a = \dfrac{v^2}{R} = \dfrac{(620 \text{ ft/s})^2}{(2800 \text{ ft})}$; $\boxed{a = 137 \text{ ft/s}^2}$

$\mathcal{N} - mg = \dfrac{mv^2}{R}$; $\mathcal{N} = \dfrac{mv^2}{R} + mg$

*10-34. (Cont.) $\mathcal{N} = \dfrac{(5 \text{ slugs})(620 \text{ ft/s})^2}{(2800 \text{ ft})} + 160 \text{ lb}$; $\boxed{\mathcal{N} = 846 \text{ lb}}$

*10-35. If it is desired that the pilot in Problem 10-34 not experience an acceleration greater than 7 times gravity (7g), what is the maximum velocity for pulling out of a dive of radius 1 km?

$a = \dfrac{v^2}{R} = 7g$; $v = \sqrt{7gR} = \sqrt{7(9.8 \text{ m/s}^2)(1000 \text{ m})}$;

$\boxed{v = 262 \text{ m/s or 943 km/h}}$

Note: *The pilot actually "feels" a force that is eight times W:*

$\mathcal{N} - mg = m(7g)$; $\mathcal{N} = 8mg$

*10-36. A 3-kg ball swings in a vertical circle at the end of an 8-m cord. When it reaches the top of its path, its velocity is 16 m/s. What is the tension in the cord? What is the critical speed at the top?   [$R = 8$ m; $m = 3$ kg; $v = 16$ m/s]

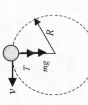

At Top: $T + mg = \dfrac{mv^2}{R}$ and $T = \dfrac{mv^2}{R} - mg$

$T = \dfrac{(3 \text{ kg})(16 \text{ m/s})^2}{(8 \text{ m})} - (3 \text{ kg})(9.8 \text{ m/s}^2)$; $\boxed{T = 66.6 \text{ N}}$

When T = 0, $v_c = \sqrt{gR} = \sqrt{(9.8 \text{ m/s}^2)(8 \text{ m})}$; $\boxed{v_c = 8.85 \text{ m/s}}$

*10-37. A 36-kg girl rides on the seat of a swing attached to two chains that are each 20 m long. If she is released from a position 8 m below the top of the swing, what force does the swing exert on the girl as she passes the lowest point?

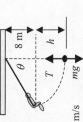

$\cos\theta = \dfrac{8 \text{ m}}{20 \text{ m}}$; $\theta = 66.4^0$; $h = 20 \text{ m} - 8 \text{ m} = 12 \text{ m}$

$\tfrac{1}{2}mv^2 = mgh$; $v = \sqrt{2gh} = \sqrt{2(9.8 \text{ m/s}^2)(12 \text{ m})}$; $v = 15.3 \text{ m/s}$

*10-37. (Cont.)   At Bottom: $T - mg = \dfrac{mv^2}{R}$ and $T = \dfrac{mv^2}{R} + mg$; $\boxed{T = 776 \text{ N}}$

$T = \dfrac{(36 \text{ kg})(15.34 \text{ m/s})^2}{(20 \text{ m})} + (36 \text{ kg})(9.8 \text{ m/s}^2)$;

Gravitation

10-38. How far apart should a 2-ton weight be from a 3-ton weight if their mutual force of attraction is equal to 0.0004 lb?   ($G = 3.44 \times 10^{-8}$ lb ft²/slug²)

$m_1 = \dfrac{(2 \text{ ton})(2000 \text{ lb/ton})}{32 \text{ ft/s}^2} = 125 \text{ slugs}$; $m_2 = \dfrac{(3 \text{ ton})(2000 \text{ lb/ton})}{32 \text{ ft/s}^2} = 187.5 \text{ slugs}$

$F = \dfrac{Gm_1m_2}{R^2}$; $R = \sqrt{\dfrac{Gm_1m_2}{F}} = \sqrt{\dfrac{(3.44 \times 10^{-8} \text{ lb ft}^2/\text{slug}^2)(125 \text{ slug})(187.5 \text{ slug})}{0.0004 \text{ lb}}}$

$\boxed{R = 1.42 \text{ ft}}$

10-39. A 4-kg mass is separated from a 2 kg mass by a distance of 8 cm. Compute the gravitational force of attraction between the two masses.

$F = \dfrac{Gm_1m_2}{R^2} = \dfrac{(6.67 \times 10^{-11} \text{ N m}^2/\text{kg}^2)(4 \text{ kg})(2 \text{ kg})}{(0.08 \text{ m})^2}$; $\boxed{F = 8.34 \times 10^{-8} \text{ N}}$

*10-40. A 3-kg mass is located 10 cm away from a 6-kg mass. What is the resultant gravitational force on a 2-kg mass located at the midpoint of a line joining the first two masses?

$F_3 = \dfrac{Gm_3m_2}{R^2} = \dfrac{(6.67 \times 10^{-11} \text{ N m}^2/\text{kg}^2)(3 \text{ kg})(2 \text{ kg})}{(0.05 \text{ m})^2}$

$F_6 = \dfrac{Gm_6m_2}{R^2} = \dfrac{(6.67 \times 10^{-11} \text{ N m}^2/\text{kg}^2)(6 \text{ kg})(2 \text{ kg})}{(0.05 \text{ m})^2}$

$F_3 = -1.6 \times 10^{-7} \text{ N}$, $F_6 = 3.20 \times 10^{-7} \text{ N}$;

$F_R = -1.6 \times 10^{-7} \text{ N} + 3.60 \times 10^{-7} \text{ N}$; $\boxed{F_R = 1.60 \times 10^{-7} \text{ N}}$

10-44. (Cont.)

$$F_c = F_g; \qquad \frac{mv^2}{R} = \frac{Gmm_e}{R^2}; \qquad v = \sqrt{\frac{Gm_e}{R}};$$

$$v = \sqrt{\frac{(6.67 \times 10^{-11} \text{ N m}^2/\text{kg}^2)(5.98 \times 10^{24} \text{ kg})}{7.18 \times 10^6 \text{ m}}}$$

$$\boxed{v = 7450 \text{ m/s}}$$

10-45. The mass of the Jupiter is 1.90×10^{27} kg and its radius is 7.15×10^7 m. What speed must a spacecraft have to circle Jupiter at a height of 6.00×10^7 m above the surface of Jupiter?

$$R = R_j + h = 7.15 \times 10^7 \text{ m} + 6 \times 10^7 \text{ m}; \quad R = 1.315 \times 10^8 \text{ m}; \quad \frac{mv^2}{R} = \frac{Gmm_e}{R^2};$$

$$v = \sqrt{\frac{Gm_e}{R+h}} = \sqrt{\frac{(6.67 \times 10^{-11})(1.9 \times 10^{27}\text{kg})}{1.315 \times 10^8 \text{ m}}}$$

$$\boxed{v = 31,400 \text{ m/s}}$$

This represents a speed of approximately 69,800 mi/h

10-46. What is the orbital speed of a satellite that moves in an orbit 1200 km above the earth's surface? *Note that:* $R = R_e + h = (6.38 \times 10^6 \text{ m}) + (1.2 \times 10^6 \text{ m}) = 7.58 \times 10^6$ m

$$F_c = F_g; \qquad \frac{mv^2}{R} = \frac{Gmm_e}{R^2}; \qquad v = \sqrt{\frac{Gm_e}{R}};$$

$$v = \sqrt{\frac{(6.67 \times 10^{-11} \text{ N m}^2/\text{kg}^2)(5.98 \times 10^{24} \text{ kg})}{7.58 \times 10^6 \text{ m}}};$$

$$\boxed{v = 7254 \text{ m/s}}$$

10-47. The radius of the moon is 1.74×10^6 m and the acceleration due to its gravity is 1.63 m/s². Apply the law of universal gravitation to find the mass of the moon.

$$mg = \frac{Gmm_m}{R_m^2}; \qquad m_m = \frac{gR_m^2}{G} = \frac{(1.63 \text{ m/s}^2)(1.74 \times 10^6 \text{ m})^2}{6.67 \times 10^{-11}\text{N m}^2/\text{kg}^2}; \qquad \boxed{m_m = 7.40 \times 10^{22} \text{ kg}}$$

***10-41.** On a distant planet, the acceleration due to gravity is 5.00 m/s². and the radius of the planet is roughly 4560 m. Use the law of gravitation to estimate the mass of this planet.

$$mg = \frac{Gmm_p}{R^2}; \qquad m_p = \frac{gR^2}{G} = \frac{(5.00 \text{ m/s}^2)(4560 \text{ m})^2}{6.67 \times 10^{-11} \text{ N m}^2/\text{kg}^2}; \qquad \boxed{m_p = 1.56 \times 10^{24} \text{ kg}}$$

****10-42.** The mass of the earth is about 81 times the mass of the moon. If the radius of the earth is 4 times that of the moon, what is the acceleration due to gravity on the moon?

$m_e = 81m_m$; $R_e = 4R_m$; *Consider test mass m on moon and then on earth:*

$$mg_m = \frac{Gmm_m}{R_m^2} \text{ and } g_m = \frac{Gm_m}{R_m^2}; \qquad mg_e = \frac{Gmm_e}{R_e^2} \text{ and } g_e = \frac{Gm_e}{R_e^2}$$

$$\frac{g_m}{g_e} = \frac{m_m R_e^2}{m_e R_m^2} = \frac{m_m (4R_m)^2}{81m_m R_m^2}; \qquad \frac{g_m}{9.8 \text{ m/s}^2} = 0.1975; \qquad \boxed{g_m = 1.94 \text{ m/s}^2}$$

****10-43.** A 60-kg mass and a 20-kg mass are separated by 10 m. At what point on a line joining these charges will another mass experience zero resultant force? [$F_2 = F_6$]

60 kg — x — m' — $10 - x$ — 20 kg; F_6, F_2

$$\frac{Gm_2m'}{(10-x)^2} = \frac{Gm_6m'}{x^2}; \qquad \frac{x^2}{(10-x)^2} = \frac{m_6}{m_2};$$

$$\frac{x}{(10-x)} = \sqrt{\frac{m_6}{m_2}} = \sqrt{\frac{60 \text{ kg}}{20 \text{ kg}}} = 1.732; \qquad x = 1.732(10-x); \qquad x = 17.32 - 1.732 x$$

$$\boxed{x = 6.34 \text{ m } \textit{from the 60-kg mass.}}$$

Kepler's Laws and Satellites

10-44. What speed must a satellite have if it is to move in a circular orbit of 800 km above the surface of the earth? [*The central force F_c must equal the gravitational force F_g.*]

Note that: $R = R_e + h = (6.38 \times 10^6 \text{ m}) + (0.8 \times 10^6 \text{ m}) = 7.18 \times 10^6$ m

*10-48. A satellite is located at a distance of 900 km above the earth's surface. What is the period of the satellite's motion? [R = 6.38 × 10⁶ m + 0.9 × 10⁶ m = 7.28 × 10⁶ m]

$$T^2 = \left(\frac{4\pi^2}{Gm_e}\right) R^3 = \frac{4\pi^2 (7.28 \times 10^6)^3}{(6.67 \times 10^{-11}\text{N m}^2/\text{kg}^2)(5.98 \times 10^{24}\text{kg})} \; ; \quad T^2 = 3.82 \times 10^7 \text{ s}^2$$

$$T = \sqrt{3.82 \times 10^7 \text{ s}^2} \; ; \quad \boxed{T = 6180 \text{ s}} \quad (\textit{about an hour and 43 minutes})$$

*10-49. How far above the earth's surface must a satellite be located if it is to circle the earth in a time of 28 h? T = 28 h (3600 s/h) = 1.01 × 10⁵ s; $T^2 = 1.02 \times 10^{10}$ s²

$$T^2 = \left(\frac{4\pi^2}{Gm_e}\right) R^3 \; ; \quad R^3 = \frac{Gm_e T^2}{4\pi^2} = \frac{(6.67 \times 10^{-11}\text{N m}^2/\text{kg}^2)(5.98 \times 10^{24}\text{kg})(1.02 \times 10^{10}\text{s}^2)}{4\pi^2}$$

$$R = \sqrt[3]{1.03 \times 10^{23}\text{m}^3} \; ; \quad R = 4.69 \times 10^7 \text{ m}; \quad h = R - R_e = \boxed{4.05 \times 10^7 \text{ m}}$$

Supplemental Problems

10-50. At what frequency should a 6-lb ball be revolved in a radius of 3 ft to produce a centripetal acceleration of 12 ft/s²? What is the tension in the cord?

$$a_c = 4\pi^2 f^2 R; \quad f^2 = \frac{a_c}{4\pi^2 R} = \frac{(12 \text{ ft/s}^2)}{4\pi^2 (3 \text{ ft})}; \quad f = \sqrt{0.1013 \text{ s}^{-2}}; \quad \boxed{f = 0.318 \text{ rev/s}}$$

$$T = ma_c = \left(\frac{6 \text{ lb}}{32 \text{ ft/s}^2}\right)(12 \text{ ft/s}^2); \quad \boxed{T = 2.25 \text{ lb}}$$

10-51. What centripetal acceleration is required to move a 2.6 kg mass in a horizontal circle of radius 300 mm if its linear speed is 15 m/s? What is the centripetal force?

$$a_c = \frac{v^2}{R} = \frac{(15 \text{ m/s})^2}{(0.300 \text{ m})}; \quad a = 750 \text{ m/s}^2$$

$$F_c = ma_c = (2.6 \text{ kg})(750 \text{ m/s}^2); \quad \boxed{F_c = 1950 \text{ N}}$$

---

*10-52. What must be the speed of a satellite located 1000 mi above the earth's surface if it is to travel in a circular path? [R = 4000 mi + 1000 mi = 5000 mi ; 5000 mi = 2.64 × 10⁷ ft]

$$\frac{mv^2}{R} = \frac{Gmm_e}{R^2} \; ; \quad v = \sqrt{\frac{Gm_e}{R}} \; ; \quad R = 2.64 \times 10^7 \text{ft}\left(\frac{0.3048 \text{ m}}{1 \text{ ft}}\right) = 8.047 \times 10^6 \text{ m}$$

$$v = \sqrt{\frac{(6.67 \times 10^{-11} \text{ N m}^2/\text{kg}^2)(5.98 \times 10^{24} \text{ kg})}{8.047 \times 10^6 \text{ m}}} \; ; \quad \boxed{v = 7041 \text{ m/s}}$$

*10-53. A 2-kg ball at swings in a vertical circle at the end of a cord 2 m in length. What is the critical velocity at the top if the orbit is to remain circular?

$$\cancel{T} + mg = \frac{mv^2}{R} \; ; \quad \textit{Critical speed } v_c \textit{ is when } T = 0$$

$$v_c = \sqrt{gR} = \sqrt{(9.8 \text{ m/s}^2)(2.0 \text{ m})} \; ; \quad \boxed{v_c = 4.42 \text{ m/s}}$$

*10-54. A 4-kg rock swings at a constant speed of 10 m/s in a vertical circle at the end of a 1.4 m cord. What are the tensions in the cord at the top and bottom of the circular path?

At Top: $T + mg = \dfrac{mv^2}{R}$ and $T = \dfrac{mv^2}{R} - mg$;

$$T = \frac{(4 \text{ kg})(10 \text{ m/s})^2}{(1.4 \text{ m})} - (4 \text{ kg})(9.8 \text{ m/s}^2) \; ; \quad \boxed{T = 247 \text{ N}}$$

At Bottom: $T - mg = \dfrac{mv^2}{R}$ and $T = \dfrac{mv^2}{R} + mg$;

$$T = \frac{(4 \text{ kg})(10 \text{ m/s})^2}{(1.4 \text{ m})} + (4 \text{ kg})(9.8 \text{ m/s}^2) \; ; \quad \boxed{T = 325 \text{ N}}$$

70

*10-55. What frequency of revolution is required to raise the flyweights in Fig. 10-16 a vertical distance of 25 mm above their lowest position. Assume that L = 150 mm.

$h = 150$ mm $- 25$ mm $= 124$ mm; $h = 0.124$ m

$$f = \frac{1}{2\pi}\sqrt{\frac{g}{h}} = \frac{1}{2\pi}\sqrt{\frac{9.8 \text{ m/s}^2}{0.125 \text{ m}}}\,; \qquad \boxed{f = 1.41 \text{ rev/s} = 84.6 \text{ rpm}}$$

*10-56. The combined mass of a motorcycle and driver is 210 kg. If the driver is to negotiate a loop-the-loop of radius 6 m, what is the critical speed at the top?

$$v_c = \sqrt{gR} = \sqrt{(9.8 \text{ m/s}^2)(6.0 \text{ m})}\,; \qquad \boxed{v_c = 7.67 \text{ m/s}}$$

*10-57. If the speed at the top of the loop in Prob. 10-56 is 12 m/s, what is the normal force at the top of the loop?

$$\text{At Top:} \quad \mathcal{N} + mg = \frac{mv^2}{R} \quad \text{and} \quad \mathcal{N} = \frac{mv^2}{R} - mg$$

$$\mathcal{N} = \frac{(210 \text{ kg})(12 \text{ m/s})^2}{(6 \text{ m})} - (210 \text{ kg})(9.8 \text{ m/s}^2)\,; \qquad \boxed{\mathcal{N} = 2980 \text{ N}}$$

10-58. The speed limit at a certain turn of radius 200 ft is 45 mi/h. What is the optimum banking angle for this situation. Are roads actually constructed at the optimum angles?

$$v = 45 \text{ mi/h} = 66.0 \text{ ft/s}; \quad \tan\theta = v^2/gR; \qquad \boxed{\theta = 34.2^0; \text{ No}}$$

*10-59. For the conical pendulum shown in Fig. 10-17, assume that a = 2 m and L = 4 m. What linear speed is required to cause the swing to move out to an angle of 20⁰?

$$b = L \sin\theta = (4 \text{ m}) \sin 20^0 = 1.37 \text{ m}; \quad R = a + b = 3.37 \text{ m};$$

$$\tan\theta = \frac{v^2}{gR}; \qquad v = \sqrt{gR\tan\theta}$$

$$v = \sqrt{(9.8 \text{ m/s}^2)(3.37 \text{ m})\tan 20^0} \qquad \boxed{v = 3.47 \text{ m/s}}$$

Critical Thinking Questions

*10-60. A coin rests on a rotating platform distance of 12 cm from the center of rotation. If the coefficient of static friction is 0.6, what is the maximum frequency of rotation such that the coin does not slip? Suppose the frequency is cut in half. Now how far from the center can the coin be placed?

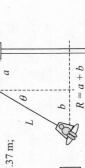

$$F_c = \mathcal{F}_s$$

The maximum frequency occurs when $F_c = \mathcal{F}_s$

$$F_c = 4\pi^2 f^2 mR; \quad \mathcal{F}_s = \mu_s mg; \quad 4\pi^2 f^2 mR = \mu_s mg; \quad f = \sqrt{\frac{\mu_s g}{4\pi^2 R}}$$

$$f = \sqrt{\frac{\mu_s g}{4\pi^2 R}} = \sqrt{\frac{(0.6)(9.8 \text{ m/s}^2)}{4\pi^2 (0.12 \text{ m})}}\,; \qquad \boxed{f = 1.11 \text{ rev/s}}$$

$$f_2 = \frac{1.114 \text{ rev/s}}{2} = 0.557 \text{ rev/s}; \quad 4\pi^2 f_2^2 mR_2 = \mu_s mg; \quad R_2 = \frac{\mu_s g}{4\pi^2 f_2^2}$$

$$R_2 = \frac{(0.6)(9.8 \text{ m/s}^2)}{4\pi^2 (0.557 \text{ rev/s})^2}\,; \qquad R = 0.480 \text{ m}; \qquad \boxed{R = 48.0 \text{ cm}}$$

*10-61. The laboratory apparatus shown in Fig. 10-19 allows a rotating mass to stretch a spring so that the supporting cord is vertical at a particular frequency of rotation. Assume the mass of the bob is 400 g and the radius of revolution is 14 cm. With a stop watch the time for 50 revolutions is found to be 35 s. What is the magnitude and direction of the force acting on the bob? *First find f in* (rev/s).

$$f = \frac{50 \text{ rev}}{35 \text{ s}} = 1.429 \text{ rev/s.} \qquad F_c = 4\pi^2 f^2 mR$$

$$F_c = 4\pi^2 (1.429 \text{ rev/s})^2 (0.4 \text{ kg})(0.14 \text{ m})\,;$$

$$\boxed{F_c = 4.51 \text{ N, directed toward the center.}}$$

The outward force ON the spring is NOT the centripetal force.

The centripetal force is ON the bob.

*10-64. The diameter of Jupiter is 11 times that of the earth, and its mass is about 320 times that of earth. What is the acceleration due to gravity near the surface of Jupiter?

$$m_j = 11m_e = 320(5.98 \times 10^{24} \text{ kg}); \quad m_j = 1.914 \times 10^{27}$$

$$R_J = 11R_e = 11(6.38 \times 10^6 \text{ m}); \quad R_J = 7.018 \times 10^7 \text{ m}; \quad mg_J = \frac{Gmm_J}{R_J^2}$$

$$\frac{Gm_J}{R_J^2} = \frac{(6.67 \times 10^{-11}\text{N m}^2/\text{kg}^2)(1.914 \times 10^{27}\text{kg})}{(7.018 \times 10^7\text{m})^2}; \quad \boxed{g_J = 25.9 \text{ m/s}^2}$$

*10-65. Assume that $L = 50$ cm and $m = 2$ kg in Fig. 10-16. How many revolutions per second are needed to make the angle $\theta = 30^0$? What is the tension in the supporting rod at that point? $[\; h = (50 \text{ cm}) \cos 30^0 = 0.433 \text{ m}; \quad m = 2.0 \text{ kg}; \quad \theta = 30^0]$

$$\tan\theta = \frac{v^2}{gR}; \quad v = \sqrt{gR\tan\theta} = \sqrt{(9.8 \text{ m/s}^2)(0.25 \text{ m})\tan(30^0)}$$

$$v = 1.19 \text{ m/s}; \quad v = 2\pi f R; \quad f = \frac{v}{2\pi R} = \frac{(1.19 \text{ m/s})}{2\pi(0.25 \text{ m})}; \quad \boxed{f = 0.757 \text{ rev/s}}$$

$$T\cos\theta = mg; \quad T = \frac{mg}{\cos\theta} = \frac{(2 \text{ kg})(9.8 \text{ m/s}^2)}{\cos 30^0}; \quad \boxed{T = 22.6 \text{ N}}$$

**10-66. A 9-kg block rests on the bed of a truck as it turns a curve of radius 86 m. Assume that $\mu_k = 0.3$ and that $\mu_s = 0.4$. Does the friction force on the block act toward the center of the turn or away? What is the maximum speed with which the truck can make the turn without slipping? What if the truck makes the turn at a much greater speed, what would be the resultant force on the block? $[\; \mathcal{F} = F_c; \quad m = 9 \text{ kg}]$

$$v_c = \sqrt{\mu_s gR} = \sqrt{(0.4)(9.8 \text{ m/s}^2)(86 \text{ m})}; \quad v_c = 18.4 \text{ m/s}; \quad \boxed{\mathcal{F}_k = F_R = 26.5 \text{ N}}$$

$$\mathcal{F}_k = \mu_k mg = (0.3)(9 \text{ kg})(9.8 \text{ m/s}^2);$$

R = 86 m; F_c; $\mathcal{F}_s$

---

*10-62. In Problem 10-61 above, assume that a 100-g mass is added to the 400-g bob? The force required to stretch the spring should be the same as before, but the rotating mass has increased. What changes when the experiment is performed again so that the centripetal force is the same as before? On what does the centripetal force act in this experiment?

Since the centripetal force must be the same, it is necessary that the velocity be reduced so that:

$$F_c = \frac{mv^2}{R}; \quad \textit{The product } mv^2 \textit{ must be the same.}$$

$$m_1 v_1^2 = m_2 v_2^2; \quad v_2^2 = \frac{m_1 v_1^2}{m_2} = \frac{(400 \text{ g})v_1^2}{(500 \text{ g})} \qquad v_1 = 2\pi f_1 R = 2\pi(1.429 \text{ rev/s})(0.14 \text{ m}) = 1.26 \text{ m/s}$$

$$v_2 = \sqrt{\frac{(400 \text{ g})v_1^2}{(500 \text{ g})}} = 0.894 \, v_1; \quad v_2 = (0.894)(1.26 \text{ m/s}); \quad \underline{v_2 = 1.13 \text{ m/s}}$$

Thus, the object moves slower and the frequency of revolution decreases so that the centripetal force acting ON the bob does not change: $m_1 v_1^2 = m_2 v_2^2$

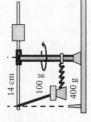

14 cm · 100 g · 400 g

*10-63. A 10-in. diameter platform turns at 78 rpm. A bug rests on the platform 1 in. from the outside edge. If the bug weighs 0.02 lb, what force acts on it? What exerts this force? Where should the bug crawl in order to reduce this force by one-half?

$$f = 78 \text{ rev/min} = \underline{1.30 \text{ rev/s}}; \quad m = W/g = 0.02 \text{ lb}/32 \text{ ft/s}^2; \quad m = 0.000625 \text{ slugs}$$

$$R = 5 \text{ in.} - 1 \text{ in.} = 4 \text{ in.}; \quad R = (4/12) \text{ ft} = 0.333 \text{ ft}; \quad F_c = 4\pi^2 f^2 \, mR$$

$$F_c = 4\pi^2 (1.3 \text{ rev/s})^2(0.000625 \text{ slug})(0.333 \text{ ft}); \quad \boxed{F_c = 0.0139 \text{ lb}}$$

The central force ON the bug is exerted BY the platform (Static friction).

Since F_c is proportional to R, halving the radius will also halve the force!

$$R_2 = \frac{(4 \text{ in.})}{2} = 2 \text{ in.}; \quad \textit{The bug should crawl to a point 2 cm from the center.}$$

Chapter 11. Rotation of Rigid Bodies

Uniform Angular Acceleration

11-1. A cable is wrapped around a drum 80 cm in diameter. How many revolutions of this drum will cause an object attached to the cable to move a linear distance of 2 m? What is the angular displacement? [$R = 0.04$ m, $s = 2$ m, $\theta = ?$]

$$\theta = \frac{s}{R} = \frac{2 \text{ m}}{0.400 \text{ m}} = 5 \text{ rad} \quad \boxed{5 \text{ rad}} \qquad \theta = (5 \text{ rad})\left(\frac{1 \text{ rev}}{2\pi \text{ rad}}\right) ; \quad \boxed{\theta = 0.796 \text{ rev}}$$

11-2. A bicycle wheel is 26 in. in diameter. If the wheel makes 60 revolutions, what linear distance will it travel? [$D = 26$ in.; $R = 13$ in. $= 1.083$ ft]

$$\theta = 60 \text{ rev}\left(\frac{2\pi \text{ rad}}{1 \text{ rev}}\right) = 377 \text{ rad}; \qquad s = \theta R = (377 \text{ rad})(1.083 \text{ ft}); \quad \boxed{s = 408 \text{ ft}}$$

11-3. A point on the edge of a large wheel of radius 3 m moves through an angle of 37^0. Find the length of the arc described by the point.

$$\theta = 37^0\left(\frac{2\pi \text{ rad}}{360^0}\right) = 0.646 \text{ rad}; \qquad s = \theta R = (0.646 \text{ rad})(3 \text{ m}); \quad \boxed{s = 1.94 \text{ m}}$$

11-4. A person sitting on the edge of a 6-ft diameter platform moves a linear distance of 2 ft. Express the angular displacement in radians, degrees, and revolutions. [$R = 3$ ft]

$$\theta = \frac{s}{R} = \frac{2 \text{ ft}}{3 \text{ ft}}; \quad \boxed{\theta = 0.667 \text{ rad}}; \quad \theta = (0.667 \text{ rad})\left(\frac{1 \text{ rev}}{2\pi \text{ rad}}\right); \quad \boxed{\theta = 0.106 \text{ rad}};$$

$$\theta = (0.667 \text{ rad})\left(\frac{360^0}{2\pi \text{ rad}}\right); \quad \boxed{\theta = 38.2^0}$$

11-5. An electric motor turns at 600 rpm. What is the angular velocity? What is the angular displacement after 6 s?

$$f = 600 \frac{\text{rev}}{\text{min}}\left(\frac{2\pi \text{ rad}}{1 \text{ rev}}\right)\left(\frac{1 \text{ min}}{60 \text{ s}}\right); \quad \boxed{\omega = 62.8 \text{ rad/s}}$$

$$\theta = \bar{\omega} t = (62.8 \text{ rad/s})(6 \text{ s}); \quad \boxed{\theta = 377 \text{ rad}}$$

11-6. A rotating pulley completes 12 rev in 4 s. Determine the average angular velocity in rev/s, rpm, and in rad/s?

$$f = \frac{12 \text{ rev}}{4 \text{ s}}; \quad \boxed{f = 3.00 \text{ rev/s}}; \quad f = 3.00 \frac{\text{rev}}{\text{s}}\left(\frac{1 \text{ rev}}{2\pi \text{ rad}}\right)\left(\frac{60 \text{ s}}{1 \text{ min}}\right); \quad \boxed{f = 28.6 \text{ rpm}}$$

$$\omega = 2\pi f = 3.00 \frac{\text{rev}}{\text{s}}\left(\frac{2\pi \text{ rad}}{1 \text{ rev}}\right); \quad \boxed{\omega = 18.8 \text{ rad/s}}$$

11-7. A bucket is hung from a rope which is wrapped many times around a circular drum of radius 60 cm. The bucket starts from rest and is lifted to a height of 20 m in 5 s. (a) How many revolutions were made by the drum. (b) What was the average angular speed of the rotating drum?

$$\theta = \frac{s}{R} = \frac{20 \text{ m}}{0.600 \text{ m}} = 33.3 \text{ rad} \qquad \theta = (33.3 \text{ rad})\left(\frac{1 \text{ rev}}{2\pi \text{ rad}}\right); \quad \boxed{\theta = 5.31 \text{ rev}}$$

$$v = \frac{s}{t} = \frac{20 \text{ m}}{5 \text{ s}}; \qquad v = 4.00 \text{ m/s}; \qquad \omega = \frac{v}{R} = \frac{4 \text{ m/s}}{0.6 \text{ m}}; \quad \boxed{\omega = 6.67 \text{ rad/s}}$$

11-8. A wheel of radius 15.0 cm starts from rest and makes 2.00 rev in 3.00 s. (a) What is its average angular velocity in rad/s? (b) What is the final linear velocity of a point on the rim of the wheel?

$$\omega = \frac{\theta}{t} = \frac{2 \text{ rev}(2\pi \text{ rad/rev})}{3 \text{ s}}; \quad \boxed{\omega = 4.19 \text{ rad/s}}$$

11-8. (Cont.)

The final angular speed is twice the average since $\omega_o = 0$: $\omega_f = 8.38$ rad/s

$v_f = \omega_f R = (8.38 \text{ rad/s})(0.15 \text{ m})$; $v_f = 1.26$ m/s

11-9.

A cylindrical piece of stock 6 in. in diameter rotates in a lathe at 800 rpm. What is the linear velocity at the surface of the cylinder? [$R = D/2 = 3$ in. $= 0.250$ ft]

$v = \omega R = 2\pi f R$; $v = 2\pi \left(800 \dfrac{\text{rev}}{\text{min}}\right)\left(\dfrac{1 \text{ min}}{60 \text{ s}}\right)(0.25 \text{ ft})$; $v = 20.9$ ft/s

11-10.

The proper tangential velocity for machining steel stock is about 70 cm/s. At what rpm should a steel cylinder 8 cm in diameter be turned in a lathe? $R = (0.08 \text{ m/2}) = 0.04$ m

$v = \omega R$; $\omega = \dfrac{v}{R} = \dfrac{0.70 \text{ m/s}}{0.04 \text{ m}} = 1.75$ rad/s; $f = \dfrac{1.75 \text{ rad/s}}{2\pi} = 0.275$ rev/s;

$f = 0.275 \dfrac{\text{rev}}{\text{s}}\left(\dfrac{60 \text{ s}}{1 \text{ min}}\right) = 16.7 \dfrac{\text{rev}}{\text{min}}$; $f = 0.279$ rev/s(60 s/min); $f = 16.7$ rpm

11-11.

For the wheel in Problem 11-8, what is the angular acceleration? What is the _linear_ acceleration of a point on the edge of the wheel? [$\omega_f = 8.38$ rad/s; $\omega_o = 0$, $t = 3$ s]

$\alpha = \dfrac{\omega_f - \omega_o}{t} = \dfrac{8.38 \text{ rad/s} - 0}{3 \text{ s}}$; $\alpha = 2.79$ rad/s^2

$a = \alpha R = (2.79 \text{ rad/s}^2)(0.15 \text{ m})$; $a = 0.419$ m/s^2

11-12.

A circular drum of radius 40 cm is initially rotating at 400 rpm. It is brought to a stop after making 50 revolutions. What was the angular acceleration and the stopping time?

$2\alpha\theta = \omega_f^2 - \omega_o^2$; $\theta = 50$ rev(2π rad/rev) = 314 rad; $f = 400$ rpm = 41.9 rad/s

$\alpha = \dfrac{\omega_f^2 - \omega_o^2}{2\theta} = \dfrac{(0)^2 - (41.9 \text{ rad/s})^2}{2(314 \text{ rad})}$; $\alpha = 2.79$ rad/s^2

$\theta = \dfrac{\omega_o + \omega_f}{2}t$; $t = \dfrac{2\theta}{\omega_f} = \dfrac{2(314 \text{ rad})}{41.9 \text{ rad/s}}$; $t = 15.0$ s

11-13.

A belt is wrapped around the edge of a pulley that is 40 cm in diameter. The pulley rotates with a constant angular acceleration of 3.50 rad/s^2. At t = 0, the rotational speed is 2 rad/s. What is the angular displacement and angular velocity of the pulley 2 s later?

$\theta = \omega_o t + \frac{1}{2}\alpha t^2$; $R = 0.40$ m/2 = 0.20 m; $\omega_o = 0$, $t = 2$ s, $\alpha = 3.5$ rad/s.

$\theta = \omega_o t + \frac{1}{2}\alpha t^2 = (2 \text{ rad/s})(2 \text{ s}) + \frac{1}{2}(3.5 \text{ rad/s}^2)(2 \text{ s})^2$; $\theta = 11.00$ rad

$\omega_f = \omega_o + \alpha t = 2 \text{ rad/s} + (3.5 \text{ rad/s}^2)(2 \text{ s})$; $\omega_f = 9.00$ rad/s

11-14.

In Problem 11-13, what is the final linear speed and linear acceleration of the pulley belt as it moves around the edge of the pulley? (*We must use the radius R = 0.20 m.*)

$v = \omega_f R = (9.00 \text{ rad/s})(0.200 \text{ m})$; $v = 1.80$ m/s

$a = \alpha R = (3.50 \text{ rad/s}^2)(0.200 \text{ m})$; $a = 0.750$ m/s^2

*11-15.

A wheel rotating initially at 6 rev/s undergoes a constant angular acceleration of 4 rad/s^2. What is the angular velocity after 5 s? How many revolutions will the wheel make?

$\omega_o = 2\pi f R = 2\pi(6 \text{ rev/s}) = 37.7$ rad/s; $\alpha = 4$ rad/s^2; $t = 5$ s

$\omega_f = \omega_o + \alpha t$; $\omega_f = 37.7 \text{ rad/s} + (4 \text{ rad/s}^2)(5 \text{ s})$; $\omega_f = 57.7$ rad/s

$\theta = \omega_o t + \frac{1}{2}\alpha t^2$; $\theta = (37.7 \text{ rad/s})(5 \text{ s}) + \frac{1}{2}(4 \text{ rad/s}^2)(5 \text{ s})^2$; $\theta = 238$ rad

$\theta = 238 \text{ rad}\left(\dfrac{1 \text{ rev}}{2\pi \text{ rad}}\right)$; $\theta = 38.0$ rev

*11-16.

A grinding disk is brought to a stop in 40 rev. If the braking acceleration was –6 rad/s^2, what was the initial frequency or revolution in rev/s? [$\theta = 40$ rev (2π) = 251 rad]

$2\alpha\theta = \omega_f^2 - \omega_o^2$; $\omega_o = \sqrt{-2\alpha\theta} = \sqrt{-2(-6 \text{ rad/s}^2)(251 \text{ rad})}$; $\omega_o = 54.9$ rad/s

$f = 54.9 \text{ rad/s}\left(\dfrac{1 \text{ rev}}{2\pi \text{ rad}}\right)$; $f = 8.74$ rev/s

11-20. A 1.2-kg bicycle wheel has a radius of 70 cm with spokes of negligible weight. If it starts from rest and receives an angular acceleration of 3 rad/s², what will be its rotational kinetic energy after 4 s? (*The bicycle wheel approximates a circular hoop.*)

$\alpha = 3.00$ rad/s²; $I = mR^2 = (1.2$ kg$)(0.70$ m$)^2$; $I = 0.588$ kg m²

$\omega_f = \omega_o + \alpha t = (0) + (3$ rad/s²$)(4$ s$)$; $\omega_f = 12.0$ rad/s

$E_k = \frac{1}{2}I\omega_f^2 = \frac{1}{2}(0.588$ kg m²$)(12.0$ rad/s$)^2$; $\boxed{E_k = 42.3 \text{ J}}$

*11-21. A 16-lb grinding disk is rotating at 400 rpm. What is the moment of inertia? [400 rpm = 41.89 rad/s] What is the radius of the disk if its kinetic energy is 54.8 ft lb?

$m = (16$ lb$/32$ ft/s²$) = 0.500$ slugs; $E_k = \frac{1}{2}I\omega^2 = 54.8$ ft lb; $I = \frac{1}{2}mR^2$

$I = \dfrac{2E_k}{\omega^2} = \dfrac{2(54.8 \text{ ft lb})}{(41.89 \text{ rad/s})^2}$; $\boxed{I = 0.625 \text{ slug ft}^2}$

$I = \frac{1}{2}mR^2$; $R = \sqrt{\dfrac{2I}{m}} = \sqrt{\dfrac{2(0.0625 \text{ slug ft}^2)}{0.50 \text{ kg}}}$; $\boxed{R = 0.500 \text{ ft or } 6.00 \text{ in.}}$

*11-22. What must be the radius of a 4-kg circular disk if it is to have the same moment of inertia as a 1-kg rod,1 m long and pivoted at its midpoint? $[I_D = \frac{1}{2}mR^2; \; I_R = (1/12)mL^2]$

$\frac{1}{2}m_dR^2 = \dfrac{m_rL^2}{12}$; $R = \sqrt{\dfrac{m_rL^2}{6m_d}} = \sqrt{\dfrac{(1 \text{ kg})(1 \text{ m})^2}{6(4 \text{ kg})}}$; $R = 0.204$ m

---

*11-17. A pulley 320 mm in diameter and rotating initially at 4 rev/s receives a constant angular acceleration of 2 rad/s². What is the linear velocity of a belt around the pulley after 8 s? What is the tangential acceleration of the belt? [$R = 0.320/2) = 0.160$ m]

$\omega_o = 4$ rev/s $(2\pi$ rad/rev$) = 25.1$ rad/s; $\alpha = 2$ rad/s²; $t = 8$ s

$\omega_f = \omega_o + \alpha t = 25.1$ rad/s $+ (2$ rad/s²$)(8$ s$)$; $\omega_f = 41.1$ rad/s

$v = \omega_f R = (41.1$ rad/s$)(0.160$ m$)$; $\boxed{v = 6.58 \text{ m/s}}$

$a = \alpha R = (2$ rad/s²$)(0.160$ m$)$; $\boxed{a = 0.320 \text{ m/s}^2}$

*11-18. A person initially at rest 4 m from the center of a rotating platform covers distance of 100 m in 20 s. What is the angular acceleration of the platform? What is the angular velocity after 4 s?

Find linear acceleration first: $s = \cancel{v_0 t}^{\,0} + \frac{1}{2}at^2$; $a = \dfrac{2s}{t^2} = \dfrac{2(100 \text{ m})}{(20 \text{ s})^2} = 0.500 \text{ m/s}^2$

$a = \alpha R$; $\alpha = \dfrac{a}{R} = \dfrac{0.500 \text{ rad/s}^2}{4 \text{ m}}$; $\boxed{\alpha = 0.125 \text{ rad/s}^2}$

$\omega_f = \cancel{\phi_o}^{\,0} + \alpha t$; $\omega_f = (0.125$ rad/s²$)(4$ s$)$; $\boxed{\omega_f = 0.500 \text{ rad/s}}$

Rotational Kinetic Energy; Moment of Inertia

11-19. A 2-kg mass and a 6-kg mass are connected by a light 30-cm bar. The system is then rotated horizontally at 300 rpm about an axis 10 cm from the 6-kg mass. What is the moment of inertia about this axis? What is the rotational kinetic energy?

$I = \Sigma mR^2 = (2$ kg$)(0.2$ m$)^2 + (6$ kg$)(0.1$ m$)^2$

$\boxed{I = 0.140 \text{ kg m}^2}$ $\omega = 300$ rpm $= 31.4$ rad/s

$E_k = \frac{1}{2}I\omega^2 = \frac{1}{2}(0.140$ kg m²$)(31.4$ rad/s$)^2$; $\boxed{E_k = 69.1 \text{ J}}$

*11-23. A wagon wheel 60 cm in diameter is mounted on a central axle where it spins at 200 rpm. The wheel can be thought of as a circular hoop of mass 2 kg, and each of 12 wooden 500-g spokes can be thought of as thin rods rotating about their ends. Calculate the moment of inertia for the entire wheel? What is the rotational kinetic energy?

$m_w = 2$ kg, $R_w = 0.30$ m; $m_s = 0.5$ kg, $L_s = 0.30$ m, $I_T = I_w + 12I_s$

$I_T = m_w R^2 + 12(\frac{1}{3}mL^2)$; $I_T = (2$ kg$)(0.3$ m$)^2 + 4(0.5$ kg$)(0.3)^2$;

$$I = 0.360 \text{ kg m}^2$$

$\omega = 200$ rpm $= 20.94$ rad/s;

$E_k = \frac{1}{2}I\omega^2 = \frac{1}{2}(0.360 \text{ kg m}^2)(20.94 \text{ rad/s})^2$; $\boxed{E_k = 78.9 \text{ J}}$

*11-24. Compare the rotational kinetic energies of three objects of equal radius and mass: A circular hoop, a circular disk, and a solid sphere.

The rotational inertias are: $I_H = mR^2$; $I_D = \frac{1}{2}mR^2$; $I_S = \frac{2}{5}mR^2$:

For purposes of comparing, suppose we set $m = 1$ kg and $R = 1$ m

We see that: $I_H = 1$ kg m²; $I_D = 0.5$ kg m²; $I_S = 0.4$ kg m²

Now $E_k = \frac{1}{2}I\omega^2$, so at a given rotational speed, the hoop has the largest kinetic energy, followed by the disk, and then by the sphere.

Newton's Second Law and Rotation

11-25. A rope wrapped around a 5-kg circular drum pulls with a tension of 400 N. If the radius of the drum is 20 cm and it is free to rotate about its central axis, what is the angular acceleration?

F = 400 N

$\tau = FR = I\alpha$; $I = \frac{1}{2}mR^2$

$FR = (\frac{1}{2}mR^2)\alpha$; $\alpha = \frac{2F}{mR} = \frac{2(400 \text{ N})}{(5 \text{ kg})(0.20 \text{ m})}$; $\boxed{\alpha = 800 \text{ rad/s}^2}$

---

*11-26. The flywheel of an engine has a moment inertia of 24 slug ft². What torque is required to accelerate the wheel from rest to an angular velocity of 400 rpm in 10 s.

$\omega_f = 400$ rpm $= 41.9$ rad/s; $\omega_o = 0$; $t = 10$ s, $I = 24$ slug ft²

$\alpha = \frac{\omega_f - \omega_o}{t} = \frac{41.9 \text{ rad/s} - 0}{10 \text{ s}} = 4.19$ rad/s² ;

$\tau = I\alpha = (24 \text{ slug ft}^2)(4.19 \text{ rad/s}^2)$; $\boxed{\tau = 1010 \text{ N m}}$

*11-27. A 3-kg thin rod is 40 cm long and pivoted about its midpoint. What torque is required to cause it to make 20 rev while its rotational speed increases from 200 rpm to 600 rpm?

L = 0.40 m

m = 3 kg

$\theta = 20$ rev$(2\pi$ rad$) = 126$ rad; $\omega_o = 200$ rpm $= 20.94$ rad/s

$\omega_f = 600$ rpm $= 62.8$ rad/s; $m = 3$ kg; $L = 0.40$ m

$2\alpha\theta = \omega_f^2 - \omega_o^2$; $2\alpha(126 \text{ rad}) = (62.8 \text{ rad/s})^2 - (20.94 \text{ rad/s})^2$; $\alpha = 13.9$ rad/s²

$I = \frac{1}{12}mL^2$ $\quad \tau = I\alpha = \frac{1}{12}mL^2\alpha = \frac{1}{12}(3 \text{ kg})(0.40 \text{ m})^2(13.9 \text{ rad/s}^2)$; $\boxed{\tau = 0.558 \text{ N m}}$

*11-28. A large 120-kg turbine wheel has a radius of gyration of 1 m. A frictional torque of 80 N m opposes the rotation of the shaft. What torque must be applied to accelerate the wheel from rest to 300 rpm in 10 s? $\omega_o = 0$, $\omega_f = 300$ rpm $= 31.4$ rad/s, $t = 2$ s

$\alpha = \frac{\omega_o - \omega_f}{t} = \frac{31.4 \text{ rad/s} - 0}{2 \text{ s}} = 15.7$ rad/s²; $I = mk^2 = (120 \text{ kg})(1 \text{ m})^2$

$I = 120$ kg m²; $\tau = I\alpha = (120 \text{ kg m}^2)(15.7 \text{ rad/s}^2)$; $\boxed{\tau = 1885 \text{ N m}}$

11-29. A 2-kg mass swings in a circle of radius 50-cm at the end of a light rod. What resultant torque is required to give an angular acceleration of 2.5 rad/s².

$I = mR^2 = (2 \text{ kg})(0.5 \text{ m})^2 = 0.5$ kg m²;

$\tau = I\alpha = (0.5 \text{ kg m}^2)(2.5 \text{ rad/s}^2)$; $\tau = 1.25$ N m

*11-30. A rope is wrapped several times around a cylinder of radius 0.2 m and mass 30 kg. What is the angular acceleration of the cylinder if the tension in the rope is 40 N and it turns without friction.

$$\tau = FR = I\alpha; \quad FR = (\tfrac{1}{2}mR^2)\alpha; \quad \alpha = \frac{2F}{mR} = \frac{2(40\ N)}{(30\ kg)(0.20\ m)}; \quad \boxed{\alpha = 13.3\ rad/s^2}$$

*11-31. An 8-kg grinding disk has a diameter of 60 cm and is rotating at 600 rpm. What braking force must be applied tangentially to the disk if it is to stop rotating in 5 s?

$$\omega_0 = 600\ rpm = 62.8\ rad/s, \quad \omega_f = 0, \quad \alpha = \frac{\omega_0 - \omega_f}{t} = \frac{62.8\ rad/s - 0}{5\ s} = 12.6\ rad/s^2$$

$$\tau = FR = I\alpha; \quad FR = (\tfrac{1}{2}mR^2)\alpha; \quad F = \tfrac{1}{2}mR\alpha = \tfrac{1}{2}(8\ kg)(0.30\ m)(12.6\ rad/s^2)$$

$$\boxed{F = 15.1\ N}$$

11-32. An unbalanced torque of 150 N·m imparts an angular acceleration of 12 rad/s² to the rotor of a generator. What is the moment of inertia?

$$\tau = I\alpha; \quad I = \frac{\tau}{\alpha} = \frac{150\ N\ m}{12\ rad/s^2}; \quad \boxed{I = 12.5\ kg\ m^2}$$

Rotational Work, Energy, and Power

11-33. A rope wrapped around a 3-kg disk 20 cm in diameter is pulled for a linear distance of 5 m with a force of 40 N. What is the linear work done by the 40-N force? What is the rotational work done on the disk? [R = 20/2 = 10 cm or 0.10 m]

$$Work = F\ s = (40\ N)(5\ m); \quad \boxed{Work = 200\ J}$$

$$\theta = \frac{s}{R} = \frac{5\ m}{0.10\ m} = 50\ rad$$

$$Work = \tau\theta = FR\theta = (40\ N)(0.10\ m)(50\ rad); \quad \boxed{Work = 200\ J}$$

*11-34. Use the work-energy theorem to calculate the final angular velocity of the disk in Problem 11-33 if it starts from rest.

$$Work = \tfrac{1}{2}I\omega_f^2 - (0); \quad I = \tfrac{1}{2}mR^2; \quad Work = \tfrac{1}{2}(\tfrac{1}{2}mR^2)\omega_f^2;$$

$$\omega_f = \sqrt{\frac{4(200\ J)}{mR^2}} = \sqrt{\frac{4(200\ J)}{(3\ kg)(0.10\ m)^2}}; \quad \boxed{\omega_f = 163\ rad/s}$$

*11-35. A 1.2 kW motor acts for 8 s on a wheel having a moment of inertia of 2 kg·m². Assuming the wheel was initially at rest, what average angular speed was developed?

$$P = \frac{Work}{t}; \quad Work = Pt = (1200\ W)(8\ s) = 9600\ J$$

$$Work = \tfrac{1}{2}I\omega_f^2 - (0); \quad 9600\ J = \tfrac{1}{2}(2\ kg\ m^2)\omega_f^2; \quad \boxed{\omega_f = 98.0\ rad/s}$$

*11-36. A cord is wrapped around the rim of a cylinder that has a mass of 10 kg and a radius of 30 cm. If the rope is pulled with a force of 60 N, what is the angular acceleration of the cylinder? What is the linear acceleration of the rope?

$$I = \tfrac{1}{2}mR^2 = \tfrac{1}{2}(10\ kg)(0.30\ m)^2 = 0.450\ kg\ m^2; \quad \tau = (60\ N)(0.3\ m) = 18\ N\ m$$

$$\tau = I\alpha; \quad \alpha = \frac{\tau}{I} = \frac{18\ N\ m}{0.450\ kg\ m^2}; \quad \boxed{\alpha = 40\ rad/s^2}$$

11-37. A 600-W motor drives a pulley with an average angular velocity of 20 rad/s. What torque is developed?

$$P = \tau\bar{\omega}; \quad \tau = \frac{P}{\omega} = \frac{600\ W}{20\ rad/s}; \quad \boxed{\tau = 30.0\ N\ m}$$

11-38. The crankshaft on an automobile develops 350 lb·ft of torque at 1800 rpm. What is the output horsepower?   1800 rpm = 188.5 rad/s ;

$$P = \tau\omega = (350\ ft\ lb)(188.5\ rad/s) = 65,973\ ft\ lb/s \quad or \quad \boxed{120\ hp}$$

Angular Momentum

11-39. A 500-g steel rod 30 cm in length is pivoted about its center and rotated at 300 rpm.

What is the angular momentum? [ω = 300 rpm = 31.4 rad/s; m = 0.5 kg]

$$I = \tfrac{1}{2}mL^2 = \tfrac{1}{2}(0.50\ \text{kg})(0.30\ \text{m})^2; \qquad I = 0.00375\ \text{kg m}^2$$

$$I\omega = (0.00375\ \text{kg m}^2)(31.4\ \text{rad/s}); \qquad \boxed{I\omega = 0.118\ \text{kg m/s}^2}$$

11-40. In Problem 11-39, what average torque must be applied to stop the rotation in 2 s?

$$\alpha = \frac{\omega_f - \omega_0}{t} = \frac{0 - (31.4\ \text{rad/s})}{2\ \text{s}} = -15.7\ \text{rad/s}^2$$

$$\tau = I\alpha = (0.00375\ \text{kg m}^2)(15.7\ \text{rad/s}^2); \qquad \boxed{\tau = 0.0589\ \text{N m}}$$

*11-41. A sudden torque of 400 N m is applied to the edge of a disk initially at rest. If the rotational inertia of the disk is 4 kg m², and the torque acts for 0.02 s, what is the change in angular momentum? What is the final angular speed?

change in angular momentum = Angular impulse; $\qquad \tau \Delta t = I\omega_f - I\omega_0^{\;0}$

$$\tau \Delta t = (400\ \text{N m})(0.02\ \text{s}) = \boxed{8.00\ \text{kg m/s}^2}$$

$$\tau \Delta t = I\omega_f = 8.00\ \text{kg m/s}^2 \qquad \omega_f = \frac{8.00\ \text{kg m/s}^2}{4\ \text{kg m}^2}; \qquad \boxed{\omega_f = 2.00\ \text{rad/s}}$$

*11-42. In Fig. 11-12, a 6-kg disk A rotating clockwise at 400 rpm engages with a 3-kg disk B initially at rest. The radius of disk A is 0.4 m and the radius of disk B is 0.2 m. What is the combined angular speed after the two disks are meshed?

$$I_A = \tfrac{1}{2}(6\ \text{kg})(0.4\ \text{m})^2 = 0.480\ \text{kg m}^2; \quad I_B = \tfrac{1}{2}(3\ \text{kg})(0.2\ \text{m})^2 = 0.060\ \text{kg m}^2$$

$$\omega_{Ao} = 400\ \text{rpm} = 41.9\ \text{rad/s}; \quad \omega_{Bo} = 0; \quad \omega_{Af} = \omega_{Bf} = \omega_c;$$

Conservation of Momentum: $\qquad I_A\omega_{Ao} + I_B\omega_{Bo} = (I_A + I_B)\,\omega_c$

---

*11-42. (Cont.) $\qquad \omega_c = \dfrac{I_A\omega_{Ao}}{I_A + I_B} = \dfrac{(0.48\ \text{kg m}^2)(41.9\ \text{rad/s})}{0.48\ \text{kg m}^2 + 0.060\ \text{kg m}^2};$ $\qquad \boxed{\omega_c = 37.2\ \text{rad/s}}$

*11-43. Assume that disk B in Problem 11-42 is initially rotating clockwise at 200 rpm in the same direction as disk A. What is the common angular speed as they mesh?

Choose clockwise as positive and use rpm's for angular speed.

$$I_A\omega_{Ao} + I_B\omega_{Bo} = (I_A + I_B)\,\omega_c$$

$$(0.48\ \text{kg m}^2)(400\ \text{rpm}) + (0.06\ \text{kg m}^2)(200\ \text{rpm}) = (0.48\ \text{kg m}^2 + 0.060\ \text{kg m}^2)\omega_c$$

$$204\ \text{kg m}^2\ \text{rpm} = 0.54\omega_c; \qquad \boxed{\omega_c = 378\ \text{rpm}}$$

*11-44. Assume the same conditions as Problem 11-42 except that the disk B is rotating counterclockwise and A is rotating clockwise. What is the combined angular velocity after the disks are meshed?

$$(0.48\ \text{kg m}^2)(400\ \text{rpm}) + (0.06\ \text{kg m}^2)(-200\ \text{rpm}) = (0.48\ \text{kg m}^2 + 0.060\ \text{kg m}^2)\omega_c$$

$$180\ \text{kg m}^2\ \text{rpm} = 0.54\omega_c; \qquad \boxed{\omega_c = 333\ \text{rpm}}$$

11-45. The rod connecting the two weights in Fig. 11-13 has negligible weight but is configured to allow the weights to slip outward. At the instant when the angular speed is 600 rpm, the 2-kg masses are 10 cm apart. What is the rotational speed later when the masses are 34 cm apart?

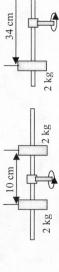

$$I_o = (2\ \text{kg})(0.05\ \text{m})^2 + (2\ \text{kg})(0.05\ \text{m})^2; \quad I_f = (2\ \text{kg})(0.17\ \text{m})^2 + (2\ \text{kg})(0.17\ \text{m})^2$$

$$I_0 = 0.010\ \text{kg m}^2; \quad I_f = 0.68\ \text{kg m}^2; \quad \omega_o = 600\ \text{rpm}; \quad I_o\omega_o = I_f\omega_f$$

$$(0.010\ \text{kg m}^2)(600\ \text{rpm}) = (0.116\ \text{kg m}^2)\omega_f; \qquad \boxed{\omega_f = 51.9\ \text{rpm}.}$$

Supplementary Problems

*11-46. The 6-kg circular grinding disk is rotating initially at 500 rpm. The radius of the disk is 40 cm. What is the angular acceleration of the disk if the ax exerts a tangential force of 120 N at the edge. How many revolutions will the disk make before stopping? What is work is done and what power is lost in the process? [ω_0 = 500 rpm = 52.35 rad/s]

$\tau = FR$ = (120 N)(0.40 m) = 48 N m; $I = \frac{1}{2}mR^2 = \frac{1}{2}(6 \text{ kg})(0.4 \text{ m})^2$ = 0.48 kg m²

$\tau = I\alpha$; $\alpha = \frac{\tau}{I} = \frac{-(48 \text{ N m})}{0.48 \text{ kg m}^2}$; $\boxed{\alpha = -100 \text{ rad/s}^2}$

$2\alpha\theta = \omega_f^2 - \omega_0^2$; $\theta = \frac{-\omega_0^2}{2\alpha} = \frac{-(52.35 \text{ rad/s})^2}{2(-100 \text{ rad/s}^2)}$; $\boxed{\theta = 13.7 \text{ rad} = 2.18 \text{ rev}}$

$Work = \tau\theta$ = (48 N m)(13.7 rad); $\boxed{Work = 658 \text{ J}}$

$P = \frac{Work}{t}$ $\overline{\omega} = \frac{\omega_0 + \omega_f}{2} = \frac{(52.35 \text{ rad/s}) + 0}{2}$ = 26.2 rad/s; $P = \overline{\tau\omega}$

P = (48 N m)(26.18 rad/s); $\boxed{P = 1.26 \text{ kW}}$

*11-47 A 3-kg wheel with spokes of negligible mass is free to rotate about its center without friction. The edge of the wheel of radius 40 cm is struck suddenly with an average tangential force of 600 N lasting for 0.002 s. (a) What angular impulse is imparted to the wheel? (b) If the wheel was initially at rest, what was its angular speed at the end of the 0.002-s interval?

$\tau = FR$ = (600 N)(0.40 m) = 240 N m;

$I = mR^2$ = (3 kg)(0.40 m)²; $\boxed{I = 0.48 \text{ kg m}^2}$

$\tau \Delta t$ = (240 N m)(0.002 s); $\tau \Delta t$ = 0.48 N m s

$\tau \Delta t = I\omega_f - 0$; $\omega_f = \frac{\tau \Delta t}{I} = \frac{0.48 \text{ N m s}}{0.480 \text{ kg m}^2}$; $\boxed{\omega_f = 1.00 \text{ rad/s}}$

*11-48. Disk A has three times the rotational inertia of Disk B. Disk A is rotating initially clockwise at 200 rpm and Disk B is rotating in the opposite direction at 800 rpm. (a) If the two are meshed together, what is the common rate of rotation of the combined disks?

Assume clockwise is positive: $I_A\omega_{Ao} + I_B\omega_{Bo} = (I_A + I_B)\omega_c$; $I_A = 3 I_B$

(3 I_B)(200 rpm) + I_B(-800 rpm) = (3I_B + I_B)ω_c

-(200 rpm)$I_B = 4I_B \omega_c$; $\omega_c = \frac{-200 \text{ rpm}}{4}$; $\boxed{\omega_c = -50.0 \text{ rpm}}$

*11-49. What if the disks in Problem 11-48 are initially rotating in the same direction? What would be the common angular speed after meshing? (*Clockwise positive*)

(3 I_B)(200 rpm) + I_B(+800 rpm) = (3I_B + I_B)ω_c

(1400 rpm)$I_B = 4I_B \omega_c$; $\omega_c = \frac{1400 \text{ rpm}}{4}$; $\boxed{\omega_c = 350 \text{ rpm}}$

*11-50. The radius of gyration of an 8-kg wheel is 50 cm. Find its moment of inertia and its kinetic energy if it is rotating at 400 rpm. ω = 400 rpm = 41.9 rad/s

$I = mk^2$ = (8 kg)(0.5 m)²; $\boxed{I = 2.00 \text{ kg m}^2}$

$E_k = \frac{1}{2}I\omega^2 = \frac{1}{2}(2 \text{ kg m}^2)(41.9 \text{ rad/s})^2$; $\boxed{E_k = 1750 \text{ J}}$

*11-51. How much work is required to slow the wheel in Problem 11-50 to 100 rpm?

Work = change in kinetic energy

$Work = \frac{1}{2}Iw_f^2 - \frac{1}{2}Iw_0^2$

ω_0 = 41.9 rad/s; ω_f = 100 rpm = 10.5 rad/s

$Work = \frac{1}{2}(2 \text{ kg m}^2)(10.5 \text{ rad/s})^2 - \frac{1}{2}(2 \text{ kg m}^2)(41.9 \text{ rad/s})^2$

$\boxed{Work = -1644 \text{ J}}$

11-52. A wheel of radius 2 ft has a moment of inertia of 8.2 slug ft². A constant force of 12 lb acts tangentially at the edge of the wheel that is initially at rest. What is the angular acceleration?

$\tau = I\alpha$; $\tau = FR = (12\ lb)(2\ ft) = 24\ lb\ ft$;

$\alpha = \dfrac{\tau}{I} = \dfrac{(24\ lb\ ft)}{8.2\ slug\ ft^2}$; $\boxed{\alpha = 2.93\ rad/s^2}$

*11-53. In Problem 11-52, the wheel was brought to rest in 5 s. How much work was done? What horsepower was developed?

$\theta = \omega_0 t + \tfrac{1}{2}\alpha t^2 = 0 + \tfrac{1}{2}(2.93\ rad/s^2)(5\ s)^2$; $\theta = 36.6\ rad$

$Work = \tau\theta = (24\ lb\ ft)(36.6\ rad)$; $\boxed{Work = 878\ ft\ lb}$

$P = \dfrac{Work}{t} = \dfrac{878\ ft\ lb}{5\ s}$; $\boxed{P = 175.7\ ft\ lb/s\ or\ 0.319\ hp}$

*11-54. An engine operating at 1800 rpm develops 200 hp. What is the torque developed?

$\omega = 1800\ rpm = 188.5\ rad/s$; $P = 200\ hp = 110{,}000\ ft\ lb$

$P = \tau\omega$; $\tau = \dfrac{P}{\omega} = \dfrac{(110{,}000\ ft\ lb/s)}{188.5\ rad/s}$; $\tau = 584\ lb\ ft$

11-55. A constant force of 200 N acts at the edge of a wheel 36 cm in diameter causing it to make 20 rev in 5 s. What power is developed?

$\tau = FR = (200\ N)(0.18\ m)$; $\tau = 36.0\ N\ m$;

$\omega = \dfrac{\theta}{t} = \dfrac{2\pi(20\ rev)}{5\ s} = 25.13\ rad/s$

$P = \tau\omega = (36\ N\ m)(25.13\ rad/s)$; $\boxed{P = 904\ W}$

---

*11-56. A 2-kg circular hoop rolls down an inclined plane from an initial height of 20 m. The kinetic energy that develops is shared between rotation and translation. What will be the speed when it reaches the bottom of the incline. [$h = 20\ m$, $v_o = \omega_o = 0$.]

$mgh = \tfrac{1}{2}mv^2 + \tfrac{1}{2}I\omega^2$; $I = mR^2$; $\omega^2 = (v^2/R^2)$

$mgh = \tfrac{1}{2}mv^2 + \tfrac{1}{2}(mR^2)(v^2/R^2)$; $mgh = \tfrac{1}{2}mv^2 + \tfrac{1}{2}mv^2$

$v^2 = gh = (9.8\ m/s^2)(20\ m)$; $\boxed{v = 14.0\ m/s}$

*11-57. Suppose a circular disk rolls down the same incline as in Problem 11-56. What is its speed when it reaches the bottom? (Same as Prob. 11-56 except that $I = \tfrac{1}{2}mR^2$)

$mgh = \tfrac{1}{2}mv^2 + \tfrac{1}{2}I\omega^2$; $I = \tfrac{1}{2}mR^2$; $\omega^2 = (v^2/R^2)$

$mgh = \tfrac{1}{2}mv^2 + \tfrac{1}{2}(\tfrac{1}{2}mR^2)(v^2/R^2)$; $mgh = \tfrac{1}{2}mv^2 + \tfrac{1}{4}mv^2$

$\tfrac{3}{4}v^2 = gh$; $v^2 = \dfrac{4gh}{3} = \dfrac{4(9.8\ m/s^2)(20\ m)}{3}$; $\boxed{v = 16.2\ m/s}$

Critical Thinking Questions

11-58. A circular hoop of mass 2-kg and radius 60 cm spins freely about its center connected by light central spokes. A force of 50 N acts tangent to the edge of the wheel for a time of 0.02 s. (a) What is the angular impulse? (b) What is the change in angular momentum? (c) If the hoop was initially at rest, what was the final angular speed? (d) Use the work-energy theorem to calculate the angular displacement. $\tau = FR$; $Impulse = \tau\ \Delta t$

$\tau\ \Delta t = FR\ \Delta t = (50\ N)(0.6\ m)(002\ s)$ $\boxed{\tau\ \Delta t = 0.600\ N\ m\ s}$

$I\omega_f - I\omega_o = \tau\ \Delta t$; $\boxed{Change\ in\ momentum = 0.600\ kg\ m^2/s}$

$I = (2\ kg)(0.60\ m)^2 = 1.2\ kg\ m^2$; $I\omega_f - I\omega_o = 0.600\ kg\ m^2/s$

11-58. (Cont.) $I = mR^2$; $\omega_f = \dfrac{0.600 \text{ kg m}^2/s}{mR^2} = \dfrac{0.600 \text{ kg m}^2/s}{(2 \text{ kg})(0.6 \text{ m})^2}$ $\boxed{\omega_f = 0.833 \text{ rad/s}}$

Work = $\tau\theta$ = FRθ; FRθ = ½$I\omega_f^2$ - 0;

$\theta = \dfrac{I\omega_f^2}{2FR} = \dfrac{(0.600 \text{ kg m}^2/s)(0.833 \text{ rad/s})^2}{2(50 \text{ N})(0.6 \text{ m})}$; $\boxed{\theta = 0.00833 \text{ rad}}$

11-59. The spin cycle on a washer slows from 900 rpm to 300 rpm in 4 s. Determine the angular acceleration. Does a force act to throw off the water from the clothes or is it the lack of a force? When operating at 900 rpm, the output power is 4 kW. What is the torque developed? If the radius of the tub is 30 cm, what is the linear speed of the clothes near the inside edge?

ω_0 = 90 rpm = 94.25 rad/s; ω_f = 600 rpm = 62.83 rad/s; R = 0.30 m

$\alpha = \dfrac{\omega_f - \omega_0}{t} = \dfrac{62.83 \text{ rad/s} - 94.25 \text{ rad/s}}{4 \text{ s}}$; $\boxed{\alpha = -7.86 \text{ rad/s}^2}$

$P = \tau\omega$; $\tau = \dfrac{P}{\omega} = \dfrac{4000 \text{ W}}{94.25 \text{ rad/s}}$; $\boxed{\tau = 42.4 \text{ N m}}$

$v = \omega R = (94.25 \text{ rad/s})(0.30 \text{ m})$; $\boxed{v = 27.7 \text{ m/s}}$

11-60. A block is attached to a cord passing over a pulley through a hole in a horizontal table top as shown in Fig. 11-14. Initially the block is revolving at 4 rad/s at a distance r from the center of the hole. If the cord is pulled from below until its radius is r/4, what is the new angular velocity?

Angular momentum is conserved: $I_o\omega_o = I_f\omega_f$; $(\cancel{mr_o^2})\omega_o = (\cancel{mr_f^2})\omega_f$

$\omega_f = \dfrac{r_0^2\omega_o}{r_f^2} = \omega_0\left(\dfrac{r_0}{r_f}\right)^2$; $\omega_f = (4 \text{ rad/s})\left(\dfrac{r_0}{r_0/4}\right)^2 = (4 \text{ rad/s})(16)$ $\boxed{\omega_f = 64 \text{ rad/s}}$

*11-61. Suppose in Fig. 11-14 the block has a mass of 2 kg and is rotating at 3 rad/s when r = 1 m. At what distance r will the tension in the cord be 25 N?

$I_o\omega_o = I_f\omega_f$; $(mr_o^2)\omega_o = (mr_f^2)\omega_f$; $\omega_f = \dfrac{r_0^2\omega_0}{r_f^2}$; $v^2 = \omega^2 r^2$

$F = \dfrac{mv_f^2}{r_f}$; $F = \dfrac{m\omega_f^2 r_f^2}{r_f} = m\omega_f^2 r_f$; $m\omega_f^2 r_f = 25$ N

Substitute $\omega_f = \dfrac{r_0^2\omega_0}{r_f^2}$ into $m\omega_f^2 r_f = 25$ N and solve for r_f:

$m\left(\dfrac{r_0^4\omega_0^2}{r_f^4}\right)r_f = 25$ N; $r_f^3 = \dfrac{mr_0^4\omega_0^2}{25 \text{ N}}$; $r_f = \sqrt[3]{\dfrac{mr_0^4\omega_0^2}{25 \text{ N}}}$

$r_f = \sqrt[3]{\dfrac{(2kg)(1 \text{ m})^4(3 \text{ rad/s})^2}{25 \text{ N}}}$; $\boxed{r_f = 0.849 \text{ m or } 84.9 \text{ cm}}$

*11-62. Consider Fig. 11-15 in which m = 2 kg, M = 8 kg, R = 60 cm, and h = 6 m. Write Newton's second law for the disk in terms of the tension in the rope, the moment of inertia of the disk, and the angular acceleration. Next write Newton's second law for the falling mass in terms the tension in the rope, the mass, and the linear acceleration. Eliminate T from these two equations. Find the linear acceleration of the 2-kg mass by recalling that $v = \omega R$, $a = \alpha R$, and $I = ½mR^2$.

(a) $\tau = FR = I\alpha$; $TR = (½MR^2)\left(\dfrac{a}{R}\right)$; $T = ½Ma$

(b) $mg - T = ma$; $mg - (½Ma) = ma$

(c) $2mg - Ma = 2ma$; $2mg = Ma + 2ma$

$a = \dfrac{2mg}{M+2m} = \dfrac{2(2 \text{ kg})(9.8 \text{ m/s}^2)}{[8 \text{ kg} + 2(2 \text{ kg})]}$; $\boxed{a = 3.27 \text{ m/s}^2}$

*11-63. Use conservation of energy to find the velocity of the 2-kg mass in Fig. 11-15 just

before it strikes the floor 6 m below. Use data given in Problem 11-62.

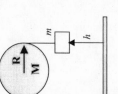

Given: $m = 2$ kg, $M = 8$ kg, $R = 60$ cm, and $h = 6$ m, $I = \frac{1}{2}MR^2$

E_{po} of falling mass $= E_{kf}$ of falling mass $+ E_{kf}$ of rotating disk

$$mgh = \frac{1}{2}mv^2 + \frac{1}{2}I\omega_f^2 \ ; \quad I = \frac{1}{2}MR^2; \quad \omega_f^2 = v^2/R^2$$

$$mgh = \frac{1}{2}mv + \frac{1}{2}(\frac{1}{2}MR^2)\left(\frac{v^2}{R^2}\right); \quad mgh = \frac{1}{2}mv^2 + \frac{1}{4}Mv^2$$

$$(2 \text{ kg})(9.8 \text{ m/s}^2)(6 \text{ m}) = \frac{1}{2}(2 \text{ kg})v^2 + \frac{1}{4}(8 \text{ kg})v^2; \quad v^2 = 39.2 \text{ m}^2/\text{s}^2; \quad \boxed{v = 6.26 \text{ m/s}}$$

*11-64. A student stands on a platform with arms outstretched, holding weights in each hand so

that the rotational inertial is 6.0 kg m². The platform is then set into constant, frictionless

rotation at 90 rpm. Now the student is able to reduce the rotational inertia to 2 kg m² by

pulling the weights in to the body. (a) What will be the new rate of rotation in the

absence of external torque? (b) What is the ratio of the final kinetic energy to the initial

kinetic energy? Explain increase in energy. [$\omega_o = 90$ rpm, $I_o = 6$ kg m², $I_f = 2$ kg m²]

Conservation of momentum: $I_o\omega_o = I_f\omega_f$

$(6 \text{ kg m}^2)(90 \text{ rpm}) = (2 \text{ kg m}^2)\,\omega_f; \quad \boxed{\omega_f = 270 \text{ rpm}}$

$\omega_o = 90$ rpm $= 9.425$ rad/s; $\quad \omega_f = 270$ rpm $= 28.27$ rad/s

$$\frac{E_{kf}}{E_{ko}} = \frac{\frac{1}{2}I_f\omega_f^2}{\frac{1}{2}I_o\omega_o^2} = \frac{\frac{1}{2}(2 \text{ kg m}^2)(28.27 \text{ rad/s})^2}{\frac{1}{2}(6 \text{ kg m}^2)(9.425 \text{ rad/s})^2}; \quad \boxed{E_k/E_f = 3.00}$$

The final kinetic energy is three times the initial energy. The increase in energy comes

for doing work on the masses to bring them closer to the body.

11-65. The large pulley shown in Fig. 11-16 can be considered as a 6-kg disk of radius 50 cm.

The right mass is 4 kg and the left mass is 2 kg. Consider both rotational and

translational energies and find the velocity just before the 4-kg mass strikes the floor?

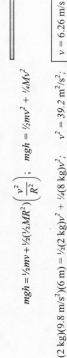

<u>Conservation of energy</u>: The initial potential energy of the right mass

must equal the sum of the final potential and kinetic energies

including rotational E_k and translational E_k

Three masses: $m_2gh = m_1gh + \frac{1}{2}m_2v^2 + \frac{1}{2}m_1v^2 + \frac{1}{2}I\omega^2$

Substitute $I = \frac{1}{2}MR^2$ and $\omega_f^2 = v^2/R^2$.

$$m_2gh = m_1gh + \frac{1}{2}m_2v^2 + \frac{1}{2}m_1v^2 + \frac{1}{2}(\frac{1}{2}MR^2)(v^2/R^2)$$

$$m_2gh = m_1gh + \frac{1}{2}m_2v^2 + \frac{1}{2}m_1v^2 + \frac{1}{4}Mv^2 = m_2gh - m_1gh$$

$$\frac{1}{2}m_2v^2 + \frac{1}{2}m_1v^2 + \frac{1}{4}Mv^2 = m_2gh - m_1gh$$

$$\frac{1}{2}(4 \text{ kg})v^2 + \frac{1}{2}(2 \text{ kg})v^2 + \frac{1}{4}(6 \text{ kg})v^2 = (4 \text{ kg})(9.8 \text{ m/s}^2)(6 \text{ m}) - (2 \text{ kg})(9.8 \text{ m/s}^2)(6 \text{ m})$$

$$2v^2 + v^2 + 1.5\ v^2 = 117.6 \text{ m}^2/\text{s}^2; \quad \boxed{v = 5.11 \text{ m/s}}$$

Chapter 12. Simple Machines

Simple Machines, Efficiency, and Mechanical Advantage

12-1. A 25 percent efficient machine performs external work of 200 J. What input work is required?

$E = \dfrac{Work\,out}{Work\,in}$; $\quad Work\,in = \dfrac{Work\,out}{E} = \dfrac{200\,J}{0.25}$; $\quad \boxed{Work\,in = 800\,J}$

12-2. What is the input work of a 30 percent efficient gasoline engine if during each cycle it performs 400 J of useful work?

$E = \dfrac{Work\,out}{Work\,in}$; $\quad Work\,in = \dfrac{Work\,out}{E} = \dfrac{400\,J}{0.30}$; $\quad \boxed{Work\,in = 1333\,J}$

12-3. A 60-W motor lifts a 2-kg mass to a height of 4 m in 3 s. Compute the output power.

$P = \dfrac{Work}{t} = \dfrac{Fs}{t}$; $\quad P = \dfrac{(2\,kg)(9.8\,m/s^2)(4\,m)}{3\,s}$; $\quad \boxed{P = 26.1\,W}$

12-4. What is the efficiency of the motor in Problem 12-3? What is the rate at which work is done against friction?

$P_{in} = 60\,W$; $\quad E = \dfrac{Power\,out}{Power\,in} = \dfrac{26.1\,W}{60\,W}$; $\quad \boxed{E = 43.5\%}$

$P_{loss} = 60\,W - 26.1\,W$; $\quad \boxed{P_{loss} = 33.9\,W}$

12-5. A 60 percent efficient machine lifts a 10-kg mass at a constant speed of 3 m/s. What is the required input power?

$P_{out} = Fv = mgv = (10\,kg)(9.8\,m/s^2)(3\,m/s)$; $\quad P_{out} = 294\,W$

$P_{in} = \dfrac{P_{out}}{E} = \dfrac{294\,W}{0.60}$; $\quad P_{in} = 490\,W$

12-6. During the operation of a 300-hp engine, energy is lost to friction at the rate of 200 hp. What is the useful output power and what is the efficiency of the engine?

$P_{out} = 300\,hp - 200\,hp = \boxed{100\,hp}$; $\quad E = \dfrac{P_{out}}{P_{in}} = \dfrac{100\,hp}{300\,hp}$; $\quad \boxed{E = 33.3\%}$

12-7. A frictionless machine lifts a 200-lb load through a vertical distance of 10 ft. The input force moves through a distance of 300 ft. What is the ideal mechanical advantage of the machine? What is the magnitude of the input force?

$M_I = \dfrac{s_i}{s_o} = \dfrac{300\,ft}{10\,ft} = \boxed{30}$; $\quad F_I = \dfrac{F_o}{30} = \dfrac{200\,lb}{30} = \boxed{6.67\,lb}$

Applications of the Lever Principle

12-8. One edge of a 50-kg safe is lifted with a 1.2-m steel rod. What input force is required at the end of the rod if a fulcrum is placed 12 cm from the safe? (Hint: To lift one edge, a force equal to one-half the weight of the safe is required.)

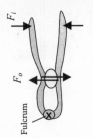
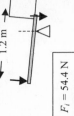

$W = mg = (50\,kg)(9.8\,m/s^2) = 490\,N$; $\quad F = W/2 = 245\,N$

$M_I = \dfrac{r_i}{r_o} = \dfrac{1.08\,m}{0.12\,m} = 9$; $\quad F_I = \dfrac{F_o}{M_I} = \dfrac{490\,N}{9}$; $\quad \boxed{F_i = 54.4\,N}$

12-9. For the nutcracker in Fig. 12-4a, the nut is located 2 cm from the fulcrum and an input force of 20-N is applied at the handles which are 10 cm from the fulcrum. What is the force applied to crack the nut?

$M_I = \dfrac{r_i}{r_o} = \dfrac{10\,cm}{2\,cm} = 5$; $\quad F_o = M_I F_i = 5(20\,N)$; $\quad \boxed{F_o = 100\,N}$

12-10. For the wheelbarrow in Fig. 12-4b, the center of gravity of a net load of 40 kg is located 50 cm from the wheel. What upward lift must be applied at a point on the handles that is 1.4 m from the wheel?

$$M_1 = \frac{r_i}{r_o} = \frac{1.4 \text{ m}}{0.5 \text{ m}} = 2.8; \qquad F_i = \frac{F_o}{M_1}$$

$$F_i = \frac{(40 \text{ kg})(9.8 \text{ m/s}^2)}{2.8}; \qquad \boxed{F_i = 140 \text{ N}}$$

12-11. What is the ideal mechanical advantage of the wheelbarrow in Problem 12-10?

$$M_1 = \frac{r_i}{r_o} = \frac{1.4 \text{ m}}{0.5 \text{ m}} = 2.8; \qquad \boxed{M_i = 2.8}$$

12-12. Find the ideal mechanical advantage of the crowbar in Fig. 12-4c if the input force is applied 30 cm from the nail and the fulcrum is located 2 cm from the nail?

$$M_1 = \frac{r_i}{r_o} = \frac{30 \text{ cm} - 2 \text{ cm}}{2 \text{ cm}} = 14; \qquad \boxed{M_i = 14.0}$$

12-13. The input force exerted by a muscle in the forearm (see Fig. 12-4d) is 120 N and acts a distance of 4 cm from the elbow. The total length of the forearm is 25 cm. What weight is being lifted?

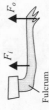

$$M_1 = \frac{r_i}{r_o} = \frac{F_o}{F_i}; \qquad F_o = \frac{r_i F_i}{r_o} = \frac{(4 \text{ cm})(120 \text{ N})}{25 \text{ cm}};$$

$$\boxed{F_o = 19.2 \text{ N}}$$

12-14. A wheel 20 cm in diameter is attached to an axle with a diameter of 6 cm. If a weight of 400 N is attached to the axle, what force must be applied to the rim of the wheel to lift the weight at constant speed? Neglect friction.

$$M_1 = \frac{F_o}{F_i} = \frac{R}{r}; \qquad F_i = \frac{F_o r}{R} = \frac{(400 \text{ N})(3 \text{ cm})}{10 \text{ cm}}$$

$$\boxed{F_i = 120 \text{ N}}$$

12-15. A 20-kg mass is to be lifted with a rod 2 m long. If you can exert a downward force of 40 N on one end of the rod, where should you place a block of wood to act as a fulcrum?

$$M_1 = M_A = \frac{F_o}{F_i} = \frac{(20 \text{ kg})(9.8 \text{ m/s}^2)}{(40 \text{ N})}; \qquad M_1 = 4.9$$

$$M_1 = \frac{r_i}{r_o} = 4.9; \qquad r_i = 4.9 r_o; \qquad r_o + r_i = 2 \text{ m}; \qquad \text{Substitute:} \qquad r_o + (4.9 r_o) = 2 \text{ m}$$

Solving for r_o gives: $\boxed{r_o = 0.339 \text{ m}}$ *The fulcrum should be 33.9 cm from the weight.*

We could also find r_i: $r_i = 4.9(0.339 \text{ m})$ or $r_i = 1.66 \text{ m}$

12-16. Determine the force F required to lift a 200-N load W with the pulley shown in Fig. 12-16a.

$$M_1 = 2; \qquad M_1 = M_A = \frac{F_o}{F_i}; \qquad F_i = \frac{F_o}{M_A} = \frac{200 \text{ N}}{2}; \qquad \boxed{F_i = 100 \text{ N}}$$

12-17. What input force is needed to lift the 200-N load with the arrangement in Fig. 12-16b?

$$M_1 = 4; \qquad M_1 = M_A = \frac{F_o}{F_i}; \qquad F_i = \frac{F_o}{M_A} = \frac{200 \text{ N}}{4}; \qquad \boxed{F_i = 50 \text{ N}}$$

12-18. What input forces are needed to lift the 200-N load for Fig. 12-16c and d?

$$M_1 = 5; \qquad M_1 = M_A = \frac{F_o}{F_i}; \qquad F_i = \frac{F_o}{M_A} = \frac{200 \text{ N}}{5}; \qquad \boxed{F_i = 40 \text{ N}}$$

$$M_1 = 4; \qquad M_1 = M_A = \frac{F_o}{F_i}; \qquad F_i = \frac{F_o}{M_A} = \frac{200 \text{ N}}{4}; \qquad \boxed{F_i = 50 \text{ N}}$$

12-19. What is the mechanical advantage of a screwdriver used as a wheel and axle if its blade is 0.3 in. wide and the handle is 0.8 in?

0.8 in.

0.3 in.

$M_I = \dfrac{0.8 \text{ in.}}{0.3 \text{ in.}}$; $\boxed{M_I = 2.67}$

**12-20. The chain hoist in Fig. 12-17 is a combination of the wheel and axle and the block and tackle. Show that the ideal mechanical advantage of such a device is given by

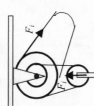

$Work\ out = Work\ in$; $F_i s_i = F_o s_o$

$s_i = 2\pi R$ $s_o = \dfrac{2\pi(R-r)}{2}$ $F_i(2\pi R) = F_o\left[\dfrac{2\pi(R-r)}{2}\right]$

$M_I = \dfrac{F_o}{F_i} = \dfrac{2R}{R-r}$; $\boxed{M_I = \dfrac{2R}{R-r}}$

*12-21. Assume that the larger radius in Fig. 12-17 is three times the smaller radius. What nput force is required to lift a 10-kg load with no friction.

$F_o = mg = (10\text{ kg})(9.8\text{ m/s}^2) = 98.0\text{ N}$; $R = 3r$

$M_I = \dfrac{2R}{R-r} = \dfrac{2(3r)}{3r-r} = 3$; $M_I = \dfrac{F_o}{F_i}$; $F_i = \dfrac{98\text{ N}}{3}$; $\boxed{F_i = 32.7\text{ N}}$

The Transmission of Torque

12-22. A 1500 rpm motor has a drive pulley 3 in. in diameter, and the driven pulley is 9 in. in diameter. Find the ideal mechanical advantage and the rpm for the output pulley.

$M_I = \dfrac{D_o}{D_i} = \dfrac{9\text{ in.}}{3\text{ in.}} = 3$; $M_I = \dfrac{D_o}{D_i} = \dfrac{\omega_i}{\omega_o} = 3$;

$\omega_o = \dfrac{\omega_i}{3} = \dfrac{(1500\text{ rpm})}{3}$ $\boxed{\omega_o = 500\text{ rpm}}$

12-23. A 30 cm diameter input pulley turns at 200 rpm on a belt drive connected to an output pulley 60 cm in diameter. What is the ratio of the output torque to the input torque? What is the output rpm?

$\dfrac{\tau_o}{\tau_i} = \dfrac{D_o}{D_i} = \dfrac{60\text{ cm}}{30\text{ cm}}$; $\boxed{\dfrac{\tau_o}{\tau_i} = 2}$

$M_I = \dfrac{D_o}{D_i} = \dfrac{\omega_i}{\omega_o} = 2$; $\omega_o = \dfrac{\omega_i}{2} = \dfrac{200\text{ rpm}}{2}$; $\boxed{\omega_o = 100\text{ rpm}}$

12-24. A V-belt pulley system has output and input drives of diameters 6 in. and 4 in., respectively. A torque of 200 lb in. is applied to the input drive. Find the output torque?

$\dfrac{\tau_o}{\tau_i} = \dfrac{D_o}{D_i} = \dfrac{6\text{ in.}}{4\text{ in.}}$ $\dfrac{\tau_o}{\tau_i} = 1.5$; $\tau_o = 1.5(200\text{ lb in.})$; $\boxed{\tau_o = 300\text{ lb ft}}$

12-25. The ratio of output speed to input speed for a gear drive is 2 to 1. What is the mechanical advantage?

$M_I = \dfrac{D_o}{D_i} = \dfrac{\omega_i}{\omega_o}$; $\dfrac{\omega_o}{\omega_i} = \dfrac{1}{M_I} = \dfrac{2}{1}$; $\boxed{M_I = \tfrac{1}{2}}$

12-26. A set of two spur gears has 40 teeth and 10 teeth. What are the possible ideal mechanical advantages.

$M_I = \dfrac{D_o}{D_i} = \dfrac{N_o}{N_i}$;   Possible ratios : $\dfrac{40}{10}$ and $\dfrac{10}{40}$

$\boxed{M_I = 4.0 \text{ and } 0.250}$

12-27. For the spur gears in Problem 12-26, what is the rotational speed of the smaller gear, if the speed of the larger gear is 200 rpm?

$\dfrac{D_L}{D_s} = \dfrac{N_L}{N_s} = \dfrac{\omega_s}{\omega_L}$; $\omega_s = \dfrac{N_L \omega_L}{N_s} = \dfrac{40(200\text{ rpm})}{10}$; $\boxed{\omega_s = 800\text{ rpm}}$

Applications of the Inclined Plane

12-28. What must be the thickness of the base, if the wedge is 20 cm long and it is desired that the input force be one-tenth of the output force?

$M_I = \frac{L}{t} = 10$; $t = \frac{L}{10} = \frac{20\ cm}{10}$; $t = 2.00\ cm$

12-29. What should be the apex angle of a wedge if it is to have a mechanical advantage of 10?

$\tan\theta = \frac{t}{L}$; $M_I = \frac{L}{t} = 10$; $\tan\theta = \frac{1}{10}$; $\theta = 5.71^0$

12-30. A 10-kg crate is moved from the ground to a loading platform by means of a ramp 6 m long and 2 m high. Assume that $\mu_k = 0.25$. What are the ideal and actual mechanical advantages of the ramp? [$\sin\theta = 2/6$; $\theta = 19.5^0$]

$M_I = \frac{L}{t} = \frac{6\ m}{2\ m}$; $M_I = 3.00$

$F_o = mg = (10\ kg)(9.8\ m/s^2)$; $F_o = 98.0\ N$

$\mathcal{F}_k = \mu_k \mathcal{N} = \mu_k mg\cos\theta$; $\mathcal{F}_k = (0.25)(98\ N)\cos 19.5^0 = 23.1\ N$

$F_i - \mathcal{F}_k - mg\sin\theta = 0$; $F_i - 23.1\ N - (98\ N)\sin 19.5^0 = 0$; $F_i = 55.77\ N$

$M_A = \frac{F_o}{F_i} = \frac{98.0\ N}{55.77\ N}$; $M_A = 1.76$

12-31. For the ramp in Problem 11-30, what is the efficiency of the ramp?

$E = \frac{M_A}{M_I} = \frac{1.76}{3}$; $E = 0.586$; $E = 58.6\%$

---

*12-32. An input force of 20 lb is applied to the 6-in. handle of a wrench. used to tighten a ¼ in.-diameter bolt? An actual output force of 600 lb is produced. If the bolt has 10 threads per inch, what is the ideal mechanical advantage., and what is the efficiency?

$P = 1/10$ in/thread $= 0.167$ in.; $M_I = \frac{2\pi R}{P} = \frac{2\pi(6\ in.)}{0.1\ in.} = 377$; $M_I = 377$

$M_A = \frac{F_o}{F_i} = \frac{600\ lb}{20\ lb} = 30$; $E = \frac{M_A}{M_I} = \frac{30}{377}$; $E = 8.00\%$

12-33. The lever of a screw jack is 24 in. long. The screw has six threads per inch. What is the ideal mechanical advantage?

$P = 1/6$ in/thread $= 0.167$ in.; $M_I = \frac{2\pi R}{P} = \frac{2\pi(24\ in.)}{0.167\ in.} = 904$; $M_I = 904$

12-34. If the screw jack in Problem 11-33 is 15 percent efficient, what force is needed to lift 2000-lb?

$M_A = E\,M_A = (0.15)(904) = 136$;

$M_A = \frac{F_o}{F_i} = 136$; $F_i = \frac{2000\ lb}{136}$; $F_i = 14.7\ lb$

Supplementary Problems

*12-35. An inclined plane is 6 m long and 1 m high. The coefficient of kinetic friction is 0.2. What force is required to pull a weight of 2400 N up the incline at constant speed? What is the efficiency of the inclined plane? [$\sin\theta = 1/6$; $\theta = 9.59^0$]

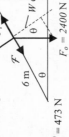

$M_I = \frac{L}{t} = \frac{6\ m}{1\ m}$; $M_I = 6.00$; $F_o = 2400\ N$

$\mathcal{F}_k = \mu_k \mathcal{N} = \mu_k W\cos\theta$; $\mathcal{F}_k = (0.2)(2400\ N)\cos 9.59^0 = 473\ N$

$F_i - \mathcal{F}_k - mg\sin\theta = 0$; $F_i - 473\ N - (2400\ N)\sin 9.59^0 = 0$; $F_i = 873\ N$

$M_A = \frac{F_o}{F_i} = \frac{98.0\ N}{55.77\ N}$; $M_A = 1.76$ $E = \frac{M_A}{M_T} = \frac{1.76}{6} = 29.3\%$

*12-36. A wheel and axle is used to raise a mass of 700-kg. The radius of the wheel is 0.50 m, and the radius of the axle is 0.04 m. If the actual efficiency is 60%, what input force must be applied to the wheel?

$F_o = W = mg = (700 \text{ kg})(9.8 \text{ m/s}^2)$; $F_o = 6860 \text{ N}$; $E_A = 0.60$; $R = 0.50 \text{ m}$

$M_I = \dfrac{R}{r} = \dfrac{0.5}{0.04} = 12.5$; $E = \dfrac{M_A}{M_I} = 0.60$; $M_A = 0.60(12.5) = 7.5$

$M_A = \dfrac{F_o}{F_i} = 7.5$; $F_i = \dfrac{6860 \text{ N}}{7.5}$; $\boxed{F_i = 915 \text{ N}}$

*12-37. A shaft rotating at 800 rpm delivers a torque of 240 N m to an output shaft that is rotating at 200 rpm. If the efficiency of the machine is 70%, compute the output torque.

What is the output power? [$\omega_o = 200 \text{ rpm} = 20.94 \text{ rad/s}$]

$E = \dfrac{\tau_o \omega_o}{\tau_i \omega_i} = 0.70$; $\tau_o = \dfrac{0.70(240 \text{ N m})(800 \text{ rpm})}{200 \text{ rpm}}$; $\boxed{\tau_o = 672 \text{ N m}}$

$P_o = \tau_o \omega_o = (672 \text{ N m})(20.94 \text{ rad/s})$; $\boxed{P_o = 14.1 \text{ kW}}$

*12-38. A screw jack has a screw whose pitch is 0.25 in. Its handle is 16 in. long, and a load of 1.9 tons is being lifted. Neglecting friction, what force is required at the end of the handle? What is the mechanical advantage?

$M_I = \dfrac{2\pi R}{P} = \dfrac{2\pi(16 \text{ in.})}{0.25 \text{ in.}}$; $M_I = 402$

Neglecting friction: $M_A = M_I = \dfrac{F_o}{F_i}$; $F_i = \dfrac{1.9 \text{ ton}(2000 \text{ lb/ton})}{402}$; $\boxed{F_i = 9.45 \text{ lb}}$

In absence of friction, $M_A = M_I = 402$; $\boxed{M_A = 402}$

---

*12-39. A certain refrigeration compressor comes equipped with a 250-mm-diameter pulley and is designed to operate at 600 rpm. What should be the diameter of the motor pulley if the motor speed is 2000 rpm?

$M_I = \dfrac{D_o}{D_i} = \dfrac{\omega_i}{\omega_o}$; $D_i = \dfrac{\omega_o D_o}{\omega_i} = \dfrac{(600 \text{ rpm})(250 \text{ mm})}{2000 \text{ rpm}}$; $\boxed{D_i = 75.0 \text{ mm}}$

*12-40. In a fan belt, the driving wheel is 20 cm in diameter and the driven wheel is 50 cm in diameter. The power input comes from a 4-kW motor that causes the driving wheel to rotate at 300 rpm. If the efficiency is 80 percent, calculate the rpm and the torque delivered to the driven wheel. [300 rpm = 31.4 rad/s]

$M_I = \dfrac{D_o}{D_i} = \dfrac{50 \text{ cm}}{20 \text{ cm}} = 2.5$; $M_A = EM_I = 0.8(2.5) = 2$

$P_i = \tau_i \omega_i$; $\tau_i = \dfrac{P_i}{\omega_i} = \dfrac{4000 \text{ W}}{31.4 \text{ rad/s}} = 127.3 \text{ N m}$

$\tau_o = M_A \tau_i = 2(127.3 \text{ N m})$; $\boxed{\tau_o = 255 \text{ N m}}$

$\omega_o = \dfrac{D_i \omega_i}{D_o} = \dfrac{(20 \text{ cm})(300 \text{ rpm})}{50 \text{ cm}}$; $\boxed{\omega_o = 120 \text{ rpm}}$

12-41. A log-splitting wedge has a side length of 16 cm and the angle at the apex is 10°. What is the ideal mechanical advantage?

$t = L \sin \theta = (16 \text{ cm}) \sin 10^0 = 2.78 \text{ cm}$; $M_I = \dfrac{L}{t} = \dfrac{16 \text{ cm}}{2.78 \text{ cm}}$; $\boxed{M_I = 5.76}$

12-42. A machine has an efficiency of 72 percent. An input force of 500 N moves through parallel distance of 40 cm. How much energy is lost in the process.

$Work\ in = (500 \text{ N})(0.40 \text{ m}) = 200 \text{ J}$; $Work\ out = 0.72(200 \text{ J}) = 144 \text{ J}$

$Energy\ Lost = Work\ in - Work\ out = 200 \text{ J} - 144 \text{ J}$; $\boxed{Loss = 56.0 \text{ J}}$

*12-43. A motor with an efficiency of 80 percent operates a winch with an efficiency of 50 percent. If the power supplied to the motor is 6 kW, how far will the winch lift a 400-kg mass in a time of 4 s?

$E_T = (0.80)(0.50) = 0.40$; Work in = (6000 W)(4 s) = 24,000 J

Work out = 0.40(24,000 J) = 9600 J; Work out = $F_o s_o$

$s_o = \dfrac{Work\ out}{F_o} = \dfrac{9600\ J}{(400\ kg)(9.8\ m/s^2)}$; $\boxed{s_o = 2.45\ m}$

Critical Thinking Questions

12-44. A 60-N weight is lifted in the three different ways shown in Fig. 12-18. Compute the ideal mechanical advantage and the required input force for each application.

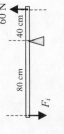
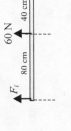
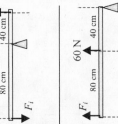

$M_I = \dfrac{r_i}{r_o} = \dfrac{80\ cm}{40\ cm}$ $\boxed{M_I = 2.00}$

$F_i = \dfrac{F_o}{M_I} = \dfrac{60\ N}{2.0}$; $\boxed{F_i = 30\ N}$

$M_I = \dfrac{r_i}{r_o} = \dfrac{120\ cm}{40\ cm}$ $\boxed{M_I = 3.00}$

$F_i = \dfrac{F_o}{M_I} = \dfrac{60\ N}{3.0}$; $\boxed{F_i = 20\ N}$

$M_I = \dfrac{r_i}{r_o} = \dfrac{40\ cm}{120\ cm}$ $\boxed{M_I = 0.333}$

$F_i = \dfrac{F_o}{M_I} = \dfrac{60\ N}{0.333}$; $\boxed{F_i = 180\ N}$

The above are examples of the three classes of levers. Note the advantages and disadvantages of each type of lever in terms of the mechanical advantage and the required input forces.

*12-45. A worm drive similar to that shown in Fig. 12-11 has n teeth in the gear wheel. (If n = 80, one complete turn of the worm will advance the wheel one-eightieth of a revolution.) Derive an expression for the ideal mechanical advantage of the worm gear in terms of the radius of the input pulley R, the radius of the output shaft r, and the number of teeth n in the gear wheel.

Work in = Work out; $F_i s_i = F_o s_o$; $s_i = 2\pi R$, $s_o = \dfrac{2\pi r}{n}$

$F_i(2\pi R) = F_o\left(\dfrac{2\pi r}{n}\right)$; $M_I = \dfrac{F_o}{F_i} = \dfrac{nR}{r}$; $\boxed{M_I = \dfrac{nR}{r}}$

*12-46. The worm drive of previous problem has 80 teeth in the gear wheel. If the radius of the input wheel is 30 cm and the radius of the output shaft is 5 cm, what input force is required to lift a 1200-kg load? Assume an efficiency of 80%.

$M_I = \dfrac{nR}{r} = \dfrac{(80)(30\ cm)}{5\ cm} = 480$; $M_A = EM_I = (0.8)(480) = 384$

$F_i = \dfrac{(1200\ kg)(9.8\ m/s^2)}{384}$; $\boxed{F_i = 30.6\ N}$

*12-47. The oarlock on a 3.5 m oar is 1 m from the handle end. A person in a rowboat applies a force of 50 N to the handle end. What is the ideal mechanical advantage and output force? Does moving the oarlock closer to the handle end increase or decrease the mechanical advantage? How far from the handle end should the oarlock be placed to produce a 20% increase in the output force?

$M_I = \dfrac{r_i}{r_o} = \dfrac{1\ m}{2.5\ m}$ $\boxed{M_I = 0.400}$

Moving oarlock closer to hands produces a smaller mechanical advantage: $\boxed{Smaller}$

12-47. (Cont.) A 20% increase in F_o means the new mechanical advantage is $1.2M_A$.

$$M'_A = 1.2(0.40) = 0.48;$$

$$\frac{r_i}{r_o} = 0.48; \quad r_i = 0.48 r_o = 0.48(3.5 \text{ m} - r_i); \quad r_i = 1.68 - 0.48 r_i$$

$\boxed{r_i = 1.14 \text{ m}}$ The oarlock should be placed 1.14 m from the hand.

*12-48. Sketch a block and tackle system with a mechanical advantage of 5.

The system drawn to the right has five lifting ropes pulling the weight upward, and thus has a mechanical advantage of 5.

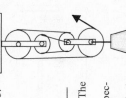

*12-49. A 60-W motor drives the input pulley of a belt drive at 150 rpm. The diameters of the input and output pulleys are 60 cm and 20 cm, respectively. Assume an actual mechanical advantage of 0.25. (a) What is the output torque? (b) What is the output power? (c) What is the efficiency?

$$M_i = \frac{D_o}{D_i} = \frac{20 \text{ cm}}{60 \text{ cm}} = 0.333 \quad \omega_o = \frac{D_i \omega_i}{D_o} = \frac{(60 \text{ cm})(150 \text{ rpm})}{20 \text{ cm}} \quad \omega_o = 450 \text{ rpm}$$

$$E = \frac{M_A}{M_i} = \frac{0.25}{0.333}; \quad \boxed{E = 0.750 \text{ or } 75.0\%}$$

$$P_o = 0.75 P_i = 0.75(60 \text{ W}) = 45 \text{ W}; \quad \boxed{P_o = 45 \text{ W}}$$

$$\tau_o \omega_o = 45 \text{ W}; \quad \omega_o = 450 \text{ rpm} = 47.1 \text{ rad/s}; \quad \tau_o = \frac{45 \text{ W}}{47.1 \text{ rad/s}}; \quad \boxed{\tau_o = 0.955 \text{ N m}}$$

*12-50. A pair of step pulleys (Fig. 12-19) makes it possible to change output speeds merely by shifting the belt. If an electric motor turns the input pulley at 2000 rpm, find the possible angular speeds of the output shaft. The pulley diameters are 4, 6, and 8 cm.

---

*12-50. (Cont.) First consider the 4-in. pulley, which can drive 4-in., 6 in.., and 8-in. output pulley. Case 1 has $d_i = 4$ in. and $d_o = 4$ in.

(a) $\omega_o d_o = \omega_i d_i$ $\omega_o = \left(\dfrac{d_i}{d_o}\right)\omega_i$ $\omega_i = 2000$ rpm

$$\omega_o = \left(\frac{4 \text{ in.}}{4 \text{ in.}}\right)(2000 \text{ rpm}); \quad \omega_o = 2000 \text{ rpm}$$

$$\omega_o = \left(\frac{4 \text{ in.}}{6 \text{ in.}}\right)(2000 \text{ rpm}); \quad \omega_o = 1333 \text{ rpm}$$

$$\omega_o = \left(\frac{4 \text{ in.}}{8 \text{ in.}}\right)(2000 \text{ rpm}); \quad \omega_o = 1000 \text{ rpm}$$

(b) Next we consider the 6-in. pulley as the input pulley

$$\omega_o = \left(\frac{6 \text{ in.}}{4 \text{ in.}}\right)(2000 \text{ rpm}); \quad \omega_o = 3000 \text{ rpm}$$

$$\omega_o = \left(\frac{6 \text{ in.}}{6 \text{ in.}}\right)(2000 \text{ rpm}); \quad \omega_o = 2000 \text{ rpm}$$

$$\omega_o = \left(\frac{6 \text{ in.}}{8 \text{ in.}}\right)(2000 \text{ rpm}); \quad \omega_o = 1500 \text{ rpm}$$

(c) Next we consider the 8-in. pulley as the input pulley

$$\omega_o = \left(\frac{8 \text{ in.}}{4 \text{ in.}}\right)(2000 \text{ rpm}); \quad \omega_o = 4000 \text{ rpm}$$

$$\omega_o = \left(\frac{8 \text{ in.}}{6 \text{ in.}}\right)(2000 \text{ rpm}); \quad \omega_o = 2667 \text{ rpm}$$

$$\omega_o = \left(\frac{8 \text{ in.}}{8 \text{ in.}}\right)(2000 \text{ rpm}); \quad \omega_o = 2000 \text{ rpm}$$

Chapter 13. Elasticity

Elastic Properties of Matter

13-1. When a mass of 500 g is hung from a spring, the spring stretches 3 cm. What is the spring constant? [$m = 0.500$ kg; $x = 0.03$ m, $F = W = mg$]

$$F = -kx; \quad k = \frac{F}{x} = \frac{(0.50 \text{ kg})(9.8 \text{ m/s}^2)}{0.03 \text{ m}}; \quad \boxed{k = 163 \text{ N/m}}$$

13-2. What will be the increase in stretch for the spring of Problem 13-1 if an additional 500-g mass is hung blow the first? [$F = W = mg$]

$$\Delta x = \frac{\Delta F}{k} = \frac{(0.500 \text{ kg})(9.8 \text{ m/s}^2)}{163 \text{ N/m}}; \quad \boxed{\Delta x = 3.00 \text{ cm}}$$

13-3. The spring constant for a certain spring is found to be 3000 N/m. What force is required to compress the spring for a distance of 5 cm?

$$F = kx = (3000 \text{ N/m})(0.05 \text{ m}); \quad \boxed{F = 150 \text{ N}}$$

13-4. A 6-in. spring has a 4-lb weight hung from one end, causing the new length to be 6.5 in. What is the spring constant? What is the strain? [$\Delta x = 6.5 \text{ in.} - 6.0 \text{ in.} = 0.50 \text{ in.}$]

$$k = \frac{F}{x} = \frac{(4 \text{ lb})}{0.5 \text{ in.}}; \quad \boxed{k = 8.00 \text{ lb/in.}}$$

$$Strain = \frac{\Delta L}{L} = \frac{0.50 \text{ in.}}{6.00 \text{ in.}}; \quad \boxed{Strain = 0.0833}$$

13-5. A coil spring 12 cm long is used to support a 1.8-kg mass producing a strain of 0.10. How far did the spring stretch? What is the spring constant?

$$Strain = \frac{\Delta L}{L}; \quad \Delta L = L_o (strain) = (12.0 \text{ cm})(0.10); \quad \Delta L = 1.20 \text{ cm}$$

$$k = \frac{\Delta F}{\Delta L} = \frac{(1.8 \text{ kg})(9.8 \text{ m/s}^2)}{0.0120 \text{ m}}; \quad \boxed{k = 1470 \text{ N/m}}$$

13-6. For the coil of Problem 13-5, what total mass should be hung if an elongation of 4 cm is desired?

$$F = mg = kx; \quad m = \frac{kx}{g} = \frac{(1470 \text{ N/m})(0.04 \text{ m})}{9.80 \text{ m/s}^2}; \quad \boxed{m = 6.00 \text{ kg}}$$

Young's Modulus

13-7. A 60-kg weight is suspended by means of a cable having a diameter of 9 mm. What is the stress? [$F = mg = (60 \text{ kg})(9.8 \text{ m/s}^2);$ $F = 588 \text{ N};$ $D = 0.009 \text{ m}$]

$$A = \frac{\pi D^2}{4} = \frac{\pi (0.009 \text{ m})^2}{4} = 6.36 \times 10^{-5} \text{ m}^2;$$

$$Stress = \frac{F}{A} = \frac{588 \text{ N}}{0.00707 \text{ m}^2}; \quad \boxed{Stress = 9.24 \times 10^6 \text{ Pa}}$$

13-8. A 50-cm length of wire is stretched to a new length of 50.01 cm. What is the strain?

$$\Delta L = 50.01 - 50 \text{ cm}; \quad Strain = \frac{\Delta L}{L} = \frac{0.01 \text{ cm}}{50 \text{ cm}}; \quad \boxed{Strain = 2.00 \times 10^{-4}}$$

13-9. A 12-m rod receives a compressional strain of -0.0004. What is the new length of the rod?

$$Strain = \frac{\Delta L}{L}; \quad \Delta L = L_o (strain) = (12.0 \text{ m})(-0.0004); \quad \Delta L = -0.00480 \text{ m}$$

$$L = L_o + \Delta L = 12.000 \text{ m} - 0.00480 \text{ m}; \quad \boxed{L = 11.995 \text{ m}}$$

13-10. Young's modulus for a certain rod is 4×10^{11} Pa. What strain will be produced by a tensile stress of 420 Mpa?

$$Y = \frac{Stress}{Strain}; \quad Strain = \frac{Stress}{Y} = \frac{420 \times 10^6 \text{ Pa}}{4 \times 10^{11} \text{ Pa}}$$

$$\boxed{Strain = 1.05 \times 10^{-3}}$$

13-11. A 500-kg mass is hung from the end of a 2-m length of metal wire 1 mm in diameter. If the wire stretches by 1.40 cm, what are the stress and strain? What is Young's modulus for this metal? [$F = mg = (500 \text{ kg})(9.8 \text{ m/s}^2)$; $F = 4900$ N; $D = 0.001$ m; $\Delta L = 0.014$ m]

$$A = \frac{\pi D^2}{4} = \frac{\pi (0.001 \text{ m})^2}{4} = 7.85 \times 10^{-7} \text{ m}^2$$

$$Stress = \frac{F}{A} = \frac{4900 \text{ N}}{7.85 \times 10^{-7} \text{ m}^2}; \quad \boxed{Stress = 6.24 \times 10^9 \text{ Pa}}$$

$$Strain = \frac{\Delta L}{L_0} = \frac{0.014 \text{ m}}{2.00 \text{ m}}; \quad \boxed{Strain = 7.00 \times 10^{-3}}$$

$$Y = \frac{Stress}{Strain} = \frac{6.24 \times 10^9 \text{ Pa}}{7 \times 10^{-3}}; \quad \boxed{Y = 8.91 \times 10^{11} \text{ Pa}}$$

13-12. A 16 ft steel girder with a cross-sectional area of 10 in.² supports a compressional load of 20 tons. What is the decrease in length of the girder? [$Y = 30 \times 10^6$ Pa; 1 ton = 2000 lb]

$$Y = \frac{FL}{A\Delta L}; \quad \Delta L = \frac{FL}{YA} = \frac{(-40{,}000 \text{ lb})(16 \text{ ft})(12 \text{ in/ft})}{(30 \times 10^6 \text{ lb/in.}^2)(10 \text{ in.}^2)}; \quad \boxed{\Delta L = -0.0256 \text{ in.}}$$

13-13. How much will a 60 cm length of brass wire, 1.2 mm in diameter, elongate when a 3-kg mass is hung from an end? [$Y = 89.6 \times 10^9$ Pa; $D = 0.0012$ m; $L_o = 0.60$ m; $m = 3$ kg]

$$A = \frac{\pi D^2}{4} = \frac{\pi (0.0012 \text{ m})^2}{4} = 1.13 \times 10^{-6} \text{ m}^2;$$

$$F = (3 \text{ kg})(9.8 \text{ m/s}^2) = 29.4 \text{ N}; \quad Y = \frac{FL}{A\Delta L};$$

$$\Delta L = \frac{FL}{YA} = \frac{(29.4 \text{ N})(0.60 \text{ m})}{(89.6 \times 10^9)(1.13 \times 10^{-6} \text{ m}^2)}; \quad \boxed{\Delta L = 1.74 \times 10^{-4} \text{ m}}$$

*13-14. A wire of cross-section 4 mm² is stretched 0.1 mm by a certain weight. How far will a wire of the same material and length stretch if its cross-sectional area is 8 mm² and the same weight is attached?

$$Y = \frac{FL}{A_1 \Delta L_1} = \frac{FL}{A_2 \Delta L_2}; \quad A_1 \Delta L_1 = A_2 \Delta L_2$$

$$\Delta L_2 = \frac{A_1 \Delta L_1}{A_2} = \frac{(4 \text{ mm}^2)(0.10 \text{ mm})}{(8 \text{ mm}^2)}; \quad \boxed{\Delta L_2 = 0.0500 \text{ mm}}$$

13-15. A wire 15 ft long and 0.1 in.² in cross-section is found to increase its length by 0.01 ft under a tension of 2000 lb. What is Young's modulus for this wire? Can you identify the material?

$$Y = \frac{FL}{A\Delta L} = \frac{(2000 \text{ lb})(15 \text{ ft})}{(0.10 \text{ in.}^2)(0.01 \text{ ft})}; \quad \boxed{Y = 30 \times 10^6 \text{ lb/in.}^2, \; steel}$$

Shear Modulus

13-16. A shearing force of 40,000 N is applied to the top of a cube that is 30 cm on a side. What is the shearing stress? [$A = (0.30 \text{ m})(0.30 \text{ m}) = 0.09 \text{ m}^2$]

$$Stress = \frac{F}{A} = \frac{40{,}000 \text{ N}}{0.09 \text{ m}^2}; \quad \boxed{Stress = 4.44 \times 10^5 \text{ Pa}}$$

13-17. If the cube in Problem 13-16 is made of copper, what will be the lateral displacement of the upper surface of the cube?

$$S = \frac{F/A}{\phi}; \quad \phi = \frac{F/A}{S} = \frac{4.44 \times 10^5 \text{Pa}}{42.3 \times 10^9 \text{Pa}}; \quad \phi = 1.05 \times 10^{-5} \text{ rad}$$

$$\phi = \frac{d}{l}; \quad d = l\phi = (0.30 \text{ m})(1.05 \times 10^{-5} \text{ rad}); \quad \boxed{d = 3.15 \text{ μm}}$$

13-18. A shearing force of 26,000 N is distributed uniformly over the cross-section of a pin 1.3 cm in diameter. What is the shearing stress. [$A = \pi D^2/4$]

$$A = \frac{\pi D^2}{4} = \frac{\pi(0.0130 \text{ m})^2}{4} = 1.33 \times 10^{-4} \text{ m}^2 ;$$

$$Stress = \frac{F}{A} = \frac{26,000 \text{ N}}{1.33 \times 10^{-4} \text{ m}^2} ; \quad \boxed{Stress = 1.96 \times 10^8 \text{ Pa}}$$

13-19. An aluminum rod 20 mm in diameter projects 4.0 cm from the wall. The end of the bolt is subjected to a shearing force of 48,000 N. Compute the downward deflection.

$$A = \frac{\pi D^2}{4} = \frac{\pi(0.020 \text{ m})^2}{4} = 3.14 \times 10^{-4} \text{ m}^2 ; \quad l = 0.04 \text{ m}; \quad F = 48000 \text{ N}$$

$$S = \frac{F/A}{\phi} = \frac{F/A}{d/l} = \frac{Fl}{Ad}; \quad d = \frac{Fl}{SA}$$

$$d = \frac{(48,000 \text{ N})(0.04 \text{ m})}{(23.7 \times 10^9 \text{ Pa})(3.14 \times 10^{-4} \text{ m}^2)}; \quad \boxed{d = 2.58 \times 10^{-4} \text{ m}}$$

13-20. A steel rod projects 1.0 in. above a floor and is 0.5 in. in diameter. The shearing force F is 6000 lb and the shear modulus is 11.6×10^6 lb/in.². What is the shearing stress and what is horizontal deflection?

$$A = \frac{\pi D^2}{4} = \frac{\pi(0.50 \text{ in.})^2}{4} = 0.196 \text{ in.}^2; \quad l = 1.0 \text{ in.}; \quad F = 6000 \text{ lb}$$

$$Stress = \frac{F}{A} = \frac{6,000 \text{ lb}}{0.196 \text{ in.}^2}; \quad \boxed{Stress = 3.06 \times 10^4 \text{ lb/in.}^2}$$

$$d = \frac{Fl}{SA} = \frac{(6000 \text{ lb})(1.0 \text{ in.})}{(30 \times 10^6 \text{lb/in.}^2)(0.196 \text{ in.}^2)}; \quad \boxed{d = 1.02 \times 10^{-3} \text{ in.}}$$

13-21. A 1500-kg load is supported at the end of a 5-m aluminum beam as shown in Fig. 13-9. The beam has a cross-sectional area of 26 cm² and the shear modulus is 23,700 MPa.

What is the shearing stress and the downward deflection of the beam?

$$A = 26 \text{ cm}^2 (10^{-4} \text{ m}^2/\text{cm}^2) = 2.60 \times 10^{-3} \text{ m}^2; \quad S = 23.7 \times 10^9 \text{ Pa}; \quad l = 5 \text{ m}$$

$$Stress = \frac{F}{A} = \frac{(1500 \text{ kg})(9.8 \text{ m/s}^2)}{2.60 \times 10^{-3} \text{ m}^2}; \quad \boxed{Stress = 5.65 \times 10^6 \text{ Pa}}$$

$$S = \frac{F/A}{\phi}; \quad \phi = \frac{F/A}{S} = \frac{5.65 \times 10^6 \text{Pa}}{23.7 \times 10^9 \text{Pa}} \quad \phi = 2.39 \times 10^{-4} \text{ rad}$$

$$\phi = \frac{d}{l}; \quad d = l\phi = (5.0 \text{ m})(2.39 \times 10^{-4} \text{rad}) ; \quad \boxed{d = 1.19 \text{ mm}}$$

13-22. A steel plate 0.5 in. thick has an ultimate shearing strength of 50,000 lb/in.². What force must be applied to punch a ¼-in. hole through the plate?

$$A = \frac{\pi D^2}{4} = \frac{\pi(0.25 \text{ in.})^2}{4} = 0.0491 \text{ in.}^2; \quad Stress = \frac{F}{A} = 50,000 \text{ lb/in.}^2$$

$$F = (50,000 \text{ lb/in.}^2)(0.0491 \text{ in.}^2); \quad \boxed{F = 2454 \text{ lb}}$$

Bulk Modulus

13-23. A pressure of 3×10^8 Pa is applied to a block of volume 0.500 m³. If the volume decreases by 0.004 m³, what is the bulk modulus? What is the compressibility?

$$B = \frac{-P}{\Delta V/V} = \frac{-(3 \times 10^8 \text{Pa})}{-0.004 \text{ m}^3/0.500 \text{ m}^3}; \quad \boxed{B = 37.5 \times 10^9 \text{ Pa}}$$

$$k = \frac{1}{B} = \frac{1}{37.5 \times 10^9 \text{Pa}}; \quad \boxed{k = 2.67 \times 10^{-11} \text{ Pa}^{-1}}$$

*13-24. The bulk modulus for a certain grade of oil is 2.8 x 10¹⁰ Pa. What pressure is required to decrease its volume by a factor of 1.2 percent? [$\Delta V/V = -1.2\% = -0.012$]

$$B = \frac{-P}{\Delta V/V}; \quad -P = B\left(\frac{\Delta V}{V}\right) = 2.8 \times 10^{10}\text{Pa}(-0.012); \quad \boxed{P = 3.36 \times 10^8 \text{ Pa}}$$

*13-25. A solid brass sphere (B = 35,000 MPa) of volume 0.8 m³ is dropped into the ocean to a depth where the water pressure is 20 Mpa greater than it is at the surface. What is the change in volume of the sphere? [$P = 20 \times 10^6$ Pa]

$$B = \frac{-P}{\Delta V/V}; \quad \Delta V = \frac{-PV}{B} = \frac{-(20 \times 10^6 \text{Pa})(0.8 \text{ m}^3)}{35 \times 10^9 \text{Pa}}; \quad \boxed{\Delta V = -4.57 \times 10^{-4} \text{ m}^3.}$$

13-26. A certain fluid compresses 0.40 percent under a pressure of 6 MPa. What is the compressibility of this fluid? [$\Delta V/V = 0.04\% = 0.0004$]

$$k = \frac{\Delta V/V}{-P} = \frac{-0.0004}{-6 \times 10^6 \text{Pa}}; \quad \boxed{k = 6.67 \times 10^{-11} \text{ Pa}^{-1}}$$

13-27. What is the fractional decrease in the volume of water when it is subjected to a pressure of 15 MPa?

$$B = \frac{-P}{\Delta V/V}; \quad \frac{\Delta V}{V} = \frac{-P}{B} = \frac{-(15 \times 10^6 \text{Pa})}{2.10 \times 10^9 \text{Pa}}; \quad \boxed{\Delta V/V = -7.14 \times 10^{-3}}$$

Supplementary Problems

13-28. A 10-m steel wire, 2.5 mm in diameter, stretches a distance of 0.56 mm when a load is attached to its end. What was the mass of the load?

$$A = \frac{\pi D^2}{4} = \frac{\pi (0.0025 \text{ m})^2}{4} = 4.91 \times 10^{-6} \text{ m}^2; \quad F = mg; \quad Y = \frac{FL}{A\Delta L} = \frac{mgL}{A\Delta L};$$

182 Unit A   Solutions Manual

Copyright © by Glencoe/McGraw-Hill.

13-28. (Cont.)
$$m = \frac{YA\Delta L}{gL} = \frac{(207 \times 10^9 \text{Pa})(4.91 \times 10^{-6}\text{m})(0.00056 \text{ m})}{(9.8 \text{ m/s}^2)(10 \text{ m})}; \quad \boxed{m = 5.81 \text{ kg}}$$

13-29. A shearing force of 3000 N is applied to the upper surface of a copper cube 40 mm on a side. If S = 4.2 x 10¹⁰ Pa, what is the shearing angle? [A = (0.04 m)² = 1.6 x 10⁻³ m².]

$$S = \frac{F/A}{\phi}; \quad \phi = \frac{F}{AS} = \frac{3000 \text{ N}}{(1.6 \times 10^{-3} \text{ m}^2)(4.2 \times 10^{10}\text{Pa})}; \quad \boxed{\phi = 4.46 \times 10^{-5} \text{ rad}}$$

13-30. A solid cylindrical steel column is 6 m long and 8 cm in diameter. What is the decrease in length if the column supports a 90,000-kg load?

$$A = \frac{\pi D^2}{4} = \frac{\pi (0.08 \text{ m})^2}{4} = 5.03 \times 10^{-3} \text{ m}^2; \quad F = W = mg; \quad L = 6.00 \text{ m}$$

$$F = (90,000 \text{ kg})(9.8 \text{ m/s}^2) = 8.82 \times 10^5 \text{ N}; \quad Y = \frac{FL}{A\Delta L};$$

$$\Delta L = \frac{FL}{YA} = \frac{(8.82 \times 10^5 \text{N})(6.0 \text{ m})}{(207 \times 10^9)(5.03 \times 10^{-3} \text{ m}^2)}; \quad \boxed{\Delta L = -5.08 \times 10^{-3} \text{ m}}$$

13-31. A piston, 8 cm in diameter, exerts a force of 2000 N on 1 liter of benzene. What is the decrease in volume of the benzene?

$$A = \frac{\pi D^2}{4} = \frac{\pi (0.08 \text{ m})^2}{4} = 5.03 \times 10^{-3} \text{ m}^2; \quad P = \frac{F}{A} = \frac{2000 \text{ N}}{5.03 \times 10^{-3}\text{ m}^2} = 3.98 \times 10^5 \text{Pa}$$

$$B = \frac{-P}{\Delta V/V}; \quad \Delta V = \frac{-PV}{B} = \frac{-(3.98 \times 10^5 \text{Pa})(0.001 \text{ m}^3)}{1.05 \times 10^9 \text{Pa}}; \quad \boxed{\Delta V = -3.79 \times 10^{-7} \text{ m}^3}$$

13-32. How much will a 600-mm length of brass wire, 1.2 mm in diameter, stretch when a 4-kg mass is hung from its end?

$$A = \frac{\pi D^2}{4} = \frac{\pi (0.0012 \text{ m})^2}{4} = 1.13 \times 10^{-6} \text{ m}^2; \quad F = (4 \text{ kg})(9.8 \text{ m/s}^2) = 39.2 \text{ N}$$

Chapter 13   Elasticity   **183**

Copyright © by Glencoe/McGraw-Hill.

13-32. (Cont.) $\Delta L = \dfrac{FL}{YA} = \dfrac{(39.2 \text{ N})(0.60 \text{ m})}{(89.6 \times 10^9)(1.13 \times 10^{-6}\text{ m}^2)}$; $\boxed{\Delta L = 2.32 \times 10^{-4} \text{ m}}$

13-33. A solid cylindrical steel column is 12 feet tall and 6 in. in diameter. What load does it support if its decrease in length is -0.0255 in.?

$A = \dfrac{\pi D^2}{4} = \dfrac{\pi(6 \text{ in.})^2}{4} = 28.3 \text{ in.}^2$; $Y = \dfrac{FL}{A\Delta L}$; $L = 12 \text{ ft} = 144 \text{ in.}$

$F = \dfrac{YA\Delta L}{L} = \dfrac{(30 \times 10^6 \text{lb/in.}^2)(28.3 \text{ in.}^2)(0.0255 \text{ in.})}{(144 \text{ in.})}$; $\boxed{F = 1.50 \times 10^5 \text{ lb}}$

13-34. Compute the volume contraction of mercury if its original volume of 1600 cm³ is subjected to a pressure of 400,000 Pa. [1600 cm³ = 1.6 × 10⁻³ m³]

$B = \dfrac{-P}{\Delta V / V}$; $\Delta V = \dfrac{-PV}{B} = \dfrac{-(400,000 \text{ Pa})(1.6 \times 10^{-3}\text{ m}^3)}{27.0 \times 10^9 \text{Pa}}$; $\boxed{\Delta V = -2.37 \times 10^{-8}\text{ m}^3}$.

13-35. What is the minimum diameter of a brass rod if it is to undergo a 400 N tension without exceeding the elastic limit? [Elastic limit = 379 × 10⁶ Pa]

$\dfrac{F}{A} = 379 \times 10^6 \text{Pa}$; $A = \dfrac{\pi D^2}{4} = \dfrac{F}{379 \times 10^6 \text{Pa}}$; $D^2 = \dfrac{4F}{\pi(379 \times 10^6 \text{Pa})}$

$D^2 = \dfrac{4(400 \text{ N})}{\pi(379 \times 10^6 \text{Pa})} = 1.34 \times 10^{-6}\text{ m}^2$; $\boxed{D = 1.16 \text{ mm}}$

13-36. A cubical metal block 40 cm on a side is given a shearing force of 400,000 N at the top edge. What is the shear modulus if the upper edge deflects a distance of 0.0143 mm.

$\phi = \dfrac{d}{l} = \dfrac{0.0143 \text{ mm}}{400 \text{ mm}} = 3.575 \times 10^{-5}$; $A = (0.40 \text{ m})^2 = 0.160 \text{ m}^2$

$S = \dfrac{F/A}{\phi} = \dfrac{400,000 \text{ N}}{(3.575 \times 10^{-3})(0.160 \text{ m}^2)}$; $\boxed{S = 6.99 \times 10^{10} \text{ Pa}}$

13-37. A steel piano wire has an ultimate strength of about 35,000 lb/in.². How large a load can a 0.5-in.-diameter steel wire hold without breaking?

$A = \dfrac{\pi D^2}{4} = \dfrac{\pi(0.5 \text{ in.})^2}{4} = 0.196 \text{ in.}^2$; $\dfrac{F}{A} = 35,000 \text{ lb/in.}^2$;

$F = (35,000 \text{ lb/in.}^2)(0.196 \text{ in.}^2)$; $\boxed{F = 6870 \text{ lb}}$

Critical Thinking Questions

*13-38. A metal wire increases its length by 2 mm when subjected to tensile force. What elongation can be expected from this same force if the diameter of the wire was reduced to one-half of its initial value? Suppose the metal wire maintains its diameter, but doubles its length. What elongation would be expected for the same load?

$Y = \dfrac{FL}{A\Delta L}$; $\Delta L = \dfrac{FL}{AY} = \dfrac{4FL}{\pi D^2 Y}$; $\Delta L\, D^2 = \dfrac{4FL}{\pi Y}$; $\Delta L_1 D_1^2 = \Delta L_2 D_2^2$

$\Delta L_2 = \Delta L_1\left(\dfrac{D_1^2}{D_2^2}\right) = (2 \text{ mm})\left(\dfrac{D}{2D}\right)^2 = \dfrac{2 \text{ mm}}{4}$; $\boxed{\Delta L_2 = 0.500 \text{ mm}}$

Since $\Delta L \propto L$, doubling L would also double ΔL. $\boxed{\Delta L_2 = 4.00 \text{ mm}}$

13-39. A cylinder 4 cm in diameter is filled with oil. What total force must be exerted on the oil to produce a 0.8 percent decrease in volume? Compare the forces necessary if the oil is replaced by water? By mercury? [ΔV/V = -0.008]

$A = \dfrac{\pi D^2}{4} = \dfrac{\pi(0.04 \text{ m})^2}{4} = 1.26 \times 10^{-3}\text{ m}^2$; $B = \dfrac{-P}{\Delta V/V} = \dfrac{-F}{A\left(\Delta V/V\right)}$

$F = (1.005 \times 10^{-5}\text{ m}^2)B$

$B = \dfrac{-F}{(1.26 \times 10^{-3})(-0.008)}$; $F = (1.005 \times 10^{-5}\text{ m}^2)(1.7 \times 10^9 \text{ Pa})$;

For oil: $F = (1.005 \times 10^{-5}\text{ m}^2)(1.7 \times 10^9 \text{ Pa})$; $F_{oil} = 17,090 \text{ N}$

13-39. (Cont.)   For water: $F = (1.005 \times 10^{-5}\text{ m}^2)(2.1 \times 10^9\text{ Pa})$; $F_w = 21{,}100\text{ N}$

For mercury: $F = (1.005 \times 10^{-5}\text{ m}^2)(27 \times 10^9\text{ Pa})$; $F_m = 271{,}400\text{N}$

**13-40. A 15 kg ball is connected to the end of a steel wire 6 m long and 1.0 mm in diameter. The other end of the wire is connected to a high ceiling, forming a pendulum. If we ignore the small change in length, what is the maximum speed that the ball may have as it passes through its lowest point without exceeding the elastic limit? How much will the length of the wire increase under the limiting stress? What effect will this change have on the maximum velocity? [D = 1 mm = 0.001 m]

$$A = \frac{\pi D^2}{4} = \frac{\pi(0.001\text{ m})^2}{4} = 7.85 \times 10^{-7}\text{ m}^2$$

The maximum speed is that for which the tension causes the stress to exceed the elastic limit for steel (2.48 x 10⁸ Pa).

$\dfrac{F}{A} = 2.48 \times 10^8\text{Pa}$; $T = F = (2.48 \times 10^8\text{Pa})(7.85 \times 10^{-7}\text{ m}^2)$; $T_{max} = 195\text{ N}$

$T - mg = \dfrac{mv^2}{R}$; $mv^2 = TR - mgR$; $v^2 = \dfrac{R(T - mg)}{m}$; $mg = (15\text{ kg})(9.8\text{ m/s}^2) = 147\text{ N}$

$v = \sqrt{\dfrac{(6\text{ m})(195\text{ N} - 147\text{ N})}{15\text{ kg}}}$; $\boxed{v_{max} = 4.37\text{ m/s}}$

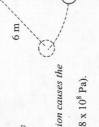

$Y = \dfrac{FL}{A\Delta L}$; $\Delta L = \dfrac{FL}{AY} = \dfrac{(195\text{ N})(6\text{ m})}{(7.85 \times 10^{-7}\text{ m}^2)(207 \times 10^9\text{Pa})}$; $\boxed{\Delta L = 7.19\text{ mm}}$

The stretch ΔL of the wire under this load will increase the radius R of the path from 6.000 m to 6.007 m. The larger radius provides a smaller centripetal force so that $(T = F_c + mg)$ is reduced. That would then permit a slightly greater maximum velocity up to the point where the tension again reaches the maximum allowed.

---

*13-41. A cylinder 10 in. in diameter is filled to a height of 6 in. with glycerin. A piston of the same diameter pushes downward on the liquid with a force of 800 lb. The compressibility of glycerin is 1.50 x 10⁻⁶ in.²/lb. What is the stress on the glycerin? How far down does the piston move?   [R = 5 in.;   A = πR² = 78.5 in.²]

$stress = P = \dfrac{F}{A} = \dfrac{800\text{ lb}}{78.5\text{ in.}^2}$; $\boxed{P = 10.2\text{ lb/in.}^2}$

$V_o = Ah_o = (78.5\text{ in.}^2)(6\text{ in.}) = 471.2\text{ in.}^3$; $k = -\dfrac{\Delta V}{PV_0}$

$\Delta V = -kPV_o = -(1.5 \times 10^{-6}\text{ in.}^2/\text{lb})(10.2\text{ lb/in.}^2)(471.2\text{ in.}^3)$; $\Delta V = 0.00721\text{ in.}^3$

$\Delta V = A\,\Delta h$ $\Delta h = \dfrac{\Delta V}{A} = \dfrac{0.00721\text{ in.}^3}{78.5\text{ in.}^2}$; $\boxed{\Delta h = 9.18 \times 10^{-5}\text{ in.}}$

*13-42. The twisting of a cylindrical shaft (Fig. 13-10) through an angle θ is an example of a shearing strain. An analysis of the situation shows that the angle of twist in radians is

$$\theta = \frac{2\tau\ell}{\pi SR^4}$$

where τ is the applied torque, l is the length of cylinder, R is the radius of cylinder, and S is the shear modulus. If a torque of 100 lb ft is applied to the end of a cylindrical steel shaft 10 ft long and 2 in. in diameter, what will be the angle of twist in radians?

Be careful of the consistent units: $\tau = 100\text{ lb ft} = 1200\text{ lb in.}$; $l = 10\text{ ft} = 120\text{ in.}$

$$\theta = \frac{2\tau l}{\pi SR^4} = \frac{2(1200\text{ lb in.})(120\text{ in.})}{\pi(12 \times 10^6\text{lb/in.}^2)(1\text{ in.})^4}$$; $\boxed{\theta = 0.00764\text{ rad}}$

Periodic Motion and the Reference Circle

14-1. A rock swings in a circle at constant speed on the end of a string, making 50 revolutions in 30 s. What is the frequency and the period for this motion?

$$f = \frac{50 \text{ rev}}{30 \text{ s}} = 1.67 \text{ rev/s}; \quad \boxed{f = 1.67 \text{ Hz}} \quad T = \frac{1}{f} = \frac{1}{1.67 \text{ hz}}; \quad \boxed{T = 0.600 \text{ s}}$$

14-2. A child sits at the edge of a platform rotating at 30 rpm. The platform is 10 m in diameter. What is the period of the motion and what is the child's speed? [$R = (D/2) = 5$ m]

$$30 \frac{\text{rev}}{\text{min}}\left(\frac{1 \text{ min}}{60 \text{ s}}\right) = 0.500 \text{ rev/s}; \quad f = 0.500 \text{ Hz}; \quad T = \frac{1}{f} = \frac{1}{0.500 \text{ hz}}; \quad \boxed{T = 2.00 \text{ s}}$$

$$v = \frac{2\pi R}{T} = \frac{2\pi(5 \text{ m})}{2.00 \text{ s}}; \quad \boxed{v = 15.7 \text{ m/s}}$$

14-3. A rubber ball swings in a horizontal circle 2 m in diameter and makes 20 revolutions in one minute. The shadow of the ball is projected on a wall by a distant light. What are the amplitude, frequency, and period for the motion of the shadow?

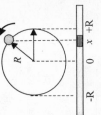

$$\boxed{A = R = 1.00 \text{ m}} \quad f = 20 \frac{\text{rev}}{\text{min}}\left(\frac{1 \text{ min}}{60 \text{ s}}\right) = 0.333 \text{ rev/s};$$

$$\boxed{f = 0.333 \text{ Hz}} \quad T = \frac{1}{f} = \frac{1}{0.333 \text{ hz}}; \quad \boxed{T = 3.00 \text{ s}}$$

14-4. Assume a ball makes 300 rpm while moving in a circle of radius 12 cm. What are the amplitude, frequency, and period for the motion of its shadow projected on a wall?

$$\boxed{A = R = 12 \text{ cm}} \quad f = 300 \frac{\text{rev}}{\text{min}}\left(\frac{1 \text{ min}}{60 \text{ s}}\right) = 5.00 \text{ rev/s}; \quad \boxed{f = 5.00 \text{ Hz}}$$

$$T = 1/f = 1/5 \text{ s}; \quad \boxed{T = 0.200 \text{ s}}$$

---

*13-43. An aluminum shaft 1 cm in diameter and 16 cm tall is subjected to a torsional shearing stress as explained in the previous problem. What applied torque will cause a twist of 1^0 as defined in Fig. 13-10. [$\theta = 1^0 = 0.01745$ rad; $R = (D/2) = 0.005$ m]

$$\theta = \frac{2\tau l}{\pi S R^4}; \quad \tau = \frac{\pi \tau S R^4}{2l} = \frac{\pi(0.01745 \text{ rad})(23.7 \times 10^9 \text{Pa})(0.005 \text{ m})^4}{2(0.16 \text{ m})} \quad \boxed{\tau = 2.54 \text{ N m}}$$

*13-44. Two sheets of aluminum on an aircraft wing are to be held together by aluminum rivets of cross-sectional area 0.25 in.^{2}. The shearing stress on each rivet must not exceed one-tenth of the elastic limit for aluminum. How many rivets are needed if each rivet supports the same fraction of the total shearing force of 25,000 lb?

The maximum stress allowed for each rivet is

$$\frac{F}{A} = \frac{1}{10}(19{,}000 \text{ lb/in.}^2) = 1900 \text{ lb/in.}^2$$

This means a shearing force of: $F = (1900 \text{ lb/in.}^2)(0.25 \text{ in.}^2) = 475 \text{ lb/rivet}$

Now we can find the number of rivets N as follows:

$$N = \frac{25{,}000 \text{ lb}}{475 \text{ lb/rivet}} = 52.7 \text{ rivets}; \quad \boxed{N = 53 \text{ rivets}}$$

14-5. A mass oscillates at a frequency of 3 Hz and an amplitude of 6 cm. What are its positions at time t = 0 and t = 2.5 s?

At t = 0: $x = A \cos (2\pi ft) = $ (6 cm) cos [2π(3 Hz)(0)]; $\boxed{x = 6.00 \text{ cm}}$

At t = 2.5 s: $x = A \cos (2\pi ft) = $ (6 cm) cos [2π(3 Hz)(2.5 s)]; $\boxed{x = 1.85 \text{ cm}}$

14-6. A 50-g mass oscillates with SHM of frequency 0.25 Hz. Assume t = 0 when the mass is at its maximum displacement. At what time will its displacement be zero? At what time will it be located at half of its amplitude? $f = 0.25$ s, $T = 1/f = 4.0$ s

One complete vibration takes 4 s, Therefore the mass reaches zero in one-fourth of that time, or $t = 4\text{s}/4 = \boxed{1.00 \text{ s}}$. *Now we find the time to reach x = A/2:*

$$x = \frac{A}{2} = A\cos(2\pi ft); \quad \cos(2\pi ft) = 0.5; \quad (2\pi ft) = \cos^{-1}(0.5) = 1.047 \text{ rad}$$

$2\pi ft = 1.047$ rad; $\quad t = \dfrac{1.047 \text{ rad}}{2\pi(0.25 \text{ Hz})}; \quad \boxed{t = 0.677 \text{ s}}$

Note that the time to reach A/2 is not equal to one-half the time to reach x = 0. That is because the restoring force is not constant. It reaches x = 0 in 1 s, but it covers half that distance in a time of 0.667 s.

14-7. When a mass of 200-g is hung from a spring, the spring is displaced downward a distance of 1.5 cm. What is the spring constant k? [$F = mg$; x = 1.5 cm = 0.015 m]

$$k = \frac{F}{x} = \frac{(0.200 \text{ kg})(9.8 \text{ m/s}^2)}{0.015 \text{ m}}; \quad \boxed{k = 131 \text{ N/m}}$$

14-8. An additional mass of 400 kg is added to the initial 200-g mass in Problem 14-7. What will be the increase in downward displacement? (*ΔF is due only to the added mass.*)

$$k = \frac{\Delta F}{\Delta x}; \quad \Delta x = \frac{\Delta F}{k} = \frac{(0.400 \text{ kg})(9.8 \text{ m/s}^2)}{131 \text{ N/m}}; \quad \boxed{\Delta x = 2.99 \text{ cm}}$$

---

*14-9. A mass at the end of a spring vibrates up and down with a frequency of 0.600 Hz and an amplitude of 5 cm. What is its displacement 2.56 s after it reaches a maximum?

$$x = A \cos(2\pi ft) = (5 \text{ cm}) \cos [2\pi(0.6 \text{ Hz})(2.56 \text{ s})]; \quad \boxed{x = -4.87 \text{ cm}}$$

*14-10. An object vibrates with an amplitude of 6 cm and a frequency of 0.490 Hz. Starting from maximum displacement in the positive direction, when will be the first time that its displacement is 2 cm?

$x = A \cos(2\pi ft); \quad \cos(2\pi ft) = \dfrac{x}{A} = \dfrac{2 \text{ cm}}{6 \text{ cm}} = 0.333; \quad (2\pi ft) = \cos^{-1}(0.333);$

$2\pi ft = 1.23$ rad; $\quad t = \dfrac{1.23 \text{ rad}}{2\pi(0.490 \text{ Hz})}; \quad \boxed{t = 0.400 \text{ s}}$

Velocity in Simple Harmonic Motion

14-11. A body vibrates with a frequency of 1.4 Hz and an amplitude of 4 cm. What is the maximum velocity? What is its position when the velocity is zero?

$v = -2\pi fA \sin(2\pi ft); \quad v_{max}$ *occurs when* $\sin\theta = 1, \quad v_{max} = 2\pi fA$

$v_{max} = 2\pi(1.4 \text{ Hz})(4 \text{ cm}); \quad \boxed{v_{max} = 35.2 \text{ cm/s}}$

When v = 0, $\quad x = \pm A \quad or \quad \boxed{x = \pm 4.00 \text{ cm}}$

14-12. An object oscillates at a frequency of 5 Hz and an amplitude of 6 cm. What is the maximum velocity?

$$v_{max} = -2\pi fA = -2\pi(1.4 \text{ Hz})(4 \text{ cm}); \quad \boxed{v_{max} = \pm 35.2 \text{ cm/s}}$$

14-13. A smooth block on a frictionless surface is attached to a spring, pulled to the right a distance of 4 cm and then released. Three seconds later it returns to the point of release.

What is the frequency and what is the maximum speed? [$T = 3.00$ s]

$f = 1/T = \boxed{0.333 \text{ Hz}}$; $\quad v_{max} = 2\pi fA = 2\pi(0.333 \text{ Hz})(4 \text{ cm})$; $\quad \boxed{v_{max} = 8.38 \text{ cm/s}}$

14-14. In Problem 14-13, what are the position and velocity 2.55 s after release?

$x = A\cos(2\pi ft) = (4 \text{ cm})\cos[2\pi(0.333 \text{ Hz})(2.55 \text{ s})]$; $\quad \boxed{x = 2.35 \text{ cm}}$

$v = -2\pi fA\sin(2\pi ft) = -2\pi(0.333 \text{ Hz})(4 \text{ cm})\sin[2\pi(0.333 \text{ Hz})(2.55 \text{ s})]$;

$\boxed{v = 6.78 \text{ cm/s}}$ *The location is 2.35 cm to the right (+) of center, and the body is moving to the right (+) at 6.78 cm/s.*

*14-15. Show that the velocity of an object in SHM can be written as a function of its amplitude and displacement: (Look at the reference circle: $\theta = 2\pi ft$)

$\sin\theta = \dfrac{y}{A}$ $\quad v = -2\pi fA\sin\theta = -2\pi fA\left(\dfrac{y}{A}\right)$; $\quad v = 2\pi fy$

But, $y = \sqrt{A^2 - x^2}$ from Pythagoras's theorem, Thus: $\quad v = \pm2\pi f\sqrt{A^2 - x^2}$

NOTE: *This expression can also be derived from conservation of energy principles. The equation derived in this example is so important for many applications, that the author strongly suggests it be assigned to every student.*

14-16. Use the relation derived in Problem 14-15 to verify the answers obtained for position and velocity in Problem 14-14.

$v = \pm2\pi f\sqrt{A^2 - x^2} = \pm2\pi(0.333 \text{ Hz})\sqrt{(4 \text{ cm})^2 - (2.35 \text{ cm})^2}$; $\quad \boxed{v = \pm 6.78 \text{ cm/s}}$

14-17. A mass vibrating at a frequency of 0.5 Hz has a velocity of 5 cm/s as it passes the center of oscillation. What are the amplitude and the period of vibration?

$v_{max} = 2\pi fA = 5 \text{ cm/s}$ $\quad A = \dfrac{v_{max}}{2\pi f} = \dfrac{5 \text{ cm/s}}{2\pi(0.5 \text{ Hz})}$; $\quad \boxed{A = 1.59 \text{ cm}}$

$T = \dfrac{1}{f} = \dfrac{1}{0.5 \text{ Hz}}$; $\quad \boxed{T = 2.00 \text{ s}}$

*14-18. A body vibrates with a frequency of 8 Hz and an amplitude of 5 cm. At what time after it is released from x = +5 cm will its velocity be equal to +2.00 m/s?

$v = -2\pi fA\sin(2\pi ft)$; $\quad \sin(2\pi ft) = \dfrac{v}{-2\pi fA} = \dfrac{2 \text{ m/s}}{-2\pi(8 \text{ Hz})(0.05 \text{ m})} = -0.796$;

$(2\pi ft) = \sin^{-1}(-0.796)$; $\quad 2\pi ft = -0.920$; $\quad t = \dfrac{0.921}{-2\pi(8 \text{ Hz})}$; $\quad t = -18.3 \text{ ms}$

NOTE: *The negative sign for time, means that the velocity was +2 m/s, 18.3 ms BEFORE its displacement was +5 cm. There will be two times within the first period of the vibration, that the velocity will be + 5 m/s. One is 18.3 ms before reaching the end of the first period (t = -18.3 ms), the second is 18.3 s after reaching half of the period. Thus, to find the first time that the velocity was +2 m/s after release from +5 cm, we need to ADD 18.3 ms to one-half of the period T.*

$T = \dfrac{1}{f} = \dfrac{1}{8 \text{ Hz}} = 0.125 \text{ s}$, $\quad t = \dfrac{T}{2} + 18.3 \text{ ms} = \dfrac{125 \text{ ms}}{2} + 18.3 \text{ ms}$

$t = 62.5 \text{ ms} + 18.3 \text{ ms}$; $\quad \boxed{t = 80.8 \text{ ms}}$

Acceleration in Simple Harmonic Motion

14-19. A 400-g mass is attached to a spring causing it to stretch a vertical distance of 2 cm. The mass is then pulled downward a distance of 4 cm and released to vibrate with SHM as shown in Fig. 14-10. What is the spring constant? What is the magnitude and direction of the acceleration when the mass is located 2 cm below its equilibrium position?

$k = \dfrac{(0.400 \text{ kg})(9.8 \text{ m/s}^2)}{0.02 \text{ m}}$; $\boxed{k = 196 \text{ N/m}}$; Consider down as +.

$a = -\dfrac{k}{m}x = \dfrac{-(196 \text{ N/m})(0.02 \text{ m})}{0.400 \text{ kg}}$ $\boxed{a = -9.8 \text{ m/s}^2, \text{ directed upward}}$

14-20. What is the maximum acceleration for the system described in Problem 14-19 and what is its acceleration when it is located 3 cm above its equilibrium position? (down +)

$a_{max} = -\dfrac{k}{m}A = \dfrac{-(196 \text{ N/m})(0.04 \text{ m})}{0.400 \text{ kg}}$ $\boxed{a = -19.6 \text{ m/s}^2, \text{ directed upward}}$

$a = -\dfrac{k}{m}x = \dfrac{-(196 \text{ N/m})(-0.03 \text{ m})}{0.400 \text{ kg}}$ $\boxed{a = 14.7 \text{ m/s}^2, \text{ directed downward}}$

14-21. A body makes one complete oscillation in 0.5 s. What is its acceleration when it is displaced a distance of x = +2 cm from its equilibrium position? (T = 0.5 s)

$f = \dfrac{1}{T} = \dfrac{1}{0.5 \text{ s}} = 2.00 \text{ Hz}$; $a = -4\pi^2 f^2 x = -4\pi^2(2 \text{ Hz})^2(0.02 \text{ m})$; $\boxed{a = -3.16 \text{ m/s}^2}$

14-22. Find the maximum velocity and the maximum acceleration of an object moving in SHM of amplitude 16 cm and frequency 2 Hz.

$v_{max} = -2\pi f A = -2\pi(2 \text{ Hz})(0.16 \text{ m})$; $\boxed{v_{max} = \pm 2.01 \text{ m/s}}$

$a_{max} = -4\pi^2 f^2 A = -4\pi^2(2 \text{ Hz})^2(0.16 \text{ m})$ $\boxed{a_{max} = \pm 25.3 \text{ m/s}^2}$

*14-23. An object vibrating with a period of 2 seconds is displaced a distance of x = +6 cm and released. What are the velocity and acceleration 3.20 s after release? [f = 1/T = 0.5 Hz]

$v = -2\pi f A \sin(2\pi ft) = -2\pi(0.5 \text{ Hz})(0.06 \text{ m})\sin[(2\pi(0.5 \text{ Hz})(3.2 \text{ s})]$;

$v = +0.111 \text{ m/s}$; $\boxed{v = +11.1 \text{ cm/s}, \text{ in + direction}}$

$a = -4\pi^2 f^2 A \cos(2\pi ft) = -4\pi^2(0.5 \text{ Hz})^2(0.06 \text{ m}) \cos[2\pi(0.5 \text{ Hz})(3.2 \text{ s})]$

$\boxed{a = +0.479 \text{ m/s}^2, \text{ in positive direction}}$

14-24. A body vibrates with SHM of period 1.5 s and amplitude 6 in. What are its maximum velocity and acceleration? [f = 1/T = (1/1.5 s) = 0.667 Hz ; A = 6 in. = 0.5 ft]

$v_{max} = -2\pi f A = -2\pi(0.667 \text{ Hz})(0.5 \text{ ft})$; $\boxed{v_{max} = \pm 2.09 \text{ ft/s}}$

$a_{max} = -4\pi^2 f^2 A = -4\pi^2(0.667 \text{ Hz})^2(0.5 \text{ ft})$ $\boxed{a_{max} = \pm 8.77 \text{ ft/s}^2}$

*14-25. For the body in Problem 14-24, what are its velocity and acceleration after a time of 7 s?

$v = -2\pi f A \sin(2\pi ft) = -2\pi(0.667 \text{ Hz})(0.5 \text{ ft})\sin[(2\pi(0.667 \text{ Hz})(7 \text{ s})]$;

$v = +1.81 \text{ ft/s}$; $\boxed{v = +1.81 \text{ ft/s}, \text{ in + direction}}$

$a = -4\pi^2 f^2 A \cos(2\pi ft) = -4\pi^2(0.667 \text{ Hz})^2(0.5 \text{ ft}) \cos[2\pi(0.5 \text{ Hz})(7 \text{ s})]$

$\boxed{a = +4.39 \text{ ft/s}^2, \text{ in positive direction}}$

Period and Frequency

*14-26. The prong of a tuning fork vibrates with a frequency of 330 Hz and an amplitude of 2 mm. What is the velocity when the displacement is 1.5 mm? (See Prob. 14-15)

$v = \pm 2\pi f \sqrt{A^2 - x^2} = \pm 2\pi(330 \text{ Hz})\sqrt{(2.0 \text{ mm})^2 - (1.5 \text{ mm})^2}$

$v = \pm 2743 \text{ mm/s}$; $\boxed{v = \pm 2.74 \text{ m/s}}$

Another approach is to find time when x = 1.5 mm, then use in equation for v(t).

*14-27. A 400g mass stretches a spring 20 cm. The 400-g mass is then removed and replaced with an unknown mass m. When the unknown mass is pulled down 5 cm and released, it vibrates with a period of 0.1 s. Compute the mass of the object.

$$k = \frac{F}{\Delta x} = \frac{(0.40 \text{ kg})(9.8 \text{ m/s}^2)}{0.20 \text{ m}} = 19.6 \text{ N/m} \text{ ; } T = 2\pi\sqrt{\frac{m}{k}}$$

$$T^2 = 4\pi^2\left(\frac{m}{k}\right) \text{ ; } m = \frac{T^2 k}{4\pi^2} = \frac{(0.10 \text{ s})^2(19.6 \text{ N/m})}{4\pi^2} \text{ ; } \boxed{m = 0.00496 \text{ kg} = 4.96 \text{ g}}$$

*14-28. A long, thin piece of metal is clamped at its lower end and has a 2-kg ball fastened to its top end. When the ball is pulled to one side and released, it vibrates with a period of 1.5 s. What is the spring constant for this device?

$$T = 2\pi\sqrt{\frac{m}{k}} \text{ ; } T^2 = \frac{4\pi^2 m}{k} \text{ ; } k = \frac{4\pi^2 m}{T^2}$$

$$k = \frac{4\pi^2 (2 \text{ kg})}{(1.5 \text{ s})^2} \text{ ; } \boxed{k = 35.1 \text{ N/m}}$$

*14-29. A car and its passengers have a total mass of 1600 kg. The frame of the car is supported by four springs, each having a force constant of 20,000 N/m. Find the frequency of vibration of the car when it drives over a bump in the road.

Each spring supports ¼(1600 kg) *or* 400 kg; $k = 20,000$ N/m.

$$f = \frac{1}{T} = \frac{1}{2\pi}\sqrt{\frac{k}{m}} \text{ ; } f = \frac{1}{2\pi}\sqrt{\frac{(20,000 \text{ N/m})}{400 \text{ kg}}} \text{ ; } \boxed{f = 1.13 \text{ Hz}}$$

The Simple Pendulum

14-30. What are the period and frequency of a simple pendulum 2 m in length?

$$T = 2\pi\sqrt{\frac{L}{g}} = 2\pi\sqrt{\frac{2 \text{ m}}{9.8 \text{ m/s}^2}} \text{ ; } \boxed{T = 2.84 \text{ s}} \text{ ; } f = 1/T \text{ ; } \boxed{f = 0.352 \text{ Hz}}$$

*14-31. A simple pendulum clock beats seconds every time the bob reaches its maximum amplitude on either side. What is the period of this motion? What should be the length of the pendulum at the point where g = 9.80 m/s²?

$$\boxed{T = 2.00 \text{ s/vib}} \quad T = 2\pi\sqrt{\frac{L}{g}} \text{ ; } T^2 = \frac{4\pi^2 L}{g} \text{ ; } L = \frac{T^2 g}{4\pi^2}$$

$$L = \frac{(2.0 \text{ s})^2(9.8 \text{ m/s}^2)}{4\pi^2} \text{ ; } \boxed{L = 0.993 \text{ m}}$$

14-32. A 10 m length of cord is attached to a steel bob hung from the ceiling. What is the period of its natural oscillation?

$$T = 2\pi\sqrt{\frac{L}{g}} = 2\pi\sqrt{\frac{10 \text{ m}}{9.8 \text{ m/s}^2}} \text{ ; } \boxed{T = 6.35 \text{ s}}$$

*14-33. On the surface of the moon, the acceleration due to gravity is only 1.67 m/s². A pendulum clock adjusted for the earth is taken to the moon. What fraction of its length on earth must the new length be in order to keep time accurately?

$$T_e = 2\pi\sqrt{\frac{L_e}{g_e}} \text{ ; } T_m = 2\pi\sqrt{\frac{L_m}{g_m}} \text{ ; } adjustment\ requires\ that\ T_e = T_m$$

$$\sqrt{\frac{L_e}{g_e}} = \sqrt{\frac{L_m}{g_m}} \text{ ; } \frac{L_m}{L_e} = \frac{g_m}{g_e} \text{ ; } \frac{L_m}{L_e} = \frac{1.67 \text{ m/s}^2}{9.8 \text{ m/s}^2} = 0.170 \text{ ; } \boxed{L_m = 0.17 L_e}$$

*14-37. A disk 20 cm in diameter forms the base of a torsional pendulum. A force of 20 N applied to the rim causes it to twist an angle of 12^0. If the period of the angular vibration after release is 0.5 s, what is the moment of inertia of the disk? [$R = D/2 = 0.10$ m]

$$\tau = FR = (20\ \text{N})(0.10\ \text{m}) = 2.0\ \text{N m}; \quad \tau = I\alpha = -k'\theta = 2.0\ \text{N m};$$

$$k' = \frac{2\ \text{N m}}{\theta} = \frac{2\ \text{N m}}{12^0(\pi/180)} = 9.55\ \text{N/rad};$$

$$T = 2\pi\sqrt{\frac{I}{k'}}; \quad T^2 = 4\pi^2\left(\frac{I}{k'}\right)$$

$$I = \frac{T^2 k'}{4\pi^2} = \frac{(0.5\ \text{s})^2(9.55\ \text{N/rad})}{4\pi^2}; \quad \boxed{I = 0.0605\ \text{kg m}^2}$$

*14-38. An irregular object is suspended by a wire as a torsion pendulum. A torque of 40 lb ft causes it to twist through an angle of 15^0. When released, the body oscillates with a frequency of 3 Hz. What is the moment of inertia of the irregular body?

$$k' = \frac{\tau}{\theta} = \frac{40\ \text{lb ft}}{15^0(\pi/180)} = 152.8\ \text{lb ft/rad}; \quad f = \frac{1}{2\pi}\sqrt{\frac{k'}{I}}; \quad f^2 = \frac{k'}{4\pi^2 I}$$

$$I = \frac{k'}{4\pi^2 f^2} = \frac{152.8\ \text{lb ft/rad}}{4\pi^2(3\ \text{Hz})^2}; \quad \boxed{I = 0.430\ \text{lb ft}^2}$$

Supplementary Problems

14-39. The spring constant of a metal spring is 2000 N/m. What mass will cause this spring to stretch a distance of 4 cm?

Given: $\Delta x = 0.04$ m, $k = 2000$ N/m, $F = mg$

$$k = \frac{\Delta F}{\Delta x} = \frac{mg}{x}; \quad m = \frac{kx}{g} = \frac{(2000\ \text{N/m})(0.04\ \text{m})}{9.8\ \text{m/s}^2}; \quad m = 8.16\ \text{kg}$$

*14-34. A student constructs a pendulum of length 3 m and determines that it makes 50 complete vibrations in 2 min and 54 s. What is the acceleration due to gravity at this student's location?   [2 min = 120 s;   t = 120 s + 54 s = 174 s]

$$T = \frac{174\ \text{s}}{50\ \text{vib}} = 3.48\ \text{s}; \quad T = 2\pi\sqrt{\frac{L}{g}}; \quad T^2 = \frac{4\pi^2 L}{g}$$

$$g = \frac{4\pi^2 L}{T^2} = \frac{4\pi^2(3.0\ \text{m})}{(3.48\ \text{s})^2}; \quad \boxed{g = 9.78\ \text{m/s}^2}$$

The Torsional Pendulum

*14-35. A torsion pendulum oscillates at a frequency of 0.55 Hz. What is the period of its vibration? What is the angular acceleration when its angular displacement is 60^0.

$$T = (1/f) = 1.82\ \text{s}; \quad \tau = I\alpha; \quad \tau = -k\theta; \quad I\alpha = -k\theta; \quad \frac{I}{k} = \frac{-\theta}{\alpha}$$

$$T = 2\pi\sqrt{\frac{I}{k'}}; \quad \frac{I}{k'} = \frac{T^2}{4\pi^2} = \frac{(1.82\ \text{s})^2}{4\pi^2}; \quad \frac{I}{k'} = 0.0837\ \text{s}^2$$

$$\theta = 60^0(\pi/180) = 0.333\pi \quad \text{and} \quad \frac{I}{k} = \frac{-\theta}{\alpha}$$

$$\alpha = \frac{-\theta}{I/k'} = \frac{-0.333\pi}{0.0837\ \text{s}^2}; \quad \boxed{\alpha = -12.5\ \text{rad/s}^2}$$

*14-36. The maximum angular acceleration of a torsional pendulum is 20 rad/s² when the angular displacement is 70^0. What is the frequency of vibration? (See Prob. 14-35)

$$\frac{I}{k'} = \frac{-\theta}{\alpha} = \frac{-70^0(\pi/180)}{-20\ \text{rad/s}^2}; \quad \frac{I}{k'} = 0.06109$$

$$T = 2\pi\sqrt{\frac{I}{k'}} = 2\pi\sqrt{0.06109\ \text{s}^2}; \quad \boxed{T = 1.55\ \text{s}} \quad f = \frac{1}{T}; \quad \boxed{f = 0.644\ \text{Hz}}$$

100

198 Unit A Solutions Manual

Copyright © by Glencoe/McGraw-Hill.

Chapter 14 Simple Harmonic Motion **199**

Copyright © by Glencoe/McGraw-Hill.

14-40.

A 4-kg mass hangs from a spring whose constant k is 400 N/m. The mass is pulled downward a distance of 6 cm and released? What is the acceleration at the instant of release? [x = 0.06 m, k = 400 N/m, m = 4 kg, $F = ma = -kx$]

$$a = \frac{-kx}{m} = \frac{-(400 \text{ N/m})(0.06 \text{ m})}{4 \text{ kg}} \; ; \quad \boxed{a = 6.00 \text{ m/s}^2}$$

14-41.

What is the natural frequency of vibration for the system described in Problem 14-40? What is the maximum velocity?

$$f = \frac{1}{2\pi}\sqrt{\frac{k}{m}} = \frac{1}{2\pi}\sqrt{\frac{400 \text{ N/m}}{4 \text{ kg}}}; \quad f = 1.59 \text{ Hz}$$

$$v_{max} = -2\pi f A = -2\pi(1.59 \text{ Hz})(0.06 \text{ m}); \quad \boxed{v_{max} = \pm 59.9 \text{ cm/s}}$$

*14-42.

A 50-g mass on the end of a spring (k = 20 N/m) is moving at a speed of 120 cm/s when located a distance of 10 cm from the equilibrium position. What is the amplitude of the vibration?   [v = 1.20 m/s, k = 20 N/m, x = 0.10 m, m = 0.050 kg]

$$f = \frac{1}{2\pi}\sqrt{\frac{k}{m}} = \frac{1}{2\pi}\sqrt{\frac{20 \text{ N/m}}{0.05 \text{ kg}}} = 3.18 \text{ Hz}; \quad \text{(See Eq. from Prob. 14-15)}$$

$$v = \pm 2\pi f \sqrt{A^2 - x^2} \; ; \quad v^2 = 4\pi^2 f^2 (A^2 - x^2); \quad A^2 = \frac{v^2}{4\pi^2 f^2} + x^2$$

$$A^2 = \frac{(1.20 \text{ m/s})^2}{4\pi^2 (3.183 \text{ Hz})^2} + (0.10 \text{ m})^2 ; \quad A = \sqrt{0.0136 \text{ m}^2} ; \quad \boxed{A = 11.7 \text{ cm}}$$

*14-43.

A 40-g mass is attached to a spring (k = 10 N/m) and released with an amplitude of 20 cm. What is the velocity of the mass when it is halfway to the equilibrium position?

$$f = \frac{1}{2\pi}\sqrt{\frac{k}{m}} = \frac{1}{2\pi}\sqrt{\frac{10 \text{ N/m}}{0.04 \text{ kg}}} = 2.516 \text{ Hz}; \quad v = \pm 2\pi f \sqrt{A^2 - x^2}$$

*14-43 (Cont.)

$$v = \pm 2\pi f \sqrt{A^2 - \left(\frac{A}{2}\right)^2} = \sqrt{0.75 A^2} \; ; \quad v = \pm 2\pi(2.516 \text{ Hz})(0.866)A$$

$$v = \pm 2\pi(2.516 \text{ Hz})(0.866)(0.20 \text{ m}) \quad \boxed{v = \pm 2.74 \text{ m/s}}$$

14-44.

What is the frequency of the motion for Problem 14-43?

$$f = \frac{1}{2\pi}\sqrt{\frac{k}{m}} = \frac{1}{2\pi}\sqrt{\frac{10 \text{ N/m}}{0.04 \text{ kg}}} = 2.516 \text{ Hz}; \quad \boxed{f = 2.52 \text{ Hz}}$$

14-45.

A 2-kg mass is hung form a light spring. When displaced and released, it is found that the mass makes 20 oscillations in 25 s. Find the period and the spring constant.

$$T = \frac{25 \text{ s}}{20 \text{ vib}} \qquad T = 1.25 \text{ s}; \qquad T = 2\pi\sqrt{\frac{m}{k}}; \qquad T^2 = \frac{4\pi^2 m}{k}$$

$$k = \frac{4\pi^2 m}{T^2} = \frac{4\pi^2 (2 \text{ kg})}{(1.25 \text{ s})^2} \; ; \quad \boxed{k = 50.5 \text{ N/m}}$$

*14-46.

What length of pendulum is needed if the period is 1.6 s at a point where g = 9.80 m/s²?

$$T = 2\pi\sqrt{\frac{L}{g}}; \quad L = \frac{gT^2}{4\pi^2} = \frac{(9.8 \text{ m/s}^2)(1.6 \text{ s})^2}{4\pi^2} \; ; \quad \boxed{T = 63.5 \text{ cm}}$$

*14-47.

An object is moving with SHM of amplitude 20 cm and frequency 1.5 Hz. What are the maximum acceleration and velocity?   [A = 0.20 m; f = 1.5 Hz]

$$a = -4\pi^2 f^2 A = -4\pi^2 (1.5 \text{ Hz})^2 (0.20 \text{ m}); \quad \boxed{a = \pm 17.8 \text{ m/s}^2}$$

$$v_{max} = -2\pi f A = -2\pi(1.5 \text{ Hz})(0.20 \text{ m}); \quad \boxed{v_{max} = \pm 1.88 \text{ m/s}}$$

14-50. (Cont.) Maximum velocity occurs at x = 0 because the restoring force has been acting in

the same direction for the longest time when x = 0: $\boxed{x = 0}$

Maximum acceleration occurs when restoring force is greatest, i.e., at $\boxed{x = \pm 8 \text{ cm.}}$

*14-51. A 200-g mass is suspended from a long, spiral spring. When displaced downward 10 cm, the mass is found to vibrate with a period of 2 s. What is the spring constant? What are its velocity and acceleration as it passes upward through the point +5 cm above its equilibrium position? [f = 1/T = 0.500 Hz; x = +5 cm]

$$T = 2\pi\sqrt{\frac{m}{k}}; \quad k = \frac{4\pi^2 m}{T^2} = \frac{4\pi^2(0.2\text{ kg})}{(2\text{ s})^2}; \quad \boxed{k = 1.97 \text{ N/m}}$$

$$v = \pm 2\pi f\sqrt{A^2 - x^2} = \pm 2\pi(0.5\text{ Hz})\sqrt{(0.10\text{ m})^2 - (0.05\text{ m})^2}$$

$\boxed{v = +0.272 \text{ m/s};}$ (positive because motion is upward)

$$a = \frac{-kx}{m} = \frac{-(1.97\text{ N/m})(+0.05\text{ m})}{0.200\text{ kg}} \quad \boxed{a = -0.493 \text{ m/s}^2}$$

The acceleration is downward, because the restoring force is downward.

*14-52. A pendulum clock beats seconds every time the bob passes through its lowest point. What must be the length of the pendulum at a place where g = 32.0 ft/s²? If the clock is moved to a point where g = 31.0 ft/s², how much time will it lose in 1 day?

$$T = 2.0 \text{ s}; \quad T = 2\pi\sqrt{\frac{L}{g}}; \quad L = \frac{T^2 g}{4\pi^2} = \frac{(2\text{ s})^2(32\text{ ft/s}^2)}{4\pi^2}; \quad L = 3.24 \text{ ft}$$

If g = 32 ft/s², Vib/day = $\frac{86,400\text{ s/day}}{2\text{ s/vib}}$ = 43,200 vib/day

If g = 31 ft/s², $T = 2\pi\sqrt{\frac{L}{g}} = 2\pi\sqrt{\frac{3.24\text{ ft}}{31\text{ ft/s}^2}}$ = 2.032 s/vib

---

*14-48. For the object in Problem 14-47, what are the position, velocity, and acceleration at a time of 1.4 s after it reaches its maximum displacement? [f = 1.5 s; t = 1.4 s]

$$x = A\cos(2\pi ft) = (20\text{ cm})\cos[2\pi(1.5\text{ Hz})(1.4\text{ s})]; \quad \boxed{x = 16.2 \text{ cm}}$$

$$v = -2\pi f A\sin(2\pi ft) = -2\pi(1.5\text{ Hz})(0.2\text{ m})\sin[2\pi(1.5\text{ Hz})(1.4\text{ s})]; \quad \boxed{v = -1.11 \text{ m/s}}$$

$$a = -4\pi^2 f^2 x = -4\pi^2(1.5\text{ Hz})^2(0.162\text{ cm}); \quad \boxed{a = -14.4 \text{ m/s}^2}$$

Critical Thinking Questions

*14-49. A mass m connected to the end of a spring oscillates with a frequency f = 2 Hz and an amplitude A. If the mass m is doubled what is the new frequency for the same amplitude?

If the mass is unchanged and the amplitude is doubled what is the frequency?

$$f = \frac{1}{2\pi}\sqrt{\frac{k}{m}}; \quad f^2 \propto \frac{1}{m}; \quad f_1^2 m_1 = f_2^2 m_2; \quad f_2 = \sqrt{\frac{f_1^2 m_1}{m_2}} = \sqrt{\frac{f_1^2 m_1}{2m_1}}$$

$$f_2 = \frac{f_1}{\sqrt{2}} = \frac{2\text{ Hz}}{1.414}; \quad \boxed{f_2 = 1.414 \text{ Hz}}$$

Since frequency is not a function of the mass, the frequency remains: $\boxed{f_2 = 2.00 \text{ Hz}}$

*14-50. Consider a 2-kg mass connected to a spring whose constant is 400 N/m. What is the natural frequency of vibration? If the system is stretched by +8 cm and then released, at what points are its velocity and acceleration maximized? Will it reach half its maximum velocity at half the amplitude? Calculate the maximum velocity and the velocity at

x = 4 cm to verify your answer?

$$f = \frac{1}{2\pi}\sqrt{\frac{k}{m}} = \frac{1}{2\pi}\sqrt{\frac{400\text{ N/m}}{2\text{ kg}}}; \quad \boxed{f = 2.25 \text{ Hz}}$$

Chapter 15. FLUIDS

Density

15-1. What volume does 0.4 kg of alcohol occupy? What is the weight of this volume?

$$\rho = \frac{m}{V}; \quad V = \frac{m}{\rho} = \frac{0.4 \text{ kg}}{790 \text{ kg/m}^2}; \quad \boxed{V = 5.06 \times 10^{-4} \text{ m}^3}$$

$$W = DV = \rho g V = 790 \text{ kg/m}^3 (9.8 \text{ m/s}^2)(5.06 \times 10^{-4} \text{ m}^3); \quad \boxed{W = 3.92 \text{ N}}$$

15-2. An unknown substance has a volume of 20 ft³ and weighs 3370 lb. What are the weight density and the mass density?

$$D = \frac{W}{V} = \frac{3370 \text{ lb}}{20 \text{ ft}^3}; \quad \boxed{D = 168 \text{ lb/ft}^3} \quad \rho = \frac{D}{g} = \frac{168 \text{ lb/ft}^3}{9.8 \text{ m/s}^2}; \quad \boxed{\rho = 5.27 \text{ slugs/ft}^3}$$

15-3. What volume of water has the same mass of 100 cm³ of lead? What is the weight density of lead?

First find mass of lead: $m = \rho V = (11.3 \text{ g/cm}^3)(100 \text{ cm}^3)$; $m = 1130 \text{ g}$

Now water: $V_w = \frac{m}{\rho_w} = \frac{1130 \text{ g}}{1 \text{ g/cm}^3} = 1130 \text{ cm}^3$; $\boxed{V_w = 1130 \text{ cm}^3}$ $\quad D = \rho g$

$$D = (11,300 \text{ kg/m}^3)(9.8 \text{ m/s}^2) = 110,740 \text{ N/m}^3; \quad \boxed{D = 1.11 \times 10^5 \text{ N/m}^3}$$

15-4. A 200-mL flask (1 L = 1 x 10⁻³ m³) is filled with an unknown liquid. An electronic balance indicates that the added liquid has a mass of 176 g. What is the specific gravity of the liquid? Can you guess the identity of the liquid?

$$V = 200 \text{ mL} = 0.200 \text{ L} = 2 \times 10^{-4} \text{ m}^3; \quad m = 0.176 \text{ kg}$$

$$\rho = \frac{m}{V} = \frac{0.176 \text{ kg}}{2 \times 10^{-4} \text{ m}^3}; \quad \boxed{\rho = 880 \text{ kg/m}^3, \text{ Benzene}}$$

---

*14-52. (Cont.) Which means at g = 31 ft/s, $Vib/day = \frac{86,400 \text{ s/day}}{2 \text{ s/vib}} = 42,520 \text{ vib/day}$

Vib. Lost = 43,200 – 42,520 = 680 vibrations

Time Lost = (2 s/vib)(680 vib) = 1360 s; $\boxed{\text{Time Lost} = 22.7 \text{ min.}}$

*14-53. A 500-g mass is connected to a device having a spring constant of 6 N/m. The mass is displaced to the right a distance x = +5 cm from its equilibrium position and then released.

What are its velocity and acceleration when x = +3 cm and when x = -3 cm?

$$f = \frac{1}{2\pi}\sqrt{\frac{k}{m}} = \frac{1}{2\pi}\sqrt{\frac{6 \text{ N/m}}{0.5 \text{ kg}}}; \quad f = 0.551 \text{ Hz}$$

$$v = \pm 2\pi f \sqrt{A^2 - x^2} = \pm 2\pi(0.551 \text{ Hz})\sqrt{(0.05 \text{ m})^2 - (0.03 \text{ m})^2} \quad \boxed{v = \pm 0.139 \text{ m/s}}$$

The velocity can be + or – at either +3 cm or at –3 cm.

At x = +3 cm: $a = \frac{-kx}{m} = \frac{-(6 \text{ N/m})(+0.03 \text{ m})}{0.500 \text{ kg}}$; $\boxed{a = -0.360 \text{ m/s}^2}$

At x = -3 cm: $a = \frac{-kx}{m} = \frac{-(6 \text{ N/m})(-0.03 \text{ m})}{0.500 \text{ kg}}$; $\boxed{a = +0.360 \text{ m/s}^2}$

Fluid Pressure

15-5. Find the pressure in kilopascals due to a column of mercury 60 cm high. What is this pressure in lb/in.^{2} and in atmospheres?

$$P = \rho g h = (13{,}600 \text{ kg/m}^3)(9.8 \text{ m/s}^2)(0.60 \text{ m}); \quad P = 80 \text{ kPa}$$

$$P = 80 \text{ kPa} \left[\frac{0.145 \text{ lb/in.}^2}{1 \text{ kPa}}\right]; \quad \boxed{P = 11.6 \text{ lb/in.}^2}$$

$$P = \frac{80 \text{ kPa}}{101.3 \text{ kPa/atm}}; \quad \boxed{P = 0.790 \text{ atm}}$$

15-6. A pipe contains water under a gauge pressure of 400 kPa. If you patch a 4-mm-diameter hole in the pipe with a piece of tape, what force must the tape be able to withstand?

$$A = \frac{\pi D^2}{4} = \frac{\pi (0.004 \text{ m})^2}{4} = 1.257 \times 10^{-5} \text{ m}^2; \quad P = \frac{F}{A};$$

$$F = PA = (400{,}000 \text{ Pa})(1.257 \times 10^{-5} \text{ m}^2); \quad \boxed{P = 5.03 \text{ N}}$$

15-7. A submarine dives to a depth of 120 ft and levels off. The interior of the submarine is maintained at atmospheric pressure. What are the pressure and the total force applied to a hatch 2 ft wide and 3 ft long? The weight density of sea water is around 64 lb/ft.^{3}

$$P = Dh = (64 \text{ lb/ft}^3)(120 \text{ ft}); \quad P = 7680 \text{ lb/ft}^2; \quad \boxed{P = 53.3 \text{ lb/in.}^2}$$

$$F = PA = (7680 \text{ lb/ft}^2)(3 \text{ ft})(2 \text{ ft}); \quad \boxed{F = 46{,}100 \text{ lb}}$$

15-8. If you constructed a barometer using water as the liquid instead of mercury, what height of water would indicate a pressure of one atmosphere?

$$P = \rho g h; \quad h = \frac{P}{\rho g} = \frac{101{,}300 \text{ Pa}}{(1000 \text{ kg/m}^3)(9.8 \text{ m/s}^2)};$$

$$\boxed{h = 10.3 \text{ m}} \quad \text{or} \quad 34 \text{ ft !}$$

15-9. A 20-kg piston rests on a sample of gas in a cylinder 8 cm in diameter. What is the gauge pressure on the gas? What is the absolute pressure?

$$A = \frac{\pi D^2}{4} = \frac{\pi (0.08 \text{ m})^2}{4} = 5.027 \times 10^{-3} \text{ m}^2; \quad P = \frac{F}{A} = \frac{mg}{A}$$

$$P = \frac{(20 \text{ kg})(9.8 \text{ m/s}^2)}{5.027 \times 10^{-3} \text{ m}^2} = 3.90 \times 10^4 \text{ kPa}; \quad \boxed{P = 39.0 \text{ kPa}}$$

$$P_{abs} = 1 \text{ atm} + P_{gauge} = 101.3 \text{ kPa} + 39.0 \text{ kPa}; \quad \boxed{P_{abs} = 140 \text{ kPa}}$$

*15-10. An open U-shaped tube such as the one in fig. 15-21 is 1 cm^2 in cross-section. What volume of water must be poured into the right tube to cause the mercury in the left tube to rise 1 cm above its original position?

$$\rho_m g h_m = \rho_2 g h_2; \quad h_2 = \frac{\rho_m h_m}{\rho_2} = \frac{(13.6 \text{ g/cm}^3)(1 \text{ cm})}{1 \text{ g/cm}^3} = 13.6 \text{ cm}$$

$$V = Ah = (1 \text{ cm}^2)(13.6 \text{ cm}); \quad \boxed{V = 13.6 \text{ cm}^3} \quad \text{or} \quad 13.6 \text{ mL}$$

15-11. The gauge pressure in an automobile tire is 28 lb/in.^{2}. If the wheel supports 1000 lb, what area of the tire is in contact with the ground?

$$A = \frac{F}{P} = \frac{1000 \text{ lb}}{28 \text{ lb/in.}^2}; \quad \boxed{A = 35.7 \text{ in.}^2}$$

15-12. Two liquids that do not react chemically are placed in a bent tube like the one in Fig. 15-

21. Show that the heights of the liquids above their surface of separation are inversely proportional to their densities: $\left(h_1/h_2 = \rho_2/\rho_1 \right)$

The gauge pressure must be the same for each column: $\rho g h_1 = \rho_2 g h_2$ *So that:*

$$\boxed{\frac{h_1}{h_2} = \frac{\rho_2}{\rho_1}}$$

15-13. Assume that the two liquids in the U-shaped tube in Fig. 15-21 are water and oil. Compute the density of the oil if the water stands 19 cm above the interface and the oil stand 24 cm above the interface. Refer to Prob. 15-12.

$$\frac{h_1}{h_2} = \frac{\rho_2}{\rho_1}; \quad \rho_{oil} = \frac{h_w \rho_w}{h_{oil}} = \frac{(19\ cm)(1000\ kg/m^3)}{24\ cm}; \quad \boxed{\rho_{oil} = 792\ kg/m^3}$$

15-14. A water-pressure gauge indicates a pressure of 50 lb/in.² at the foot of a building. What is the maximum height to which the water will rise in the building?

$$P = Dh; \quad h = \frac{P}{D} = \frac{(50\ lb/in.^2)(144\ in.^2/ft^2)}{62.4\ lb/ft^2}; \quad \boxed{h = 115\ ft}$$

The Hydraulic Press

15-15. The areas of the small and large pistons in a hydraulic press are 0.5 and 25 in.², respectively. What is the ideal mechanical advantage of the press? What force must be exerted to lift a ton? Through what distance must the input force move, if the load is lifted a distance of 1 in.?   [1 ton = 2000 lb]

$$M_I = \frac{A_o}{A_i} = \frac{25\ in.^2}{0.5\ in.^2}; \quad \boxed{M_I = 50} \quad F_i = \frac{2000\ lb}{50}; \quad \boxed{F_i = 40.0\ lb}$$

$$s_i = M_I s_o = (50)(1\ in.); \quad \boxed{s_i = 50\ in.}$$

15-16. A force of 400 N is applied to the small piston of a hydraulic press whose diameter is 4 cm. What must be the diameter of the large piston if it is to lift a 200-kg load?

$$\frac{F_o}{F_i} = \frac{A_o}{A_i} = \frac{d_o^2}{d_i^2}; \quad d_o = d_i \sqrt{\frac{F_o}{F_i}} = (4\ cm)\sqrt{\frac{(200\ kg)(9.8\ m/s^2)}{400\ N}};$$

$$\boxed{d_o = 8.85\ cm}$$

15-17. The inlet pipe that supplies air pressure to operate a hydraulic lift is 2 cm in diameter. The output piston is 32 cm in diameter. What air pressure (gauge pressure) must be used to lift an 1800-kg automobile.

$$P_i = P_o; \quad P_i = \frac{F_o}{A_o} = \frac{(1800\ kg)(9.8\ m/s^2)}{\pi(0.16\ m)^2}; \quad \boxed{P_i = 219\ kPa}$$

15-18. The area of a piston in a force pump is 10 in.². What force is required to raise water with the piston to a height of 100 ft?   [10 in.²(1 ft²/144 in.²) = 0.0694 ft²]

$$F = PA = (Dh)A; \quad F = (62.4\ lb/ft^3)(100\ ft)(0.0694\ ft^2); \quad \boxed{F = 433\ lb}$$

Archimedes' Principle

*15-19. A 100-g cube 2 cm on each side is attached to a string and then totally submerged in water. What is the buoyant force and what is the tension in the rope?

$$V = (0.02\ m)^3 = 8 \times 10^{-6}\ m^3; \quad m = 0.100\ kg; \quad F_B = \rho g V$$

$$F_B = (1000\ kg/m^3)(9.8\ m/s^2)(8 \times 10^{-6}\ m^3); \quad \boxed{F_B = 0.0784\ N}$$

$$\Sigma F_y = 0; \quad T + F_B - mg = 0; \quad T = mg - F_B;$$

$$T = (0.100\ kg)(9.8\ m/s^2) - 0.0784\ N; \quad T = 0.980\ N - 0.0784\ N; \quad \boxed{T = 0.902\ N}$$

*15-20. A solid object weighs 8 N in air. When it is suspended from a spring scale and submerged in water, the apparent weight is only 6.5 N. What is the density of the object?

$$\frac{W}{g} = \frac{8\ N}{9.8\ m/s^2}; \quad m = 0.816\ kg \quad \rho = \frac{m}{V}$$

To find density, we need to know the volume V of the block which is the same as the volume of the water displaced.

$$F_B = 8\ N - 6.5\ N; \quad F_B = 1.5\ N; \quad F_B = \rho g V; \quad V = \frac{F_B}{\rho g} = \frac{1.50\ N}{(1000\ kg/m^3)(9.8\ m/s^2)};$$

$$V = 1.53 \times 10^{-4}\ m^3; \quad \rho = \frac{m}{V} = \frac{0.816\ kg}{1.53 \times 10^{-4}\ m^3}; \quad \boxed{\rho = 5333\ kg/m^3}$$

*15-21. A cube of wood 5.0 cm on each edge floats in water with three-fourths of its volume submerged. (a) What is the weight of the cube? (b) What is the mass of the cube? (c) What is the specific gravity of the wood?   [$V = (0.05 \text{ m})^3 = 1.25 \times 10^{-4} \text{ m}^3$]

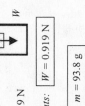

The volume of water displaced is ¾ of the volume of the block:

$$V_D = \tfrac{3}{4}(1.25 \times 10^{-4} \text{ m}^3) = 9.38 \times 10^{-5} \text{ m}^3$$

$$F_B = \rho g V_D = (1000 \text{ kg/m}^3)(9.8 \text{ m/s}^2)(9.38 \times 10^{-5} \text{ m}^3) = 0.919 \text{ N}$$

The weight is the same as the buoyant force if the block floats: $\boxed{W = 0.919 \text{ N}}$

$$m = \frac{W}{g} = \frac{0.919 \text{ N}}{9.8 \text{ m/s}^2}; \qquad m = 0.0938 \text{ kg} \quad \text{or} \quad \boxed{m = 93.8 \text{ g}}$$

Specific gravity: $\dfrac{\rho}{\rho_w} = \dfrac{\tfrac{m}{V}}{\tfrac{m}{V_w}}; \quad \dfrac{\tfrac{3}{4}(125 \text{ cm}^3)}{125 \text{ cm}^3}$; $\boxed{\text{Specific gravity} = 0.75}$

*15-22. A 20-g piece of metal has a density of 4000 kg/m³. It is hung in a jar of oil (1500 kg/m³) by a thin thread until it is completely submerged. What is the tension in the thread?

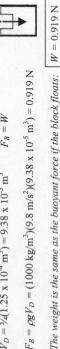

First find volume of metal from its mass and density:

$$\rho = \frac{m}{V}; \quad V = \frac{m}{\rho} = \frac{0.02 \text{ kg}}{4000 \text{ kg/m}^3} = 5 \times 10^{-6} \text{ m}^3; \quad F_B = \rho g V$$

$$F_B = (1500 \text{ kg/m}^3)(9.8 \text{ m/s}^2)(5 \times 10^{-6} \text{ m}^3); \quad F_B = 0.0735 \text{ N}$$

$$\Sigma F_y = 0; \quad T + F_B - mg = 0; \quad T = mg - F_B; \quad mg = (0.02 \text{ kg})(9.8 \text{ m/s}^2)$$

$$T = 0.196 \text{ N} - 0.0735 \text{ N}; \quad \boxed{T = 0.123 \text{ N}}$$

*15-23. The mass of a rock is found to be 9.17 g in air. When the rock is submerged in a fluid of density 873 kg/m³, its apparent mass is only 7.26 g. What is the density of this rock?

Apparent weight = true weight – buoyant force; $m_A g = mg - mg$

$$m_A = m - m_f; \quad m_f = m - m_A = 9.17 \text{ g} - 7.26 \text{ g} = 1.91 \text{ g}$$

---

*15-23. (Cont.)   The volume V_f displaced is found from the mass displaced: $m_f = 1.91 \text{ g}$

$$V_f = \frac{m_f}{\rho_f} = \frac{0.00191 \text{ kg}}{873 \text{ kg/m}^3} = 2.19 \times 10^{-6} \text{ m}^3; \qquad V_f = V_{rock} = 2.19 \times 10^{-6} \text{ m}^3$$

$$\rho_{rock} = \frac{m_{rock}}{V_{rock}} = \frac{9.16 \times 10^{-3} \text{ kg}}{2.19 \times 10^{-6} \text{ m}^3}; \qquad \boxed{\rho_{rock} = 4191 \text{ kg/m}^3}$$

*15-24. A balloon 40 m in diameter is filled with helium. The mass of the balloon and attached basket is 18 kg. What additional mass can be lifted by this balloon?

First find volume of balloon: $V_b = (4/3)\pi R^3 = (4/3)\pi(20 \text{ m})^3$

$$V_b = 3.351 \times 10^4 \text{ m}^3; \qquad F_B = W_{balloon} + W_{Helium} + W_{added}$$

$$F_b = \rho_{air} g V_b = (1.29 \text{ kg/m}^3)(9.8 \text{ m/s}^2)(3.351 \times 10^4 \text{ m}^3) = 4.24 \times 10^5 \text{ N}$$

$$W_{He} = \rho g V = (0.178 \text{ kg/m}^3)(9.8 \text{ m/s}^2)(3.351 \times 10^4 \text{ m}^3) = 5.845 \times 10^4 \text{ N}; \quad W_b = m_b g$$

$$W_{add} = F_B - W_b - W_{Helium} = 4.24 \times 10^5 \text{ N} - (18 \text{ kg})(9.8 \text{ m/s}^2) - 5.845 \times 10^4 \text{ N}$$

$$W_{add} = 3.65 \times 10^5 \text{ N}; \qquad m_{add} = \frac{W_{add}}{g} = \frac{3.65 \times 10^5 \text{ N}}{9.8 \text{ m/s}^2}; \qquad \boxed{m_{add} = 37{,}200 \text{ kg}}$$

The densities of air and helium were taken from Table 15-1 in the text.

Fluid Flow

15-25. Gasoline flows through a 1-in.-diameter hose at an average velocity of 5 ft/s. What is the rate of flow in gallons per minute? (1 ft³ = 7.48 gal). How much time is required to fill a 20-gal tank?   [$A = \pi R^2 = \pi(0.5 \text{ in.})^2 = 7.854 \text{ in}^2(1 \text{ ft}/144 \text{ in.}^2) = 0.0273 \text{ ft}^2 = 5.454 \times 10^{-3} \text{ ft}^2$]

$$R = vA = (5 \text{ ft/s})(5.454 \times 10^{-3} \text{ ft}^2) = 0.0273 \text{ ft}^3/s;$$

$$R = (0.0273 \text{ ft}^3/s)(7.48 \text{ gal/ft}^3)(60 \text{ s/min}); \quad R = 12.2 \text{ gal/min}.$$

$$Time = \frac{20 \text{ gal}}{12.2 \text{ gal/min}}; \qquad \boxed{Time = 1.63 \text{ min}}$$

15-26. Water flows from a terminal 3 cm in diameter and has an average velocity of 2 m/s. What is the rate of flow in liters per minute? (1 L = 0.001 m^3.) How much time is required to fill a 40-L container? [$A = \pi(0.015\text{ m})^2 = 7.07 \times 10^{-4}\text{ m}^2$; $V = 40\text{ L} = 0.04\text{ m}^3$]

$$R = vA = (2\text{ m/s})(7.07 \times 10^{-4}\text{ m}^2) = 1.41 \times 10^{-3}\text{ m}^3/\text{s}$$

$$\text{Time} = \frac{0.04\text{ m}^3}{1.41 \times 10^{-3}\text{ m}^3/\text{s}}; \qquad \boxed{\text{Time} = 28.3\text{ s}}$$

15-27. What must be the diameter of a hose if it is to deliver 8 L of oil in 1 min with an exit velocity of 3 m/s?

$$R = \frac{8\text{ L}}{1\text{ min}}\left(\frac{0.001\text{ m}^3}{1\text{ L}}\right)\left(\frac{1\text{ min}}{60\text{ s}}\right) = 1.33 \times 10^{-4}\text{ m}^3/\text{s}; \qquad R = vA$$

$$A = \frac{\pi D^2}{4} = \frac{R}{v}; \qquad D^2 = \frac{4R}{\pi v}; \qquad D^2 = \frac{4(1.33 \times 10^{-4}\text{ m}^3/\text{s})}{\pi(3\text{ m/s})} = 5.66 \times 10^{-4}\text{ m}^2$$

$$D = \sqrt{5.66 \times 10^{-4}\text{ m}^2}; \qquad D = 7.52 \times 10^{-3}\text{ m}; \qquad \boxed{D = 7.52\text{ mm}}$$

15-28. Water from a 2-in. pipe emerges horizontally at the rate of 8 gal/min. What is the emerging velocity? What is the horizontal range of the water if the pipe is 4 ft from the ground?

$$R = \frac{8\text{ gal}}{1\text{ min}}\left(\frac{1\text{ ft}^3}{7.48\text{ gal}}\right)\left(\frac{1\text{ min}}{60\text{ s}}\right) = 0.01782\text{ ft}^3/\text{s}; \qquad A = \frac{\pi(\tfrac{1}{12}\text{ ft})^2}{4} = 0.0218\text{ ft}^2$$

$$v = \frac{R}{A} = \frac{0.01782\text{ ft}^3/\text{s}}{0.0218\text{ ft}^2}; \qquad \boxed{v = 0.817\text{ ft/s}}$$

To find the range x, we first find time to strike ground from: $y = \tfrac{1}{2}gt^2$

$$t = \sqrt{\frac{2y}{g}} = \sqrt{\frac{2(4\text{ ft})}{32\text{ ft/s}^2}} = 0.500\text{ s}; \qquad \textit{Now range is } x = v_x t$$

Range: $x = vt = (0.817\text{ ft/s})(0.5\text{ s}); \qquad x = 0.409\text{ ft}$ or $\boxed{x = 4.90\text{ in.}}$

15-29. Water flowing at 6 m/s through a 6-cm pipe is connected to a 3-cm pipe. What is the velocity in the small pipe? Is the rate of flow greater in the smaller pipe?

$$A_1v_1 = A_2v_2 \qquad v_2 = \frac{A_1v_1}{A_2} = \frac{d_1^2 v_1}{d_2^2} = \left(\frac{6\text{ cm}}{3\text{ cm}}\right)^2(6\text{ m/s}): \qquad \boxed{v_2 = 24.0\text{ m/s}}$$

The rate of flow is the same in each pipe.

Applications of Bernoulli's Equation

15-30. Consider the situation described by Problem 15-29. If the centers of each pipe are on the same horizontal line, what is the difference in pressure between the two connecting pipes?

For a horizontal pipe, $h_1 = h_2$: $P_1 + \cancel{\rho g h_1} + \tfrac{1}{2}\rho v_1^2 = P_2 + \cancel{\rho g h_2} + \tfrac{1}{2}\rho v_2^2$

$$P_1 - P_2 = \tfrac{1}{2}\rho v_2^2 - \tfrac{1}{2}\rho v_1^2 = \tfrac{1}{2}\rho(v_2^2 - v_1^2); \qquad \rho = 1000\text{ kg/m}^3$$

$$P_1 - P_2 = \tfrac{1}{2}(1000\text{ kg/m}^3)[(24\text{ m/s})^2 - (6\text{ m/s})^2] = 2.70 \times 10^5\text{ Pa}; \qquad \boxed{\Delta P = 270\text{ kPa}}$$

15-31. What is the emergent velocity of water from a crack in its container 6 m below the surface? If the area of the crack is 1.2 cm^2, at what rate of flow does water leave the container? [*The pressures are the same at top and at crack:* $P_1 = P_2$]

$$\cancel{P_1} + \rho g h_1 + \tfrac{1}{2}\rho v_1^2 = \cancel{P_2} + \rho g h_2 + \tfrac{1}{2}\rho v_2^2;$$

$$\rho g h_1 + \tfrac{1}{2}\rho v_1^2 = \rho g h_2 + \tfrac{1}{2}\rho v_2^2$$

Notice that ρ cancels out and recall that v_1 can be considered as zero.

Setting $v_1 = 0$, we have: $\rho g h_1 = \rho g h_2 + \tfrac{1}{2}\rho v_2^2$ or $v_2^2 = 2g(h_1 - h_2)$

$$v_2^2 = 2(9.8\text{ m/s}^2)(6\text{ m}); \qquad \boxed{v_2 = 10.8\text{ m/s}}$$

$$A = (1.2\text{ cm}^2)(1 \times 10^{-4}\text{ m}^2/\text{cm}^2) = 1.20 \times 10^{-4}\text{ m}^2;$$

$$R = vA \qquad R = (10.84\text{ m/s})(1.20 \times 10^{-4}\text{ m}^2);$$

$$\boxed{R = 1.41 \times 10^{-3}\text{ m}^3/\text{s}} \qquad \text{or} \qquad R = 1.41\text{ L/s}$$

15-32. A 2-cm-diameter hole is in the side of a water tank, and it is located 5 m below the water level in the tank. What is the emergent velocity of the water from the hole? What volume of water will escape from this hole in 1 min? [*Apply Torricelli's theorem*]

$$v = \sqrt{2gh} = \sqrt{2(9.8\ m/s^2)(6\ m)}\ ; \quad \boxed{v = 9.90\ m/s}$$

$$A = \frac{\pi D^2}{4} = \frac{\pi(0.02\ m)^2}{4} = 3.18 \times 10^{-5} m^2; \quad R = vA$$

$$R = (9.90\ m/s)(3.18 \times 10^{-5} m^2); \quad R = 3.11 \times 10^{-4} m^3/s$$

$$R = \frac{3.11 \times 10^{-4} m^3}{1\ s}\left(\frac{60\ s}{1\ min}\right)\left(\frac{1\ L}{0.001\ m^3}\right); \quad \boxed{R = 187\ L/min}$$

**15-33. Water flows through a horizontal pipe at the rate of 82 ft³/min. A pressure gauge placed on a 6-in. cross-section of this pipe reads 16 lb/in.². What is the gauge pressure in a section of pipe where the diameter is 3 in.?

$$A_1 = \pi(3\ in.)^2 = 28.3\ in.^2 = 0.1964\ ft^2$$

$$A_1 = \pi(1.5\ in.)^2 = 7.07\ in.^2 = 0.0491\ ft^2$$

$$R_1 = R_2 = 82\ ft^3/min(1\ min/60\ s) = 1.37\ ft^3/s; \quad v_1A_1 = v_2A_2\ ;$$

$$v_1 = \frac{R}{A_1} = \frac{1.37\ ft^3/s}{0.1964\ ft^2} = 6.959\ ft/s; \quad v_2 = \frac{R}{A_2} = \frac{1.37\ ft^3/s}{0.0491\ ft^2} = 27.84\ ft/s$$

Now find absolute pressure: $P_1 = 16\ lb/in.^2 + 14.7\ lb/in.^2 = 30.7\ lb/in.^2$;

$$P_1 = \left(30.7\ \frac{lb}{in.^2}\right)\left(\frac{144\ in.^2}{1\ ft^2}\right) = 4421\ lb/ft^2 \quad (Absolute\ pressure\ pipe\ 1)$$

$$D = \rho g; \quad \rho = \frac{D}{g} = \frac{62.4\ lb/ft^3}{32\ ft/s^2} = 1.95\ slugs/ft^3$$

Use consistent units for all terms: ft, slugs)

**15-33. (Cont.) $P_1 = 4421\ lb/ft^2$; $v_1 = 6.959\ ft/s$; $v_2 = 27.84\ ft/s$; $\rho = 1.95\ slugs/ft^3$;

Since $h_1 = h_2$, $P_1 + \frac{1}{2}\rho v_1^2 = P_2 + \frac{1}{2}\rho v_2^2$ *and* $P_2 = P_1 + \frac{1}{2}\rho v_1^2 - \frac{1}{2}\rho v_2^2$

$$P_2 = 4421\ lb/ft^2 + \frac{1}{2}(1.95\ slugs/ft^3)(6.959\ ft/s)^2 - \frac{1}{2}(1.95\ slugs/ft^3)(27.84\ ft/s)^2$$

$$P_2 = 4421\ lb/ft^2 + 47.22\ lb/ft^2 - 755.7\ lb/ft^2; \quad P_2 = 3713\ lb/ft^2$$

$$P_2 = 3713\ \frac{lb}{ft^2}\left(\frac{1\ ft^2}{144\ in.^2}\right) = 25.8\ lb/in.^2; \quad (Absolute\ pressure\ in\ pipe\ 2)$$

Gauge pressure $P_2 = 25.8\ lb/in.^2 - 14.7\ lb/in.^2$; $\boxed{P_2 = 11.1\ lb/in.^2}$

*15-34. Water flows at the rate of 6 gal/min through an opening in the bottom of a cylindrical tank. The water in the tank is 16 ft deep. What is the rate of escape if an added pressure of 9 lb/in.² is applied to the source of the water?

The rate of escape is proportional to the difference in pressure between input and output.

$$\Delta P = \rho g h = Dh = (62.4\ lb/ft^3)(16\ ft); \quad \Delta P = 998.4\ lb/ft^2 = 6.933\ lb/in.^2$$

Thus, ΔP *of 6.933 lb/in.² produces a rate of 6.0 gal/min. Now the new* ΔP *is:*

$$\Delta P' = 6.933\ lb/in.^2 + 9\ lb/in.^2 = 15.93\ lb/in.^2, \quad By\ ratio\ and\ proportion,\ we\ have$$

$$\frac{R}{15.93\ lb/in.^2} = \frac{6\ gal/min}{6.933\ lb/in.^2} \quad and \quad \boxed{R = 13.8\ gal/min}$$

*15-35. Water moves through a small pipe at 4 m/s under an absolute pressure of 200 kPa. The pipe narrows to one-half of its original diameter. What is the absolute pressure in the narrow part of the pipe? [$v_1 d_1^2 = v_2 d_2^2$]

$$v_1 = 4\ m/s; \quad v_2 = \left(\frac{2d_2}{d_2}\right)^2 (4\ m/s) = 16\ m/s \quad and \quad P_2 = P_1 + \frac{1}{2}\rho v_1^2 - \frac{1}{2}\rho v_2^2$$

*15-39. A block of wood weighs 16 lb in air. A lead sinker with an apparent weight of 28 lb in water, is attached to the wood, and both are submerged in water. If their combined apparent weight in water is 18 lb, find the density of the wooden block?

$$F_B = 28\ lb + 16\ lb - 18\ lb = 26\ lb; \quad F_B = DV$$

$$V = \frac{F_B}{D} = \frac{26\ lb}{62.4\ lb/ft^3} = 0.417\ ft^3; \quad D_{wood} = \frac{16\ lb}{0.417\ ft^3}; \quad \boxed{D = 38.4\ lb/ft^3}$$

*15-40. A 100-g block of wood has a volume of 120 cm^3. Will it float in water? Gasoline?

For water: $F_B = \rho g h = (1000\ kg/m^3)(9.8\ m/s^2)(120 \times 10^{-6}\ m^3) = 1.176\ N$

$W = mg = (0.1\ kg)(9.8\ m/s^2) = 0.980\ N \quad F_B > W \quad \boxed{YES}$

For gasoline: $F_B = \rho g h = (680\ kg/m^3)(9.8\ m/s^2)(120 \times 10^{-6}\ m^3) = 0.800\ N$

$W = mg = (0.1\ kg)(9.8\ m/s^2) = 0.980\ N \quad F_B < W \quad \boxed{NO}$

*15-41. A vertical test tube has 3 cm of oil (0.8 g/cm^3) floating on 9 cm of water. What is the pressure at the bottom of the tube?   [$P_T = \rho_o g h_o + \rho_w g h_w$]

$P_T = (800\ kg/m^3)(9.8\ m/s^2)(0.03\ m) + (1000\ kg/m^3)(9.8\ m/s^2)(0.09\ m)$

$P_T = 235.2\ Pa + 882\ Pa = 1117\ Pa; \quad \boxed{P_T = 1.12\ kPa}$

*15-42. What percentage of an iceberg will remain below the surface of seawater ($\rho = 1030\ kg/m^3$)?

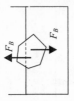

If iceberg floats, then: $F_B = mg$ and $F_B = \rho_a g V_w$

$mg = \rho_i V_i\, g;$ therefore, $\rho_i V_i\, g = \rho_a g V_w$

So that: $\dfrac{V_w}{V_i} = \dfrac{\rho_i}{\rho_w} = \dfrac{920\ kg/m^3}{1030\ kg/m^3} = 0.893$ or $\boxed{89.3\%}$

Thus, 89.3 percent of the iceberg remains underwater, hence the expression: "That's just the tip of the iceberg."

---

*15-35. (Cont.) $P_2 = P_1 + \tfrac{1}{2}\rho v_1^2 - \tfrac{1}{2}\rho v_2^2; \quad \rho = 1000\ kg/m^3; \quad v_1 = 4\ m/s; \quad v_2 = 16\ m/s$

$P_2 = 200,000\ Pa + \tfrac{1}{2}(1000\ kg/m^3)(4\ m/s)^2 - \tfrac{1}{2}(1000\ kg/m^3)(16\ m/s)^2$

$P_2 = 200,000\ Pa + 8000\ Pa - 128,000\ Pa = 80,000\ Pa; \quad \boxed{P_2 = 80.0\ kPa}$

*15-36. Water flows steadily through a horizontal pipe. At a point where the absolute pressure is 300 kPa, the velocity is 2 m/s. The pipe suddenly narrows, causing the absolute pressure to drop to 100 kPa. What will be the velocity of the water in this constriction?

$P_1 + \tfrac{1}{2}\rho v_1^2 = P_2 + \tfrac{1}{2}\rho v_2^2$

$\tfrac{1}{2}\rho v_2^2 = P_1 + \tfrac{1}{2}\rho v_1^2 - P_2$

$\tfrac{1}{2}(1000\ kg/m^3)v_2^2 = 300,000\ Pa + \tfrac{1}{2}(1000\ kg/m^3)(2\ m/s)^2 - 100,000\ Pa$

$(500\ kg/m^3)v_2^2 = 202,000\ Pa; \quad \boxed{v_2 = 20.1\ m/s}$

Supplementary Problems

*15-37. Human blood of density 1050 kg/m^3 is held a distance of 60 cm above an arm of a patient to whom it is being administered. How much higher is the pressure at this position than it would be if it were held at the same level as the arm?

$P = \rho g h = (1050\ kg/m^3)(9.8\ m/s^2)(0.6\ m); \quad \boxed{P = 6.17\ kPa}$

*15-38. A cylindrical tank 50 ft high and 20 ft in diameter is filled with water. (a) What is the water pressure on the bottom of the tank? (b) What is the total force on the bott0m? (c) What is the pressure in a water pipe that is located 90 ft below the water level in the tank?

(a) $P = (62.4\ lb/ft^3)(50\ ft) = 3120\ lb/ft^2$ or $\boxed{21.7\ lb/in.^2}$ *(Gauge pressure)*

(b) $F = PA = (3120\ lb/ft^2)[\pi(10\ ft)^2]; \quad \boxed{F = 9.80 \times 10^5\ lb}$

(c) $P = (63.4\ lb/ft^3)(90\ ft) = 5616\ lb/ft^2; \quad \boxed{P = 39.0\ lb/in.^2}$ *(Gauge pressure)*

**15-43. What is the smallest area of ice 30 cm thick that will support a 90-kg man? The ice is floating in fresh water ($\rho = 1000$ kg/m³). [$V = Ah$ so that $A = V/h$]

The question becomes: What volume of ice will support a 90-kg person?

$F_B = W_{ice} + W_{man}$; $F_B = \rho_w g V_w$; $W_{ice} = \rho_{ice} g V_{ice}$; $W_{man} = mg$

$\rho_w g V_w = \rho_{ice} g V_{ice} + mg$; *(gravity divides out)*

The smallest area occurs when the ice is level with the surface and $V_{ice} = V_w$

$\rho_w V_w = \rho_{ice} V_w + m$ or $(1000 \text{ kg/m}^3)V_w - (920 \text{ kg/m}^3)V_w = 90$ kg

$V_w = 1.125$ m³; *Now since* $V = Ah$, *we have*

$A = \frac{V_w}{h} = \frac{1.125 \text{ m}^3}{0.300 \text{ m}}$ and $\boxed{A = 3.75 \text{ m}^2}$

*15-44. A spring balance indicates a weight of 40 N when an object is hung in air. When the same object is submerged in water, the indicated weight is reduced to only 30 N. What is the density of the object? [$F_B = 40 \text{ N} - 30 \text{ N} = 10$ N]

$F_B = \rho_w g V_w$; $\quad V_w = \frac{F_B}{\rho_w g} = \frac{10 \text{ N}}{(1000 \text{ kg/m}^3)(9.8 \text{ m/s}^2)}$; $\quad V_w = 1.02 \times 10^{-3}$ m³

The volume of the object is the same as the water displaced: $V = 1.02 \times 10^{-3}$ m³

$\frac{W}{g} = \frac{40 \text{ N}}{9.8 \text{ m/s}^2} = 4.08$ kg; $\quad \rho = \frac{m}{V} = \frac{4.08 \text{ kg}}{1.02 \times 10^{-3} \text{ m}^3}$ $\quad \boxed{\rho = 4000 \text{ kg/m}^3}$

*15-45. A thin-walled cup has a mass of 100 g and a total volume of 250 cm³. What is the maximum number of pennies that can be placed in the cup without sinking in the water? The mass of a single penny is 3.11 g.

$F_B = \rho g V = m_c g + m_p g$; $\quad m_p = \rho V - m_c$; $\quad m_p = (1 \text{ g/cm}^3)(250 \text{ cm}^3) - 100$ g

$m_p = 150$ g; Since each penny is 3.11 g, $\boxed{\text{Nbr of pennies} = 48}$

**15-46. What is the absolute pressure at the bottom of a lake that is 30 m deep?

$P_{abs} = 1 \text{ atm} + \rho g h = 101,300 \text{ Pa} + (1000 \text{ kg/m}^3)(9.8 \text{ m/s}^2)(30 \text{ m})$; $\boxed{P = 395 \text{ kPa}}$

15-47. A fluid is forced out of a 6-mm-diameter tube so that 200 mL emerges in 32 s. What is the average velocity of the fluid in the tube? [$R = vA$; 200 mL $= 2 \times 10^{-4}$ m³]

$A = \frac{\pi d^2}{4} = \frac{\pi (0.006 \text{ m})^2}{4} = 2.83 \times 10^{-5} \text{ m}^2$; $\quad R = \frac{2 \times 10^{-4} \text{ m}^3}{32 \text{ s}} = 6.25 \times 10^{-6} \text{ m}^3/\text{s}$

$v = \frac{R}{A} = \frac{6.25 \times 10^{-6} \text{ m}^3/\text{s}}{2.83 \times 10^{-5} \text{ m}^2}$; $\quad \boxed{v = 0.221 \text{ m/s}}$

*15-48. A pump of 2-kW output power discharges water from a cellar into a street 6 m above. At what rate in liters per second is the cellar emptied?

$Power = \frac{Fs}{t} = \frac{mgh}{t}$; $\quad \frac{m}{t} = \frac{Power}{gh} = \frac{2000 \text{ W}}{(9.8 \text{ m/s}^2)(6 \text{ m})} = 34.0$ kg/s

Now, $\rho_w = (1000 \text{ kg/m}^3)(0.001 \text{ m}^3/\text{L}) = 1$ kg/L;

Therefore, 1 kg of water is one liter: $\boxed{Rate = 34.0 \text{ L/s}}$

15-49. A horizontal pipe of diameter 120 mm has a constriction of diameter 40 mm. The velocity of water in the pipe is 60 cm/s and the pressure is 150 kPa (a) What is the velocity in the constriction? (b) What is the pressure in the constriction?

$v_1 d_1^2 = v_2 d_2^2$; $\quad v_2 = v_1 \left(\frac{d_1}{d_2}\right)^2 = (60 \text{ cm/s})\left(\frac{120 \text{ mm}}{40 \text{ mm}}\right)^2$; $\quad \boxed{v_2 = 540 \text{ cm/s}}$

$P_1 + \frac{1}{2}\rho v_1^2 = P_2 + \frac{1}{2}\rho v_2^2$ $\quad$ *and* $\quad$ $P_2 = P_1 + \frac{1}{2}\rho v_1^2 - \frac{1}{2}\rho v_2^2$

$P_2 = 150,000 \text{ Pa} + \frac{1}{2}(1000 \text{ kg/m}^3)(0.06 \text{ m/s})^2 - \frac{1}{2}(1000 \text{ kg/m}^3)(5.4 \text{ m/s})^2$

$P_2 = 150,000 \text{ Pa} + 180 \text{ Pa} - 14,580 \text{ Pa} = 136,000 \text{ Pa}$; $\quad \boxed{P_2 = 136 \text{ kPa}}$

*15-50. The water column in the container shown in Fig. 15-20 stands at a height H above the base of the container. Show that the depth h required to give the horizontal range x is given by

$$h = \frac{H}{2} \pm \frac{\sqrt{H^2 - x^2}}{2}$$

Use this relation to show that the holes equidistant above and below the midpoint will have the same horizontal range? [y = H − h]

The emergent velocity v_x is: $v_x = \sqrt{2gh}$ and $x = v_x t$ and $y = \frac{1}{2}gt^2$

$t = \frac{x}{v_x} = \frac{x}{\sqrt{2gh}}$; $t^2 = \frac{x^2}{2gh}$; (Now substitute t^2 into $y = \frac{1}{2}gt^2$)

$y = \frac{1}{2}g\frac{x^2}{2gh}$; $y = \frac{gx^2}{4h}$; $y = H - h = \frac{gx^2}{4h}$

Multiply both sides by "h" and rearrange: $h^2 - Hh + x^2/4 = 0$

Now, $h = \frac{-b \pm \sqrt{b^2 - 4ac}}{2a}$ where $a = 1$, $b = H$, and $c = \frac{x^2}{4}$

$h = \frac{H \pm \sqrt{H^2 - 4x^2/4}}{2(1)}$; $\boxed{h = \frac{H}{2} \pm \frac{\sqrt{H^2 - x^2}}{2}}$

The midpoint is (H/2), and the ± term indicates the distance above and below that point.

*15-51. A column of water stands 16 ft above the base of its container. What are two hole depths at which the emergent water will have a horizontal range of 8 ft?

From Problem 15-50: $h = \frac{H}{2} \pm \frac{\sqrt{H^2 - x^2}}{2}$

$h = \frac{16\text{ ft}}{2} \pm \frac{\sqrt{(16\text{ ft})^2 - (8\text{ ft})^2}}{2} = 8\text{ ft} \pm 6.93\text{ ft}$; $\boxed{h = 1.07\text{ ft and } 14.9\text{ ft}}$

*15-52. Refer to Fig. 15-20 and Problem 15-50. Show that the horizontal range is given by

$$x = 2\sqrt{h(H - h)}$$

Use this relation to show that the maximum range is equal to the height H of the water column.

From Problem 15-50: $H - h = x^2/4h$ or $x^2 = 4hH - 4h^2$

From which we have: $\boxed{x = 2\sqrt{h(H - h)}}$

The maximum range x_{max} occurs when $h = (H/2)$

$x^2 = 4h(H - h)$

$x_{max} = 2\sqrt{\frac{H}{2}\left(H - \frac{H}{2}\right)} = 2\sqrt{\frac{H^2}{4}}$ and $\boxed{x_{max} = H}$

*15-53. Water flows through a horizontal pipe at the rate of 60 gal/min (1 ft³ = 7.48 gal). What is the velocity in a narrow section of the pipe that is reduced from 6 to 1 in. in diameter?

$R = 60\frac{\text{gal}}{\text{min}}\left(\frac{1\text{ ft}^3}{7.48\text{ gal}}\right)\left(\frac{1\text{ min}}{60\text{ s}}\right) = 0.1337\text{ ft}^3/\text{s};$ $d_1 = 6\text{ in.} = 0.5\text{ ft}$

$v_1 = \frac{R}{A_1} = \frac{0.1337\text{ ft}^3/\text{s}}{\pi(0.25\text{ ft})^2};$ $v_1 = 0.6809\text{ ft/s}$

$v_1 d_1^2 = v_2 d_2^2;$ $v_2 = v_1\left(\frac{d_1}{d_2}\right)^2 = (0.6809\text{ ft/s})\left(\frac{6\text{ in.}}{1\text{ in.}}\right)^2;$ $\boxed{v_2 = 24.5\text{ ft/s}}$

15-54. What must be the gauge pressure in a fire hose if the nozzle is to force water to a height of 20 m?

$\Delta P = \rho gh = (1000\text{ kg/m}^3)(9.8\text{ m/s}^2)(30\text{ m});$ $\boxed{\Delta P = 196\text{ kPa}}$

15-55. Water flows through the pipe shown in Fig. 15-22 at the rate of 30 liters per second.

The absolute pressure a point A is 200 kPa, and the point B is 8 m higher than point A.

The lower section of pipe has a diameter of 16 cm and the upper section narrows to a

diameter of 10 cm. (a) Find the velocities of the stream at points A and B. (b) What is the

absolute pressure at point B? [$R = 30$ L/s $= 0.030$ m^3/s]

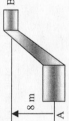

$A_A = \pi(0.08\ m)^2 = 0.0201\ m^3$

$A_B = \pi(0.05\ m)^2 = 0.00785\ m^3$

$v_A = \dfrac{R}{A_A} = \dfrac{0.030\ m^3/s}{0.0201\ m^2} = 1.49\ m/s$; $v_2 = \dfrac{R}{A_2} = \dfrac{0.030\ m^3/s}{0.00785\ m^2} = 3.82\ m/s$

$\boxed{v_1 = 1.49\ m/s}$ and $\boxed{v_2 = 3.82\ m/s}$

The rate of flow is the same at each end, but

To find pressure at point B, we consider the height $h_A = 0$ for reference purposes:

$P_A + \rho g h_A^{\;0} + \tfrac{1}{2}\rho v_A^2 = P_B + \rho g h_B + \tfrac{1}{2}\rho v_B^2$; $P_B = P_A + \tfrac{1}{2}\rho v_A^2 - \rho g h_B - \tfrac{1}{2}\rho v_B^2$

$P_B = 200{,}000\ Pa + \tfrac{1}{2}(1000\ kg/m^3)(1.49\ m/s)^2$

$- (1000\ kg/m^3)(9.8\ m/s^2)(8\ m) - \tfrac{1}{2}(1000\ kg/m^3)(3.82\ m/s)^2$

$P_B = 200{,}000\ Pa + 1113\ Pa - 78{,}400\ Pa - 7296\ Pa$; $\boxed{P_B = 115\ kPa}$

Critical Thinking Questions

15-56. A living room floor has floor dimensions of 4.50 m and 3.20 m and a height of 2.40 m.

The density of air is 1.29 kg/m^3. What does the air in the room weigh? What force does

the atmosphere exert on the floor of the room? $V = (4.50\ m)(3.20\ m)(2.40\ m)$;

$V = 34.56\ m^3$, $A_{floor} = (4.5\ m)(3.2\ m) = 14.4\ m^2$; $\rho = \dfrac{m}{V}$; $W = mg$

$m = \rho V = (1.29\ kg/m^3)(34.56\ m^3) = 44.6\ kg$; $W = (44.6\ kg)(9.8\ m/s^2)$; $\boxed{W = 437\ N}$

$F = PA = (101{,}300\ Pa)(14.4\ m^2)$; $\boxed{F = 1{,}460{,}000\ N}$

15-57. A tin coffee can floating in water (1.00 g/cm^3) has an internal volume of 180 cm^3 and a

mass of 112 g. How many grams of metal can be added to the can without causing it to

sink in the water. [*The buoyant force balances total weight.*]

$F_B = \rho g V = m_c g + m_m g$; $m_m = \rho V - m_c$;

The volume of the can and the volume of displaced water are the same.

$m_m = (1\ g/cm^3)(180\ cm^3) - 112\ g$ $\boxed{m_m = 68.0\ g}$

*15-58. A wooden block floats in water with two-thirds of its volume submerged. The same

block floats in oil with nine-tenths of its volume submerged. What is the ratio of the

density of the oil to the density of water (the specific gravity)?

The buoyant force is same for oil and water, $F_B(oil) = F_B(water)$

$\rho_{oil} g V_{oil} = \rho_w g V_w$; $\dfrac{\rho_{oil}}{\rho_w} = \dfrac{V_w}{V_{oil}} = \dfrac{2/3}{9/10}$; $\boxed{Specific\ gravity = 0.741}$

*15-59. An aircraft wing 25 ft long and 5 ft wide experiences a lifting force of 800 lb. What is the

difference in pressure between the upper and lower surfaces of the wing?

$P_1 - P_2 = \dfrac{800\ lb}{(25\ ft)(5\ ft)} = 6.40\ lb/ft^2$; $\boxed{\Delta P = 0.0444\ lb/in.^2}$

*15-60. Assume that air (ρ = 1.29 kg/m^3) flows past the top surface of an aircraft wing at 36 m/s.

The air moving past the lower surface of the wing has a velocity of 27 m/s. If the wing

has a weight of 2700 N and an area of 3.5 m^2, what is the buoyant force on the wing?

Assume $h_1 = h_2$ for small wing: $P_1 + \tfrac{1}{2}\rho v_1^2 = P_2 + \tfrac{1}{2}\rho v_2^2$

$P_1 - P_2 = \tfrac{1}{2}(1.29\ kg/m^3)(36\ m/s)^2 - \tfrac{1}{2}(1.29\ kg/m^3)(27\ m/s)^2$; $\Delta P = 365.7\ Pa$

$\Delta P = \dfrac{F}{A} = 365.7\ Pa$; $F = (365.7\ Pa)(3.50\ m^2)$; $\boxed{F = 1280\ N}$

*15-61. Seawater has a weight density of 64 lb/ft³. This water is pumped through a system of pipes (see Fig. 15-23) at the rate of 4 ft³/min. Pipe diameters at the lower and upper ends are 4 and 2 in., respectively. The water is discharged into the atmosphere at the upper end, a distance of 6 ft higher than the lower section. What are the velocities of flow in the upper and lower pipes? What are the pressures in the lower and upper sections?

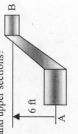

$R = 4\,\frac{ft^3}{min}\left(\frac{1\ min}{60\ s}\right) = 0.0667\ ft^3/s$ $d_A = 4$ in.; $d_B = 2$ in.

$A_A = \frac{\pi(\frac{1}{3}ft)^2}{4} = 0.0873\ ft^2$; $A_B = \frac{\pi(\frac{1}{6}ft)^2}{4} = 0.0218\ ft^2$

$v_A = \frac{R}{A_A} = \frac{0.0667\ ft^3/s}{0.0873\ ft^2} = 0.764\ ft/s$; $v_2 = \frac{R}{A_2} = \frac{0.0667\ ft^3/s}{0.0218\ ft^2} = 3.06\ ft/s$

$v_A = 0.764\ ft/s$ and $v_B = 3.06\ ft/s$

The rate of flow is the same at each end, but

Pressure at point B is 1 atm = 2116 lb/ft². Consider $h_A = 0$ for reference purposes.

$D = \rho g$; $\rho = \frac{D}{g} = \frac{64\ lb/ft^3}{32\ ft/s^2}$; $\rho = 2.00$ slugs/ft³

$P_A + \rho g h_A^{\,0} + \tfrac{1}{2}\rho v_A^2 = P_B + \rho g h_B + \tfrac{1}{2}\rho v_B^2$; $P_A = P_B + \tfrac{1}{2}\rho v_B^2 + \rho g h_B - \tfrac{1}{2}\rho v_A^2$

$P_A = 2116\ lb/ft^2 + \tfrac{1}{2}(2\ slugs/ft^3)(3.06\ ft/s)^2$
$+ (2\ slugs/ft^3)(32\ ft/s^2)(6\ ft) - \tfrac{1}{2}(2\ slugs/ft^3)(0.764\ ft/s)^2$

$P_A = 2116\ lb/ft^2 + 9.36\ lb/ft^2 + 384\ lb/ft^2 - 0.584\ lb/ft^2$; $P_A = 2509\ lb/ft^2$

$P_A = 2209\ \frac{lb}{ft^2}\left(\frac{1\ ft^2}{144\ in.^2}\right)$; $P_A = 17.4\ lb/in.^2$ *(absolute)*

Chapter 16. Temperature and Expansion

16-1. Body temperature is normal at 98.6°F. What is the corresponding temperature on the Celsius scale?

$t_C = \frac{5}{9}(t_F - 32^0) = \frac{5}{9}(98.6^0 - 32^0)$; $t_C = 37^0C$

16-2. The boiling point of sulfur is 44.5°C. What is the corresponding temperature on the Fahrenheit scale?

$t_F = \frac{9}{5}t_C + 32^0 = \frac{9}{5}(444.5^0) + 32^0$; $t_F = 832^0F$

16-3. A steel rail cools from 70 to 30°C in 1 h. What is the change of temperature in Fahrenheit degrees for the same time period?

$\Delta t = 70^0C - 30^0C = 40C^0$; $\Delta t = 40C^0\left(\frac{9\ F^0}{5\ C^0}\right)$; $\Delta t = 72\ F^0$

*16-4. At what temperature will the Celsius and Fahrenheit scales have the same numerical reading?

$\frac{5}{9}(x - 32^0) = \frac{9}{5}x + 32^0$; $x = -40^0C$ or -40^0F

16-5. A piece of charcoal initially at 180°F experiences a decrease in temperature of 120 F°. What is the final temperature on the Celsius scale?

Express this change of temperature in Celsius degrees.

$\Delta t = 120\ F^0$; $120\ F^0\left(\frac{5\ C^0}{9\ F^0}\right) = 66.7\ C^0$; $\Delta t = 66.7\ C^0$

The final temperature is 180°F - 120 F° = 60°F which must be converted to °C:

$t_C = \frac{5}{9}(t_F - 32^0) = \frac{5}{9}(60^0 - 32^0)$; $t_C = 15.6\ ^0C$

16-6. Acetone boils at 56.5°C and liquid nitrogen boils at -196°C. Express these specific temperatures on the Kelvin scale. What is the difference in these temperatures on the Celsius scale?

Acetone: $T = t_C + 273°$ m $= 56.5° + 273°$; $T = 329.5$ K

Nitrogen: $T = t_C + 273°$ m $= -196° + 273°$; $T = 77.0$ K

$\Delta t = 56.5°C - (-196°C) = 252.5\ C°$, $\boxed{\Delta t = 252.5\ C°}$

Note: The difference in kelvins is the same as in Celsius degrees.

16-7. The boiling point of oxygen is -297.35°F. Express this temperature in kelvins and in degrees Celsius.

$t_C = {}^5/_9(-297.35° - 32°)$; $\boxed{t_C = -183°C}$

$T = t_C + 273° = -183°C + 273°$; $\boxed{T = 90.0\ K}$

16-8. If oxygen cools from 120° to 70°F, what is the change of temperature in kelvins?

$\Delta t = 120°F - 70°F = 50\ F°$,

$50\ F° \left(\dfrac{5\ C°}{9\ F°}\right) = 27.8\ C°$; $1\ K = 1\ C°$; $\boxed{\Delta t = 27.8\ K}$

16-9. A wall of firebrick has an inside temperature of 313°F and an outside temperature of 73°F. Express the difference of temperature in kelvins.

$\Delta t = 313°F - 73°F = 240\ F°$;

$240\ F° \left(\dfrac{5\ C°}{9\ F°}\right) = 133\ C°$; $1\ K = 1\ C°$; $\boxed{\Delta t = 133\ K}$

16-10. Gold melts at 1336K. What is the corresponding temperature in degrees Celsius and in degrees Fahrenheit.

$t_C = 1336\ K - 273° = 1063°C$; $\boxed{t_C = 1060°C}$

$t_F = {}^9/_5\,t_C + 32° = {}^9/_5(1063°) + 32°$; $\boxed{t_F = 1950°F}$

16-11. A sample of gas cools from -120 to -180°C. Express the change of temperature in kelvins and in Fahrenheit degrees. [Since $1\ K = 1\ C°$, the change in kelvins is the same as in $C°$.]

$\Delta t = -180°C - (-120°C) = -60\ C°$; $\boxed{\Delta T = -60\ K}$

$\Delta t = -60\ C° \left(\dfrac{9\ F°}{5\ C°}\right) = -108\ F°$; $\boxed{\Delta t = -108\ F°}$

Temperature and Expansion

16-12. A slab of concrete is 20 m long. What will be the increase in length if the temperature changes from 12°C to 30°C. Assume that $\alpha = 9 \times 10^{-6}/C°$.

$\Delta L = \alpha L_0 \Delta t = (9 \times 10^{-6}/C°)(20\ m)(30°C - 12°C)$; $\boxed{\Delta L = 3.24\ mm}$

16-13. A piece of copper tubing is 6 m long at 20°C. How much will it increase in length when heated to 80°C?

$\Delta L = \alpha L_0 \Delta t = (1.7 \times 10^{-5}/C°)(6\ m)(80°C - 20°C)$; $\boxed{\Delta L = 6.12\ mm}$

16-14. A silver bar is 1 ft long at 70°F. How much will it increase in length when it is placed into boiling water (212°F)?

$\Delta L = \alpha L_0 \Delta t = (1.1 \times 10^{-5}/F°)(1\ ft)(212°F - 70°F)$; $\Delta L = 0.00156$ ft

$\Delta L = 0.00156$ ft(1 in./12 ft); $\boxed{\Delta L = 0.0187\ in.}$

16-15. The diameter of a hole in a steel plate is 9 cm when the temperature is 20°C. What will be the diameter of the hole at 200°C?

$\Delta L = \alpha L_0 \Delta t = (1.2 \times 10^{-5}/C^0)(9 \text{ cm})(200^0C - 20^0C)$; $\Delta L = 0.0194$ cm

$L = L_0 + \Delta L = 9.00 \text{ cm} + 0.0194 \text{ cm}$; $\boxed{L = 9.02 \text{ cm}}$

*16-16. A brass rod is 2.00 m long at 15°C. To what temperature must the rod be heated so that its new length is 2.01 m?   [$\Delta L = 2.01 \text{ m} - 2.00 \text{ m} = 0.01 \text{ m}$]

$\Delta L = \alpha L_0 \Delta t$; $\Delta t = \dfrac{\Delta L}{\alpha L_o} = \dfrac{0.010 \text{ m}}{(1.8 \times 10^{-5}/C^0)(2.00 \text{ m})}$; $\Delta t = 278$ C^0

$t = t_0 + \Delta t = 15^0C + 278 \text{ C}^0$; $\boxed{t = 293^0C}$

16-17. A square copper plate 4 cm on a side at 20°C is heated to 120°C. What is the increase in the area of the copper plate?   [$\gamma = 2\alpha = 2(1.7 \times 10^{-5}/C^0) = 3.4 \times 10^{-5}/C^0$]

$\Delta A = \gamma A_0 \Delta t = (3.4 \times 10^{-5}/C^0)(4 \text{ cm})^2(120^0C - 20^0C)$;

$\boxed{\Delta A = 0.0544 \text{ cm}^2.}$

*16-18. A circular hole in a steel plate has a diameter of 20.0 cm at 27°C. To what temperature must the plate be heated in order that the area of the hole be 314 cm^2?

$A = \dfrac{\pi D^2}{4} = \dfrac{\pi (20 \text{ cm})^2}{4} = 314.16 \text{ cm}^2$ at 27^0C

The change in area must be 314 cm^2 – 314.16 cm^2: $\Delta A = -0.16$ cm

$\Delta A = 2\alpha A_0 \Delta t$; $\Delta t = \dfrac{\Delta A}{2\alpha A_0} = \dfrac{-0.16 \text{ cm}}{2(1.2 \times 10^{-5}/C^0)(314.16 \text{ cm})} = -21.2 \text{ C}^0$

Thus, the final temperature is $27^0C - 21.2^0C$: $\boxed{t = 5.88^0C}$

16-19. What is the increase in volume of 16.0 liters of ethyl alcohol when the temperature is increased by 30 C^0?

$\Delta V = \beta V_0 \Delta t = (11 \times 10^{-4}/C^0)(16 \text{ L})(50^0C - 20^0C)$; $\boxed{\Delta V = 0.528 \text{ L}}$

16-20. A Pyrex beaker has an inside volume of 600 mL at 20°C. At what temperature will the inside volume be 603 mL?   [$\Delta V = 603 \text{ mL} - 600 \text{ mL} = 3 \text{ mL}$]

$\Delta V = \beta V_0 \Delta t$; $\Delta t = \dfrac{\Delta V}{\beta V_0} = \dfrac{3 \text{ mL}}{(0.3 \times 10^{-5}/C^0)(600 \text{ mL})} = 556 \text{ C}^0$

$t = 20^0 C + 556^0 C$; $\boxed{t = 576^0C}$

16-21. If 200 cm^3 of benzene exactly fills an aluminum cup at 40°C, and the system cools to 18°C, how much benzene (at 18°C) can be added to the cup without overflowing?

$\Delta V = \Delta V_B - \Delta V_{AL} = \beta_B V_0 \Delta t - (3\alpha)V_0 \Delta t$; $\Delta t = (18 - 40) = -22 \text{ C}^0$

$\Delta V = (12.4 \times 10^{-4}/C^0)(200 \text{ cm}^3)(-22 C^0) - 3(2.4 \times 10^{-5}/C^0)(200 \text{ cm}^3)(-22 C)$

$\Delta V = -5.456 \text{ cm}^3 + 0.3168 \text{ cm}^3 = -5.14 \text{ cm}^3$; $\boxed{V_B = 5.14 \text{ cm}^3}$

16-22. A Pyrex glass beaker is filled to the top with 200 cm^3 of mercury at 20°C. How much mercury will overflow if the temperature of the system is increased to 68°C?

$V_o = 200 \text{ cm}^3$; $\beta_m = 1.8 \times 10^{-4}/C^0$; $\alpha_p = 0.3 \times 10^{-5}/C^0$; $\Delta t = 68^0C - 20^0C = 48 \text{ C}^0$;

$\Delta V = \Delta V_m - \Delta V_p = \beta_m V_0 \Delta t - (3\alpha_p)V_0 \Delta t$;

$\Delta V = (1.8 \times 10^{-4}/C^0)(200 \text{ cm}^3)(48 C^0) - 3(0.3 \times 10^{-5}/C^0)(200 \text{ cm}^3)(48 C^0)$

$\Delta V = 1.728 \text{ cm}^3 - 0.0864 \text{ cm}^3 = 5.14 \text{ cm}^3$; $\boxed{V_B = 1.64 \text{ cm}^3}$

Supplementary Problems

*16-23. The diameter of the hole in a copper plate at 20°C is 3.00 mm. To what temperature must the copper be cooled if its diameter is to be 2.99 mm. [$\Delta L = (2.99 - 3.00) = -.01$ mm]

$$\Delta L = \alpha L_o \Delta t; \quad \Delta t = \frac{\Delta L}{\alpha L_o} = \frac{-0.010 \text{ m}}{(1.7 \times 10^{-5}/C^0)(3.00 \text{ m})}; \quad \Delta t = -196 \ C^0$$

$$t = t_o + \Delta t = 20^0C - 196 \ C^0; \quad \boxed{t = -176^0C}$$

16-24. A rectangular sheet of aluminum measures 6 by 9 cm at 28°C. What is its area at 0°C?

$$A_o = (6 \text{ cm})(9 \text{ cm}) = 54 \text{ cm}^2; \quad \Delta t = 0^0 - 28^0C = -28^0C; \quad \gamma = 2\alpha$$

$$\Delta A = 2\alpha A_o \Delta t = 2(2.4 \times 10^{-5}/C^0)(54 \text{ cm}^2)(-28 \ C^0) = -0.0726 \text{ cm}^2$$

$$A = 54 \text{ cm}^2 - 0.0726 \text{ cm}^2; \quad \boxed{A = 53.9 \text{ cm}^2}$$

**16-25. A steel tape measures the length of an aluminum rod as 60 cm when both are at 8°C. What will the tape read for the length of the rod if both are at 38°?

The aluminum rod will expand more than does the steel tape. Thus the tape will give a smaller reading based on the difference in the change of length.

$$\Delta L_{AL} = \alpha_{AL} L_o \Delta t = (2.4 \times 10^{-5}/C^0)(60 \text{ cm})(30 \ C^0); \quad \Delta L_{AL} = 0.0432 \text{ cm}$$

$$\Delta L_s = \alpha_s L_o \Delta t = (1.2 \times 10^{-5}/C^0)(60 \text{ cm})(30 \ C^0); \quad \Delta L_{AL} = 0.0216 \text{ cm}$$

The reading will be less by the difference in the expansions.

$$Reading = 60 \text{ cm} + (0.0432 \text{ cm} - 0.0216 \text{ cm}); \quad Reading = 60.02 \text{ cm}$$

16-26. At 20°C, a copper cube measures 40 cm on a side. What is the volume of the cube when the temperature reaches 150°C? [$V_0 = (40 \text{ cm})^3 = 64,000 \text{ cm}^3$; $\Delta t = 150 - 20 = 130 \ C^0$]

$$V = V_0 + 3\alpha V_0 \Delta t = 64,000 \text{ cm}^3 + 3(1.7 \times 10^{-5}/C^0)(64,000 \text{ cm}^3)(130 \ C^0)$$

$$V = 64,000 \text{ cm}^3 + 424 \text{ cm}^3; \quad \boxed{V = 64,420 \text{ cm}^3}$$

16-27. A Pyrex beaker ($\alpha = 0.3 \times 10^{-5}/C^0$) is filled to the top with 200 mL of glycerine ($\beta = 5.1 \times 10^{-4}/C^0$). How much glycerine will overflow the top if the system is heated from 20°C to 100°C? [$V_o = 200$ mL; $\beta_g = 5.1 \times 10^{-4}/C^0$; $\alpha_p = 0.3 \times 10^{-5}/C^0$;

$$\Delta V = \Delta V_m - \Delta V_p = \beta_m V_0 \Delta t - (3\alpha_p)V_0 \Delta t; \quad \Delta t = 100^0C - 20^0C = 80 \ C^0;$$

$$\Delta V = (5.1 \times 10^{-4}/C^0)(200 \text{ mL})(80 \ C^0) - 3(0.3 \times 10^{-5}/C^0)(200 \text{ mL})(80 \ C^0)$$

$$\Delta V = 8.16 \text{ mL} - 0.1444 \text{ mL} = 8.016 \text{ mL}; \quad \boxed{V_B = 8.02 \text{ mL}}$$

16-28. A stove is at 450°F. If the temperature drops by 50 kelvins, what is the new temperature in degrees Celsius?

$$t_C = \tfrac{5}{9}(t_F - 32) = \tfrac{5}{9}(450 - 32); \quad t_C = 232.2^0C$$

$$Since \ 1 \text{ K} = 1 \ C^0: \quad t = 232.2^0 - 50^0 \quad and \quad \boxed{t = 182^0C}$$

*16-29. A 100-ft steel tape correctly measures distance when the temperature is 20°C. What is the true measurement if this tape indicates distance of 94.62 ft on a day when the temperature is 36°C?

$$\Delta L = \alpha L_o \Delta t = (1.2 \times 10^{-5}/C^0)(100 \text{ ft})(36^0C - 20^0C) = 0.0192 \text{ ft}$$

$$L = L_o + \Delta L = 94.62 \text{ ft} + 0.0192 \text{ ft}; \quad \boxed{L = 94.64 \text{ ft}}$$

*16-30. The diameter of a steel rod is 3.000 mm when the temperature is 20°C. Also at 20°C, the diameter of a brass ring is 2.995 mm. At what common temperature will the brass ring slip over the steel rod smoothly?

$$\Delta L_b - \Delta L_s = 3.000 \text{ mm} - 2.999 \text{ mm} = 0.001 \text{ mm}$$

$$(1.8 \times 10^{-5}/C^0)(3.000 \text{ mm}) \Delta t - (1.2 \times 10^{-5}/C^0)(2.999 \text{ mm}) \Delta t = 0.001 \text{ mm}$$

$$From \ which: \quad \Delta t = 55.2 \ C^0 \quad and \quad t = 20^0C + 55.2^0 \text{ C} \quad \boxed{t = 75.2^0C}$$

Critical Thinking Questions

16-35. The laboratory apparatus for measuring the coefficient of linear expansion is illustrated in Fig. 16-17. The temperature of a metal rod is increased by passing steam through an enclosed jacket. The resulting increase in length is measured with the micrometer screw at one end. Since the original length and temperature are known, the expansion coefficient can be calculated from Eq. (16-8). The following data were recorded during an experiment with a rod of unknown metal:

$L_o = 600$ mm $t_o = 23^0\text{C}$

$\Delta L = 1.04$ mm $t_f = 98^0\text{C}$

What is the coefficient of linear expansion for this metal? Can you identify the metal?

$\alpha = \dfrac{\Delta L}{L_0 \Delta t} = \dfrac{1.04 \text{ mm}}{(600 \text{ mm})(98^0\text{C} - 23^0\text{C})}$ $\boxed{\alpha = 2.3 \times 10^{-5}/\text{C}^0; \quad \text{Aluminum}}$

*16-36. Assume that the end points of a rod are fixed rigidly between two walls to prevent expansion with increasing temperature. From the definitions of Young's modulus (Chapter 13) and your knowledge of linear expansion, show that the compressive force F exerted by the walls will be given by

$$F = \alpha A Y \Delta t$$

where A = cross-section of the rod, Y = Young's modulus, and Δt = increase in temperature of rod. From Chap. 15, young's modulus Y is:

$Y = \dfrac{FL}{A\Delta L}$; $F = YA\left(\dfrac{\Delta L}{L}\right)$; and $\Delta L = \alpha L_0 \Delta t$ or $\dfrac{\Delta L}{L} = \alpha \Delta t$

Eliminating $(\Delta L/L)$, *we have:* $\boxed{F = YA\alpha \Delta t}$

---

*16-31. A certain metal cube increases its volume by 0.50 percent when its temperature increases by 100 C°. What is the linear expansion coefficient for this metal? [0.5 % = 0.005]

$\Delta V = \beta V_0 \Delta t = 3\alpha V_0 \Delta t$; $\alpha = \dfrac{1}{3\Delta t}\left(\dfrac{\Delta V}{V_0}\right) = \dfrac{1}{3(100 \text{ C}^0)}(0.0050)$

$\boxed{\alpha = 1.67 \times 10^{-5}/\text{C}^0}$

16-32. By what percentage does a brass cube increase its volume when heated from 20°C to 100°C? [$\beta = 3\alpha$ and $\Delta t = 100°\text{C} - 20°\text{C} = 80 \text{ C}^0$]

$\Delta V = \beta V_0 \Delta t = 3\alpha V_0 \Delta t$; $\dfrac{\Delta V}{V_0} = 3\alpha \Delta t = 3(1.8 \times 10^{-5}/\text{C}^0)(80 \text{ C}^0)$

$\dfrac{\Delta V}{V_0} = 4.32 \times 10^{-3}$; $\boxed{(\Delta V/V) = 0.432 \%}$

16-33. A round brass plug has a diameter of 8.001 cm at 28°C. To what temperature must the plug be cooled if it is to fit snugly into an 8.000 cm hole?

$\Delta L = \alpha L_0 \Delta t$; $\Delta t = \dfrac{\Delta L}{\alpha L_o} = \dfrac{-0.001 \text{ cm}}{(1.8 \times 10^{-5}/\text{C}^0)(8.001 \text{ cm})}$; $\Delta t = -6.94 \text{ C}^0$

$t = t_o + \Delta t = 28^0\text{C} - 6.94 \text{ C}^0$; $\boxed{t = 21.1°\text{C}}$

16-34. Five hundred cubic centimeters of ethyl alcohol completely fill a Pyrex beaker. If the temperature of the system increases by 70 C°, what volume of alcohol overflows?

$V_o = 500 \text{ cm}^3$; $\beta_m = 11 \times 10^{-4}/\text{C}^0$; $\alpha_p = 0.3 \times 10^{-5}/\text{C}^0$

$\Delta V = \Delta V_m - \Delta V_p = \beta_m V_0 \Delta t - (3\alpha_p)V_0 \Delta t$; $\Delta t = 70 \text{ C}^0$;

$\Delta V = (11 \times 10^{-4}/\text{C}^0)(500 \text{ cm}^3)(70 \text{ C}^0) - 3(0.3 \times 10^{-5}/\text{C}^0)(500 \text{ cm}^3)(70 \text{ C}^0)$

$\Delta V = 38.5 \text{ cm}^3 - 0.315 \text{ cm}^3 = 5.14 \text{ cm}^3$; $\boxed{V_B = 38.2 \text{ cm}^3}$

*16-37. Prove that the density of a material changes with temperature so that the new density ρ is given by

$$\rho = \frac{\rho_o}{1 + \beta \Delta t}$$

where ρ_o = original density, β = volume expansion coefficient, and Δt = change in temperature.

$$V_f = V_o + \beta V_o \Delta t = V_o(1 + \alpha \Delta t) \quad \text{from which} \quad \frac{V_f}{V_0} = 1 - \beta \Delta t;$$

Now, $\rho = m/V$ or $V = m/\rho$, so that: $\quad \dfrac{m/\rho}{m/\rho_0} = 1 + \beta \Delta t$

$$\frac{\rho_o}{\rho} = 1 + \beta \Delta t; \qquad \boxed{\rho = \frac{\rho_0}{1 + \beta \Delta t}}$$

16-38. The density of mercury at 0^0C is 13.6 g/cm³. Use the relation in the previous example to find the density of mercury at 60^0C?

$$\rho = \frac{\rho_0}{1 + \beta \Delta t} = \frac{(13.6 \text{ g/cm}^3)}{1 + (1.8 \times 10^{-4}/C^0)(60 \ C^0)}; \qquad \boxed{\rho = 13.5 \text{ g/cm}^3}$$

16-39. A steel ring has an inside diameter of 4.000 cm at 20^0C. The ring is to be slipped over a copper shaft that has a diameter of 4.003 cm at 20^0C. (a) To what temperature must the ring be heated? (b) If the ring and the shaft are cooled uniformly, at what temperature will the ring just slip off the shaft? [ΔL_s = 4.003 cm − 4.00 cm = 0.003 cm]

(a) $\Delta L_s = \alpha L_o \Delta t$; $\quad \Delta t = \dfrac{0.003 \text{ cm}}{(1.2 \times 10^{-5}/C^0)(4.000 \text{ cm})} = 62.5 \ C^0$

The steel ring must be heated to: 20^0C + 62.5^0 or $\boxed{82.5^0 C}$

*16-39. (Cont.) (b) Find temperature at which ring slips off easily.

Begin at 20^0C where $L_s = 4.000$ cm and $L_c = 4.003$ cm, next cool both until the diameters are the same. That occurs when the copper rod shrinks more than the steel ring such that: $\Delta L_{copper} - \Delta L_{steel} = 0.003$ cm

$\alpha_c L_c \Delta t - \alpha_s L_s \Delta t = 0.003$ cm; $\quad \Delta t = \dfrac{0.003 \text{ cm}}{\alpha_c L_c - \alpha_s L_s}$

$$\Delta t = \frac{0.003 \text{ cm}}{(1.7 \times 10^{-5}/C^0)(4.003 \text{ cm}) - (1.2 \times 10^{-5}/C^0)(4.000 \text{ cm})} = 150 \ C^0$$

Thus the temperature of both copper and steel must decrease by 150^0C.

$t_f = t_0 - 150 \ C^0 = 20^0$C − 150 C^0; $\quad \boxed{t_f = -130^0 C}$

Chapter 17. Quantity of Heat

NOTE: Refer to Tables 17-1 and 17-2 for accepted values for specific heat, heat of vaporization, and heat of fusion for the substances in the problems below

Quantity of heat and Specific Heat Capacity

17-1. What quantity of heat is required to change the temperature of 200 g of lead from 20 to 100^0C? [Answer given in calories--also worked below for joules.]

$Q = mc\Delta t = (0.20 \text{ kg})(130 \text{ J/kg·K})(100^0\text{C} - 20^0\text{C});$ $\boxed{Q = 2080 \text{ J}}$

$Q = mc\Delta t = (200 \text{ g})(0.031 \text{ cal/g·}C^0)(100^0\text{C} - 20^0\text{C});$ $\boxed{Q = 496 \text{ cal}}$

17-2. A certain process requires 500 J of heat. Express this energy in calories and in Btu.

$Q = 500 \text{ J}\left(\dfrac{1 \text{ cal}}{4.186 \text{ J}}\right)$ $\boxed{Q = 119 \text{ cal}}$

$Q = 500 \text{ J}\left(\dfrac{1 \text{ cal}}{4.186 \text{ J}}\right)\left(\dfrac{\text{Btu}}{252 \text{ cal}}\right)$ $\boxed{Q = 0.474 \text{ Btu}}$

17-3. An oven applies 400 kJ of heat to a 4 kg of a substance causing its temperature to increase by $80\ C^0$. What is the specific heat capacity?

$c = \dfrac{Q}{m\Delta t} = \dfrac{400,000 \text{ J}}{(4 \text{ kg})(80\ C^0)};$ $\boxed{c = 1250 \text{ J/kg } C^0}$

17-4. What quantity of heat will be released when 40 lb of copper cools form 78 to 32^0F?

$Q = (40 \text{ lb})(0.093 \text{ Btu/lb } F^0)(78^0\text{F} - 32^0\text{F});$ $\boxed{Q = 171 \text{ Btu}}$

17-5. A lawn mower engine does work at the rate of 3 kW. What equivalent amount of heat will be given off in one hour?

$P = 3000 W = 3000\dfrac{\text{J}}{\text{s}}\left(\dfrac{3600 \text{ s}}{1 \text{ h}}\right);$ $Q = 10,800,000 \text{ J/h};$ $\text{Q} = 10.8 \text{ MJ/h}$

236 Unit A   Solutions Manual

Copyright © by Glencoe/McGraw-Hill.

17-6. An air conditioner is rated at 15,000 Btu/h. Express this power in kilowatts and in calories per second?

$P = 15,000\ \dfrac{\text{Btu}}{\text{h}}\left(\dfrac{252 \text{ cal}}{1 \text{ Btu}}\right)\left(\dfrac{1 \text{ h}}{3600 \text{ s}}\right);$ $\boxed{P = 1050 \text{ cal/s}}$

17-7. Hot coffee is poured into a 0.5-kg ceramic cup with a specific heat of 880 J/kg C^0. How much heat is absorbed by the cup if its temperature increases from 20 to 80^0C?

$Q = mc\Delta t = (0.5 \text{ kg})(880 \text{ J/kg } C^0)(80^0\text{C} - 20^0\text{C});$ $\boxed{Q = 26.4 \text{ kJ}}$

17-8. A 2 kW electric motor is 80 percent efficient. How much heat is lost in one hour?

$\text{Loss} = 0.20(2 \text{ kW}) = 400 \text{ W} = 400 \text{ J/s};$

$\text{Loss} = 400 \text{ J/s}(3600 \text{ s/h});$ $\boxed{\text{Loss} = 1.44 \text{ MJ}}$

17-9. An 8-kg copper sleeve must be heated from 25^0C to 140^0C in order that it will expand to fit over a shaft. How much heat is required?

$Q = mc\Delta t = (8 \text{ kg})(390 \text{ J/kg } C^0)(140^0\text{C} - 25^0\text{C});$ $\boxed{Q = 359 \text{ kJ.}}$

17-10. How many grams of iron at 20^0C must be heated to 100^0C in order to be able to release 1800 cal of heat as it returns to its original temperature?

$m = \dfrac{Q}{c\Delta t} = \dfrac{1800 \text{ cal}}{(0.113 \text{ cal/g·}C^0)(100^0\text{C} - 20^0\text{C})};$ $\boxed{m = 199 \text{ g}}$

17-11. A 4-kg chunk of metal (c = 320 J/kg C^0) is initially at 300^0C. What will its final temperature be if it loses 50 kJ of heat energy?

$\Delta t = \dfrac{Q}{mc} = \dfrac{-50,000 \text{ J}}{(4 \text{ kg})(320 \text{ J/kg } C^0)};$ $\Delta t = -39.1\ C^0$

$t = 300^0\text{C} - 39.1^0\text{C};$ $\boxed{t = 261^0\text{C}}$

Chapter 17   Quantity of Heat   237

Copyright © by Glencoe/McGraw-Hill.

17-12. In a heat-treatment, a hot copper part is quenched with water, cooling it from 400°C to 30°C. What was the mass of the part if it loses 80 kcal of heat?

$$m = \frac{Q}{c\Delta t} = \frac{-80,000 \text{ cal}}{(0.093 \text{ cal/g C}^0)(30^0C - 400^0C)}; \quad m = 2325 \text{ g}; \quad \boxed{m = 2.32 \text{ kg}}$$

Conservation of Energy: Calorimetry

*17-13. A 400-g copper pipe initially at 200°C is dropped into a container filled with 3 kg of water at 20°C. Ignoring other heat exchanges, what is the equilibrium temperature of the mixture?

Heat lost by copper pipe = Heat gained by water; $m_c c_c \Delta t = m_w c_w \Delta t;$

$$(400 \text{ g})(0.093 \text{ cal/g C})(200^0C - t_e) = (3000 \text{ kg})(1 \text{ ca/g C})(t_e - 20^0C)$$

Solving for t_e we obtain: $\boxed{t_e = 22.2^0C}$

17-14. How much aluminum (c = 0.22 cal/g C°) at 20°C must be added to 400 g of hot water at 80°C in order that the equilibrium temperature be 30°C?

$$m_w c_w (80^0C - 30^0C) = m_{AL} c_{Al} (30^0C - 20^0C)$$

$$(400 \text{ g})(1 \text{ cal/g C}^0)(50 \text{ C}^0) = m_{Al} (0.22 \text{ cal/g C}^0)(10 \text{ C}^0)$$

$$m_{Al} = \frac{20,000 \text{ cal}}{2.2 \text{ cal/g}} = 9090 \text{ g}; \quad \boxed{m_{Al} = 9.09 \text{ kg}}$$

17-15. A 450-g chunk of metal is heated to 100°C and then dropped into a 50-g aluminum calorimeter cup containing 100-g of water. The initial temperature of cup and water is 10°C and the equilibrium temperature is 21.1°C. Find the specific heat of the metal?

Heat lost by metal = heat gained by cup + heat gained by water

$$m_x c_x(100^0C - 21.1^0C) = m_{Al}c_{Al}(21.1^0C - 10^0C) + m_w c_w(21.1^0C - 10^0C)$$

17-15. (Cont.)

$$m_x c_x (78.9 \text{ C}^0) = m_{Al}c_{Al}(11.1 \text{ C}^0) + m_w c_w(11.1 \text{ C}^0)$$

$$(450 \text{ g}) c_x (78.9 \text{ C}^0) = (50 \text{ g})(0.22 \text{ cal/g C}^0)(11.1 \text{ C}^0) + (100 \text{ g}) (1 \text{ cal/g C}^0)(11.1 \text{ C}^0)$$

$$(35,505 \text{ g C}^0) c_x = 122.1 \text{ cal} + 1110 \text{ cal}; \quad \boxed{c_x = 0.0347 \text{ cal/g C}^0}$$

17-16. What mass of water initially at 20°C must be mixed with 2 kg of iron to bring the iron from 250°C to an equilibrium temperature of 25°C?

$$m_w c_w (25^0C - 20^0C) = m_{iron} c_{iron} (250^0C - 25^0C)$$

$$m_w (4186 \text{ J/kg C}^0)(5 \text{ C}^0) = (2 \text{ kg})(470 \text{ J/kg C}^0)(225 \text{ C}^0)$$

$$m_w = \frac{211,500 \text{ J}}{20,930 \text{ J/kg}} = 10.1 \text{ kg}; \quad \boxed{m_{Al} = 10.1 \text{ kg}}$$

*17-17. A worker removes a 2-kg piece of iron from an oven and places it into a 1-kg aluminum container partially filled with 2 kg of water. If the temperature of the water rises from 21 to 50°C, what was the initial temperature of the iron? [$\Delta t_w = 50^0C - 21^0C = 29 \text{ C}^0$]

Heat lost by iron = heat gained by aluminum + heat gained by water

$$(2 \text{ kg})(470 \text{ J/kg C}^0)(t_i - 50^0C) = m_{Al}c_{Al}(29 \text{ C}^0) + m_w c_w(29 \text{ C}^0)$$

$$(940 \text{ J/C}^0)(t_i - 50^0C) = (1 \text{ kg})(920 \text{ J/kg C}^0)(29 \text{ C}^0) + (2 \text{ kg})(4186 \text{ J/kg C}^0)(29 \text{ C}^0)$$

$$(940 \text{ J/C}^0) \, t_i - 47,000 \text{ J} = 26,680 \text{ J} + 242,788 \text{ J}$$

$$t_i = \frac{222,468 \text{ J}}{940 \text{ J/C}^0}; \quad \boxed{t_i = 337^0C}$$

17-18. How much iron at 212°F must be mixed with 10-lb of water at 68°F in order to have an equilibrium temperature of 100°F? [The "lb" used here is the pound-mass (1/32) slug.]

$$\Delta t_i = 212^0F - 100^0F = 112 \text{ F}^0; \quad \Delta t_w = 100^0F - 68^0F = 32 \text{ F}^0;$$

$$m_x (0.113 \text{ Btu/lb F}^0)(112 \text{ F}^0) = (10 \text{ lb})(1 \text{ Btu/lb F}^0)(32 \text{ F}^0)$$

$$\boxed{m_x = 25.3 \text{ lb}}$$

17-22. How much heat is needed to melt completely 20 g of silver at its melting temperature?

$Q_2 = mL_f = (0.020\ kg)(960.8\ J/kg)$; $\boxed{Q_2 = 19.2\ J}$

17-23. What quantity of heat is needed to convert 2 kg of ice at -25°C to steam at 100°C?

Total $Q = Q_1$ to reach 0°C + Q_2 to melt + Q_3 to reach 100°C + Q_4 to vaporize

$Q_1 = mc\Delta t = (2\ kg)(2300\ J/kg\ C°)(25\ C°)$; $Q_1 = 1.150 \times 10^5\ J$

$Q_2 = mL_f = (2\ kg)(334.00\ J/kg)$; $Q_2 = 6.680 \times 10^5$

$Q_3 = mc\Delta t = (2\ kg)(4186\ J/kg\ C°)(100\ C°)$; $Q_3 = 8.372 \times 10^5\ J$

$Q_4 = mL_v = (2\ kg)(2,256,000\ J/kg)$; $Q_4 = 45.12 \times 10^5\ J$

$Q_T = Q_1 + Q_2 + Q_3 + Q_4 = 1,465,000\ cal$; $\boxed{Q_T = 6.13 \times 10^6\ J}$

17-24. If 7.57 x 10⁶ J of heat are absorbed in the process of completely melting a 1.60-kg chunk of an unknown metal, what is the latent heat of fusion and what is the metal?

$L_f = \dfrac{Q}{m} = \dfrac{7.57 \times 10^6\ J}{1.60\ kg}$; $\boxed{L_f = 4.73 \times 10^6\ \dfrac{J}{kg}};$ Copper

17-25. How many grams of steam at 100°C must be mixed with 200-g of water at 20°C in order for the equilibrium temperature to be 50°C?

$m_s L_v + m_s c_w(100°C - 50°C) = m_w c_w(50°C - 20°C)$

$(540\ cal/g)m_s + (50\ C°)(1\ cal/g\ C°)m_s = (200\ g)(1\ cal/g\ C°)(30\ C°)$

$(590\ cal/g)m_s = 6000\ cal$; $\boxed{m_s = 10.2\ g}$

17-26. What total heat is released when 0.500 lb of steam at 212°F changes to ice at 10°F?

Total Heat lost = (0.5 lb)(970 Btu/lb) + (0.5 lb)(1 Btu/lb F°)(212°F − 32°F)
+ (0.5 lb)(144 Btu/lb) + (0.5 lb)(0.5 Btu/lb F°)(10 F°)

Heat Lost = 485 Btu + 90 Btu + 72 Btu + 2.5 Btu; $\boxed{Heat\ lost = 650\ Btu}$

17-19. A 1.3-kg copper block is heated to 200°C and then dropped into an insulated container partially filled with 2-kg of water at 20°C. What is the equilibrium temperature?

$(1.3\ kg)(390\ J/kg\ C°)(200°C - t_e) = (2\ kg)(4186\ J/kg\ C°)(t_e - 20°)$

$101,400\ J - (507\ J/C°)t_e = 8372\ J/C°)t_e - 167,440\ J$

$t_e = \dfrac{268,840\ J}{8879\ J/C°}$; $\boxed{t_e = 30.3°C}$

17-20. Fifty grams of brass shot are heated to 200°C and then dropped into a 50-g aluminum cup containing 160 g of water. The cup and water are initially 20°C. What is the equilibrium temperature?

Heat lost by shot: (50 g)(0.094 cal/g C°)(200°C − t_e) = 940 cal − (4.70 cal/C°)t_e

Heat Gained by AL: (50 g)(0.22 cal/g C°)(t_e − 20°C) = (11 cal/C°)t_e − 220 cal

Heat Gained by Water: (160 g)(1 cal/g C°)(t_e − 20°C) = (160 cal/C°)t_e − 3200 cal

Heat lost by shot = Heat gained by aluminum + Heat gained by water

940 cal − (4.70 cal/C°)t_e = [(11 cal/C°)t_e − 220 cal] + [(160 cal/C°)t_e − 3200 cal]

Simplify and solve for t_e: $\boxed{t_e = 24.8°C}$

Heat of Fusion and Heat of Vaporization

17-21. A foundry has an electric furnace that can completely melt 540 kg of copper. If the copper was initially at 20°C, what total heat is needed to melt the copper?

First we raise temperature to boiling point, then we must melt at that temperature:

$Q_1 = mc\Delta t = (540\ kg)(390\ J/kg\ C°)(1080°C - 20°C) = 2.23 \times 10^8\ J$

$Q_2 = mL_f = (540\ kg)(134,000\ J/kg)$; $Q_2 = 7.24 \times 10^7\ J$; $\boxed{Q_2 = 7.24 \times 10^7}$

$Q_T = Q_1 + Q_2 = 22.3 \times 10^7\ J + 7.24 \times 10^7\ J$; $\boxed{Q_T = 2.96 \times 10^8\ J}$

17-31. A heating element supplies an output power of 12 kW. How much time is needed to melt completely a 2-kg silver block? Assume no power is wasted.

$$Q = mL_f = (2\ kg)(88.3 \times 10^3\ J/kg) = 176,600\ J; \qquad P = 12,000\ J/s$$

$$P = \frac{Heat}{t}; \qquad t = \frac{Heat}{P} = \frac{176,600\ J}{12,000\ J/s}; \qquad \boxed{t = 14.7\ s}$$

*17-32. How much ice at -10^0C must be added to 200 g of water at 50^0C to bring the equilibrium temperature to 40^0C? (The ice must first be brought to 0^0C, then it must be melted, and the resulting water brought to the equilibrium temperature.)

$$m_ic_i(10\ C^0) + m_iL_f + m_ic_w(40^0C - 0^0C) = m_sc_w(50^0C - 40^0C)$$

$$m_i(0.5\ cal/g\ C^0)(10\ C^0) + (80\ cal/g)m_i + (40\ C^0)(1\ cal/g\ C^0)m_i = (200\ g)(1\ cal/g\ C^0)(10\ C^0)$$

$$(125\ cal/g)m_s = 2000\ cal; \qquad \boxed{m_s = 16.0\ g}$$

*17-33. Assume that 5 g of steam at 100^0C are mixed with 20-g of ice at 0^0C. What will be the equilibrium temperature? (Total heat lost by steam = Total heat gained by ice)

$$m_sL_v + m_sc_w(100^0C - t_e) = m_iL_f + m_ic_w(t_e - 0^0C)$$

$$(5\ g)(540\ cal/g) + (5\ g)(1\ cal/g\ C^0)(100^0C - t_e) = (20\ g)(80\ cal/g) + (20\ g)(1\ cal/g\ C^0)t_e$$

$$2700\ cal + 500\ cal - (5\ cal/C^0)t_e = 1600\ cal + (20\ cal/C^0)t_e$$

$$(25\ cal/C^0)t_e = 1600\ cal; \qquad \boxed{t_e = 64.0^0C}$$

*17-34. How much heat is developed by the brakes of a 4000-lb truck to bring it to a stop from a speed of 60 mi/h? $Work = \frac{1}{2}mv_f^2 - \frac{1}{2}mv_o^2$ $\quad v_o = 60\ mi/h = 88\ ft/s;$ $\quad v_f = 0;$ $\quad m = W/g$

$$m = \frac{4000\ lb}{32\ ft/s^2} = 125\ slugs; \qquad Work = 0 - \frac{1}{2}(125\ sl)(88\ ft/s)^2 = -484,000\ ft\ lb$$

$$Heat = -484,000\ ft\ lb\left(\frac{1\ Btu}{778\ ft\ lb}\right); \qquad \boxed{Heat = 622\ Btu}$$

Chapter 17 Quantity of Heat **243**

17-27. One hundred grams of ice at 0^0C is mixed with 600 g of water at 25^0C. What will be the equilibrium temperature for the mixture?

$$(600\ g)(1\ cal/g\ C^0)(25\ C^0 - t_e) = (100\ g)(80\ cal/g) + (100\ g)(t_e - 0^0)$$

$$15,000\ cal - 600t_e = 8000\ cal + 100t_e - 0$$

$$t_e = \frac{7000\ cal}{700\ cal/C^0}; \qquad \boxed{t_e = 10.0^0C}$$

17-28. A certain grade of gasoline has a heat of combustion of $4.6 \times 10^7\ J/kg$. Assuming 100% efficiency, how much gasoline must be burned to completely melt 2-kg of copper at its melting temperature?

$$Q = mH = (2\ kg)(4.6 \times 10^7\ J/kg) = 9.2 \times 10^7\ J;$$

$$\boxed{Q = 9.2 \times 10^7\ J}$$

Supplementary Problems

17-29. If 1600 J of heat is applied to a brass ball, its temperature rises from 20 to 70^0C. What is the mass of the ball?

$$m = \frac{Q}{c\Delta t} = \frac{1600\ J}{(390\ J/kg\ C^0)(70^0C - 20^0C)};$$

$$m = 0.0821\ kg; \qquad \boxed{m = 82.1\ g}$$

17-30. How much heat does an electric freezer absorb in lowering the temperature of 2 kg of water from 80^0C to 20^0C?

$$Q = mc\Delta t = (2\ kg)(4186\ J/kg\ C^0)(80^0C - 20^0C); \qquad \boxed{Q = 5.02 \times 10^5\ J}$$

$$Alternatively: \quad Q = (2000\ g)(1\ cal/g\ C^0)(80^0C - 20^0C); \qquad \boxed{Q = 120\ kcal}$$

*17-35. Two hundred grams of copper at 300^0C is dropped into a 310-g copper calorimeter cup partially filled with 300 g of water. If the initial temperature of the cup and water was 15^0C, what is the equilibrium temperature?

Heat lost by copper: $(200 \text{ g})(0.093 \text{ cal/g C}^0)(300^0C - t_e) = 5580 \text{ cal} - (18.6 \text{ cal/C}^0)t_e$

Heat Gained by cup: $(310 \text{ g})(0.093 \text{ cal/g C}^0)(t_e - 15^0C) = (28.83 \text{ cal/C}^0)t_e - 432.5 \text{ cal}$

Heat Gained by Water: $(300 \text{ g})(1 \text{ cal/g C}^0)(t_e - 15^0C) = (300 \text{ cal/C}^0)t_e - 4500 \text{ cal}$

Heat lost by copper = Heat gained by cup + Heat gained by water

$5580 \text{ cal} - (18.6 \text{ cal/C}^0)t_e = [(28.8 \text{ cal/C}^0)t_e - 432.5 \text{ cal}] + [(300 \text{ cal/C}^0)t_e - 4500 \text{ cal}]$

Simplify and solve for t_e: $\boxed{t_e = 30.3 \ ^0C}$

*17-36. How many pounds of coal must be burned to melt completely 50 lb of ice in a heater that is 60% efficient?

$m_x(mH_c) = m_iL_f$ $m_x = \dfrac{(50 \text{ lb})(144 \text{ Btu/lb})}{0.60(13{,}000 \text{ Btu/lb})}$;

$\boxed{m_x = 0.923 \text{ lb}}$

*17-37. If 80 g of molten lead at 327.3^0C are poured into a 260-g iron casting initially at 20^0C, what will be the equilibrium temperature neglecting other losses?

Heat to solidify lead: $Q = mL_f = (0.080 \text{ kg})(24{,}500 \text{ J/kg}) = 1960 \text{ J}$

Heat lost to reach t_e: $Q = (0.080 \text{ kg})(130 \text{ J/kg C}^0)(327.3^0C - t_e) = 3404 \text{ J} - (10.4 \text{ J/C}^0) \, t_e$

Heat gained by iron: $Q = (0.260 \text{ kg})(470 \text{ J/kg C}^0)(t_e - 20^0C) = (122 \text{ J/C}^0)t_e - 2444 \text{ J}$

Heat lost in solidifying + heat to reach t_e = *heat gained by iron*

$1960 \text{ J} + 3404 \text{ J} - (10.4 \text{ J/C}^0)t_e = (122 \text{ J/C}^0)t_e - 2444 \text{ J}$

Simplify and solve for t_e: $\boxed{t_e = 58.9^0C}$

---

*17-38. What equilibrium temperature is reached when 2 lb of ice at 0^0F is dropped into a 3-lb aluminum cup containing 7.5 lb of water? The cup and water are initially at 200^0F.

$m_ic(32^0F - 0^0F) + m_iL_f + m_ic_w(t_e - 32^0F) = m_wc_w(200^0F - t_e) + m_{Al}c_{Al}(200^0F - t_e)$

Heat gained: $(2 \text{ lb})(0.5 \text{ Btu/lb F}^0)(32 \text{ F}^0)+(2 \text{ lb})(144 \text{ Btu/lb})+(2 \text{ lb})(1 \text{ Btu/lb F}^0)(t - 32^0F)$

Heat gained: $32 \text{ Btu} + 288 \text{ Btu} + (2 \text{ lb/F}^0)t_e - 64 \text{ Btu} = \underline{256 \text{ Btu} + (2 \text{ lb/F}^0)t_e}$

Heat Lost: $(7.5 \text{ lb})(1 \text{ Btu/lb F}^0)(200^0F - t_e) + (3 \text{ lb})(0.22 \text{ Btu/lb F}^0)(200^0F - t_e)$

Heat lost: $1500 \text{ Btu}-(7.5 \text{ Btu/F}^0)t_e +132 \text{ Btu} -(0.66 \text{ Btu/F}^0)t_e = \underline{1632 \text{ Btu} - (8.16 \text{ Btu/F}^0)t_e}$

Heat lost = Heat Gained: $256 \text{ Btu} + (2 \text{ lb/F}^0)t_e = 1632 \text{ Btu} - (8.16 \text{ Btu/F}^0)t_e$

Solving for t_e *we have:* $\boxed{t_e = 135^0F}$

*17-39. A solar collector has an area of 5 m² and the power of sunlight is delivered at 550 W/m². This power is used to increase the temperature of 200 g of water from 20^0C to 50^0C. How much time is required?

$P = (550 \text{ W/m}^2)(5 \text{ m}^2) = 2750 \text{ W} = 2750 \text{ J/s}$

$Q = mc\Delta t = (0.200 \text{ kg})(4186 \text{ J/kg C}^0)(50^0C - 20^0C);$ $Q = 25{,}116 \text{ J}$

$t = \dfrac{Q}{P} = \dfrac{25{,}116 \text{ J}}{2750 \text{ J/s}};$ $\boxed{t_e = 9.13 \text{ s}}$

*17-40. If 10 g of milk at 12^0C is added to 180 g of coffee at 95^0C, what is the equilibrium temperature. Assume milk and coffee are essentially water.

Heat gained by milk = heat lost by coffee.

$(10 \text{ g})(1 \text{ cal/g C}^0)(t_e - 12^0C) = (80 \text{ g})(1 \text{ cal/g C}^0)(95^0C - t_e)$

$(10 \text{ cal/C}^0)t_e - 120 \text{ cal} = 7600 \text{ cal} - (80 \text{ cal/C}^0) t_e$

Solving for t_e *we obtain:* $\boxed{t_e = 85.8^0C}$

Critical Thinking Questions

*17-44. An large, insulated container holds 120 g of coffee at $85°C$. How much ice at $0°C$ must be added to cool the coffee to $50°C$? Now, how much coffee at $100°C$ must be added to return the contents to $85°C$? How many grams are finally in the container?

(a) $m_i L_f + m_i c_w(50°C - 0°C) = (120 \text{ g})(1 \text{ cal/g C}°)(85°C - 50°)$

$m_i(80 \text{ cal/g}) + m_i(1 \text{ cal/g C}°)(50 \text{ C}°) = (120 \text{ g})(1 \text{ cal/g C}°)(35 \text{ C}°)$

$(130 \text{ cal/g})m_i = 4200 \text{ cal}$; $\boxed{m_i = 32.3 \text{ g}}$

(b) $m_c(1 \text{ cal/g C}°)(100°C - 85°C) = (120 \text{ g} + 32.3 \text{ g})(1 \text{ cal/g C}°)(85°C - 50°C)$

$(15 \text{ cal/g})m_c = 5330.5 \text{ cal}$; $\boxed{m_c = 355 \text{ g}}$

(c) $m_T = 120 \text{ g} + 32.3 \text{ g} + 355.4 \text{ g} = 508 \text{ g}$; $\boxed{m_T = 508 \text{ g}}$

*17-45. Four 200-g blocks are constructed out of copper, aluminum, Silver, and Lead so that they have the same mass and the same base area (although of different heights). The temperature of each block is raised from $20°C$ to $100°C$ by applying heat at the rate of 200 J/s. Find the time required for each block to reach $100°C$.

Copper: $Q = mc\Delta t = (0.2 \text{ kg})(390 \text{ J/kg C}°)(80 \text{ C}°)$; $Q = 6240 \text{ J}$

$t = \dfrac{6240 \text{ J}}{200 \text{ J/s}}$ $\boxed{t = 31.2 \text{ s}}$

Aluminum: $Q = mc\Delta t = (0.2 \text{ kg})(920 \text{ J/kg C}°)(80 \text{ C}°)$; $t = \dfrac{14{,}720 \text{ J}}{200 \text{ J/s}}$ $\boxed{t = 73.6 \text{ s}}$

Silver: $Q = mc\Delta t = (0.2 \text{ kg})(230 \text{ J/kg C}°)(80 \text{ C}°)$; $t = \dfrac{3680 \text{ J}}{200 \text{ J/s}}$ $\boxed{t = 18.4 \text{ s}}$

Lead : $Q = mc\Delta t = (0.2 \text{ kg})(130 \text{ J/kg C}°)(80 \text{ C}°)$; $t = \dfrac{2080 \text{ J}}{200 \text{ J/s}}$ $\boxed{t = 10.4 \text{ s}}$

Note that materials with lower specific heat capacities take less time to reach $100°C$.

---

*17-41. How many grams of steam at $100°C$ must be added to 30 g of ice at $0°C$ in order to produce an equilibrium temperature of $40°C$?

$m_s L_v + m_s c_w(100°C - 40°C) = m_i L_f + m_i c_w(40°C - 0°C)$

$m_s(540 \text{ cal/g}) + m_s(1 \text{ cal/g C}°)(60 \text{ C}°) = (30 \text{ g})(80 \text{ cal/g}) + (30 \text{ g})(1 \text{ cal/g C}°)(40 \text{ C}°)$

$(600 \text{ cal/g})m_s = 2400 \text{ cal} + 1200 \text{ cal}$; $\boxed{m_s = 6.00 \text{ g}}$

*17-42. A 5-g lead bullet moving at 200 m/s embeds itself into a wooden block. Half of its initial energy is absorbed by the bullet. What is the increase in temperature of the bullet?

Heat $= \frac{1}{2}(\frac{1}{2}mv^2) = \frac{1}{4}(0.005 \text{ kg})(200 \text{ m/s})^2 = 50 \text{ J}$

$Q = mc\Delta t$; $\Delta t = \dfrac{Q}{mc} = \dfrac{50 \text{ J}}{(0.005 \text{ kg})(130 \text{ J/kg C}°)}$; $\boxed{\Delta t = 76.9 \text{ C}°}$

*17-43. If 4 g of steam at $100°C$ is mixed with 20 g of ice at $-5°C$, find the final temperature of the mixture.

$m_s L_v + m_s c_w(100°C - t_e) = m_i c(5 \text{ C}°) + m_i L_f + m_i c_w(t_e - 0°C)$

Heat gained $= (4 \text{ g})(540 \text{ cal/g}) + (4 \text{ g})(1 \text{ cal/g C}°)(100 \text{ C}° - t_e)$

$= 2160 \text{ cal} + 400 \text{ cal} - (4 \text{ cal/C}°)t_e$

Heat lost $= (20 \text{ g})(0.5 \text{ cal/g C}°)(5 \text{ C}°) + (20 \text{ g})(80 \text{ cal/g}) + (20 \text{ g})(1 \text{ cal/g C}°)t_e$

$= 50 \text{ cal} + 1600 \text{ cal} + (20 \text{ cal/C}°)t_e$

$50 \text{ cal} + 1600 \text{ cal} + (20 \text{ cal/C}°)t_e = 2160 \text{ cal} + 400 \text{ cal} - 4 \text{ cal/C}°$

$(24 \text{ cal/C}°)t_e = 910 \text{ cal}$; $\boxed{t_e = 37.9°C}$.

*17-46. Each of the blocks in the previous example are placed on a large block of ice. Find out how much ice is melted by each block when all reach equilibrium at 0°C? Which sinks deepest and which sinks the least?

$m_i L_f = m_c c_c \Delta t$; $m_i(3.34 \times 10^5 \text{ J/kg}) = (0.2 \text{ kg})(390 \text{ J/kg C}^0)(100 \text{ C}^0)$; $m_c = 23.4$ g

$m_i L_f = m_A c_A \Delta t$; $m_i(3.34 \times 10^5 \text{ J/kg}) = (0.2 \text{ kg})(920 \text{ J/kg C}^0)(100 \text{ C}^0)$; $m_A = 55.1$ g

$m_i L_f = m_c c_s \Delta t$; $m_i(3.34 \times 10^5 \text{ J/kg}) = (0.2 \text{ kg})(230 \text{ J/kg C}^0)(100 \text{ C}^0)$; $m_s = 13.8$ g

$m_i L_f = m_c c_l \Delta t$; $m_l(3.34 \times 10^5 \text{ J/kg}) = (0.2 \text{ kg})(130 \text{ J/kg C}^0)(100 \text{ C}^0)$; $m_l = 7.78$ g

Note that the materials of higher heat capacity melt more ice. Thus, the aluminum block sinks deepest and the lead block sinks the least.

*17-47. In an experiment to determine the latent heat of vaporization for water, a student measures the mass of an aluminum calorimeter cup to be 50 g. After a quantity of water is added, the combined mass of the water and cup is 120 g. The initial temperature of the cup and water is 18°C. A quantity of steam at 100°C is passed into the calorimeter, and the system is observed to reach equilibrium at 47.4°C. The total mass of the final mixture is 124 g. What value will the student obtain for the heat of vaporization?

First determine the mass of water: $m_w = 120 \text{ g} - 50$ g; $m_w = 70$ g

$m_s = 124 \text{ g} - 120$ g; $m_s = 4.00$ g

Now find mass of steam:

$m_s L_v + m_s c_w(100°\text{C} - 47.4°\text{C}) = m_w c_w(47.4°\text{C} - 18°\text{C}) + m_c c_c(47.4°\text{C} - 18°\text{C})$

$(4 \text{ g})L_v + (4 \text{ g})(1 \text{ cal/g C}^0)(52.6 \text{ C}^0) = (70 \text{ g})(1 \text{ cal/g C}^0)(29.4 \text{ C}^0)$
$+ (50 \text{ g})(0.22 \text{ cal/g C}^0)(29.4 \text{ C}^0)$

$(4 \text{ g})L_v + 210.4 \text{ cal/C}^0 = 2058 \text{ cal/C}^0 + 323.4 \text{ cal/C}^0$

$\boxed{L_v = 543 \text{ cal/g}}$

**17-48. If equal masses of ice at 0°C, water at 50°C, and steam at 100°C are mixed and allowed to reach equilibrium. Will all of the steam condense? What will be the temperature of the final mixture? What percent of the final mixture will be water and what percent will be steam? (Let m be the initial mass of water, ice, and steam.)

Because the heat of vaporization is the largest, lets assume that the equilibrium temperature is 100°C and that only mass m_x condenses. Then look at the results.

$m_x L_v = mL_f + mc_w(100 \text{ C}^0) + mc_w(100°\text{C} - 50°\text{C})$

$\dfrac{m_x}{m} L_v = L_f + c_w(100 \text{ C}^0) + c_w(50 \text{ C}^0)$; $\dfrac{m_x}{m} L_v = L_f + (150 \text{ C}^0)c_w$

$\dfrac{m_x}{m} = \dfrac{L_f + (150 \text{ C}^0)c_w}{L_v} = \dfrac{80 \text{ cal/g} + (150 \text{ C}^0)(1 \text{ cal/g C}^0)}{540 \text{ cal/g}}$; $\dfrac{m_x}{m} = 0.426$

This answer is reasonable based on the assumptions. Thus, all the steam does NOT condense and $\boxed{t_e = 100°\text{C}}$

The total mass is $m_s + m_w + m_s = 3m$ and $m_x = 0.426$ m (condensed), Thus

$Percent \ steam = \dfrac{m - 0.426 \, m}{3m} = \dfrac{0.574 \, m}{3m} = 0.191$; $\boxed{19.1\% \ steam}$

The remainder is water; $\boxed{80.9\% \ water}$

**17-49. If 100 g of water at 20°C is mixed with 100 g of ice at 0°C and 4 g of steam at 100°C, find the equilibrium temperature and the composition of the mixture?.

First let's assume that not all of the ice melts, then check to see if answer is reasonable.

Heat lost = Heat gained: $m_s L_v + m_s c_w(100°\text{C} - 0°\text{C}) + m_w c_w(20°\text{C} - 0°\text{C}) = m_x L_f$

$(4 \text{ g})(540 \text{ cal/g}) + (4 \text{ g})(1 \text{ cal/g C}^0)(100 \text{ C}^0) + (100 \text{ g})(1 \text{ cal/g C}^0)(20 \text{ C}^0) = m_x(80 \text{ cal/g})$

$m_x = 57$ g;   This means that 100 g $- 57$ g or 43 g of ice remain unmelted

$\boxed{\text{Total water} = 4 \text{ g} + 100 \text{ g} + 57 \text{ g} = 161 \text{ g}; \text{ Total ice} = 43 \text{ g}}$

17-50. Ten grams of ice at -5^0C is mixed with 6 g of steam at 100^0C. Find the final temperature and the composition of the mixture. *(Let's assume that only a mass m_x of steam condenses and that the final temperature is 100^0C, then check solution.)*

$m_x(540 \text{ cal/g}) = (10 \text{ g})(0.5 \text{ cal/g C}^0)(5 \text{ C}^0) + (10 \text{ g})(80 \text{ cal/g}) + (10 \text{ g})(1 \text{ cal/g C}^0)(100 \text{ C}^0)$

Solving for m_x we obtain: $m_x = 3.38$ g of steam condensed; 2.92 g of steam remain.

Total water = 3.38 g + 10 g = 13.4 g; Total steam = 2.92 g

Chapter 18. Transfer of Heat

Note: Refer to Tables 18-1 and 18-2 for thermal conductivities and other constants needed in the solution of the problems in this section.

Thermal Conductivity

18-1. A block of copper has a cross-section of 20 cm^2 and a length of 50 cm. The left end is maintained at 0^0C and the right end is at 100^0C. What is the rate of heat flow in watts?

$k = 385$ W/m K; $\Delta t = 100^0\text{C} - 0^0\text{C} = 100 \text{ C}^0$, $20 \text{ cm}^2 = 20 \times 10^{-4} \text{ m}^2$

$$H = \frac{kA\Delta t}{L} = \frac{(385 \text{ W/m C}^0)(20 \times 10^{-4} \text{ m}^2)(100 \text{ C}^0)}{0.50 \text{ m}}; \quad \boxed{H = 154 \text{ W}}$$

18-2. In Problem 18-1, what is the heat flow if the copper block is replaced with a block of glass having the same dimensions?

$k_G = 0.80$ W/m K; $A = 20 \times 10^{-4} \text{ m}^2$; $L = 0.50$ m; $\Delta t = 100 \text{ C}^0$

$$H = \frac{kA\Delta t}{L} = \frac{(0.80 \text{ W/m C}^0)(20 \times 10^{-4} \text{ m}^2)(100 \text{ C}^0)}{0.50 \text{ m}}; \quad \boxed{H = 0.320 \text{ W}}$$

18-3. A 50-cm long brass rod has a diameter of 3 mm. The temperature of one end is 76 C^0 higher than the other end. How much heat is conducted in one minute?

$$A = \frac{\pi D^2}{4} = \frac{\pi(0.003 \text{ m})^2}{4} = 7.07 \times 10^{-6} \text{ m}^2; \quad L = 0.50 \text{ m}; \quad \Delta t = 76 \text{ C}^0$$

$$H = \frac{kA\Delta t}{L} = \frac{(109 \text{ W/m C}^0)(7.07 \times 10^{-6} \text{ m}^2)(76 \text{ C}^0)}{0.50 \text{ m}}; \quad H = 0.117 \text{ W}$$

$$H = \frac{Q}{t}; \quad Q = Ht = (0.117 \text{ J/s})(60 \text{ s}); \quad \boxed{Q = 7.03 \text{ J}}$$

*18-8. A composite wall 6 m long and 3 m high consists of 12 cm of concrete joined with 10 cm of corkboard. The inside temperature is 10°C and the outside temperature is 40°C. Find the temperature at the interface of the two materials. [$\Delta t = 40°C - 10°C = 30 \text{ C}°$]

$H_{steel} = H_{silver}$; $\quad \dfrac{k_1 A \Delta t}{L_1} = \dfrac{k_2 A \Delta t}{L_2}$

$\dfrac{(50.2 \text{ kcal/m s C}°)(95°C - t)}{0.30 \text{ m}} = \dfrac{(406 \text{ kcal/m s C}°)(t - 5°C)}{0.60 \text{ m}}$; $\boxed{t = 22.8°C}$

*18-9. What is the steady-state rate of heat flow through the composite wall of Problem 18-8?

$H_1 = H_2 = \dfrac{(406 \text{ kcal/m s C}°)(22.8°C - 5°C)(4 \times 10^{-4}\text{m}^2)}{0.60 \text{ m}}$; $\boxed{H = 4.83 \text{ J/s}}$

Thermal Radiation

18-10. What is the power radiated from a spherical blackbody of surface area 20 cm² if its temperature is 250°C?

$R = \dfrac{P}{A} = e\sigma T^4$; $\quad T = 250°C + 273° = 523 \text{ K}$; $\quad 20 \text{ cm}^2 = 20 \times 10^{-4} \text{ m}^2$

$P = e\sigma A T^4 = (1)(5.67 \times 10^{-8}\text{ W/m}^2\text{K}^4)(20 \times 10^{-4}\text{m}^2)(523 \text{ K})^4$; $\boxed{P = 8.48 \text{ W}}$

18-11. What is the rate of radiation for a spherical blackbody at a temperature of 327°C? Will this rate change if the radius is doubled for the same temperature?

$T = 327°C + 273° = 600 \text{ K}$; $\quad e = 1$; $\quad R = e\sigma T^4$

$R = (1)(5.67 \times 10^{-8}\text{ W/m}^2\text{K}^4)(600 \text{ K})^4$; $\boxed{R = 7.35 \text{ kW/m}^2}$

$R = \dfrac{P}{A} = e\sigma T^4$ so that changing the radius does NOT change the rate of radiation.

18-4. A pane of window glass is 10 in. wide, 16 in. long, and 1/8 in. thick. The inside surface is at 60°F and the outside surface is at 20°F. How many Btu are transferred to the outside in a time of 2 h? [$L = (1/8)$ in. = 0.125 in.; $A = (10 \text{ in.})(16 \text{ in.}) = 160 \text{ in.}^2$]

$A = (160 \text{ in.}^2)\left(\dfrac{1 \text{ ft}^2}{144 \text{ in.}^2}\right) = 1.11 \text{ ft}^2$; $\quad \Delta t = 60°F - 20°F = 40 \text{ F}°$

$Q = \dfrac{kA\Delta t\, \tau}{L} = \dfrac{(5.6 \text{ Btu in./ft}^2\text{h F}°)(1.11 \text{ ft}^2)(40 \text{ F}°)(2 \text{ h})}{0.125 \text{ in.}}$; $\boxed{Q = 3980 \text{ Btu}}$

18-5. One end of an iron rod 30 cm long and 4 cm² in cross-section is placed in a bath of ice and water. The other end is placed in a steam bath. How many minutes are needed to transfer 1.0 kcal of heat? In what direction does the heat flow?

$\tau = \dfrac{QL}{kA\Delta t} = \dfrac{(1 \text{ kcal})(0.30 \text{ m})}{(1.2 \times 10^{-2}\text{kcal/m s C}°)(4 \times 10^{-4}\text{m}^2)(100 \text{ C}°)}$; $\tau = 625$ s; $\boxed{\tau = 10.4 \text{ min}}$

The direction of heat flow is from the stem bath to the ice and water.

18-6. A steel plate of thickness 20 mm has a cross-section of 600 cm². One side is at 170°C and the other is at 120°C. What is the rate of heat transfer?

$H = \dfrac{(50.2 \text{ W/m K})(600 \times 10^{-4}\text{m}^2)(170°C - 120°C)}{0.020 \text{ m}}$; $\boxed{H = 7530 \text{ W}}$

18-7. How much heat is lost in 12 h through a 3-in. brick firewall 10 ft² area if one side is at 330°F and the other is at 78°F?

$\Delta t = 330°F - 78°F = 252 \text{ F}°$; $\quad A = 10 \text{ ft}^2$; $\quad \tau = 12$ h; $\quad L = 3$ in.

$Q = \dfrac{(5 \text{ Btu in./ft}^2\text{h F}°)(10 \text{ ft}^2)(252 \text{ F}°)(12 \text{ h})}{3 \text{ in.}}$; $\boxed{Q = 50,400 \text{ Btu}}$

*18-12. The emissivity of a metallic sphere is 0.3 and at a temperature of 500 K its radiates a power of 800 W. What is the radius of the sphere?

$$R = e\sigma T^4 = (0.3)(5.67 \times 10^{-8} \text{ W/m}^2\text{K}^4)(500 \text{ K})^4 = 1063 \text{ W/m}^2; \quad R = \frac{P}{A}$$

$$A = \pi r^2 = \frac{P}{R}; \quad r = \sqrt{\frac{P}{\pi R}}; \quad r = \sqrt{\frac{800 \text{ W}}{\pi(1063 \text{ W/m}^2)}}; \quad \boxed{r = 0.489 \text{ m}}$$

*18-13. A certain body absorbs 20 percent of the incident thermal radiation, what is its emissivity? What energy will be emitted by this body in 1 min if its surface area is 1 m² and its temperature is 727°C?

$$e = 20\% = \boxed{0.2}; \quad T = 273^0 + 727^0 = 1000 \text{ K}; \quad \tau = 60 \text{ s};$$

$$R = e\sigma T^4 = (0.2)(5.67 \times 10^{-8} \text{ W/m}^2\text{K}^4)(1000 \text{ K})^4; \quad R = 11{,}340 \text{ W/m}^2$$

$$R = \frac{E}{A\tau}; \quad E = RA\tau = (11{,}340 \text{ W/m}^2)(1 \text{ m}^2)(60 \text{ s}); \quad \boxed{E = 680 \text{ kJ}}$$

*18-14. The operating temperature of the filament in a 25-W lamp is 2727°C. If the emissivity is 0.3, what is the surface area of the filament? [T = 2727^{0}C + 273^0 = 3000 K]

$$P = e\sigma AT^4; \quad A = \frac{25 \text{ W}}{(0.3)(5.67 \times 10^{-8} \text{ W/m}^2\text{K}^4)(3000 \text{ K})^4};$$

$$A = 1.81 \times 10^{-5} \text{ m}^2 \quad \text{or} \quad \boxed{A = 0.181 \text{ cm}^2}$$

Supplementary Problems

18-15. A glass window pane is 60 cm wide 1.8 m tall and 3 mm thick. The inside temperature is 20^{0}C and the outside temperature is -10^{0}C. How much heat leaves the house through this window in one hour? A = (0.6 m)(1.8 m) = 1.08 m²; Δt = [20 - (-10)] = 30 C^0

$$Q = \frac{kA\Delta t \tau}{L} = \frac{(0.8 \text{ W/m}^2\text{K})(1.08 \text{ m}^2)(30 \text{ C}^0)(3600 \text{ s})}{0.003 \text{ m}}; \quad Q = 3.11 \times 10^7 \text{ J}$$

18-16. A 20-cm thickness of fiberglass insulation covers a 20 m by 15 m attic floor. How many calories of heat are lost to the attic if the temperatures on the sides of the insulation are -10^{0}C and +24^{0}C. [Δt = 24 - (-10) = 34 C^0, A = (20 m)(15 m) = 300 m²]

$$Q = \frac{kA\Delta t \tau}{L} = \frac{(1 \times 10^{-5} \text{ kcal/m s C}^0)(300 \text{ m}^2)(34 \text{ C}^0)}{0.20 \text{ m}}; \quad \boxed{Q = 0.165 \text{ kcal}}$$

18-17. The bottom of an aluminum pan is 3 mm thick and has a surface area of 120 cm². How many calories per minute are conducted through the bottom of the pan if the temperature of the outer and inner surfaces are 114^{0}C and 117^{0}C. [Δt = 117^0 - 114^0 = 3 C^0]

$$Q = \frac{(0.05 \text{ kcal/m s C}^0)(120 \times 10^{-4} \text{ m}^2)(3 \text{ C}^0)}{0.003 \text{ m}}; \quad \boxed{Q = 36 \text{ kcal}}$$

18-18. A solid wall of concrete is 80 ft high, 100 ft wide and 6 in. thick. The surface temperatures on the sides of the concrete are 30^{0}F and 100^{0}F. What time is required for 400,000 Btu of heat to be transferred? [A = (80 ft)(100 ft) = 8000 ft²; Δt = 100^0 - 30^0 = 70 F^0]

$$\tau = \frac{QL}{kA\Delta t} = \frac{(400{,}000 \text{ Btu})(6 \text{ in.})}{(5.6 \text{ Btu in./ft}^2\text{h F}^0)(8000 \text{ ft}^2)(70 \text{ F}^0)}; \quad \boxed{\tau = 0.765 \text{ h or } 45.9 \text{ min}}$$

18-19. The bottom of a hot metal pan has an area of 86 cm² and a temperature of 98^{0}C. The pan is placed on top of a corkboard 5 mm thick.. The Formica table top under the corkboard is maintained at a constant temperature of 20^{0}C. How much heat is conducted through the cork in 2 min?

Δt = 98^0 - 20^0 = 78 C^0; A = 86 cm² = 86 × 10⁻⁴ m²; τ = 2 min = 120 s

$$Q = \frac{(0.04 \text{ W/m C}^0)(86 \times 10^{-4} \text{ m}^2)(78 \text{ C}^0)(120 \text{ s})}{0.005 \text{ m}}; \quad \boxed{Q = 644 \text{ J}}$$

*18-20. What thickness of copper is required to have the same insulating value as 2 in. of corkboard? *First find the R-value for 2 in. of corkboard.*

$$R = (2 \text{ in.})(3.3 \text{ ft}^2 \text{ h F}°/\text{Btu}) = 6.6 \text{ ft}^2 \text{ h F}°/\text{Btu}$$

Copper: $L(0.00038 \text{ ft}^2 \text{ h F}°/\text{Btu}) = 6.6 \text{ ft}^2 \text{ h F}°/\text{Btu}$; $L = 17{,}370 \text{ in.}$ or $\boxed{1450 \text{ ft}}$

*18-21. What thickness of concrete is required to have the same insulating value as 6 cm of fiberglass? *For the same insulating value, the ratio's (L/k) must be the same.*

$$\frac{L_{con}}{k_{con}} = \frac{L_{fib}}{k_{fib}}; \quad L_{con} = \frac{k_{con}L_{fib}}{k_{fib}} = \frac{(0.8 \text{ W/m K})(6 \text{ cm})}{(0.04 \text{ W/m K})}; \quad \boxed{L_{con} = 120 \text{ cm}}$$

18-22. A plate-glass window in an office building measures 2 by 6 m and is 1.2 cm thick. Its outer surface is at $23°C$ and its inner surface is at $25°C$. How many joules of heat pass through the glass in an hour?

$$A = (2 \text{ m})(6 \text{ m}) = 12 \text{ m}^2; \quad \Delta t = 25° - 23° = 2 \text{ C}°$$

$$Q = \frac{(0.8 \text{ W/m C}°)(12 \text{ m}^2)(2 \text{ C}°)(3600 \text{ s})}{0.012 \text{ m}}; \quad \boxed{Q = 5760 \text{ kJ}}$$

18-23. What must be the temperature of a black body if its rate of radiation is 860 W/m²?

$$R = e\sigma T^4; \quad T^4 = \frac{R}{e\sigma} = \frac{860 \text{ W/m}^2}{(1)(5.67 \times 10^{-8} \text{ W/m}^2\text{K}^4)} = 1.517 \times 10^{10} \text{K}^4; \quad \boxed{T = 351 \text{ K}}$$

18-24. A gray steel ball has an emissivity of 0.75 and when its temperature is $570°C$, the power radiated is 800 W. What is the surface area of the ball? [$T = 273° + 570° = 843 \text{ K}$]

$$P = e\sigma AT^4; \quad A = \frac{P}{e\sigma T^4} = \frac{(800 \text{ W})}{(0.75)(5.67 \times 10^{-8} \text{ W/m}^2\text{K}^4)(843 \text{ K})^4}$$

$$A = 0.0373 \text{ m}^2 \text{ or } \boxed{373 \text{ cm}^2}$$

18-25. A 25-W lamp has a filament of area 0.212 cm². If the emissivity is 0.35, what is the operating temperature of the filament?

$$T^4 = \frac{P}{e\sigma A} = \frac{25 \text{ W}}{(0.35)(5.67 \times 10^{-8} \text{ W/m}^2\text{K}^4)(0.212 \times 10^{-4} \text{ m}^2)} = 5.94 \times 10^{13} \text{ K}^4$$

$$T = \sqrt[4]{5.94 \times 10^{13} \text{ K}^4}; \quad \boxed{T = 2776 \text{ K}}$$

Critical Thinking Questions

*18-26. The wall of a freezing plant consists of 6 in. of concrete and 4 in. of corkboard. The temperature of the inside cork surface is $-15°F$ and the temperature of the outside surface is $70°F$. What is the temperature at the interface between the cork and concrete? How much heat is conducted through each square foot of wall in one hour?

For steady state: $H_{con} = H_{cork}$

$$\frac{k_1 A(70°C - t_i)}{L_1} = \frac{k_2 A(t_i - (-15°C))}{L_2}$$

$$\frac{(5.6 \text{ Btu in./ft}^2\text{h F}°)(70°C - t_i)}{6 \text{ in.}} = \frac{(0.30 \text{ Btu in./ft}^2\text{h F}°)(t_i + 15°C)}{4 \text{ in.}}$$

$$(0.933 \text{ Btu/ft}^2 \text{ h})(70°C - t_i) = (0.075 \text{ Btu/ft}^2 \text{ h})(t_i + 15°F)$$

Solving for t_i, we obtain: $\boxed{t_i = 63.7°F}$

The heat conducted per square foot is the same. Suppose we choose the concrete, then

$$\frac{H}{A} = \frac{(5.6 \text{ Btu in./ft}^2\text{h F}°)(70°C - 63.7°C)}{(6 \text{ in.})}; \quad \boxed{H/A = 5.92 \text{ Btu/ft}^2 \text{ h}}$$

After some time the heat per unit area per unit of time is the same throughout the wall.

If the same rates of heat transfer are to be realized, then the thicknesses must be chosen so that the R values are the same:

$$\frac{L_A}{k_A} = \frac{L_B}{k_B} \qquad L_B = \frac{k_B L_A}{k_A} = \frac{k_B(6\text{ cm})}{2k_B} = 3\text{ cm}; \qquad \boxed{L_B = 3.00\text{ cm}}$$

Material B needs to be only half the thickness of Material A to provide the same insulating value.

*18-27. A wooden icebox has walls that are 4 cm thick, and the overall effective surface area is 2 m². How many grams of ice will be melted in 1 min if the inside temperatures of the walls are 4°C and the outside temperatures are 20°C?

Inside and outside temperatures are surface temperatures:

$$Q = \frac{kA\Delta t\,\tau}{L}; \qquad Q = m_i L_f = \frac{kA\Delta t\,\tau}{L}$$

$$m_i = \frac{kA\Delta t\,\tau}{LL_f} = \frac{(0.10\text{ W/m}^2\text{K})(2\text{ m}^2)(60\text{ s})(20^0\text{C} - 4^0\text{C})}{(0.04\text{ m})(334\times10^3\text{ J/kg})}; \qquad \boxed{m_i = 14.4\text{ g}}$$

Note: If the inside and outside temperatures were air temperatures, this would involve both convection and conduction, making the solution much more complicated.

*18-28. The filament in a lamp operates at a temperature of 727°C and is surrounded by an envelope at 227°C. If the filament has an emissivity of 0.25 and a surface area of 0.30 cm², what is the operating power of the lamp?

$$P = e\sigma A(T_1^4 - T_2^4) = e\sigma A[(1000\text{ K})^4 - (500\text{ K})^4] = e\sigma A(9.375\times10^{11}\text{ K}^4)$$

$$P = (0.25)(5.67\times10^{-8}\text{ W/m}^2\text{ K}^4)(3\times10^{-5}\text{ m}^2)(9.375\times10^{11}\text{ K}^4)$$

$$\boxed{P = 0.399\text{ W}}$$

*18-29. The thermal conductivity of material A is twice that for material B. Which has the greater R value? When 6 cm of material A is between two walls the rate of conduction is 400 W/m². What thickness of material B is needed to provide the same rate of heat transfer if other factors remain constant?

$$k_A = 2k_B; \qquad \text{The R-value is } (L/k), \text{ so that}$$

$$\left(\frac{L}{k_A}\right) = \left(\frac{L}{2k_B}\right) = \frac{1}{2}\left(\frac{L}{k_B}\right) \qquad \text{Thus,} \qquad \boxed{R_A = \tfrac{1}{2}R_B}$$

Chapter 19. Thermal Properties of Matter

General Gas Laws: Initial and Final States

19-1. An ideal gas occupies a volume of 4.00 m^3 at 200 kPa absolute pressure. What will be the new pressure if the gas is slowly compressed to 2.00 m^3 at constant temperature?

$$P_1V_1 = P_2V_2; \quad P_2 = \frac{P_1V_1}{V_2} = \frac{(200 \text{ kPa})(4.00 \text{ m}^3)}{(2.00 \text{ m}^3)} \qquad \boxed{P_2 = 400 \text{ kPa}}$$

19-2. The absolute pressure of a sample of ideal gas is 300 kPa at a volume of 2.6 m^3. If the pressure decreases to 101 kPa at constant temperature, what is the new volume?

$$P_1V_1 = P_2V_2; \quad V_2 = \frac{P_1V_1}{P_2} = \frac{(300 \text{ kPa})(2.6 \text{ m}^3)}{(101 \text{ kPa})} \qquad \boxed{V_2 = 7.72 \text{ m}^3}$$

19-3. Two hundred cubic centimeters of an ideal gas at 20^{0}C expands to a volume of 212 cm^3 at constant pressure. What is the final temperature. [$T_1 = 20^0 + 273^0 = 293$ K]

$$\frac{V_1}{T_1} = \frac{V_2}{T_2}; \quad T_2 = \frac{T_1V_2}{V_1} = \frac{(293 \text{ K})(212 \text{ cm}^3)}{200 \text{ cm}^3} ; \quad T_2 = 310.6 \text{ K}$$

$$t_C = 310.6 - 273^0 = 37.6^0\text{C}; \qquad \boxed{t_C = 37.6^0\text{C}}$$

19-4. The temperature of a gas sample decreases from 55^{0}C to 25^{0}C at constant pressure. If the initial volume was 400 mL, what is the final volume?

$$T_1 = 55^0 + 273^0 = 328 \text{ K}; \quad T_2 = 25^0 + 273^0 = 298 \text{ K}; \quad V_1 = 400 \text{ mL}$$

$$\frac{V_1}{T_1} = \frac{V_2}{T_2}; \quad V_2 = \frac{T_2V_1}{T_1} = \frac{(298 \text{ K})(400 \text{ mL})}{328 \text{ K}} \qquad \boxed{V_2 = 363 \text{ mL}}$$

19-5. A steel cylinder contains an ideal gas at 27^{0}C. The gauge pressure is 140 kPa. If the temperature of the container increases to 79^{0}C, what is the new gauge pressure?

$$T_1 = 27^0 + 273^0 = 300 \text{ K}; \quad T_2 = 79^0 + 273^0 = 352 \text{ K};$$

$$P_1 = 140 \text{ kPa} + 101.3 \text{ kPa} = 241.3 \text{ kPa};$$

$$\frac{P_1}{T_1} = \frac{P_2}{T_2}; \quad P_2 = \frac{P_1T_2}{T_1} = \frac{(241.3 \text{ kPa})(352 \text{ K})}{300 \text{ K}} = 283.1 \text{ kPa}$$

$$Gauge \; Pressure = 283.1 \text{ kPa} - 101.3 \text{ kPa}; \qquad \boxed{P_2 = 182 \text{ kPa}}$$

19-6. The absolute pressure of a sample of gas initially at 300 K doubles as the volume remains constant. What is the new temperature? [$P_2 = 2P_1$]

$$\frac{P_1}{T_1} = \frac{P_2}{T_2}; \quad T_2 = \frac{P_2T_1}{P_1} = \frac{(2P_1)(300 \text{ K})}{P_1}; \qquad \boxed{T_2 = 600 \text{ K}}$$

19-7. A steel cylinder contains 2.00 kg of an ideal gas. Overnight the temperature and volume remain constant, but the absolute pressure decreases from 500 kPa down to 450 kPa. How many grams of the gas leaked out over night?

$$\frac{P_1V_1}{m_1T_1} = \frac{P_2V_2}{m_2T_2}; \quad m_2 = \frac{m_1P_2}{P_1} = \frac{(2.00 \text{ kg})(450 \text{ kPa})}{500 \text{ kPa}} ; \qquad m_2 = 1.80 \text{ kg}$$

$$Lost = 2.00 \text{ kg} - 1.80 \text{ kg} = 0.200 \text{ kg}; \qquad \boxed{\text{Amt. Leaked} = 200 \text{ g}}$$

19-8. Five liters of a gas at 25^{0}C has an absolute pressure of 200 kPa. If the absolute pressure reduces to 120 kPa and the temperature increases to 60^{0}C, what is the final volume?

$$T_1 = 25^0 + 273^0 = 298 \text{ K}; \quad T_2 = 60^0 + 273^0 = 333 \text{ K}$$

$$\frac{P_1V_1}{T_1} = \frac{P_2V_2}{T_2}; \quad V_2 = \frac{P_1V_1T_2}{T_1P_2} = \frac{(200 \text{ kPa})(5 \text{ L})(333 \text{ K})}{(298 \text{ K})(120 \text{ kPa})}$$

$$\boxed{V_2 = 9.31 \text{ L}}$$

19-9. An air compressor takes in 2 m³ of air at 20°C and one atmosphere (101.3 kPa) pressure. If the compressor discharges into a 0.3-m³ tank at an absolute pressure of 1500 kPA, what is the temperature of the discharged air? $[T_1 = 20^0 + 273^0 = 293 \text{ K}]$

$\frac{P_1V_1}{T_1} = \frac{P_2V_2}{T_2}$; $T_2 = \frac{P_2V_2T_1}{P_1V_1} = \frac{(1500 \text{ kPa})(0.3 \text{ m}^3)(293 \text{ K})}{(101.3 \text{ kPa})(2.0 \text{ m}^3)}$; $\boxed{T_2 = 651 \text{ K}}$

19-10. A 6-L tank holds a sample of gas under an absolute pressure of 600 kPa and a temperature of 57°C. What will be the new pressure if the same sample of gas is placed into a 3-L container at 7°C. $[T_1 = 57^0 + 273^0 = 330 \text{ K}; \quad T_2 = 7^0 + 273^0 = 280 \text{ K}]$

$\frac{P_1V_1}{T_1} = \frac{P_2V_2}{T_2}$; $P_2 = \frac{P_1V_1T_2}{T_1V_2} = \frac{(600 \text{ kPa})(6 \text{ L})(280 \text{ K})}{(330 \text{ K})(3 \text{ L})}$; $\boxed{P_2 = 1020 \text{ kPa}}$

19-11. If 0.8 L of a gas at 10°C is heated to 90°C at constant pressure. What is the new volume?

$T_1 = 10^0 + 273^0 = 283 \text{ K}$; $T_2 = 90^0 + 273^0 = 363 \text{ K}$

$\frac{V_1}{T_1} = \frac{V_2}{T_2}$; $V_2 = \frac{T_2V_1}{T_1} = \frac{(363 \text{ K})(0.8 \text{ L})}{283 \text{ K}}$; $\boxed{V_2 = 1.03 \text{ L}}$

19-12. The inside of an automobile tire is under a gauge pressure of 30 lb/in.² at 4°C. After several hours, the inside air temperature rises to 50°C. Assuming constant volume, what is the new gauge pressure?

$P_1 = 30 \text{ lb/in.}^2 + 14.7 \text{ lb/in.}^2 = 44.7 \text{ lb/in.}^2$

$T_1 = 273^0 + 4^0 = 277 \text{ K}$; $T_2 = 273^0 + 50^0 = 323 \text{ K}$

$\frac{P_1}{T_1} = \frac{P_2}{T_2}$; $P_2 = \frac{P_1T_2}{T_1} = \frac{(44.7 \text{ lb/in.}^2)(323 \text{ K})}{(277 \text{ K})} = 52.1 \text{ lb/in.}^2$

$P_2 = 52.1 \text{ lb/in.}^2 - 14.7 \text{ lb/in.}^2 = 37.4 \text{ lb/in.}^2$; $\boxed{P_2 = 37.4 \text{ lb/in.}^2}$

19-13. A 2-L sample of gas has an absolute pressure of 300 kPa at 300 K. If both pressure and volume experience a two-fold increase, what is the final temperature?

$\frac{P_1V_1}{T_1} = \frac{P_2V_2}{T_2}$; $T_2 = \frac{P_2V_2T_1}{P_1V_1} = \frac{(600 \text{ kPa})(4 \text{ L})(300 \text{ K})}{(300 \text{ kPa})(2 \text{ L})}$ $\boxed{T_2 = 1200 \text{ K}}$

Molecular Mass and the Mole

19-14. How many moles are contained in 600 g of air (M = 29 g/mole)?

$n = \frac{m}{M} = \frac{600 \text{ g}}{29 \text{ g/mol}}$; $\boxed{n = 20.7 \text{ mol}}$

19-15. How many moles of gas are there in 400 g of nitrogen gas (M = 28 g/mole)? How many molecules are in this sample?

$n = \frac{m}{M} = \frac{400 \text{ g}}{28 \text{ g/mol}}$; $n = 14.3 \text{ mol}$ $n = \frac{N}{N_A}$

$N = nN_A = (14.3 \text{ mol})(6.023 \times 10^{23} \text{ molecules/mol})$;

$\boxed{N = 8.60 \times 10^{24} \text{ molecules}}$

19-16. What is the mass of a 4-mol sample of air (M = 29 g/mol)?

$n = \frac{m}{M}$; $m = nM = (4 \text{ mol})(29 \text{ g/mol})$; $\boxed{m = 116 \text{ g}}$

19-17. How many grams of hydrogen gas (M = 2 g/mol) are there in 3.0 moles of hydrogen? How many grams of air (M = 29 g/mol) are there in 3.0 moles of air?

$n = \frac{m}{M}$; $m = nM = (3 \text{ mol})(2 \text{ g/mol})$; $\boxed{m = 6.00 \text{ g}}$

$n = \frac{m}{M}$; $m = nM = (3 \text{ mol})(29 \text{ g/mol})$; $\boxed{m = 87.0 \text{ g}}$

*19-18. How many molecules of hydrogen gas (M = 2 g/mol) are needed to have the same mass as 4 g of oxygen (M = 32 g/mol)? How many moles are in each sample?

$n = \dfrac{m}{M} = \dfrac{N}{N_A}$; $N_H = \dfrac{m_H N_A}{M_H} = \dfrac{(4\ g)(6.023 \times 10^{23}\,molecules/mol)}{2\ g/mol}$

$$N_H = 1.20 \times 10^{24}\ molecules\ of\ H_2$$

$n_H = \dfrac{m_H}{M_H} = \dfrac{4\ g}{2\ g/mol}$; $\boxed{n_H = 2\ mol}$

$n_O = \dfrac{m_O}{M_O} = \dfrac{4\ g}{32\ g/mol}$; $\boxed{n_H = 0.125\ mol}$

*19-19. What is the mass of one molecule of oxygen (M = 32 g/mol)?

$n = \dfrac{m}{M} = \dfrac{N}{N_A}$; $m = \dfrac{NM}{N_A} = \dfrac{(1\ molecule)(32\ g/mol)}{6.023 \times 10^{23}\,molecules/mol}$; $m = 5.31 \times 10^{-23}\ g$

$m = 5.31 \times 10^{-23}\,g \left(\dfrac{1\ kg}{1000\ g}\right)$; $\boxed{m = 5.31 \times 10^{-26}\ kg}$

*19-20. The molecular mass of CO_2 is 44 g/mol. What is the mass of a single molecule of CO_2?

$n = \dfrac{m}{M} = \dfrac{N}{N_A}$; $m = \dfrac{NM}{N_A} = \dfrac{(1\ molecule)(44\ g/mol)}{6.023 \times 10^{23}\,molecules/mol}$; $m = 7.31 \times 10^{-23}\ g$

$m = 7.31 \times 10^{-23}\,g \left(\dfrac{1\ kg}{1000\ g}\right)$; $\boxed{m = 7.31 \times 10^{-26}\ kg}$

The Ideal Gas Law

19-21. Three moles of an ideal gas have a volume of 0.026 m³ and a pressure of 300 kPa. What is the temperature of the gas in degrees Celsius?

$PV = nRT$; $T = \dfrac{PV}{nR} = \dfrac{(300,000\ Pa)(0.026\ m^3)}{(3\ mol)(8.314\ J/mol \cdot K)}$

$T = 313\ K$; $t_C = 313^0 - 273^0$; $\boxed{t_C = 39.7°C}$

19-22. A 16-L tank contains 200 g of air (M = 29 g/mol) at 27°C. What is the absolute pressure of this sample? [$T = 27^0 + 273^0 = 300\ K$; $V = 16\ L = 16 \times 10^{-3}\ m^3$]

$PV = \dfrac{m}{M}RT$; $P = \dfrac{mRT}{MV} = \dfrac{(200\ g)(8.314\ J/mol \cdot K)(300\ K)}{(29\ g/mol)(16 \times 10^{-3}\,m^3)}$; $\boxed{P = 1.08 \times 10^6\ Pa}$

19-23. How many kilograms of nitrogen gas (M = 28 g/mol) will occupy a volume of 2000 L at an absolute pressure of 202 kPa and a temperature of 80°C? [$T = (80 + 273) = 353\ K$]

$PV = \dfrac{m}{M}RT$; $m = \dfrac{MPV}{RT} = \dfrac{(28\ g/mol)(202,000\ Pa)(2\ m^3)}{(353\ K)(8.314\ J/mol \cdot K)}$;

$m = 3854\ g$; $m = 3.85\ kg$

19-24. What volume is occupied by 8 g of nitrogen gas (M = 28 g/mol) at standard temperature and pressure (STP)? [$T = 273\ K$, $P = 101.3\ kPa$]

$PV = \dfrac{m}{M}RT$; $V = \dfrac{mRT}{MP} = \dfrac{(8\ g)(8.314\ J/mol \cdot K)(273\ K)}{(28\ g/mol)(101,300\ Pa)}$; $V = 6.40 \times 10^{-3}\ m^3$

$V = 6.40 \times 10^{-3}\ m^3$; $\boxed{V = 6.40\ L}$

19-25. A 2-L flask contains 2 x 10²³ molecules of air (M = 29 g/mol) at 300 K. What is the absolute gas pressure?

$PV = \dfrac{N}{N_A}RT$; $P = \dfrac{NRT}{N_A V} = \dfrac{(2 \times 10^{23}\,molecules)(8.314\ J/mol \cdot K)(300\ K)}{(6.023 \times 10^{23}\,molecules/mol)(2 \times 10^{-3}\,m^3)}$

$$\boxed{P = 414\ kPa}$$

19-26. A 2 m³ tank holds nitrogen gas (M = 28 g/mole) under a gauge pressure of 500 kPa. If the temperature is 27°C, what is the mass of gas in the tank? [$T = 27^0 + 273^0 = 300\ K$]

$PV = \dfrac{m}{M}RT$; $m = \dfrac{MPV}{RT} = \dfrac{(28\ g/mol)(500,000\ Pa)(2\ m^3)}{(300\ K)(8.314\ J/mol \cdot K)}$; $\boxed{m = 11.2\ kg}$

19-27. How many moles of gas are contained in a volume of 2000 cm³ at conditions of standard temperature and pressure (STP)?

$$PV = nRT; \quad n = \frac{PV}{RT} = \frac{(101,300 \text{ Pa})(2 \times 10^{-3}\text{ m}^3)}{(273 \text{ K})(8.314 \text{ J/mol·K})}; \quad \boxed{n = 0.0893 \text{ mol}}$$

19-28. A 0.30 cm³ cylinder contains 0.27 g of water vapor (M = 18 g/mol) at 340°C. What is its absolute pressure assuming the water vapor is an ideal gas? [T = 340° + 273° = 613 K]

$$PV = \frac{m}{M}RT; \quad P = \frac{mRT}{MV} = \frac{(0.27 \text{ g})(8.314 \text{ J/mol·K})(613 \text{ K})}{(18 \text{ g/mol})(0.3 \times 10^{-6}\text{ m}^3)}$$

$$\boxed{P = 2.55 \times 10^8 \text{ Pa}}$$

Humidity

19-29. If the air temperature is 20°C and the dew point is 12°C, what is the relative humidity?

Remember that the actual vapor pressure at a given temperature is the same as the saturated vapor pressure for the dew-point temperature. The table values for 20°C and 12°C are used here, and the relative humidity is found as follows:

$$Relative \ Humidity = \frac{10.64 \text{ mmHg}}{17.4 \text{ mmHg}} = 0.608; \quad \boxed{60.8\%}$$

19-30. The dew point is 20°C. What is the relative humidity when the air temperature is 24°C?

$$Relative \ Humidity = \frac{17.5 \text{ mmHg}}{22.4 \text{ mmHg}}; \quad \boxed{\text{Rel. hum.} = 78.1\%}$$

19-31. The relative humidity is 77 percent when the air temperature is 28°C. What is the dew point? From the table, at 28°C, saturation vapor pressure is 28.3 mmHg.

vapor pressure = 0.77(28.3 mmHg) = 21.8 mmHg

$\boxed{Dew \ point = 23.5°C}$ From Table

19-32. What is the pressure of water vapor in the air on a day when the temperature is 86°F and the relative humidity is 80 percent? [*For 86°F the sat. vapor pressure is 31.8 mm Hg*]

$$\frac{x}{31.8 \text{ mmHg}} = 0.80; \quad \boxed{x = 25.4 \text{ mm Hg}}$$

19-33. The air temperature in a room during the winter is 28°C. What is the relative humidity if moisture first starts forming on a window when the temperature of its surface is at 20°C?

$$\frac{17.5 \text{ mmHg}}{28.3 \text{ mmHg}} = 0.618 \quad \boxed{Rel. Hum. = 61.8\%}$$

Supplementary Problems

19-34. A sample of gas occupies 12 L at 7°C and at an absolute pressure of 102 kPa. Find its temperature when the volume reduces to 10 L and the pressure increases to 230 kPa.

$$V_1 = 12 \text{ L} = 12 \times 10^{-3}\text{ m}^3; \quad V_2 = 10 \text{ L} = 10 \times 10^{-3}\text{ m}^3; \quad T_1 = 7° + 273° = 280 \text{ K}$$

$$\frac{PV_1}{T_1} = \frac{P_2 V_2}{T_2}; \quad T_2 = \frac{P_2 V_2 T_1}{PV_1} = \frac{(230 \text{ kPa})(10 \text{ L})(280 \text{ K})}{(102 \text{ kPa})(12 \text{ L·m}^3)}; \quad \boxed{T_2 = 526 \text{ K}}$$

19-35. A tractor tire contains 2.8 ft³ of air at a gauge pressure of 70 lb/in.². What volume of air at one atmosphere of pressure is required to fill this tire if there is no change in temperature or volume?   [$P_2 = 70 \text{ lb/in.}^2 + 14.7 \text{ lb/in.}^2 = 84.7 \text{ lb/in.}^2$]

$$P_1 V_1 = P_2 V_2; \quad V_2 = \frac{P_2 V_2}{P_1} = \frac{(84.7 \text{ lb/in.}^2)(2.8 \text{ ft}^3)}{14.7 \text{ lb/in.}^2}; \quad \boxed{V_2 = 16.1 \text{ ft}^3.}$$

19-36. A 3-L container is filled with 0.230 mol of an ideal gas at 300 K. What is the pressure of the gas? How many molecules are in this sample of gas?

$$P = \frac{nRT}{V} = \frac{(0.230 \text{ mol})(8.314 \text{ J/mol·K})(300 \text{ K})}{3 \times 10^{-3}\text{ m}^3}; \quad P = 191 \text{ kPa} \qquad n = \frac{N}{N_A}$$

$$N = nN_A = (0.230 \text{ mol})(6.023 \times 10^{23} \text{ molecules/mol}) = \boxed{1.39 \times 10^{23} \text{ molecules}}$$

19-37. How many moles of helium gas (M = 4 g/mol) are there in a 6-L tank when the pressure is 2×10^5 Pa and the temperature is 27^0C? What is the mass of the helium?

$$n = \frac{PV}{RT} = \frac{(2 \times 10^6 \text{Pa})(6 \times 10^{-3} \text{m}^3)}{(8.314 \text{ J/mol} \cdot \text{K})(300 \text{ K})}; \qquad n = 0.481 \text{ mol}$$

$$n = \frac{m}{M}; \qquad m = nM = (0.481 \text{ mol})(4 \text{ g/mol}); \qquad \boxed{m = 1.92 \text{ g}}$$

19-38. How many grams of air (M = 29 g/mol) must be pumped into an automobile tire if it is to have a gauge pressure of 31 lb/in.² Assume the volume of the tire is 5000 cm³ and its temperature is 27^0C?

P = 31 lb/in.² + 14.7 lb/in.² = 45.7 lb/in.²; $V = 5000 \text{ cm}^3 = 5$ L

$$PV = \frac{m}{M}RT; \qquad m = \frac{PVM}{RT} = \frac{(45.7 \text{ lb/in.}^2)(5 \times 10^{-3} \text{m}^3)}{(8.314 \text{ J/mol} \cdot \text{K})(300 \text{ K})};$$

$$m = 9.16 \times 10^{-5} \text{ g or } \boxed{m = 9.16 \times 10^{-8} \text{ kg}}$$

19-39. The air temperature inside a car is 26^0C. The dew point is 24^0C. What is the relative humidity inside the car?

$$x = \frac{22.4 \text{ mmHg}}{25.2 \text{ mmHg}} = 0.889 \qquad \boxed{\text{Rel. hum.} = 88.9\%}$$

19-40. The lens in a sensitive camera is clear when the room temperature is 71.6°F and the relative humidity is 88 percent. What is the lowest temperature of the lens if it is not to become foggy from moisture?

At 71.6^{0}C, saturated pressure is 19.8 mmHg

Actual pressure = 0.88(19.8 mmHg) = 17.4 mmHg

Thus, from tables, the dewpoint is: $\boxed{67.8^0\text{F}}$

*19-41. What is the density of oxygen gas (M = 32 g/mol) at a temperature of 23^0C and atmospheric pressure?

$$PV = \frac{m}{M}RT; \qquad \rho = \frac{m}{V} = \frac{PM}{RT} = \frac{(101,300 \text{ Pa})(32 \text{ g/mol})}{(8.314 \text{ J/mol} \cdot \text{K})(296 \text{ K})} = 1320 \text{ g/m}^3$$

$$\boxed{\rho = 1.32 \text{ kg/m}^3}$$

*19-42. A 5000-cm³ tank is filled with carbon dioxide (M = 44 g/mol) at 300 K and 1 atm of pressure. How many grams of CO_2 can be added to the tank if the maximum absolute pressure is 60 atm and there is no change in temperature? [5000 cm³ = 5 L]

At 1 atm: $\quad m = \dfrac{PVM}{RT} = \dfrac{(1 \text{ atm})(5 \text{ L})(44 \text{ g/mol})}{(0.0821 \text{ L} \cdot \text{atm/mol} \cdot \text{K})(300 \text{ K})} = 8.932 \text{ g}$

At 60 atm: $\quad m = \dfrac{PVM}{RT} = \dfrac{(60 \text{ atm})(5 \text{ L})(44 \text{ g/mol})}{(0.0821 \text{ L} \cdot \text{atm/mol} \cdot \text{K})(300 \text{ K})} = 535.9 \text{ g}$

Mass added = 535.9 g – 8.932 g; Added = 527 g

*19-43. The density of an unknown gas at STP is 1.25 kg/m³. What is the density of this gas at 18 atm and 60^0C?

$P_1 = 1$ atm; $T_1 = 273$ K; $P_2 = 18$ atm; $T_2 = 60^0 + 273^0 = 333$ K

$$PV = \frac{m}{M}RT; \qquad \rho = \frac{m}{V} = \frac{PM}{RT} \qquad \frac{\rho_1}{\rho_2} = \frac{MP_1/RT_1}{MP_2/RT_2} = \frac{P_1T_2}{P_2T_1}$$

$$\frac{\rho_1}{\rho_2} = \frac{P_1T_2}{P_2T_1}; \qquad \rho_2 = \frac{\rho_1 P_2 T_1}{P_1 T_2}$$

$$\rho_2 = \frac{\rho_1 P_2 T_1}{P_1 T_2} = \frac{(1.25 \text{ kg/m}^3)(18 \text{ atm})(273 \text{ K})}{(1 \text{ atm})(333 \text{ K})}; \qquad \boxed{\rho = 18.4 \text{ kg/m}^3}$$

Critical Thinking Questions

*19-44. A tank with a capacity of 14 L contains helium gas at 24°C under a gauge pressure of 2700 kPa. (A) What will be the volume of a balloon filled with this gas if the helium expands to an internal absolute pressure of 1 atm and the temperature drops to -35°C?

(b) Now suppose the system returns to its original temperature (24°C). What is the final volume of the balloon?

(a) $P_1 = 2700$ kPa $+ 101.3$ kPa $= 2801.3$ kPa; $P_2 = 101.3$ kPa; $V_1 = 14$ L

$T_1 = 24^0 + 273^0 = 297$ K; $T_2 = -35^0 + 273^0 = 238$ K

$\frac{P_1V_1}{T_1} = \frac{P_2V_2}{T_2}$; $V_2 = \frac{P_1V_1T_2}{P_2T_1} = \frac{(2801\ kPa)(14\ L)(238\ K)}{(101.3\ kPa)(297\ K)}$; $\boxed{V_2 = 310\ L}$

(b) $P_2 = P_3 = 1$ atm; $T_2 = 238$ K, $V_2 = 310$ L, $T_3 = 297$ K

$\frac{P_2V_2}{T_2} = \frac{P_3V_3}{T_3}$; $V_3 = \frac{V_2T_3}{T_2} = \frac{(310\ L)(297\ K)}{238\ K}$; $\boxed{V_3 = 387\ L}$

*19-45. A steel tank is filled with oxygen. One evening when the temperature is 27°C, the gauge at the top of the tank indicates a pressure of 400 kPa. During the night a leak develops in the tank. The next morning it is noticed that the gauge pressure is only 300 kPa and that the temperature is 15°C. What percentage of the original gas remains in the tank?

$P_1 = 400$ kPa $+ 101.3$ kPa $= 501.3$ kPa; $P_2 = 300$ kPa $+ 101.3$ kPa $= 401.3$ kPa

$T_1 = 273^0 + 27^0 = 300$ K; $T_2 = 273^0 + 15^0 = 288$ K; $V_1 = V_2$

$\frac{P_1V_1}{m_1T_1} = \frac{P_2V_2}{m_2T_2}$; $\frac{m_2}{m_1} = \frac{P_2T_1}{P_1T_2} = \frac{(401.3\ kPa)(300\ K)}{(501.3\ kPa)(288\ K)}$;

$\frac{m_2}{m_1} = 0.834$; $\boxed{Mass\ remaining = 83.4\%}$

**19-46. A 2-L flask is filled with nitrogen (M = 28 g/mol) at 27°C and 1 atm of absolute pressure. A stopcock at the top of the flask is opened to the air and the system is heated to a temperature of 127°C. The stopcock is then closed and the system is allowed to return to 27°C. What mass of nitrogen is in the flask? What is the final pressure?

(a) *The mass remaining in the flask after heating to 127°C is found as follows:*

$T = 127^0 + 273^0 = 400$ K; $R = 0.0821$ atm L/mol K

$PV = \frac{m}{M}RT$; $m = \frac{PVM}{RT} = \frac{(1\ atm)(2\ L)(28\ g/mol)}{(0.0821\ L \cdot atm/mol \cdot K)(400\ K)}$; $\boxed{m = 1.705\ g}$

(b) *This same mass remains when it returns to* $T = 27^0 + 273^0 = 300$ K, *therefore,*

$P = \frac{mRT}{MV} = \frac{(1.705\ g)(0.0821\ L \cdot atm/mol \cdot K)(300\ K)}{(28\ g/mol)(2\ L)}$; $\boxed{P = 0.750\ atm}$

*19-47. What is the volume of 8 g of sulfur dioxide (M = 64 g/mol) if it has an absolute pressure of 10 atm and a temperature of 300 K? If 10^{20} molecules leak from this volume every second, how long will it take to reduce the pressure by one-half?

$PV = \frac{m}{M}RT$; $V = \frac{mRT}{MP} = \frac{(8\ g)(0.0821\ L \cdot atm/mol \cdot K)(300\ K)}{(64\ g/mol)(10\ atm)}$; $\boxed{V = 0.308\ L}$

$n = \frac{m}{M} = \frac{N_1}{N_A}$; $N_1 = \frac{N_A m}{M} = \frac{(6.023 \times 10^{23}\ molecules/mol)(8\ g)}{64\ g/mol}$

$N_1 = 7.529 \times 10^{22}$ molecules in original sample

Now, the pressure P is proportional to the number of molecules so that:

$\frac{P_1}{P_2} = \frac{N_1}{N_2}$ and $N_2 = \frac{N_1(\frac{1}{2}P_1)}{P_1} = \frac{N_1}{2} = \frac{7.529 \times 10^{22}\ molecules}{2}$

$N_2 = 3.765 \times 10^{22}$ molecules; *Molecules lost* $= N_1 - N_2 = 3.765 \times 10^{22}$ molecules

$time = \frac{3.764 \times 10^{22}\ molecules}{10^{22}\ molecules/s}$; $\boxed{time = 371\ s}$

Chapter 20. Thermodynamics

The First Law of Thermodynamics

20-1. In an industrial chemical process, 600 J of heat is supplied to a system while 200 J of work is done BY the system. What is the increase in the internal energy of the system?

Work done BY the system is positive, heat INTO a system is positive. Apply first law:

$$\Delta Q = \Delta U + \Delta W; \quad \Delta Q = 600 \text{ J}; \quad \Delta W = 200 \text{ J}$$

$$\Delta U = \Delta Q - \Delta W = 600 \text{ J} - 200 \text{ J}; \quad \boxed{\Delta U = 400 \text{ J}}$$

20-2. Assume that the internal energy of a system decreases by 300 J while 200 J of work is done by a gas. What is the value of Q? Is heat lost or gained by the system?

$$\Delta U = -300 \text{ J}; \quad \Delta W = +200 \text{ J}; \quad \Delta Q = \Delta U + \Delta W$$

$$\Delta Q = (-300 \text{ J}) + (200 \text{ J}) = -100 \text{ J}; \quad \boxed{Heat\ Lost:\ \Delta Q = -100 \text{ J}}$$

20-3. In a thermodynamic process, the internal energy of the system increases by 500 J. How much work was done by the gas if 800 J of heat is absorbed?

$$\Delta U = +500 \text{ J}; \quad \Delta Q = +800 \text{ J}; \quad \Delta Q = \Delta U + \Delta W$$

$$\Delta W = \Delta Q - \Delta U = 800 \text{ J} - 500 \text{ J}; \quad \boxed{\Delta W = 300 \text{ J}}$$

20-4. A piston does 3000 ft lb of work on a gas, which then expands performing 2500 ft lb of work on its surroundings. What is the change in internal energy of the system if net heat exchange is zero? [*Assume $\Delta Q = 0$, then $\Delta Q = \Delta U + \Delta W = 0$ and $\Delta U = -\Delta W$*]

$$\Delta U = -(Work_{out} - Work_{in}) = -(2500 \text{ ft lb} - 3000 \text{ ft lb}); \quad \boxed{\Delta U = +500 \text{ ft lb} = 0.643 \text{ Btu}}$$

---

*19-48. A flask contains 2 g of helium (M = 4 g/mol) at 57°C and 12 atm absolute pressure. The temperature then decreases to 17°C and the pressure falls to 7 atm. How many grams of helium have leaked out of the container? [$T_1 = 57^0 + 273^0 = 330$ K; $T_2 = 290$ K]

$$V_1 = \frac{mRT_1}{MP_1} = \frac{(2 \text{ g})(0.0821 \text{ L} \cdot \text{atm/mol} \cdot \text{K})(330 \text{ K})}{(4 \text{ g/mol})(12 \text{ atm})}; \quad \boxed{V_1 = 1.13 \text{ L}}$$

$$m_2 = \frac{MP_2V_2}{RT_2} = \frac{(4 \text{ g/mol})(7 \text{ atm})(1.129 \text{ L})}{(0.0821 \text{ L} \cdot \text{atm/mol} \cdot \text{K})(290 \text{ K})}; \quad m_2 = 1.328 \text{ g}$$

$$m_1 = 2.00 \text{ g}; \quad mass\ lost = 2.00 - 1.328 = \boxed{0.672 \text{ g}}$$

*19-49. What must be the temperature of the air in a hot-air balloon in order that the mass of the air be 0.97 times that of an equal volume of air at a temperature of 27°C?

$$m_2 = 0.97 m_1; \quad T_2 = 27^0 + 273^0 = 300 \text{ K}; \quad Assume\ V_1 = V_2 \quad T_1 = ?$$

Note: The pressure inside a balloon will always be equal to the pressure of the atmosphere, since that is the pressure applied to the surface of the balloon, so $P_1 = P_2$.

$$V_1 = \frac{m_1RT_1}{MP_1} = V_2; \quad \frac{m_1RT_1}{MP_1} = \frac{(0.97m_1)RT_2}{MP_2}; \quad T_1 = 0.97T_2$$

$$T_2 = \frac{T_1}{0.97} = \frac{300 \text{ K}}{0.97}; \quad \boxed{T_2 = 309 \text{ K}}$$

20-5. In a chemical laboratory, a technician applies 340 J of energy to a gas while the system surrounding the gas does 140 J of work ON the gas. What is the change in internal energy? [$\Delta Q = +340$ J; $\Delta W = -140$ J (work ON gas is negative)]

$$\Delta U = \Delta Q - \Delta W = (340\ \text{J}) - (-140\ \text{J}); \quad \boxed{\Delta U = 480\ \text{J}}$$

20-6. What is the change in internal energy for Problem 20-5 if the 140 J of work is done BY the gas instead of ON the gas? [Work BY gas is positive, $\Delta W = +140$ J]

$$\Delta U = \Delta Q - \Delta W = (340\ \text{J}) - (+140\ \text{J}); \quad \boxed{\Delta U = 200\ \text{J}}$$

20-7. A system absorbs 200 J of heat as the internal energy increases by 150 J. What work is done by the gas? [$\Delta Q = +200$ J, $\Delta U = +150$ J]

$$\Delta W = \Delta Q - \Delta U = 200\ \text{J} - 150\ \text{J} = 50\ \text{J}; \quad \Delta W = 50\ \text{J}$$

*20-8. The specific heat of water is 4186 J/kg C°. How much does the internal energy of 200 g of water change as it is heated from 20°C to 30°C? Assume the volume is constant.

$$\Delta Q = mc\Delta T = (0.2\ \text{kg})(4186\ \text{J/kg})(30^{0}\text{C} - 20^{0}\text{C}); \quad \Delta Q = 8372\ \text{J}$$

Since $\Delta V = 0$, ΔW is also zero: $\Delta U = \Delta Q$: $\boxed{\Delta U = +8370\ \text{J}}$

*20-9. At a constant pressure of 101.3 kPA, one gram of water (1 cm³) is vaporized completely and has a final volume of 1671 cm³ in its vapor form. What work is done by the system against its surroundings? (1 cm³ = 1 x 10⁻⁶ m³) What is the increase in internal energy?

$$Work = P\Delta V = (101{,}300\ \text{Pa})(1671\ \text{cm}^3 - 1\text{cm}^3)(10^{-6}\ \text{m}^3/\text{cm}^3); \quad \Delta W = 169\ \text{J}$$

*20-9. (Cont.) $\Delta Q = mL_f = (0.001\ \text{kg})(2.256 \times 10^6\ \text{J/kg}) = 2256$ J

$$\Delta U = \Delta Q - \Delta W = 2256\ \text{J} - 169\ \text{J}; \quad \Delta U = 2090\ \text{J}$$

*20-10. A 10-kg block slides down a plane from a height of 10 in, and has a velocity of 10 m/s when it reaches the bottom, how many calories of heat were lost due to friction?

Thermodynamic Processes

20-11. An ideal gas expands isothermally while absorbing 4.80 J of heat. The piston has a mass of 3 kg. How high will the piston rise above its initial position? [$\Delta U = 0$ (isothermal)]

$$\Delta Q = \Delta U + \Delta W; \quad \Delta W = \Delta Q = +4.80\ \text{J}; \quad Work = Fh = 4.80\ \text{J}$$

$$h = \frac{Work}{F} = \frac{4.80\ \text{J}}{(3\ \text{kg})(9.8\ \text{m/s}^2)}; \quad \boxed{h = 0.163\ \text{m or } 16.3\ \text{cm}}$$

20-12. The work done on a gas during an adiabatic compression is 140 J. Calculate the increase in internal energy of the system in calories.

For an adiabatic process, $\Delta Q = 0$ and work ON gas is $\Delta W = -140$ J

$$\Delta U + \Delta W = 0; \quad \Delta U = -\Delta W = -(-140\ \text{J}); \quad \boxed{\Delta U = +140\ \text{J}}$$

The internal energy increases as work is done in compressing the gas.

20-13. During an isobaric expansion a steady pressure of 200 kPa causes the volume of a gas to change from 1 L to 3 L. What work is done by the gas? [1 L = 1 x 10⁻³ m³]

$$Work = P(V_f - V_i) = (200{,}000\ \text{Pa})(3 \times 10^{-3}\ \text{m}^3 - 1 \times 10^{-3}\ \text{m}^3)$$

$$\boxed{Work = 400\ \text{J}}$$

20-14. A gas is confined to a copper can. How much heat must be supplied to increase the internal energy by 59 J? What type of thermodynamic process is involved?

Since the gas is confined, no work is done on or by the gas, so that: $\Delta Q = \Delta U$

$$\boxed{\Delta Q = \Delta U = 59 \text{ J}; \quad An\ isochoric\ process}$$

20-15. A gas confined by a piston expands almost isobarically at 100 kPa. When 20,000 J of heat are absorbed by the system, its volume increases from 0.100 m³ to 0.250 m³. What work is done and what is the change in internal energy?

$Work = P\,\Delta V = (100{,}000 \text{ Pa})(0.250 \text{ m}^3 - 0.100 \text{ m}^3);$ $\boxed{Work = 15.0 \text{ kJ}}$

$\Delta Q = \Delta U + \Delta W; \quad \Delta U = \Delta Q - \Delta W = 20{,}000 \text{ J} - 15{,}000 \text{ J};$ $\boxed{\Delta U = 5.00 \text{ kJ}}$

20-16. The specific heat of brass is 390 J/kg C⁰. A 4-kg piece of brass is heated isochorically causing the temperature to rise by 10 C⁰. What is the increase in Internal energy.

In an isochoric process, we assume negligible heat expansion $(\Delta W = 0)$

$\Delta U = \Delta Q = mc\Delta t = (4 \text{ kg})(390 \text{ J/kg C}^0)(10 \text{ C}^0);$ $\boxed{\Delta U = 15.6 \text{ kJ}}$

*20-17. Two liters of an ideal gas has a temperature of 300 K and a pressure of 2 atm. It undergoes an isobaric expansion while increasing its temperature to 500 K. What work is done by the gas? [$P = 2$ atm $= 202.6$ kPa; $V = 2$ L $= 2 \times 10^{-3}$ m³]

$\dfrac{P_1 V_1}{T_1} = \dfrac{P_2 V_2}{T_2}; \quad V_2 = \dfrac{V_1 T_2}{T_1} = \dfrac{(2 \text{ L})(500 \text{ K})}{300 \text{ K}} = 3.33 \text{ L}; \quad Work = P\Delta V$

$Work = (202{,}600 \text{ Pa})(3.33 \times 10^{-3} \text{ m}^3 - 2.00 \times 10^{-3} \text{ m}^3) = 270 \text{ kJ}$

---

*20-18. The diameter of a piston is 6.00 cm and the length of its stroke is 12 cm. Assuming a constant force of 340 N moves the piston for a full stroke. Calculate the work first based on force and distance. Then verify by considering pressure and volume?

$A = \dfrac{\pi D^2}{4} = \dfrac{\pi(0.06 \text{ m})^2}{4} = 2.83 \times 10^{-3}\,\text{m}^2 \qquad h = 0.12 \text{ m}$

$\Delta V = Ah = (0.00283 \text{ m}^2)(0.12 \text{ m}) = 3.40 \times 10^{-4}\,\text{m}^3$

$Work = Fh = (340 \text{ N})(0.12 \text{ m}) = 40.8 \text{ J};$ $\boxed{Work = 40.8 \text{ J}}$

$P = \dfrac{F}{A} = \dfrac{340 \text{ N}}{0.00283 \text{ m}^2} = 1.20 \times 10^5 \text{Pa}$

$Work = P\Delta V = (3.4 \times 10^{-4} \text{ m}^3)(1.20 \times 10^5 \text{ Pa});$ $\boxed{Work = 40.8 \text{ J}}$

*20-19. For adiabatic processes, it can be shown that the pressure and volume are related by:

$$PV_1^\gamma = PV_2^\gamma \qquad (20\text{-}13)$$

where γ is the adiabatic constant which is 1.40 for diatomic gases and also for the gasoline vapor/air mixture in combustion engines. Use the ideal gas law to prove the companion relationship:

$$T_1 V_1^{\lambda-1} = T_2 V_2^{\lambda-1} \qquad (20\text{-}14)$$

From the general gas law: $\dfrac{PV_1}{T_1} = \dfrac{P_2 V_2}{T_2}; \quad \dfrac{P_1}{P_2} = \dfrac{T_1 V_2}{T_2 V_1} = \dfrac{TV^{-1}}{TV^{-1}}$

Now, from Eq (20-13): $\dfrac{P_1}{P_2} = \dfrac{V_2^\gamma}{V_1^\gamma}$ Eliminating (P_1/P_2), we have

$$\dfrac{T_1 V_1^{-1}}{T_2 V_2^{-1}} = \dfrac{V_2^\gamma}{V_1^\gamma} \quad \text{or} \quad T_1 V_1^{\lambda-1} = T_2 V_2^{\lambda-1}$$

*20-20. The compression ratio for a certain diesel engine is 15. The air-fuel mixture ($\gamma = 1.4$) is taken in at 300 K and 1 atm of pressure. Find the pressure and temperature of the gas after compression. (Refer to Problem 20-19.) [$(V_1/V_2) = 15$ or $V_1 = 15 V_2$]

$$P_1V_1^\gamma = P_2V_2^\gamma; \quad \frac{P_2}{P_1} = \frac{V_1^\gamma}{V_2^\gamma} = \left(\frac{V_1}{V_2}\right)^\gamma \quad \frac{P_2}{P_1} = \left(\frac{15V_2}{V_2}\right)^\gamma = (15)^{1.4} = 44.3$$

$$P_2 = 44.3\, P_1 = 44.3\ (101.3 \text{ kPa}) \qquad \boxed{P_2 = 4490 \text{ kPa}}$$

$$\frac{P_1V_1}{T_1} = \frac{P_2V_2}{T_2}; \quad T_2 = \frac{T_1 P_2 V_2}{P_1 V_1} = \frac{(300\text{ K})(4490\text{ kPa})\, V_2}{(101.3\text{ kPa})(15\, V_2)}; \quad \boxed{T_2 = 886 \text{ K}}$$

The final temperature can also be found from Eq. (20-14) in Prob. 20-19.

The Second Law of Thermodynamics

20-21. What is the efficiency of an engine that does 300 J of work in each cycle while discarding 600 J to the environment?

$$Q_{in} - Q_{out} = W_{out}: \quad Q_{in} = 300 \text{ J} + 600 \text{ J}; \quad Q_{in} = 900 \text{ J}$$

$$E = \frac{W_{out}}{Q_{in}} = \frac{300 \text{ J}}{900 \text{ J}}; \quad \boxed{E = 33.3\%}$$

20-22. During a complete cycle, a system absorbs 600 cal of heat and rejects 200 cal to the environment. How much work is done? What is the efficiency?

$$W_{out} = Q_{in} - Q_{out} = 600 \text{ cal} - 200 \text{ cal}; \quad W_{in} = 400 \text{ cal} \text{ or } \boxed{1674 \text{ J}}$$

$$E = \frac{W_{out}}{Q_{in}} = \frac{400 \text{ cal}}{600 \text{ cal}}; \quad \boxed{E = 66.7\%}$$

---

*20-23. An 37 percent-efficient engine loses 400 J of heat during each cycle. What work is done and how much heat is absorbed in each cycle?

$$E = \frac{Q_{in} - Q_{out}}{Q_{in}} = 0.37; \quad Q_{in} - 400 \text{ J} = 0.37\, Q_{in} \qquad \boxed{Q_{in} = 635 \text{ J}}$$

$$Work = Q_{in} - Q_{out} = 635 \text{ J} - 400 \text{ J}; \quad \boxed{Work = 235 \text{ J}}$$

20-24. What is the efficiency of an engine that operates between temperatures of 525 K and 300 K?

$$E = \frac{T_{in} - T_{out}}{T_{in}} = \frac{525 \text{ K - 300 K}}{525 \text{ K}}; \quad \boxed{E = 42.9\%}$$

20-25. A steam engine takes superheated steam from a boiler at 200°C and rejects it directly into the air at 100°C. What is the ideal efficiency?

$$E = \frac{T_{in} - T_{out}}{T_{in}} = \frac{473 \text{ K - 373 K}}{473 \text{ K}}; \quad \boxed{E = 21.1\%}$$

20-26. In a Carnot cycle, the isothermal expansion of a gas takes place at 400 K and 500 cal of heat is absorbed by the gas. How much heat is lost if the system undergoes isothermal compression at 300 K?

$$E = \frac{T_{in} - T_{out}}{T_{in}} = \frac{400 \text{ K - 300 K}}{400 \text{ K}}; \quad E = 25\%$$

$$E = \frac{Q_{in} - Q_{out}}{Q_{in}} = \frac{500 \text{ cal} - Q_{out}}{500 \text{ cal}} = 0.25; \quad Q_{out} = 375 \text{ cal}$$

$$Q_{out} = (375 \text{ cal})\left(\frac{4.186 \text{ J}}{1 \text{ cal}}\right); \quad \boxed{Q_{out} = 1570 \text{ J}}$$

20-27. A Carnot engine absorbs 1200 cal during each cycle as it operates between 500 K and 300 K. What is the efficiency? How much heat is rejected and how much work is done during each cycle? *For a Carnot engine, actual and ideal efficiencies are equal.*

$$E = \frac{T_{in} - T_{out}}{T_{in}} = \frac{500\ K - 300\ K}{500\ K}; \qquad E = 40\%$$

$$E = \frac{Q_{in} - Q_{out}}{Q_{in}} = \frac{1200\ cal - Q_{out}}{1200\ cal} = 0.40; \qquad Q_{out} = 720\ cal$$

$$Work = 0.40(1200\ cal) = 480\ cal\left(\frac{4.186\ J}{1\ cal}\right); \qquad \boxed{Work = 2020\ J}$$

20-28. The actual efficiency of an engine is 60 percent of its ideal efficiency. The engine operates between temperatures of 460 K and 290 K. How much work is done in each cycle if 1600 J of heat is absorbed?

$$E = \frac{T_{in} - T_{out}}{T_{in}} = \frac{460\ K - 290\ K}{460\ K} = 37.0\% \qquad E_A = 0.60(37\%) = 22.1\%$$

$$E_A = \frac{W_{out}}{Q_{in}} = 0.221; \qquad W_{out} = (0.221)(1600\ J); \qquad \boxed{Work = 355\ J}$$

20-29. A refrigerator extracts 400 J of heat from a box during each cycle and rejects 600 J to a high temperature reservoir. What is the coefficient of performance?

$$K = \frac{Q_{cold}}{Q_{hot} - Q_{cold}} = \frac{400\ J}{600\ J - 400\ J}; \qquad \boxed{K = 2.00}$$

20-30. The coefficient of performance of a refrigerator is 5.0. How much heat is discarded if the compressor does 200 J of work during each cycle?

$$K = \frac{Q_{cold}}{W_{out}} = 5; \qquad Q_{cold} = 5(200\ J); \qquad \boxed{Q_{cold} = 1000\ J}$$

20-31. How much heat is extracted from the cold reservoir if the compressor of a refrigerator does 180 J of work during each cycle. The coefficient of performance is 4.0. What heat is rejected to the hot reservoir?

$$K = \frac{Q_{cold}}{W_{out}} = 4; \qquad Q_{cold} = 4(180\ J); \qquad \boxed{Q_{cold} = 720\ J}$$

$$Work = Q_{hot} - Q_{cold}; \qquad Q_{hot} = 180\ J + 720\ J; \qquad \boxed{Q_{hot} = 900\ J}$$

20-32. An ideal refrigerator extracts 400 J of heat from a reservoir at 200 K and rejects heat to a reservoir at 500 K. What is the ideal coefficient of performance and how much work is done in each cycle?

$$K = \frac{T_{cold}}{T_{hot} - T_{cold}} = \frac{200\ K}{500\ K - 200\ K}; \qquad \boxed{K = 0.667}$$

$$K = \frac{Q_{cold}}{W_{in}}; \qquad W_{in} = \frac{400\ J}{0.667} = 600\ J \qquad \boxed{Work = 600\ J}$$

This is an extremely inefficient refrigerator which requires 600 J of work to extract 400 J of heat in a cooling process while it rejects 1000 J to the environment!

20-33. A Carnot refrigerator has a coefficient of performance of 2.33. If 600 J of work is done by the compressor in each cycle, how many joules of heat are extracted from the cold reservoir and how much is rejected to the environment?

$$K = \frac{Q_{cold}}{W_{in}} = 2.33; \qquad Q_{cold} = 2.33\ (600\ J); \qquad \boxed{Q_{cold} = 1400\ J}$$

$$Q_{hot} = 1400\ J + 600\ J = 2000\ J \qquad \boxed{Q_{hot} = 2000\ J}$$

The compressor does 600 J of work, extracting 1400 J of energy from the cold reservoir and discarding 2000 J to the environment.

Supplementary Problems:

20-34. In a thermodynamic process, 200 Btu are supplied to produce an isobaric expansion under a pressure of 100 lb/in.². The internal energy of the system does not change. What is the increase in volume of the gas?

Since there is no change in internal energy, $\Delta U = 0$ and $\Delta Q = \Delta W = 200$ Btu.

$$\Delta W = (200\ Btu)\left(\frac{778\ ft\ lb}{1\ Btu}\right) = 155{,}600\ ft\ lb;\quad P = 100\ \frac{lb}{in.^2}\left(\frac{144\ in.^2}{1\ ft^2}\right) = 14{,}100\ lb/ft^2$$

$$\Delta W = P\Delta V;\quad \Delta V = \frac{\Delta W}{P} = \frac{155{,}600\ ft\ lb}{14{,}400\ lb/ft^2};\quad \boxed{\Delta V = 10.8\ ft^3}$$

20-35. A 100 cm³ sample of gas at a pressure of 100 kPa is heated isochorically from point A to point B until its pressure reaches 300 kPa. Then it expands isobarically to point C, where its volume is 400 cm³. The pressure then returns to 100 kPa at point D with no change in volume. Finally, it returns to its original state at point A. Draw the P-V diagram for this cycle. What is the net work done for the entire cycle?

The net work around a closed PV loop is equal to the enclosed area $\Delta P \cdot \Delta P$: (Recall that $1\ cm^3 = 10^{-6}\ m^2$.)

$$\Delta P \cdot \Delta V = (300\ kPa - 100\ kPa)(400\ cm^3 - 100\ cm^3)$$

$$Work = (200\ kPa)(300\ cm^3) = 60{,}000\ kPa \cdot cm^3$$

$$Work = (60{,}000\ kPa \cdot cm^3)\left(\frac{1000\ Pa}{1\ kPa}\right)\left(\frac{10^{-6}\ m^3}{1\ cm^3}\right);\quad \boxed{Work = 60\ J}$$

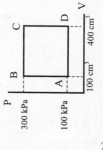

Note that zero work is done during the isochoric processes AB and CD, since $\Delta V = 0$. Positive work is done from B to C and negative work is done from D to A making the net work equal to zero. $P_B(V_C - V_B) + P_A(V_A - V_D) = 60\ J$. Same as area $\Delta P \cdot \Delta V$.

20-36. Find the net work done by a gas as it is carried around the cycle shown in Fig. 20-17.

$$Work = area = \Delta P \cdot \Delta V;\quad (1\ L = 1 \times 10^{-3}\ m^3)$$

$$Work = (200{,}000\ Pa - 100{,}000\ Pa)(5\ L - 2\ L)$$

$$Work = (100{,}000\ Pa)(3 \times 10^{-3}\ m^3) = 300\ J$$

$$\boxed{Work = 300\ J}$$

20-37. What is the net work done for the process ABCA as described by Fig. 20-18.

$$Work = area = \tfrac{1}{2}\Delta P \cdot \Delta V\quad (1\ atm = 101{,}300\ Pa)$$

$$Work = (3\ atm - 1\ atm)(5\ L - 2\ L) = 6\ atm \cdot L$$

$$Work = 6\ atm \cdot L\left(\frac{101{,}300\ Pa}{1\ atm}\right)\left(\frac{10^{-3}\ m^3}{1\ L}\right)\quad \boxed{Work = 85.0\ J}$$

*20-38. A real engine operates between 327°C and 0°C, and it has an output power of 8 kW. What is the ideal efficiency for this engine? How much power is wasted if the actual efficiency is only 25 percent?

$$T_{in} = 327^0 + 273^0 = 600\ K;\quad T_{out} = 0^0 + 273^0 = 273\ K$$

$$E = \frac{T_{in} - T_{out}}{T_{in}} = \frac{600\ K - 273\ K}{600\ K};\quad \boxed{E_I = 54.5\%};\quad E_A = 0.25(54.5\%) = 13.6\%$$

$$E_A = \frac{P_{output}}{P_{in}};\quad P_{in} = \frac{P_{output}}{E_A} = \frac{8\ kW}{0.136} = 58.7\ kW\quad P_{in} = P_{output} + P_{lost}$$

$$P_{lost} = P_{in} - P_{output};\quad P_{lost} = 58.7\ kW - 8\ kW$$

$$\boxed{Power\ wasted = 50.7\ kW}$$

*20-39. The Otto efficiency for a gasoline engine is 50 percent, and the adiabatic constant is 1.4. Compute the compression ratio.

$$E = 1 - \frac{1}{(V_1/V_2)^{\gamma-1}} = 1 - \frac{1}{C^{\gamma-1}}; \quad 1 - E = \frac{1}{C^{\gamma-1}}$$

$$C^{\gamma-1} = \frac{1}{1-E} = \frac{1}{1-0.5} = 2; \quad \gamma - 1 = 1.4 - 1 = 0.4; \quad C^{0.4} = 2$$

$$(C^{0.4})^{1/0.4} = (2)^{1/0.4}; \quad \boxed{C = 5.66} \quad \textit{(Compression ratio)}$$

*20-40. A heat pump takes heat from a water reservoir at 41°F and delivers it to a system of pipes in a house at 78°F. The energy required to operate the heat pump is about twice that required to operate a Carnot pump. How much mechanical work must be supplied by the pump to deliver 1 x 10⁶ Btu of heat energy to the house?

Must use absolute T: $T_{hot} = 78^0 + 460^0 = 538$ R; $T_{cold} = 41^0 + 460^0 = 501$ R

For HEATING, the C.O.P. is: $K = \dfrac{T_{hot}}{T_{hot} - T_{cold}} = \dfrac{538 \text{ R}}{538 \text{ R} - 501 \text{ R}} = 14.54\%$ *(ideal)*

$$K = \frac{Q_{hot}}{W_{in}}; \quad W_{in} = \frac{(1 \times 10^6 \text{Btu})(778 \text{ ft lb/Btu})}{0.1454}; \quad Work = 5.35 \times 10^7 \text{ ft lb}$$

Actual work = 2(ideal work): $\boxed{\textit{Actual work} = 1.07 \times 10^8 \text{ ft lb}}$

20-41. A Carnot engine has an efficiency of 48 percent. If the working substance enters the system at 400°C, what is the exhaust temperature? [$T_{in} = 400^0 + 273^0 = 673$ K]

$$E = \frac{T_{in} - T_{out}}{T_{in}}; \quad \frac{673 \text{ K} - T_{out}}{673 \text{ K}} = 0.48; \quad 673 \text{ K} - T_{out} = (0.48)(673)$$

$$\boxed{T_{out} = 350 \text{ K}}$$

20-42. During the compression stroke of an automobile engine, the volume of the combustible mixture decreases from 18 to 2 in.³. If the adiabatic constant is 1.4, what is the maximum possible efficiency for the engine? [*Maximum E is the ideal E*]

$$E = 1 - \frac{1}{(V_1/V_2)^{\gamma-1}}; \quad \frac{V_1}{V_2} = \frac{18 \text{ in.}^3}{2 \text{ in.}^3} = 9; \quad (\gamma - 1) = 1.4 - 1 = 0.4$$

$$E = 1 - \frac{1}{9^{0.4}}; \quad \boxed{E = 58.5\%}$$

20-43. How many joules of work must be done by the compressor in a refrigerator to change 1.0 kg of water at 20°C to ice at -10°C? The coefficient of performance is 3.5.

$$Q_{cold} = mc_w(20^0 C - 0^0 C) + mL_f + mc_i[0^0 C - (-10^0 C)]$$

$$Q_{cold} = (1 \text{ kg})(4186 \text{ J/kg C}^0)(20 \text{ C}^0) + (1 \text{ kg})(3.34 \times 10^5 \text{ J/kg})$$
$$+ (1 \text{ kg})(2300 \text{ J/kg C}^0)(10 \text{ C}^0) = 4.41 \times 10^5 \text{ J}$$

$$K = \frac{Q_{cold}}{W_{in}}; \quad W_{in} = \frac{4.41 \times 10^5 \text{ J}}{3.5}; \quad \boxed{W_{in} = 126 \text{ kJ}}$$

20-44. In a mechanical refrigerator the low-temperature coils of the evaporator are at -30°C, and the condenser has a temperature of 60°C. What is the maximum possible coefficient of performance? [$T_{cold} = -30 + 273^0 = 243$ K; $T_{hot} = 60^0 + 273^0 = 333$ K]

$$K = \frac{T_{cold}}{T_{hot} - T_{cold}} = \frac{243 \text{ K}}{333 \text{ K} - 243 \text{ K}}; \quad \boxed{K = 2.70}$$

20-45. An engine has a thermal efficiency of 27 percent and an exhaust temperature of 230°C. What is the lowest possible input temperature? [$T_{out} = 230 + 273^0 = 503$ K]

$$E = \frac{T_{in} - T_{out}}{T_{in}}; \quad \frac{T_{in} - 503 \text{ K}}{T_{in}} = 0.27; \quad 0.27T_{in} = T_{in} - 503 \text{ K}$$

$$\boxed{T_{in} = 689 \text{ K or } 416^0 C}$$

20-46. The coefficient of performance of a refrigerator is 5.0. If the temperature of the room is 28⁰C, what is the lowest possible temperature that can be obtained inside the refrigerator?

$$K = \frac{T_{cold}}{T_{hot} - T_{cold}}; \quad \frac{T_{cold}}{301\ K - T_{cold}} = 5.0; \quad T_{cold} = 1505\ K - 5T_{cold}$$

$$\boxed{T_{cold} = 251\ K \ \text{or}\ -22.2^{0}C}$$

Critical Thinking Questions

20-47. A gas expands against a movable piston, lifting it through 2 in. at constant speed. How much work is done by the gas if the piston weighs 200 lb and has a cross-sectional area of 12 in.²? If the expansion is adiabatic, what is the change in internal energy in Btu? Does ΔU represent an increase or decrease in internal energy?

$$Work = Fx = (200\ lb)(2\ in.)(1\ ft/12\ in.) = \boxed{33.3\ \text{ft lb}}$$

$$Work = 33.3\ \text{ft lb} \left(\frac{1\ \text{ft lb}}{778\ \text{Btu}} \right) = 0.0428\ \text{Btu}$$

For adiabatic process, $ΔQ = 0$, and $ΔU = -ΔW = -0.0428$ Btu; $\boxed{ΔU = -0.0428\ \text{Btu}}$

This represents a DECREASE in internal energy.

286 Unit A   Solutions Manual

---

*20-48. Consider the P-V diagram shown in Fig. 20-19, where the pressure and volume are indicated for each of the points A, B, C, and D. Starting at point A, a 100-cm³ sample of gas absorbs 200 J of heat, causing the pressure to increase from 100 kPa to 200 kPa while its volume increases to 200 cm³. Next the gas expands from B to C, absorbing an additional 400 J of heat while its volume increases to 400 cm³. (a) Find the net work done and the change in internal energy for each of the processes AB and BC. (b) What are the net work and the total change in internal energy for the process ABC? (c) What kind of process is illustrated by AB? *Recall that work is equal to the area under the curve.*

Note: (1 kPa)(1 cm³) = 0.001 Pa·m³ = 0.001 J

(a) *Area of triangle = ½(base)(height)*

$$W_{AB} = \tfrac{1}{2}(200\ cm^3 - 100\ cm^3)(200\ kPa - 100\ kPa) + (100\ kPa)(200\ cm^3 - 100\ cm^3)$$

$$W_{AB} = 5000\ \text{kPa·cm}^3 + 10{,}000\ \text{kPa·cm}^3 = 15{,}000\ \text{kPa·cm}^3$$

$$W_{AB} = 15{,}000\ \text{kPa·cm}^3 \left(\frac{0.001\ J}{1\ \text{kPa·cm}^3} \right); \quad \boxed{W_{AB} = 15.0\ J}$$

(b) *For AB,* $Q_{in} = 400\ J$, *so that:* $ΔU = Q_{in} - ΔW = 200\ J - 15\ J = 185\ J$; $\boxed{ΔU_{AB} = +185\ J}$

Now, for process BC, Work = area = (200 kPa)(400 cm³ – 200 cm³); Work = 40,000 kPa·cm³

$$W_{AB} = 40{,}000\ \text{kPa·cm}^3 \left(\frac{0.001\ J}{1\ \text{kPa·cm}^3} \right); \quad \boxed{W_{AB} = 40.0\ J}$$

For process BC, $Q_{in} = 400\ J$, *so that:* $ΔU = Q_{in} - ΔW = 400\ J - 40\ J = 360\ J$; $\boxed{ΔU_{BC} = +360\ J}$

(c) *Net Heat:* $ΔQ_{ABC} = +200\ J + 400\ J = \boxed{600\ J}$; $W_{ABC} = 15\ J + 40\ J = \boxed{55\ J}$

Net change in internal energy: +185 J + 360 J = 945 J; $\boxed{ΔU_{ABC} = +545\ J}$

First law is satisfied for ABC: $ΔQ = ΔU + ΔW$; 600 J = 545 J + 55 J

(d) *Process BC is an ISOBARIC process (constant pressure).*

Chapter 20   Thermodynamics **287**

144

*20-49. The cycle begun in the previous example now continues from C to D while an additional 200 J of heat is absorbed. (a) Find the net work and the net change in internal energy for the process CD. (b) Suppose the system now returns to its original state at point A. What is the net work for the entire cycle ABCDA, and what is the efficiency of the entire cycle?

(a) $W_{CD} = \frac{1}{2}\Delta P_1 \cdot \Delta V_1 + \Delta P_2 \cdot \Delta V_2$

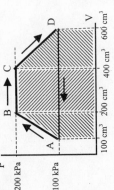

$W_{CD} = \frac{1}{2}(200 - 100)\text{kPa}(600 - 400)\text{ cm}^3$
$+ (100\text{ kPa})(600 - 400)\text{ cm}^3$

$W_{CD} = 10{,}000\text{ kPa cm}^3 + 20{,}000\text{ kPa cm}^3$; $W_{CD} = 30{,}000\text{ kPa cm}^3 = 30\text{ J}$; $\boxed{W_{CD} = 30\text{ J}}$

$\Delta U_{CD} = \Delta Q - \Delta W = 200\text{ J} - 30\text{ J} = 170\text{ J}$; $\boxed{\Delta U_{CD} = 170\text{ J}}$

(b) Work for DA = $(100\text{ kPA})(100\text{ cm}^3 - 600\text{ cm}^3) = -50{,}000\text{ kPa cm}^3$; $\underline{W_{DA} = -50\text{ J}}$

Note that work from D to A is NEGATIVE since final volume is LESS than initial volume.

When system returns to its initial state at A, the total ΔU must be ZERO for ABCDA.

Thus, $\Delta U_{DA} + \Delta U_{CD} + \Delta U_{ABC} = 0$; $\Delta U_{DA} + 170\text{ J} + 545\text{ J} = 0$; $\Delta U_{DA} = -715\text{ J}$

$\Delta Q_{DA} = \Delta U_{DA} + \Delta W = -715\text{ J} - 50\text{ J}$; $\Delta Q_{DA} = -765\text{ J}$

The efficiency of the cycle is based on the net work done for the heat put IN to the cycle.

$E = \frac{Q_{in}}{\Delta W} = \frac{35\text{ J}}{200\text{ J} + 400}$

$\boxed{E = 5.83\%}$

CTQ 2 & 3: Summary

	ΔQ	ΔU	ΔW
AB	200 J	185 J	15 J
BC	400 J	360 J	40 J
CD	200 J	170 J	30 J
DA	-765 J	-715 J	-50 J
Total	+35 J	0 J	+35 J

Study the table which illustrates the first law of thermodynamics as it applies to each of the processes described by CTQ's #2 and #3. Note that $\Delta Q = \Delta U + \Delta W$ in every case.

*20-50. Consider a specific mass of gas that is forced through an adiabatic throttling process. Before entering the valve, it has internal energy U_1, pressure P_1 and volume V_1. After passing though the valve, it has internal energy U_2 pressure P_2 and volume V_2. The net work done is the work done BY the gas minus the work done ON the gas. Show that The quantity $U + PT$, called the enthalpy, is conserved during a throttling process.

For an adiabatic process, $\Delta Q = 0$, so that $\Delta W = -\Delta U$ and $\Delta W = W_{out} - Work_{in}$

$\Delta W = P_2V_2 - P_1V_1 = -\Delta U$; $P_2V_2 - P_1V_1 = -(U_2 - U_1)$

Rearranging we have: $\boxed{U_2 + P_2V_2 = U_1 + P_1V_1}$ *Enthalpy is conserved*

*20-51. A gasoline engine takes in 2000 J of heat and delivers 400 J of work per cycle, The heat is obtained by burning gasoline which has a heat of combustion of 50 kJ/g. What is the thermal efficiency? How much heat is lost per cycle? How much gasoline is burned in each cycle? If the engine goes through 90 cycles per second, what is the output power?

$E = \frac{W_{out}}{Q_{in}} = \frac{400\text{ J}}{2000\text{ J}}$; $\boxed{E = 20\%}$

$W_{out} = Q_{in} - Q_{out}$; $Q_{out} = 2000\text{ J} - 400\text{ J}$; $\boxed{Q_{out} = 1600\text{ J}}$

$Gas\ burned: = \frac{2000\text{ J}}{50{,}000\text{ J/g}} = 0.04\text{ g}$; $\boxed{Amount\ burned = 0.0400\text{ g}}$

$P = \frac{Work}{t} = \frac{(90\text{ cycles})(400\text{ J/cycle})}{1\text{ s}}$; $\boxed{P_{out} = 36.0\text{ kW}}$

*20-52. Consider a Carnot engine of efficiency e and a Carnot refrigerator whose coefficient of performance is K. If these devices operate between the same temperatures, derive the following relationship. *Let* $T_{cold} = T_{out} = T_2$ *and* $T_{hot} = T_{in} = T_1$, *then*

$$K = \frac{T_2}{T_1 - T_2} \quad \text{and} \quad e = \frac{T_1 - T_2}{T_1}$$

$$eT_1 = T_1 - T_2; \quad T_2 = (1-e)T_1 \quad K = \frac{(1-e)T_1}{T_1 - (1-e)T_1}$$

$$K = \frac{(1-e)T_1}{T_1 - (1-e)T_1} = \frac{(1-e)T_1}{(1-1+e)T_1}; \quad \boxed{K = \frac{1-e}{e}}$$

Chapter 21. Wave Motion

Mechanical Waves

21-1. A transverse wave has a wavelength of 30 cm and vibrates with a frequency of 420 Hz.

What is the speed of this wave?   [$\lambda = 30$ cm $= 0.30$ m]

$$v = f\lambda = (420 \text{ Hz})(0.30 \text{ m}) ; \quad \boxed{v = 126 \text{ m/s}}$$

21-2. A person on a pier counts the slaps of a wave as the crests hit a post. If 80 slaps are heard in one minute and a particular crest travels a distance of 8 m in 4 s, what is the length of a single wave?

$$v = \frac{s}{t} = \frac{8 \text{ m}}{4 \text{ s}} = 2 \text{ m/s}; \quad f = \frac{80 \text{ waves}}{60 \text{ s}} = 1.33 \text{ Hz}$$

$$\lambda = \frac{v}{f} = \frac{2 \text{ m/s}}{1.33 \text{ Hz}}; \quad \boxed{\lambda = 1.5 \text{ m}}$$

21-3. A transverse wave is pictured in Fig. 21-13. Find the amplitude, wavelength, period, and speed of the wave if it has a frequency of 12 Hz.   [$A = 12$ cm, $\lambda = 28$ cm]

From the figure: $\boxed{A = 12 \text{ cm}, \lambda = 28 \text{ cm};}$

$$v = f\lambda = (12 \text{ Hz})(0.28 \text{ m}); \quad \boxed{v = 3.36 \text{ m/s}}$$

$$T = \frac{1}{f} = \frac{1}{12 \text{ Hz}}; \quad \boxed{T = 0.0833 \text{ s}}$$

21-4. For the longitudinal wave in Fig. 21-13, find the amplitude, wavelength, period, and speed of the wave if it has a frequency of 8 Hz. If the amplitude were doubled, would any of the other factors change?

From figure: $\boxed{A = 12 \text{ cm and } \lambda = 28 \text{ cm}}$

$$v = f\lambda = (8 \text{ Hz})(0.28 \text{ m}); \quad \boxed{v = 2.24 \text{ m/s};} \quad T = \frac{1}{f} = \frac{1}{8 \text{ Hz}}; \quad \boxed{T = 0.125 \text{ s}}$$

21-5. A 500-g metal wire has a length of 50 cm and is under a tension of 80 N. What is the speed of a transverse wave in the wire?

$$v = \sqrt{\frac{Fl}{m}} = \sqrt{\frac{(80 \text{ N})(0.50 \text{ m})}{0.50 \text{ kg}}} \; ; \quad \boxed{v = 8.94 \text{ m/s}}$$

21-6. If the wire in Problem 21-5 is cut in half, what will be its new mass? Show that the speed of the wave is unchanged? Why?

$$m = \frac{0.500 \text{ kg}}{2}; \quad m = 0.250 \text{ kg}; \quad v = \sqrt{\frac{Fl}{m}} = \sqrt{\frac{(80 \text{ N})(0.250 \text{ m})}{0.250 \text{ kg}}} = 8.94 \text{ m/s}$$

The speed is the same, because linear density m/l is not changed.

21-7. A 3-m cord under a tension of 200 N sustains a transverse wave speed of 172 m/s. What is the mass of the rope?

$$v = \sqrt{\frac{Fl}{m}}; \quad v^2 = \frac{Fl}{m}; \quad m = \frac{Fl}{v^2} = \frac{(200 \text{ N})(3 \text{ m})}{(172 \text{ m/s})^2}; \quad \boxed{m = 0.0203 \text{ kg}}$$

21-8. A 200-g cord is stretched over a distance of 5.2 m and placed under a tension of 500 N. Compute the speed of a transverse wave in the cord?

$$v = \sqrt{\frac{Fl}{m}} = \sqrt{\frac{(500 \text{ N})(5.2 \text{ m})}{0.200 \text{ kg}}} \; ; \quad \boxed{v = 114 \text{ m/s}}$$

21-9. What tension is needed to produce a wave speed of 12 m/s in a 900-g string that is 2 m long?

$$F = \frac{mv^2}{l} = \frac{(0.900 \text{ kg})(12 \text{ m/s})^2}{2 \text{ m}}; \quad \boxed{F = 64.8 \text{ N.}}$$

21-10. A wooden float at the end of a fishing line makes eight complete oscillations in 10 s. If it takes 3.60 s for a single wave to travel 11 m, what is the wavelength of the water waves?

$$f = \frac{8 \text{ waves}}{10 \text{ s}} = 0.800 \text{ Hz}; \quad v = \frac{11 \text{ m}}{3.6 \text{ s}} = 3.06 \text{ m/s};$$

$$\lambda = \frac{v}{f} = \frac{3.06 \text{ m/s}}{0.800 \text{ Hz}} \; ; \quad \boxed{\lambda = 3.82 \text{ m}}$$

*21-11. What frequency is required to cause a rope to vibrate with a wavelength of 20 cm when it is under a tension of 200 N. Assume the linear density of the rope to be 0.008 kg/m.

$$f = \frac{v}{\lambda}; \quad f = \frac{1}{\lambda}\sqrt{\frac{F}{1}} = \frac{1}{(0.20 \text{ m})}\sqrt{\frac{(200 \text{ N})}{0.008 \text{ kg/m}}} \; ; \quad \boxed{f = 791 \text{ Hz}}$$

*21-12. A tension of 400 N causes a 300-g wire of length 1.6 m to vibrate with a frequency of 40 Hz. What is the wavelength of the transverse waves?

$$v = \sqrt{\frac{Fl}{m}} = \sqrt{\frac{(400 \text{ N})(1.6 \text{ m})}{0.30 \text{ kg}}} = 46.2 \text{ m/s}; \quad \lambda = \frac{v}{f} = \frac{46.2 \text{ m/s}}{40 \text{ Hz}} \; ; \quad \boxed{\lambda = 1.15 \text{ m}}$$

*21-13. A horizontal spring is jiggled back and forth at one end by a device that makes 80 oscillations in 12 s. What is the speed of the longitudinal waves if condensations are separated by 15 cm as the wave progresses down the spring?

$$f = \frac{80 \text{ waves}}{12 \text{ s}} = 6.67 \text{ Hz}; \quad v = f\lambda = (6.67 \text{ Hz})(0.15 \text{ m}); \quad \boxed{v = 1.00 \text{ m/s}}$$

Energy of a Periodic Wave

21-14. A 2-m length of string has a mass of 300 g and vibrates with a frequency of 2 Hz and an amplitude of 50 mm. If the tension in the rope is 48 N, how much power must be delivered to the string?

$$\mu = \frac{m}{l} = \frac{0.30 \text{ kg}}{2 \text{ m}} = 0.159 \text{ kg/m}; \qquad v = \sqrt{\frac{F}{\mu}} = \sqrt{\frac{(48 \text{ N})}{0.15 \text{ kg/m}}} = 17.9 \text{ m/s}$$

$$P = 2\pi^2 f^2 A^2 \mu v = 2\pi^2(2 \text{ Hz})^2(0.05 \text{ m})^2(0.15 \text{ kg/m})(17.9 \text{ m/s}); \qquad \boxed{P = 0.530 \text{ W}}$$

21-15. An 80-g string has a length of 40 m and vibrates with a frequency of 8 Hz and an amplitude of 4 cm. Find the energy per unit of length passing along the string?

$$\frac{E}{l} = 2\pi^2 f^2 A^2 \mu = 2\pi^2(8 \text{ Hz})^2(0.04 \text{ m})^2\,\frac{0.08 \text{ kg}}{40 \text{ m}}; \qquad \boxed{E/l = 4.04 \times 10^{-3} \text{ J/m}}$$

21-16. If the wavelength of the transverse wave in Problem 21-15 is 1.6 m, what power is supplied by the source?

$$P = 2\pi^2 f^2 A^2 \mu v = \left(\frac{E}{l}\right)v; \qquad v = f\lambda = (8 \text{ Hz})(1.6 \text{ m}) = 12.8 \text{ m/s}$$

$$P = \left(\frac{E}{l}\right)v = (4.04 \times 10^{-3}\text{J/m})(12.8 \text{ m/s}); \qquad \boxed{P = 5.17 \times 10^{-2} \text{ W}}$$

*21-17. A 300-g string has a length of 2.50 m and vibrates with an amplitude of 8.00 mm. The tension in the string is 46 N. What must be the frequency of the waves in order that the average power be 90.0 W? $[\,P = 2\pi^2 f^2 A^2 \mu v\,]$

$$\mu = \frac{m}{l} = \frac{0.300 \text{ kg}}{2.50 \text{ m}} = 0.120 \text{ kg/m}; \qquad v = \sqrt{\frac{Fl}{m}} = \sqrt{\frac{46 \text{ N}}{0.120 \text{ kg/m}}} = 19.6 \text{ m/s}$$

$$f = \sqrt{\frac{P}{2\pi^2 A^2 \mu v}} = \sqrt{\frac{90.0 \text{ W}}{2\pi^2(0.008 \text{ m})^2(0.120 \text{ kg/m})(19.6 \text{ m/s})}}; \qquad \boxed{f = 174 \text{ Hz}}$$

Standing Wave and Characteristic Frequencies

21-18. A string vibrates with a fundamental frequency of 200 Hz. What is the frequency of the second harmonic and of the third overtone?

$$f_n = nf_1; \qquad f_2 = 2(200 \text{ Hz}); \qquad \boxed{f_2 = 400 \text{ Hz}}$$

Third overtone is the fourth harmonic: $\quad f_4 = 4(200 \text{ Hz}); \qquad \boxed{f_4 = 800 \text{ Hz}}$

21-19. If the fundamental frequency of a wave is 330 Hz, what is the frequency of the fifth harmonic and the second overtone? $\quad f_n = nf_1 = n(330 \text{ Hz})$

$$f_n = nf_1; \qquad f_2 = 5(330 \text{ Hz}); \qquad \boxed{f_5 = 1650 \text{ Hz}}$$

Second overtone is the third harmonic: $\quad f_3 = 3(330 \text{ Hz}); \qquad \boxed{f_4 = 990 \text{ Hz}}$

21-20. The linear density of a string is 0.00086 kg/m. What should be the tension in the rope in order for a 2 m length of this string to vibrate at 600 Hz for its third harmonic?

$$f_3 = \frac{3}{2l}\sqrt{\frac{F}{\mu}}; \qquad f_3^2 = \frac{9}{4l^2}\left(\frac{F}{\mu}\right); \qquad F = \frac{4l^2 \mu f_3^2}{9}$$

$$F = \frac{4(2 \text{ m})^2(0.00086 \text{ kg/m})(600 \text{ Hz})^2}{9}; \qquad F = 550 \text{ N}$$

21-21. A 10-g string, 4 m in length, has a tension of 64 N. What is the frequency of its fundamental mode of vibration? What are the frequencies of the first and second overtones?

$$f_1 = \frac{1}{2L}\sqrt{\frac{Fl}{m}} = \frac{1}{2(4 \text{ m})}\sqrt{\frac{(64 \text{ N})(4 \text{ m})}{0.0100 \text{ kg}}}; \qquad \boxed{f_1 = 20 \text{ Hz}}$$

First Overtone $= f_2 = 2(20 \text{ Hz}) = \boxed{40 \text{ Hz}}$

Second Overtone $= f_3 = 3(20 \text{ Hz}) = \boxed{60 \text{ Hz}}$

21-22. The second harmonic of a vibrating string is 200 Hz. If the length of the string is 3 m and its tension is 200 N, compute the linear density of the string.

$$f_2 = \frac{2}{2l}\sqrt{\frac{F}{\mu}}; \quad f_2^2 = \frac{1}{l^2}\left(\frac{F}{\mu}\right); \quad \mu = \frac{F}{f_2^2 l^2}$$

$$\mu = \frac{(200\ N)}{(200\ Hz)^2(3\ m)^2}; \quad \boxed{\mu = 5.56 \times 10^{-4}\ kg/m}$$

*21-23. A 0.500-g string is 4.3 m long and has a tension of 300 N. If it is fixed at each end and vibrates in three segments, what is the frequency of the standing waves?

$$f_3 = \frac{3}{2l}\sqrt{\frac{Fl}{m}} = \frac{3}{(2)(4.3\ m)}\sqrt{\frac{(300\ N)(4.3\ m)}{0.5 \times 10^{-3}\ kg}}; \quad \boxed{f_3 = 560\ Hz}$$

*21-24. A string vibrates with standing waves in five loops when the frequency is 600 Hz. What frequency will cause the string to vibrate in only two loops?

$$\frac{f_5}{f_2} = \frac{5f_1}{2f_1} = \frac{600\ Hz}{f_2}; \quad f_2 = \frac{2(600\ Hz)}{5}; \quad \boxed{f_2 = 240\ Hz}$$

*21-25. A 120-g wire fixed at both ends is 8 m long and has a tension of 100 N. What is the longest possible wavelength for a standing wave? What is the frequency?

$$v = \sqrt{\frac{Fl}{m}} = \sqrt{\frac{(100\ N)(8\ m)}{0.120\ kg}} = 81.65\ m/s$$

The longest standing wave occurs for the fundamental, when $\lambda = 2l$

$$\lambda = 2(8\ m) = 16\ m; \quad \boxed{\lambda = 16\ m}$$

The velocity of the wave is $v = f\lambda$, so that

$$f = \frac{v}{\lambda} = \frac{(81.65\ m/s)}{(16\ m)}; \quad \boxed{f_1 = 5.10\ Hz}$$

Supplemental Problems

21-26. A longitudinal wave of frequency 400 Hz has a velocity of 60 m/s. What is the wavelength?

$$\lambda = \frac{v}{f} = \frac{60\ m/s}{400\ Hz}; \quad \boxed{\lambda = 0.150\ m}$$

21-27. What is the speed of a transverse wave in a rope of length 2.00 m and mass 80 g under a tension of 400 N?

$$v = \sqrt{\frac{Fl}{m}} = \sqrt{\frac{(400\ N)(2\ m)}{0.080\ kg}}; \quad \boxed{v = 100\ m/s}$$

21-28. A transverse wave travels at a speed of 8.00 m/s. A particular particle on the string moves from its highest point to its lowest point in a time of 0.03 s. What is the wavelength? [*From high to low is a time of ½T, so that T = 2(0.03 s) = 0.06 s.*]

$$f = \frac{1}{T} = \frac{1}{0.06\ s} = 16.7\ Hz; \quad \lambda = \frac{v}{f} = \frac{8\ m/s}{16.7\ Hz}; \quad \boxed{\lambda = 0.480\ m}$$

21-29. A bass guitar string 750 mm long is stretched with sufficient force to produce a fundamental vibration of 220 Hz. What is the velocity of the transverse waves in this string?

The fundamental occurs when $\lambda = 2l = 2(0.750\ m)$; $\quad \lambda = 1.50\ m$

$$v = f\lambda = (220\ Hz)(1.50\ m); \quad \boxed{v = 330\ m/s}$$

*21-30. A 5-kg mass is hung from the ceiling by a 30-g wire 1.8 m long. What is the fundamental frequency of vibration for this wire? [F = mg = (5 kg)(9.8 m/s²)]

$$f_1 = \frac{1}{2l}\sqrt{\frac{Fl}{m}} = \frac{1}{2(1.8\ m)}\sqrt{\frac{(49\ N)(1.8\ m)}{0.030\ kg}}; \quad \boxed{f_1 = 15.1\ Hz}$$

*21-31. A steel guy wire supporting a pole is 18.9 m long and 9.5 mm in diameter. It has a linear density of 0.474 kg/m. When it is struck at one end by a hammer, the pulse returns in 0.3 s. What is the tension in the wire?

$$v = \frac{2l}{t} = \frac{2(18.9 \text{ m})}{0.3 \text{ s}} = 126 \text{ m/s}; \qquad v = \sqrt{\frac{Fl}{m}}$$

$$v^2 = \frac{F}{\mu}; \quad F = \mu v^2 = (0.474 \text{ kg/m})(126 \text{ m/s})^2; \qquad \boxed{F = 7530 \text{ N}}$$

*21-32. A 30-m wire weighing 400 N is stretched with a tension of 1800 N. How much time is required for a pulse to make a round trip if it is struck at one end?

$$m = \frac{400 \text{ N}}{9.8 \text{ m/s}^2} = 40.8 \text{ kg}; \quad v = \sqrt{\frac{Fl}{m}} = \sqrt{\frac{(1800 \text{ N})(30 \text{ m})}{40.8 \text{ kg}}}; \qquad v = 36.4 \text{ m/s}$$

$$t = \frac{2l}{v} = \frac{2(30 \text{ m})}{36.4 \text{ m/s}}; \qquad \boxed{t = 1.65 \text{ s}}$$

*21-33. Transverse waves have a speed of 20 m/s on a string whose tension is 8 N. What tension is required to give a wave speed of 30 m/s for the same string?

Velocity is proportional to the square root of the tension, therefore:

$$\frac{v_1}{v_2} = \sqrt{\frac{F_1}{F_2}}; \quad \frac{v_1^2}{v_2^2} = \frac{F_1}{F_2}; \quad F_2 = \frac{F_1 v_2^2}{v_1^2} = \frac{(8 \text{ N})(30 \text{ m/s})^2}{(20 \text{ m/s})^2}; \qquad \boxed{F_2 = 18.0 \text{ N}}$$

*21-34. The fundamental frequency for a given string is 80 Hz. If the mass of the string is doubled but other factors remain constant, what is the new fundamental frequency?

$$f_n = \frac{n}{2L}\sqrt{\frac{Fl}{m}}; \quad \frac{f_1}{f_2} = \frac{\sqrt{\frac{1}{m}}}{\sqrt{\frac{1}{2m}}} = \sqrt{2}; \quad f_2 = \frac{f_1}{\sqrt{2}} = \frac{80 \text{ Hz}}{1.414}$$

$$\boxed{f_2 = 56.6 \text{ Hz}}$$

Critical Thinking Questions

*21-35. In a laboratory experiment, an electromagnetic vibrator is used as a source of standing waves in a string. A one meter length of the string is determined to have a mass of 0.6 g.

One end of the string is connected to the tip of the vibrator and the other passes over a pulley 1 m away and is attached to a weight hanger. A mass of 392 g hanging from the free end causes the string to vibrate in three segments. What is the frequency of the vibrator? What new mass attached to the free end will cause the string to vibrate in four loops? What is the fundamental frequency?

1 m

0.392 kg

$$f_3 = \frac{3}{2l}\sqrt{\frac{Fl}{m}} = \frac{3}{2(1 \text{ m})}\sqrt{\frac{mg(1 \text{ m})}{6 \times 10^{-4}\text{kg}}}$$

$$f_3 = \frac{3}{2}\sqrt{\frac{(0.392 \text{ kg})(9.8 \text{ m/s}^2)(1 \text{ m})}{6 \times 10^{-4}\text{kg}}}; \qquad f_3 = 120 \text{ Hz}$$

Now using the same vibrator frequency, what mass will produce four loops (n = 4).

$$f_4 = \frac{4}{2L}\sqrt{\frac{Fl}{m}} = 120 \text{ Hz}; \quad \frac{16}{4(1 \text{ m}^2)}\left(\frac{Fl}{m}\right) = 1.44 \times 10^4 \text{ Hz}^2$$

$$F = \frac{4(1.44 \times 10^6 \text{ Hz}^2)(6 \times 10^{-4}\text{kg})(1 \text{ m}^2)}{16(1 \text{ m})}; \qquad F = 2.16 \text{ N}$$

$$m = \frac{W}{g} = \frac{2.16 \text{ N}}{9.8 \text{ m/s}^2}; \quad m = 0.2204 \text{ kg} \qquad \boxed{m = 22.0 \text{ g}}$$

*21-36. To understand the parameters that affect wave velocity in a vibrating string suppose that

$$v = \sqrt{\frac{F\ell}{m}} = 100 \text{ m/s}$$

What is the new wave speed v' for each of the following changes: (a) F' = 2F, (b) m' = 2m, (c) ℓ' = 2 ℓ ?

*21-39. A variable oscillator allows a laboratory student to adjust the frequency of a source to produce standing waves in a vibrating string. A 1.20-m length of string ($\mu = 0.400$ g/m) is placed under a tension of 200 N. What frequency is necessary to produce three standing loops in the vibrating string? What is the fundamental frequency? What frequency will produce five loops?

$$f_3 = \frac{3}{2l}\sqrt{\frac{F}{\mu}} = \frac{3}{2(1.2\ m)}\sqrt{\frac{(200\ N)}{(0.0004\ kg/m)}}\ ;\qquad \boxed{f_3 = 884\ Hz}$$

Since $f_3 = 3f_1$, $\quad f_1 = \dfrac{884\ Hz}{3}$; $\quad \boxed{f_1 = 295\ Hz}$

Since $f_5 = 5f_1$; $\quad f_5 = 5(295\ Hz)$ $\quad \boxed{f_1 = 1470\ Hz}$

Note the following proportions from the formula: $v^2 \propto F$, $v^2 \propto \ell$, and $v^2 \propto 1/m$

$\dfrac{F_2}{F_1} = \dfrac{v_2^2}{v_1^2}$; $\quad \dfrac{2F_1}{F_1} = \dfrac{v_2^2}{(100\ m/s)^2}$; $\quad v_2 = \sqrt{2 \times 10^4\,m^2/s^2}$; $\quad \boxed{v_2 = 141\ m/s}$

$\dfrac{\ell_2}{\ell_1} = \dfrac{v_2^2}{v_1^2}$; $\quad \dfrac{2\ell_1}{\ell_1} = \dfrac{v_2^2}{(100\ m/s)^2}$; $\quad v_2 = \sqrt{2 \times 10^4\,m^2/s^2}$; $\quad \boxed{v_2 = 141\ m/s}$

$\dfrac{F_2}{F_1} = \dfrac{y_{m_2}}{y_{m_1}}$; $\quad \dfrac{m_1}{2m_1} = \dfrac{v_2^2}{(100\ m/s)^2}$; $\quad v_2 = \sqrt{5 \times 10^3\,m^2/s^2}$; $\quad \boxed{v_2 = 70.7\ m/s}$

*21-37. A power of 2 mW generates waves down rope A, and another power source generates waves down an identical rope B. The waves in each rope are of the same frequency f and velocity v. If the amplitude in rope B is twice that of rope A, what power is supplied to rope B? [$f_B = f_A$; $v_B = v_A$; $A_B = 2A_A$; $P_1 = 0.002\ W$; $P = 2\pi^2 f^2 A^2 \mu v$; $P_B = ?$]

$$\frac{P_B}{P_A} = \frac{2\pi^2 f_B^2 A_B^2 m v}{2\pi^2 f_A^2 A_A^2 m v} = \frac{2\pi^2 f_A^2 (2A_A)^2 m v}{2\pi^2 f_A^2 A_A^2 m v} = \frac{4}{1}$$

$$P_B = 4P_A = 4(2\ mW); \qquad \boxed{P_B = 8\ mW}$$

*21-38. The fundamental frequency of a piano wire is 253 Hz. By what fraction must the tension in the wire be increased in order that the frequency be the desired "C" note (256 Hz)?

$$\frac{f_2}{f_1} = \frac{\sqrt{F_2}}{\sqrt{F_1}} = \sqrt{\frac{F_2}{F_1}};\qquad \frac{F_2}{F_1} = \frac{f_2^2}{f_1^2} = \frac{(256\ Hz)^2}{(253\ Hz)^2};\qquad \frac{F_2}{F_1} = 1.024$$

The tension must be increased by a factor of $\boxed{0.024}$

Chapter 22. Sound

Speed of Sound Waves

22-1. Young's modulus for steel is 2.07 x 10^{11} Pa and its density is 7800 kg/m^3. Compute the speed of sound in a steel rod.

$$v = \sqrt{\frac{Y}{\rho}} = \sqrt{\frac{2.07 \times 10^{11}\,\text{Pa}}{7800 \text{ kg/m}^3}} \; ; \quad \boxed{v = 5150 \text{ m/s}}$$

22-2. A 3-m length of copper rod has a density 8800 kg/m^3, and Young's modulus for copper is 1.17 x 10^{11} Pa. How much time will it take for sound to travel from one end of the rod to the other?

$$v = \sqrt{\frac{Y}{\rho}} = \sqrt{\frac{1.17 \times 10^{11}\,\text{Pa}}{8800 \text{ kg/m}^3}} \; ; \quad v = 3646 \text{ m/s}$$

$$v = \frac{s}{t} \; ; \quad t = \frac{s}{v} = \frac{2(3\text{ m})}{3646 \text{ m/s}} \; ; \quad \boxed{t = 1.65 \text{ ms}}$$

22-3. What is the speed of sound in air (M = 29 g/mol and γ = 1.4) on a day when the temperature is 30°C? Use the approximation formula to check this result.

$$v = \sqrt{\frac{\gamma RT}{M}} = \sqrt{\frac{(1.4)(8.314 \text{ J/kg K})(273^0 + 30^0)\text{K}}{0.029 \text{ kg/mol}}} \; ; \quad \boxed{v = 349 \text{ m/s}}$$

$$v = 331 \text{ m/s} + \left(0.6\,\frac{\text{m/s}}{\text{C}^0}\right)(30^0\text{C}) \; ; \quad \boxed{v = 349 \text{ m/s}}$$

22-4. The speed of longitudinal waves in a certain metal rod of density 7850 kg/m^3 is measured to be 3380 m/s. What is the Young's modulus for the metal?

$$v = \sqrt{\frac{Y}{\rho}} \; ; \quad v^2 = \frac{Y}{\rho} \; ; \quad Y = \rho v^2 = (7850 \text{ kg/m}^3)(3380 \text{ m/s})^2 \; ; \quad \boxed{Y = 8.97 \times 10^{10} \text{ Pa}}$$

22-5. If the frequency of the waves in Problem 22-4 is 312 Hz, what is the wavelength?

$$v = f\lambda \; ; \quad \lambda = \frac{v}{f} = \frac{3380 \text{ m/s}}{312 \text{ Hz}} \; ; \quad \boxed{\lambda = 10.8 \text{ m}}$$

22-6. Compare the theoretical speeds of sound in hydrogen (M = 2.0 g/mol, γ = 1.4) with helium (M = 4.0 g/mol, γ = 1.66) at 0°C.

$$v_H = \sqrt{\frac{\gamma RT}{M}} = \sqrt{\frac{(1.4)(8.314 \text{ J/mol K})(273 \text{ K})}{0.002 \text{ kg/mol}}} \; ; \quad v_H = 1260 \text{ m/s}$$

$$v_{He} = \sqrt{\frac{\gamma RT}{M}} = \sqrt{\frac{(1.66)(8.314 \text{ J/mol K})(273 \text{ K})}{0.004 \text{ kg/mol}}} \; ; \quad v_{He} = 971 \text{ m/s}$$

$$\frac{v_{He}}{v_H} = \frac{971 \text{ m/s}}{1260 \text{ m/s}} \; ; \quad \boxed{v_{He} = 0.771 \, v_H}$$

*22-7. A sound wave is sent from a ship to the ocean floor, where it is reflected and returned. If the round trip takes 0.6 s, how deep is the ocean floor? Consider the bulk modulus for sea water to be 2.1 x 10^9 Pa and its density to be 1030 kg/m^3.

$$v = \sqrt{\frac{B}{\rho}} = \sqrt{\frac{2.1 \times 10^9\,\text{Pa}}{1030 \text{ kg/m}^3}} \; ; \quad v = 1428 \text{ m/s}$$

$$h = vt = (1328 \text{ m/s})(0.3 \text{ s}) \; ; \quad \boxed{h = 428 \text{ m}}$$

Vibrating Air Columns

22-8. Find the fundamental frequency and the first three overtones for a 20-cm pipe at 20°C if the pipe is open at both ends. $v = 331 \text{ m/s} + (0.6)(30^0) = 343$ m/s.

$$f_n = \frac{nv}{2l} \; ; \quad f_1 = \frac{(1)(343 \text{ m/s})}{(2)(0.20 \text{ m})} = 858 \text{ Hz} \quad \boxed{f_1 = 858 \text{ Hz}}$$

$$f_n = nf_1 \; ; \quad f_2 = 2(857.5 \text{ Hz}) = \boxed{1715 \text{ Hz}}$$

(First overtone, n = 2)

22-8 (Cont.)

(2nd overtone, n = 3) $f_n = nf_1$; $f_2 = 3(857.5 \text{ Hz}) = \boxed{2573 \text{ Hz}}$

(3rd overtone, n = 4) $f_n = nf_1$; $f_2 = 4(857.5 \text{ Hz}) = \boxed{3430 \text{ Hz}}$

22-9. Find the fundamental frequency and the first three overtones for a 20-cm pipe at 20°C if the pipe is closed at one end.

$f_n = \frac{nv}{4l}$; $f_1 = \frac{(1)(343 \text{ m/s})}{(4)(0.20 \text{ m})} = 429 \text{ Hz}$ $\boxed{f_1 = 429 \text{ Hz}}$

(First overtone, n = 3) $f_n = nf_1$; $f_2 = 3(429 \text{ Hz}) = \boxed{1290 \text{ Hz}}$

(2nd overtone, n = 5) $f_n = nf_1$; $f_2 = 5(429 \text{ Hz}) = \boxed{2140 \text{ Hz}}$

(3rd overtone, n = 7) $f_n = nf_1$; $f_2 = 7(429 \text{ Hz}) = \boxed{3000 \text{ Hz}}$

22-10. What length of closed pipe will produce a fundamental frequency of 256 Hz at 20°C?

$f_n = \frac{nv}{4l}$; $l = \frac{(1)(343 \text{ m/s})}{4(256 \text{ Hz})}$; $l = 0.335 \text{ m}$; $\boxed{l = 33.5 \text{ cm}}$

22-11. What length of open pipe will produce a fundamental frequency of 356 Hz at 20°C?

$f_n = \frac{nv}{2l}$; $l = \frac{(1)(343 \text{ m/s})}{2(356 \text{ Hz})}$; $l = 0.482 \text{ m}$; $\boxed{l = 48.2 \text{ cm}}$

22-12 What length of open pipe will produce a frequency of 1200 Hz as it first overtone on a day when the speed of sound is 340 m/s? [For open pipe, first overtone is for n = 2]

$f_n = \frac{nv}{2l}$; $l = \frac{2(340 \text{ m/s})}{2(1200 \text{ Hz})}$; $\boxed{l = 28.3 \text{ cm}}$

22-13. The second overtone of a closed pipe is 1200 Hz at 20°C. What is the length of the pipe.

The second overtone for a closed pipe occurs when n = 5, and v = 343 m/s.

$f_n = \frac{nv}{4l}$; $l = \frac{5(343 \text{ m/s})}{4(1200 \text{ Hz})}$; $\boxed{l = 35.7 \text{ cm}}$

*22-14. In a resonance experiment, the air in a closed tube of variable length is found to resonate with a tuning fork when the air column is first 6 cm and then 18 cm long. What is the frequency of the tuning fork if the temperature is 20°C? [v = 343 m/s at 20°C.]

The distance between adjacent nodes of resonance is one-half of a wavelength.

$\frac{\lambda}{2} = 18 \text{ cm} - 6 \text{ cm}$; $\lambda = 24 \text{ cm}$; $f = \frac{v}{\lambda} = \frac{343 \text{ m/s}}{0.24 \text{ m}}$; $\boxed{f = 1430 \text{ Hz}}$

*22-15. A closed pipe and an open pipe are each 3 m long. Compare the wavelength of the fourth overtone for each pipe at 20°C.? (Only odd harmonics allowed for closed pipe.)

For an open pipe, the fourth overtone is the fifth harmonic, n = 5.

Open (fourth overtone): $\lambda_n = \frac{2l}{n}$; $\lambda_5 = \frac{2(3 \text{ m})}{5}$; $\lambda_5 = 1.20 \text{ m}$

For closed pipe, the fourth overtone is the ninth harmonic, n = 9.

Closed (fourth overtone): $\lambda_n = \frac{4l}{n}$; $\lambda_9 = \frac{4(3 \text{ m})}{9}$; $\lambda_9 = 1.33 \text{ m}$

Sound Intensity and Intensity Level

22-16. What is the intensity level in decibels of a sound whose intensity is 4×10^{-5} W/m²?

$\beta = 10\log\frac{I}{I_0} = 10\log\frac{4 \times 10^{-5} \text{W/m}^2}{1 \times 10^{-12} \text{W/m}^2}$; $\boxed{\beta = 76.0 \text{ dB}}$

22-17. The intensity of a sound is 6×10^{-8} W/m². What is the intensity level?

$\beta = 10\log\frac{I}{I_0} = 10\log\frac{6 \times 10^{-8} \text{W/m}^2}{1 \times 10^{-12} \text{W/m}^2}$; $\boxed{\beta = 47.8 \text{ dB}}$

22-18. A 60 dB sound is measured at a particular distance from a whistle. What is the intensity of this sound in W/m²?

$\beta = 10\log\frac{I}{I_0} = 60$ dB; $10^6 = \frac{I}{I_0}$; $I = (10^6)(1 \times 10^{-12}$ W/m²); $\boxed{I = 1 \times 10^{-6} \text{ W/m}^2}$

*22-19. What is the intensity of a 40 dB sound?

$\beta = 10\log\frac{I}{I_0} = 40$ dB; $10^4 = \frac{I}{I_0}$; $I = (10^4)(1 \times 10^{-12}$ W/m²); $\boxed{I = 1 \times 10^{-8} \text{ W/m}^2}$

*22-20. Compute the intensities for sounds of 10 dB, 20 dB, and 30 dB.

$\beta = 10\log\frac{I}{I_0} = 10$ dB; $10^1 = \frac{I}{I_0}$; $I = (10^1)(1 \times 10^{-12}$ W/m²); $\boxed{I = 1 \times 10^{-11} \text{ W/m}^2}$

$\beta = 10\log\frac{I}{I_0} = 20$ dB; $10^2 = \frac{I}{I_0}$; $I = (10^2)(1 \times 10^{-12}$ W/m²); $\boxed{I = 1 \times 10^{-10} \text{ W/m}^2}$

$\beta = 10\log\frac{I}{I_0} = 30$ dB; $10^3 = \frac{I}{I_0}$; $I = (10^3)(1 \times 10^{-12}$ W/m²); $\boxed{I = 1 \times 10^{-9} \text{ W/m}^2}$

22-21. Compute the intensity levels for sounds of 1 x 10⁻⁶ W/m², 2 x 10⁻⁶ W/m², and 3 x 10⁻⁶ W/m².

$\beta = 10\log\frac{I}{I_0} = 10\log\frac{1 \times 10^{-6} \text{W/m}^2}{1 \times 10^{-12} \text{W/m}^2}$; $\boxed{\beta = 60.0 \text{ dB}}$

$\beta = 10\log\frac{I}{I_0} = 10\log\frac{2 \times 10^{-6} \text{W/m}^2}{1 \times 10^{-12} \text{W/m}^2}$; $\boxed{\beta = 63.0 \text{ dB}}$

$\beta = 10\log\frac{I}{I_0} = 10\log\frac{3 \times 10^{-6} \text{W/m}^2}{1 \times 10^{-12} \text{W/m}^2}$; $\boxed{\beta = 64.8 \text{ dB}}$

22-22. An isometric source of sound broadcasts a power of 60 W. What are the intensity and the intensity level of a sound heard at a distance of 4 m from this source?

$I = \frac{P}{4\pi r^2} = \frac{60 \text{ W}}{4\pi(4 \text{ m})^2} = 0.2984 \text{ W/m}^2$; $\boxed{I = 0.298 \text{ W/m}^2}$

$\beta = 10\log\frac{I}{I_0} = 10\log\frac{0.2984 \text{ W/m}^2}{1 \times 10^{-12} \text{ W/m}^2}$; $\boxed{\beta = 115 \text{ dB}}$

22-23. A 3.0-W sound source is located 6.5 m from an observer. What are the intensity and the intensity level of the sound heard at that distance?

$I = \frac{P}{4\pi r^2} = \frac{3.0 \text{ W}}{4\pi(6.5 \text{ m})^2} = 5.65 \times 10^{-3} \text{ W/m}^2$; $\boxed{I = 5.65 \times 10^{-3} \text{ W/m}^2}$

$\beta = 10\log\frac{I}{I_0} = 10\log\frac{0.2984 \text{ W/m}^2}{1 \times 10^{-12} \text{ W/m}^2}$; $\boxed{\beta = 97.5 \text{ dB}}$

22-24. A person located 6 m from a sound source hears an intensity of 2 x 10⁻⁴ W/m². What intensity is heard by a person located 2.5 m from the source?

$I_1 r_1^2 = I_2 r_2^2$; $I_2 = \frac{I_1 r_1^2}{r_2^2} = \frac{(2 \times 10^{-4} \text{W/m}^2)(6 \text{ m})^2}{(2.5 \text{ m})^2}$; $\boxed{I = 1.15 \times 10^{-3} \text{ W/m}^2}$

*22-25. The intensity level 6 m from a source is 80 dB. What is the intensity level at a distance of 15.6 m from the same source?

$\beta = 10\log\frac{I}{I_0} = 80 \text{ dB}$; $10^8 = \frac{I}{I_0}$; $I = (10^8)(1 \times 10^{-12} \text{ W/m}^2)$; $I = 1 \times 10^{-4} \text{ W/m}^2$

$I_1 r_1^2 = I_2 r_2^2$; $I_2 = \frac{I_1 r_1^2}{r_2^2} = \frac{(1 \times 10^{-4} \text{ W/m}^2)(6 \text{ m})^2}{(15.6 \text{ m})^2}$; $I_2 = 1.48 \times 10^{-5} \text{ W/m}^2$

$\beta = 10\log\frac{I}{I_0} = 10\log\frac{1.48 \times 10^{-5} \text{ W/m}^2}{1 \times 10^{-12} \text{ W/m}^2}$; $\boxed{\beta = 71.7 \text{ dB}}$

The Doppler Effect

Assume that the speed of sound in 343 m/s for all of these problems.

22-26. A stationary source of sound emits a signal at a frequency of 290 Hz. What are the frequencies heard by an observer (a) moving toward the source at 20 m/s and (b) moving away from the source at 20 m/s? (Approach = +, recede = -)

$$f_0 = f_s \frac{V + v_0}{V - v_s} = 290 \text{ Hz} \left(\frac{343 \text{ m/s} + 20 \text{ m/s}}{343 \text{ m/s} - 0} \right) \; ; \quad \boxed{f_0 = 307 \text{ Hz}}$$

$$f_0 = f_s \frac{V + v_0}{V - v_s} = 290 \text{ Hz} \left[\frac{343 \text{ m/s} + (-20 \text{ m/s})}{343 \text{ m/s} - 0} \right] \; ; \quad \boxed{f_0 = 273 \text{ Hz}}$$

22-27. A car blowing a 560-Hz horn moves at a speed of 15 m/s as it first approaches a stationary listener and then moves away from a stationary listener at the same speed. What are the frequencies heard by the listener? (Approach = +, recede = -)

$$f_0 = f_s \frac{V + v_0}{V - v_s} = 560 \text{ Hz} \left(\frac{343 \text{ m/s} + 0}{343 \text{ m/s} - 15 \text{ m/s}} \right) \; ; \quad \boxed{f_0 = 586 \text{ Hz}}$$

$$f_0 = f_s \frac{V + v_0}{V - v_s} = 560 \text{ Hz} \left[\frac{343 \text{ m/s} + 0}{343 \text{ m/s} - (-15 \text{ m/s})} \right] \; ; \quad \boxed{f_0 = 537 \text{ Hz}}$$

22-28. A person stranded in a car blows a 400-Hz horn. What frequencies are heard by the driver of a car passing at a speed of 60 km/h? (Approach = +, recede = -)

$$v_0 = 60 \frac{\text{km}}{\text{h}} \left(\frac{1000 \text{ m}}{1 \text{ km}} \right) \left(\frac{1 \text{ h}}{3600 \text{ s}} \right) = 16.7 \text{ m/s}$$

Approaching: $f_0 = f_s \dfrac{V + v_0}{V - v_s} = 400 \text{ Hz} \left(\dfrac{343 \text{ m/s} + 16.7 \text{ m/s}}{343 \text{ m/s} - 0} \right) \; ; \quad \boxed{f_0 = 419 \text{ Hz}}$

At same point as car there is no change: $\boxed{f_0 = 400 \text{ Hz}}$

Leaving: $f_0 = f_s \dfrac{V + v_0}{V - v_s} = 400 \text{ Hz} \left[\dfrac{343 \text{ m/s} + (-16.7 \text{ m/s})}{343 \text{ m/s} - 0} \right] \; ; \quad \boxed{f_0 = 381 \text{ Hz}}$

22-29. A train moving at 20 m/s blows a 300-Hz whistle as it passes a stationary observer. What are the frequencies heard by the observer as the train passes?

Approaching: $f_0 = f_s \dfrac{V + v_0}{V - v_s} = 300 \text{ Hz} \left(\dfrac{343 \text{ m/s} + 0}{343 \text{ m/s} - 20 \text{ m/s}} \right) \; ; \quad \boxed{f_0 = 319 \text{ Hz}}$

When at the same position there is no change: $\boxed{f_0 = 300 \text{ Hz}}$

Leaving: $f_0 = f_s \dfrac{V + v_0}{V - v_s} = 300 \text{ Hz} \left[\dfrac{343 \text{ m/s} + 0}{343 \text{ m/s} - (-20 \text{ m/s})} \right] \; ; \quad \boxed{f_0 = 283 \text{ Hz}}$

*22-30. A child riding a bicycle north at 6 m/s hears a 600 Hz siren from a police car heading south at 15 m/s. What is the frequency heard by the child? (Approaches are +)

Approaching: $f_0 = f_s \dfrac{V + v_0}{V - v_s} = 600 \text{ Hz} \left(\dfrac{343 \text{ m/s} + 6 \text{ m/s}}{343 \text{ m/s} - 15 \text{ m/s}} \right) \; ; \quad \boxed{f_0 = 638 \text{ Hz}}$

*22-31. An ambulance moves northward at 15 m/s. Its siren has a frequency of 600 Hz at rest. A car heads south at 20 m/s toward the ambulance. What frequencies are heard by the car driver before and after they pass? (Approach = +, recede = -)

Before passing: $f_0 = f_s \dfrac{V + v_0}{V - v_s} = 600 \text{ Hz} \left[\dfrac{343 \text{ m/s} + 20 \text{ m/s}}{343 \text{ m/s} - 15 \text{ m/s}} \right] \; ; \quad \boxed{f_0 = 664 \text{ Hz}}$

After passing: $f_0 = f_s \dfrac{V + v_0}{V - v_s} = 600 \text{ Hz} \left[\dfrac{343 \text{ m/s} + (-20 \text{ m/s})}{343 \text{ m/s} - (-15 \text{ m/s})} \right] \; ; \quad \boxed{f_0 = 541 \text{ Hz}}$

*22-32. A truck traveling at 24 m/s overtakes a car traveling at 10 m/s in the same direction. The trucker blows a 600-Hz horn. What frequency is heard by the car driver?

The car is moving away, so $v_0 = -10$ m/s; Truck is approaching, so $v_s = +24$ m/s

$$f_0 = f_s \frac{V + v_0}{V - v_s} = 600 \text{ Hz} \left[\frac{343 \text{ m/s} + (-10 \text{ m/s})}{343 \text{ m/s} - (+24 \text{ m/s})} \right] \; ; \quad \boxed{f_0 = 626 \text{ Hz}}$$

*22-33. A 500-Hz sound source is heard by a stationary observer at a frequency of 475 Hz. What is the speed of the train? Is it moving toward the observer or away from the observer?

$$f_0 = f_s \frac{V+v_0}{V-v_s}; \quad \frac{f_o}{f_s} = \frac{V+0}{V-v_s}; \quad \frac{f_0}{f_s} = \frac{475 \text{ Hz}}{500 \text{ Hz}} = 0.950$$

$$\frac{V}{V-v_s} = 0.950; \quad V = 0.95V - 0.95v_s; \quad 0.95v_s = -0.05V$$

$$v_s = \frac{-0.05(343 \text{ m/s})}{0.950}; \quad \boxed{v_s = -18.1 \text{ m/s, away}}$$

The negative sign means the train is moving away from the observer.

Supplementary Problems

22-34. The speed of sound in a certain metal rod is 4600 m/s and the density of the metal is 5230 kg/m³. What is Young's modulus for this metal?

$$v = \sqrt{\frac{Y}{\rho}}; \quad v^2 = \frac{Y}{\rho}; \quad Y = \rho v^2 = (5230 \text{ kg/m}^3)(4600 \text{ m/s})^2; \quad \boxed{Y = 1.11 \times 10^{11} \text{ Pa}}$$

22-35. A sonar beam travels in a fluid for a distance of 200 m in 0.12 s. The bulk modulus of elasticity for the fluid is 2600 MPa. What is the density of the fluid?

$$v = \frac{200 \text{ m}}{0.12 \text{ s}} = 1667 \text{ m/s}; \quad v = \sqrt{\frac{B}{\rho}}; \quad v^2 = \frac{B}{\rho}; \quad \rho = \frac{B}{v^2} = \frac{2.60 \times 10^9 \text{Pa}}{(1667 \text{ m/s})^2}$$

$$\boxed{\rho = 936 \text{ kg/m}^3}$$

22-36. What is the frequency of the third overtone for a closed pipe of length 60 cm?

Third overtone is for n = 7: $f_7 = \frac{7v}{4l}$; $f_7 = \frac{(7)(343 \text{ m/s})}{(4)(0.60 \text{ m})}$; $\boxed{f_1 = 1000 \text{ Hz}}$

22-37. A 40-g string 2 m in length vibrates in three loops. The tension in the string is 270 N. What is the wavelength? What is the frequency?

$$\lambda = \frac{2l}{n} = \frac{2(2 \text{ m})}{3}; \quad \boxed{\lambda = 1.33 \text{ m}} \quad v = \sqrt{\frac{Fl}{m}} = \sqrt{\frac{(270 \text{ N})(2 \text{ m})}{0.040 \text{ kg}}}$$

$$v = 116 \text{ ft/s}; \quad f = \frac{v}{\lambda} = \frac{116 \text{ m/s}}{1.33 \text{ m}}; \quad \boxed{f = 87.1 \text{ Hz}}$$

22-38. How many beats per second are heard when two tuning forks of 256 Hz and 259 Hz are sounded together?

$$f' - f = 259 \text{ Hz} - 256 \text{ Hz} = \boxed{3 \text{ beats/s}}$$

*22-39. What is the length of a closed pipe if the frequency of its second overtone is 900 Hz on a day when the temperature is 20C?

The second overtone for a closed pipe occurs when n = 5, and v = 343 m/s.

$$f_n = \frac{nv}{4l}; \quad l = \frac{5(343 \text{ m/s})}{4(900 \text{ Hz})}; \quad \boxed{l = 47.6 \text{ cm}}$$

*22-40. The fundamental frequency for an open pipe is 360 Hz. If one end of this pipe is closed, what will be the new fundamental frequency? (n = 1 for fundamental)

We will first find the length of an open pipe that has a frequency of 360 Hz

$$f_n = \frac{nv}{2l}; \quad l = \frac{1(343 \text{ m/s})}{2(360 \text{ Hz})}; \quad l = 47.6 \text{ cm}$$

Now, take this length for a closed pipe to find new frequency:

$$f_1 = \frac{(1)v}{4l}; \quad f = \frac{(343 \text{ m/s})}{4(0.476 \text{ m})}; \quad \boxed{f = 180 \text{ Hz}}$$

*22-44. Find the ratio of the intensities of two sounds if one is 12 dB higher than the other?

$\beta_1 = 10\log\frac{I_1}{I_0}$; $\beta_2 = 10\log\frac{I_2}{I_0}$; $\beta_2 - \beta_1 = 10\log\frac{I_2}{I_0} - 10\log\frac{I_2}{I_0}$

Recall that: $\log A - \log B = \log (A/B)$ and apply to the above relation

$\beta_2 - \beta_1 = 10\log\frac{I_2}{I_0} - 10\log\frac{I_2}{I_0}$; $\beta_2 - \beta_1 = 10\log\frac{I_2}{I_1}$

$\beta_2 - \beta_1 = 10\log\frac{I_2}{I_1} = 12$ dB; $\log\frac{I_2}{I_1} = 1.2$; $10^{1.2} = \frac{I_2}{I_1}$

$$(I_2/I_1) = 15.8$$

*22-45. A certain loud speaker has a circular opening of area 6 cm². The power radiated by this speaker is 6 x 10⁻⁷ W. What is the intensity of the sound at the opening? What is the intensity level?

$A = 6$ cm² $= 6 \times 10^{-4}\text{m}^2$; $I = \frac{P}{A} = \frac{6\times 10^{-7}\,\text{W}}{6\times 10^{-4}\,\text{m}^2}$; $\boxed{I = 1 \times 10^{-3}\ \text{W/m}^2}$

$\beta = 10\log\frac{I}{I_0} = 10\log\frac{1\times 10^{-3}\,\text{W/m}^2}{1\times 10^{-12}\,\text{W/m}^2}$; $\boxed{\beta = 90\ \text{dB}}$

*22-46. The noon whistle at the textile mill has a frequency of 360 Hz What are the frequencies heard by the driver of a car passing the mill at 25 m/s on a day when sound travels at 343 m/s?

Approaching: $f_0 = f_s\frac{V+v_0}{V-v_s} = 360$ Hz$\left(\frac{343\text{ m/s}+25\text{ m/s}}{343\text{ m/s}-0}\right)$; $\boxed{f_0 = 386\ \text{Hz}}$

At same point as source: $\boxed{f_0 = 360\ \text{Hz}}$

Leaving: $f_0 = f_s\frac{V+v_0}{V-v_s} = 360$ Hz$\left(\frac{343\text{ m/s}-25\text{ m/s}}{343\text{ m/s}-0}\right)$; $\boxed{f_0 = 334\ \text{Hz}}$

---

*22-41. A 60-cm steel rod is clamped at one end as shown in Fig. 22-13a. Sketch the fundamental and the first overtone for these boundary conditions. What are the wavelengths in each case?

Boundary conditions = node at right, antinode to left:

$\lambda_1 = 4l = 4(0.60$ m); $\lambda_1 = 2.40$ m

First overtone adds one node, 1ˢᵗ ovt. = 3rd harmonic.

$\lambda_3 = \frac{4l}{3} = \frac{4(0.60\text{ m})}{3}$; $\lambda_3 = 0.800$ m

Fundamental

First overtone

*22-42. The 60-cm rod in Fig. 22-13b is now clamped at its midpoint. What are the wavelengths for the fundamental and first overtone?

Boundary conditions: A node must be at the center, and an antinode must be at each end in both cases.

Fundamental: $\lambda_1 = \frac{2l}{1} = \frac{2(0.60\text{ m})}{1}$ $\lambda_1 = 1.20$ m

First overtone is first possibility after the fundamental. Because of clamp at midpoint,

First overtone: $\lambda = \frac{2l}{3} = \frac{2(0.60\text{ m})}{3}$; $\lambda = 0.400$ m

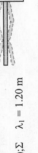

Fundamental

First overtone

*22-43. The velocity of sound in a steel rod is 5060 m/s. What is the length of a steel rod mounted as shown in Fig. 22-13a if the fundamental frequency of vibration for the rod is 3000 Hz?

$v = f\lambda$; $\lambda = \frac{v}{f} = \frac{5060\text{ m/s}}{3000\text{ Hz}}$; $\lambda = 1.69$ m

For fundamental: $\lambda_1 = 4l$; $l = \frac{\lambda}{4} = \frac{1.69\text{ m}}{4}$; $\boxed{l = 42.2\ \text{cm}}$

Fundamental

*22-47. What is the difference in intensity levels (dB) for two sounds whose intensities are

2 × 10⁻⁵ W/m² and 0.90 W/m²? [See solution for Prob. 22-44 above.]

$$\beta_2 - \beta_1 = 10\log\frac{I_2}{I_0} - 10\log\frac{I_2}{I_0}; \qquad \beta_2 - \beta_1 = 10\log\frac{I_2}{I_1}$$

$$\beta_2 - \beta_1 = 10\log\frac{0.90 \text{ W/m}^2}{2 \times 10^{-5}\text{ W/m}^2}; \qquad \boxed{\Delta\beta = 49.5 \text{ dB}}$$

Critical Thinking Questions

*22-48. By inhaling helium gas, one can raise the frequency of the voice considerably. For air

M = 29 g/mol and γ = 1.4; for helium M = 4.0 g/mol and γ = 1.66. At a temperature of

27⁰C, you sing a "C" note at 256 Hz. What is the frequency that will be heard if you

inhale helium gas and other parameters are unchanged? Notice that both v and f were

increased. How do you explain this in view of the fact that $v = f\lambda$. Discuss.

$$v_{air} = \sqrt{\frac{\gamma RT}{M}} = \sqrt{\frac{1.4)(8.314 \text{ J/mol K})(300 \text{ K})}{0.029 \text{ kg/mol}}}\; ; \qquad v_H = 347 \text{ m/s}$$

$$v_{He} = \sqrt{\frac{\gamma RT}{M}} = \sqrt{\frac{1.66)(8.314 \text{ J/mol K})(300 \text{ K})}{0.004 \text{ kg/mol}}}\; ; \qquad v_{He} = 1017 \text{ m/s}$$

The fundamental wavelength is a property of the boundary conditions which don't

change. Therefore, the frequencies are directly proportional to the velocities.

$$\frac{f_{He}}{f_{air}} = \frac{1017 \text{ m/s}}{347 \text{ m/s}} = 2.93; \qquad f_{He} = 2.93 f_{air} = 2.93(256 \text{ Hz}); \qquad \boxed{f_{He} = 750 \text{ Hz}}$$

The ratio of v/f is constant and equal to the wavelength in each case.

*22-49. A toy whistle is made out of a piece of sugar cane that is 8 cm long. It is essentially an

open pipe from the air inlet to the far end. Now suppose a hole is bored at the midpoint

so that the finger can alternately close and open the hole. (a) If the velocity of sound is

340m/s, what are the two possible fundamental frequencies obtained by closing and

opening the hole at the center of the cane? (b) What is the fundamental frequency if the

finger covers the hole and the far end is plugged?

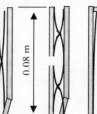

0.08 m

An opening forces an antinode to occur at that point.

(a) *With the finger closing the hole, the fundamental is:*

$$\lambda_1 = 2l = 2(0.08 \text{ m}); \qquad \lambda_1 = 1.60 \text{ m}$$

$$f_1 = \frac{340 \text{ m/s}}{1.60 \text{ m}}\; ; \qquad \boxed{f_1 = 212 \text{ Hz}}$$

Now, with the finger removed, the fundamental is: $\lambda = l = 0.08$ m, *so that*

$$f_1 = \frac{340 \text{ m/s}}{0.80 \text{ m}}\; ; \qquad \boxed{f_1 = 425 \text{ m}}$$

(b) *Now if the far end is plugged and the hole is covered,* $f_1 = 4l$:

$$\lambda = 4(0.08 \text{ m}) = 3.2 \text{ m}; \qquad f = \frac{340 \text{ m/s}}{3.20 \text{ m}}\; ; \qquad \boxed{f = 106 \text{ Hz}}$$

*22-50. A tuning fork of frequency 512 Hz is moved away from an observer and toward a flat

wall with a speed of 3 m/s. The speed of sound in the air is 340 m/s. What is the

apparent frequency of the unreflected sound? What is the apparent frequency of the

reflected sound? How many beats are heard each second?

For unreflected sound, $v_s = +3$ m/s; *for reflected sound,* $v_s = -3$ m/s

Unreflected: $f_0 = f_s\dfrac{V+v_0}{V-v_s} = (512 \text{ Hz})\left[\dfrac{340 \text{ m/s} + 0}{340 \text{ m/s} -(+3 \text{ m/s})}\right]$ $\boxed{f_0 = 517 \text{ Hz}}$

resonance positions occur at 17, 51, and 85 cm from the top of the tube. What is the velocity of sound in the air? What is the approximate temperature in the room?

The distance between adjacent resonance points must be equal to one-half of a wavelength. Therefore, the wavelength of the sound must be:

$$\lambda = 2(51\text{ cm} - 17\text{ cm}) = 68.0\text{ cm}$$

$$v = f\lambda = (512\text{ Hz})(0.680\text{ m}); \qquad \boxed{v = 348\text{ m/s}}$$

$$v = 331\text{ m/s} + \left(0.6\,\frac{\text{m/s}}{\text{C}^2}\right)t = 348\text{ m/s} \qquad \boxed{t = 28.3\,^{0}\text{C}}$$

*22-53. What is the difference in intensity levels of two sounds, one being twice the intensity of the other?

Assume $I_2 = 2I_1$: $\beta_2 - \beta_1 = 10\log\dfrac{I_2}{I_1} = 10\log\dfrac{2I_1}{I_1}$; $\boxed{\Delta\beta = 3.01\text{ dB}}$

---

*22-50. (Cont.) Reflected: $f_0 = f_s\dfrac{V + v_0}{V - v_s} = (512\text{ Hz})\left[\dfrac{340\text{ m/s} + 0}{340\text{ m/s} - (-3\text{ m/s})}\right]$ $\boxed{f_0 = 508\text{ Hz}}$

Number of beats = 517 Hz – 508 Hz = $\boxed{9\text{ beats/s}}$

*22-51. Using the logarithmic definition of decibels, derive the following expression which relates the ratio of intensities of two sounds to the difference in decibels for the sounds:

$$\beta_2 - \beta_1 = 10\log\frac{I_2}{I_1}$$

$$\beta_1 = 10\log\frac{I_1}{I_0}; \quad \beta_2 = 10\log\frac{I_2}{I_0}; \quad \beta_2 - \beta_1 = 10\log\frac{I_2}{I_0} - 10\log\frac{I_1}{I_0}$$

Recall that: $\log A - \log B = \log(A/B)$ *and apply to the above relation*

$$\beta_2 - \beta_1 = 10\log\frac{I_2}{I_0} - 10\log\frac{I_1}{I_0}; \quad \beta_2 - \beta_1 = 10\log\frac{I_2}{I_1}$$

Use this relationship to work Problems 22-44 and 22-47.

Refer to Problems 22-44 and 22-47 for applications of this formula.

22-52. The laboratory apparatus shown in Fig. 22-14 is used to measure the speed of sound in air by the resonance method. A vibrating tuning fork of frequency f is held over the open end of a tube, partly filled with water. The length of the air column can be varied by changing the water level. As the water level is gradually lowered from the top of the tube, the sound intensity reaches a maximum at the three levels shown in the figure. The maxima occur whenever the air column resonates with the tuning fork. Thus, the distance between successive resonance positions is the distance between adjacent notes for the standing waves in the air column. The frequency of the fork is 512 Hz, and the

Chapter 23. The Electric Force

Coulomb's Law

23-1. Two balls each having a charge of 3 μC are separated by 20 mm. What is the force of repulsion between them?

$$F = \frac{(9 \times 10^9 \text{N} \cdot \text{m}^2/\text{C}^2)(3 \times 10^{-6}\text{C})(3 \times 10^{-6}\text{C})}{(20 \times 10^{-3}\text{m})^2} \; ; \quad \boxed{F = 202 \text{ N}}$$

23-2. Two point charges of -3 and +4 μC are 12 mm apart in a vacuum. What is the electrostatic force between them?

$$F = \frac{(9 \times 10^9 \text{N} \cdot \text{m}^2/\text{C}^2)(-3 \times 10^{-6}\text{C})(4 \times 10^{-6}\text{C})}{(12 \times 10^{-3}\text{m})^2} \; ; \quad \boxed{F = 750 \text{ N, attraction}}$$

23-3. An alpha particle consists of two protons ($q_e = 1.6 \times 10^{-19}$ C) and two neutrons (no charge). What is the repulsive force between two alpha particles separated by 2 nm?

$$q_\alpha = 2(1.6 \times 10^{-19} \text{ C}) = 3.2 \times 10^{-19} \text{ C}$$

$$F = \frac{(9 \times 10^9 \text{N} \cdot \text{m}^2/\text{C}^2)(3.2 \times 10^{-19}\text{C})(3.2 \times 10^{-19}\text{C})}{(2.00 \times 10^{-9}\text{m})^2} \; ; \quad \boxed{F = 2.30 \times 10^{-10} \text{ N}}$$

23-4. Assume that the radius of the electron's orbit around the proton in a hydrogen atom is approximately 5.2×10^{-11} m. What is the electrostatic force of attraction?

$$F = \frac{(9 \times 10^9 \text{N} \cdot \text{m}^2/\text{C}^2)(1.6 \times 10^{-19}\text{C})(-1.6 \times 10^{-19}\text{C})}{(5.2 \times 10^{-11}\text{m})^2} \; ; \quad \boxed{F = 8.52 \times 10^{-8} \text{ N}}$$

23-5. What is the separation of two -4 μC charges if the force of repulsion between them is 200 N?

$$r = \sqrt{\frac{kqq'}{F}} = \sqrt{\frac{(9 \times 10^9 \text{N} \cdot \text{m}^2/\text{C}^2)(-4 \times 10^{-6}\text{C})^2}{200 \text{ N}}} \; ; \quad \boxed{r = 26.8 \text{ mm}}$$

23-6. Two identical charges separated by 30 mm experience a repulsive force of 980 N. What is the magnitude of each charge?

$$F = \frac{kq^2}{r^2} \; ; \quad q = \sqrt{\frac{Fr^2}{k}} = \sqrt{\frac{980 \text{ N}(0.030 \text{ m})^2}{9 \times 10^9 \text{N} \cdot \text{m}^2/\text{C}^2}} \; ; \quad \boxed{q = 9.90 \text{ μC}}$$

*23-7. A 10 μC charge and a -6 μC charge are separated by 40 mm. What is the force between them. The spheres are placed in contact for a few moments and then separated again by 40 mm. What is the new force? Is it attractive or repulsive?

$$F = \frac{(9 \times 10^9 \text{N} \cdot \text{m}^2/\text{C}^2)(-6 \times 10^{-6}\text{C})(10 \times 10^{-6}\text{C})}{(40 \times 10^{-3}\text{m})^2} \; ; \quad \boxed{F = 338 \text{ N, attraction}}$$

When spheres touch, 6 μC of charge are neutralized, leaving 4 μC to be shared by two spheres, or +2 μC on each sphere. Now they are again separated.

$$F = \frac{(9 \times 10^9 \text{N} \cdot \text{m}^2/\text{C}^2)(2 \times 10^{-6}\text{C})(2 \times 10^{-6}\text{C})}{(0.080 \text{ m})^2} \; ;$$

$$\boxed{F = 5.62 \text{ N, repulsion}}$$

-6 μC   10 μC   0.08 m

2 μC   2 μC

2 μC   2 μC   0.08 m

*23-8. Two point charges initially attract each other with a force of 600 N. If their separation is reduced to one-third of its original distance, what is the new force of attraction?

$$F \propto \frac{1}{r^2} \; ; \quad F_1 r_1^2 = F_2 r_2^2 \; ; \quad F_2 = F_1 \left(\frac{r_2^2}{r_2^2}\right) = F_1 \left(\frac{r_1}{r_2}\right)^2 \; ; \quad r_1 = 3 r_2$$

$$F_2 = F_1 \left(\frac{3r_2}{r_2}\right)^2 = 9F_1 \; ; \quad \boxed{F_2 = 5400 \text{ N}}$$

The Resultant Electrostatic Force

23-9. A +60 μC charge is placed 60 mm to the left of a +20 μC charge. What is the resultant force on a -35 μC charge placed midway between the two charges?

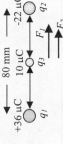

$$F_{13} = \frac{(9 \times 10^9 N \cdot m^2/C^2)(60 \times 10^{-6}C)(35 \times 10^{-6}C)}{(30 \times 10^{-3}m)^2}$$

$F_{13} = 2.10 \times 10^4$ N, *directed to the left*

$$F_{23} = \frac{(9 \times 10^9 N \cdot m^2/C^2)(20 \times 10^{-6}C)(35 \times 10^{-6}C)}{(30 \times 10^{-3}m)^2}; \quad F_{13} = 2.10 \times 10^4 \text{ N, } directed\ to\ right.$$

$F_R = F_{13} + F_{23} = (-2.10 \times 10^4 N) + (0.700 \times 10^4 N);$ $\boxed{F_R = -1.40 \times 10^4 \text{ N, left.}}$

23-10. A point charge of +36 μC is placed 80 mm to the left of a second point charge of -22 μC. What force is exerted on third charge of +10 μC located at the midpoint?

$$F_{13} = \frac{(9 \times 10^9 N \cdot m^2/C^2)(36 \times 10^{-6}C)(10 \times 10^{-6}C)}{(40 \times 10^{-3}m)^2}$$

$F_{13} = 2025$ N, *directed to the right*

$$F_{23} = \frac{(9 \times 10^9 N \cdot m^2/C^2)(22 \times 10^{-6}C)(10 \times 10^{-6}C)}{(40 \times 10^{-3}m)^2}; \quad F_{13} = 1238 \text{ N, } directed\ to\ right.$$

$F_R = F_{13} + F_{23} = 2025 N + 1238 N;$ $\boxed{F_R = 3260 \text{ N, } left.}$

23-11. For Problem 23-10, what is the resultant force on a third charge of +12 μC placed between the other charges and located 60 mm from the +36 μC charge?

$$F_{13} = \frac{(9 \times 10^9 N \cdot m^2/C^2)(36 \times 10^{-6}C)(12 \times 10^{-6}C)}{(60 \times 10^{-3}m)^2}$$

$$F_{23} = \frac{(9 \times 10^9 N \cdot m^2/C^2)(22 \times 10^{-6}C)(12 \times 10^{-6}C)}{(20 \times 10^{-3}m)^2};$$

Both to right, so $F_R = F_{13} + F_{23} = 1080 N + 5940 N;$ $\boxed{F = 7020 \text{ N, } rightward.}$

23-12. A +6 μC charge is 44 mm to the right of a -8 μC charge. What is the resultant force on a -2 μC charge that is 20 mm to the right of the -8 μC charge?

$$F_{13} = \frac{(9 \times 10^9 N \cdot m^2/C^2)(8 \times 10^{-6}C)(2 \times 10^{-6}C)}{(20 \times 10^{-3}m)^2}$$

$$F_{23} = \frac{(9 \times 10^9 N \cdot m^2/C^2)(2 \times 10^{-6}C)(6 \times 10^{-6}C)}{(24 \times 10^{-3}m)^2};$$

Both to right, so $F_R = F_{13} + F_{23} = 360 N + 187.5 N;$ $\boxed{F = 548 \text{ N, } rightward}$

*23-13. A 64-μC charge is locate 30 cm to the left of a 16-μC charge. What is the resultant force on a -12 μC charge positioned exactly 50 mm below the 16 μC charge?

$$s = \sqrt{(30 \text{ mm})^2 + (50 \text{ mm})^2} = 58.3 \text{ mm}$$

$$\tan \phi = \frac{50 \text{ mm}}{30 \text{ mm}}; \quad \phi = 59.0^0$$

$$F_{13} = \frac{(9 \times 10^9 N \cdot m^2/C^2)(64 \times 10^{-6}C)(12 \times 10^{-6}C)}{(58.3 \times 10^{-3}m)^2}$$

$$F_{13} = 2033 \text{ N, } 59.0^0 \text{ N of W}$$

$$F_{23} = \frac{(9 \times 10^9 N \cdot m^2/C^2)(16 \times 10^{-6}C)(12 \times 10^{-6}C)}{(50 \times 10^{-3}m)^2} = 691 \text{ N, upward.}$$

$F_x = 0 - F_{13} \cos 59.0^0 = -(2033 \text{ N}) \cos 59^0$; $F_x = -1047$ N

$F_y = F_{23} + F_{13} \sin 59.0^0 = 691 \text{ N} + (2033 \text{ N}) \sin 59^0$; $F_y = 2434$ N

$$F = \sqrt{(-1047 \text{ N})^2 + (2434 \text{ N})^2} = 2650 \text{ N}; \quad \tan\theta = \frac{2434 \text{ N}}{-1047 \text{ N}}; \quad \theta = 66.7^0 \text{ N of W.}$$

$\boxed{\text{Resultant force: } F_R = 2650 \text{ N, } 66.7^0 \text{ N of W (or } 113.3^0)}$

*23-14. A charge of +60 nC is located 80 mm above a -40-nC charge. What is the resultant force on a -50-nC charge located 45 mm horizontally to the right of the -40-nC charge?

$s = \sqrt{(45 \text{ mm})^2 + (80 \text{ mm})^2} = 91.8 \text{ mm}$

$\tan\phi = \dfrac{80 \text{ mm}}{45 \text{ mm}}$; $\phi = 60.64^0$

$F_{13} = \dfrac{(9 \times 10^9 \text{N}\cdot\text{m}^2/\text{C}^2)(60 \times 10^{-6}\text{C})(50 \times 10^{-6}\text{C})}{(91.8 \times 10^{-3}\text{m})^2}$

$F_{13} = 2564 \text{ N}, 60.64^0 \text{ N of W}$

$F_{23} = \dfrac{(9 \times 10^9 \text{N}\cdot\text{m}^2/\text{C}^2)(40 \times 10^{-6}\text{C})(50 \times 10^{-6}\text{C})}{(45 \times 10^{-3}\text{m})^2} = 8889 \text{ N}, rightward.$

$F_x = -F_{13} \cos 60.64^0 + F_{23} = -(2564 \text{ N}) \cos 60.64^0 + 8889 \text{ N}$; $F_x = 7632 \text{ N}$

$F_y = +F_{13} \sin 60.64^0 + 0 = (2564 \text{ N}) \sin 60.64^0$; $F_y = 2235 \text{ N}$

$F = \sqrt{(7632 \text{ N})^2 + (2235 \text{ N})^2}$; $\tan\theta = \dfrac{2235 \text{ N}}{7632 \text{ N}}$; $\boxed{F_R = 7950 \text{ N}, \theta = 16.3^0 \text{ N of E.}}$

*23-15. Three point charges q₁ = +8 μC, q₂ = -4 μC, and q₃ = +2 μC are placed at the corners of an equilateral triangle, 80 mm on each side as described by Fig. 23-15. What are the magnitude and direction of the resultant force on the +8 μC charge?

$F_{21} = \dfrac{(9 \times 10^9 \text{N}\cdot\text{m}^2/\text{C}^2)(4 \times 10^{-6}\text{C})(8 \times 10^{-6}\text{C})}{(80 \times 10^{-3}\text{m})^2}$

$F_{21} = 45.0 \text{ N}, 60^0 \text{ S of E}$

$F_{31} = \dfrac{(9 \times 10^9 \text{N}\cdot\text{m}^2/\text{C}^2)(2 \times 10^{-6}\text{C})(8 \times 10^{-6}\text{C})}{(80 \times 10^{-3}\text{m})^2}$

$F_{31} = 22.5 \text{ N}, 60^0 \text{ N of E}$; $F_x = (22.5 \text{ N}) \cos 60^0 + (45 \text{ N}) \cos 60^0 = 33.8 \text{ N}$

$F_y = (22.5 \text{ N}) \sin 60^0 - (45 \text{ N}) \sin 60^0 = -19.5 \text{ N}$

*23-15. (Cont.) $F = \sqrt{(33.8 \text{ N})^2 + (-19.5 \text{ N})^2} = 39.0 \text{ N}$; $\tan\theta = \dfrac{-19.5 \text{ N}}{33.8 \text{ N}}$; $\theta = -30^0$

Resultant electric force: $\boxed{F_R = 39.0 \text{ N}, \ \theta = 330.0^0}$

Supplementary Problems

23-16. What should be the separation of two +5-uC charges so that the force of repulsion is 4 N?

$r = \sqrt{\dfrac{kqq'}{F}} = \sqrt{\dfrac{(9 \times 10^9 \text{N}\cdot\text{m}^2/\text{C}^2)(5 \times 10^{-6}\text{C})^2}{4.00 \text{ N}}}$; $\boxed{r = 23.7 \text{ cm}}$

23-17. The repulsive force between two pith balls is found to be 60 μN. If each pith ball carries a charge of 8 nC, what is their separation?

$r = \sqrt{\dfrac{kqq'}{F}} = \sqrt{\dfrac{(9 \times 10^9 \text{N}\cdot\text{m}^2/\text{C}^2)(8 \times 10^{-9}\text{C})^2}{60 \times 10^{-6} \text{ N}}}$; $\boxed{r = 98.0 \text{ mm}}$

23-18. Two identical unknown charges experience a mutual repulsive force of 48 N when separated by 60 mm. What is the magnitude of each charge?

$F = \dfrac{kq^2}{r^2}$; $q = \sqrt{\dfrac{Fr^2}{k}} = \sqrt{\dfrac{(48 \text{ N})(0.060 \text{ m})^2}{9 \times 10^9 \text{N}\cdot\text{m}^2/\text{C}^2}}$; $\boxed{q = 4.38 \text{ μC}}$

23-19. One object contains an excess of 5 x 10¹⁴ electrons and another has a deficiency of 4 x 10¹⁴ electrons. What is the force each exerts on the other if the objects are 30 mm apart? Is it attraction or repulsion? (1e = 1.6 x 10⁻¹⁹ C, excess =-, deficiency =+.)

$q_1 = (5 \times 10^{14}\ e)(1.6 \times 10^{-19}\ C/e) = -80 \text{ μC}$; $q_2 = (4 \times 10^{14}\ e)(1.6 \times 10^{-19}\ C/e) = +64 \text{ μC}$

$F = \dfrac{(9 \times 10^9 \text{N}\cdot\text{m}^2/\text{C}^2)(80 \times 10^{-6}\text{C})(64 \times 10^{-6}\text{C})}{(30 \times 10^{-3}\text{m})^2}$; $\boxed{F = 5.12 \times 10^4 \text{ N, attraction}}$

23-20. If it were possible to put 1 C of charge on each of two spheres separated by a distance of 1 m, what would be the repulsive force in newtons.

$$F = \frac{(9 \times 10^9\,N \cdot m^2/C^2)(1\,C)(1\,C)}{(1\,m)^2}\;; \quad \boxed{F = 9 \times 10^9\,N\,!}$$

The coulomb is a very large unit for electrostatics applications.

23-21. How many electrons must be placed on each of two spheres separated by 4 mm in order to produce a repulsive force of one 400 N?

$$F = \frac{kq^2}{r^2}; \quad q = \sqrt{\frac{Fr^2}{k}} = \sqrt{\frac{(400\,N)(0.004\,m)^2}{9 \times 10^9\,N \cdot m^2/C^2}}\;; \quad q = 843\,nC$$

$$q = 843 \times 10^{-9}\,C\left(\frac{1\,e}{1.6 \times 10^{-19}\,C}\right)\;; \quad \boxed{q = 5.27 \times 10^{12}\ \text{electrons}}$$

23-22. A –40-nC charge is placed 40 mm to the left of a +6-nC charge. What is the resultant force on a –12-nC charge place 8 mm to the right of the +6-nC charge?

$$F_1 = \frac{(9 \times 10^9\,N \cdot m^2/C^2)(40 \times 10^{-9}\,C)(12 \times 10^{-9}\,C)}{(48 \times 10^{-3}\,m)^2}$$

$$F_2 = \frac{(9 \times 10^9\,N \cdot m^2/C^2)(6 \times 10^{-9}\,C)(12 \times 10^{-9}\,C)}{(8 \times 10^{-3}\,m)^2}\;;$$

Both to right, so $F_R = F_1 + F_2 = 1.88$ mN $– 10.1$ mN; $\boxed{F = -8.25\ \text{mN, }\textit{leftward}}$

-40 nC q_1 — 40 mm — 6 nC — 8 mm — q_3 = -12 nC q_2 — F_1 — F_2

23-23. A 5-μC charge is placed 6 cm to the right of a 2-μC charge. What is the resultant force on a –9 nC charge placed 2 cm to the left of the 2-μC charge?

$$F_1 = \frac{(9 \times 10^9\,N \cdot m^2/C^2)(9 \times 10^{-9}\,C)(2 \times 10^{-6}\,C)}{(2 \times 10^{-2}\,m)^2}\;;$$

$F_1 = +405$ mN, *to right*

-9 nC — 2 cm — 2 μC q_1 — 6 cm — 5 μC q_2 ; F_1 ; F_2

$$F_2 = \frac{(9 \times 10^9\,N \cdot m^2/C^2)(5 \times 10^{-6}\,C)(9 \times 10^{-9}\,C)}{(8 \times 10^{-2}\,m)^2}\;; \quad F_2 = +63.3\ \text{mN, }\textit{to right}$$

Resultant force: $\quad F_R = 405$ mN $+ 63.3$ mN; $\boxed{F_R = 468\ \text{mN}}$

23-24. An equal number of electrons is placed on two metal spheres 3.0 cm apart in air. How many electrons are on each sphere if the resultant force is 4500 N?

$$F = \frac{kq^2}{r^2}; \quad q = \sqrt{\frac{Fr^2}{k}} = \sqrt{\frac{(4500\,N)(0.03\,m)^2}{9 \times 10^9\,N \cdot m^2/C^2}}\;; \quad q = 21.2\ \mu C$$

$$q = 21.2 \times 10^{-6}\,C\left(\frac{1\,e}{1.6 \times 10^{-19}\,C}\right)\;; \quad \boxed{q = 1.33 \times 10^{14}\ \text{electrons}}$$

23-25. A 4-nC charge is placed on a 4-g sphere that is free to move. A fixed 10-μC point charge is 4 cm away. What is the initial acceleration of the 4-μC charge?

$$F_2 = \frac{(9 \times 10^9\,N \cdot m^2/C^2)(4 \times 10^{-9}\,C)(10 \times 10^{-6}\,C)}{(4 \times 10^{-2}\,m)^2}\;; \quad F_2 = 225\ \text{mN}$$

$$a = \frac{F}{m} = \frac{0.225\,N}{0.004\,kg}\qquad \boxed{a = 56.2\ \text{m/s}^2}$$

*23-26. What is the resultant force on a +2 μC charge that is 60 mm from each of two –4-μC charges that are 80 mm apart in air?

$$\tan\phi = \frac{40\,mm}{60\,mm}; \qquad \phi = 48.2^0$$

$$F_2 = \frac{(9 \times 10^9\,N \cdot m^2/C^2)(4 \times 10^{-6}\,C)(2 \times 10^{-6}\,C)}{(60 \times 10^{-3}\,m)^2}$$

$$F_2 = 20.0\ \text{N, } 48.2^0\ \text{S of E}$$

$$F_1 = \frac{(9 \times 10^9\,N \cdot m^2/C^2)(2 \times 10^{-6}\,C)(4 \times 10^{-6}\,C)}{(60 \times 10^{-3}\,m)^2}\;; \quad F_1 = 20.0\ \text{N, } 48.2^0\ \text{S of W}$$

$q_1 = 2\ \mu C$; ϕ ; F_2 ; $q_2 = -4\ \mu C$; 60 mm ; q_3 ; -4 μC ; 40 mm ; 60 mm ; F_1

*23-26. (Cont.) $F_x = (20 N) \cos 48.2^0 + (20 N) \cos 48.2^0 = 13.33 N - 13.33 N$; $F_x = 0$

$F_y = (20 N) \sin 48.2^0 + (20 N) \sin 48.2^0 = 14.9 N + 14.9 N$; $F_y = -29.8 N$

$$\boxed{\text{Resultant force: } F_R = 29.8\ N, \text{ downward}}$$

*23-27. Two charges of +25 and +16 μC are 80 mm apart. A third charge of +60 μC is placed between the other charges 30 mm from the +25 μC charge. Find the resultant force on the third charge?

$$F_1 = \frac{(9 \times 10^9 N \cdot m^2/C^2)(60 \times 10^{-6}C)(25 \times 10^{-6}C)}{(30 \times 10^{-3}m)^2}$$

$F_1 = 15\ kN$, directed to the right

$$F_2 = \frac{(9 \times 10^9 N \cdot m^2/C^2)(60 \times 10^{-6}C)(16 \times 10^{-6}C)}{(50 \times 10^{-3}m)^2};\quad F_{13} = 3.46\ kN, \text{ directed to left.}$$

$F_R = F_1 + F_2 = 15\ kN + 3.46\ kN$; $\boxed{F_R = 11.5\ kN, \text{ right.}}$

*23-28. A 0.02-g pith ball is suspended freely. The ball is given a charge of +20 μC and placed 0.6 m from a charge of +50 μC. What will be the initial acceleration of the pith ball?

$$F = \frac{(9 \times 10^9 N \cdot m^2/C^2)(20 \times 10^{-6}C)(50 \times 10^{-6}C)}{(0.600\ m)^2};\quad F = 25.0\ N$$

$a = \dfrac{F}{m} = \dfrac{25.0\ N}{2 \times 10^{-5} kg}$; $\boxed{a = 1.25 \times 10^6\ m/s}$

**23-29. A 4 μC charge is located 6 cm from an 8 μC charge. At what point on a line joining the two charges will the resultant force be zero?

$F_1 = F_2$; $\dfrac{kq_3q_1}{x^2} = \dfrac{kq_3q_2}{(6-x)^2}$

$F_1 = F_2$; $\dfrac{q_1}{x^2} = \dfrac{q_2}{(6-x)^2}$; $x^2 = \left(\dfrac{q_1}{q_2}\right)(6-x)^2$

Take square root of both sides: $x = \sqrt{\dfrac{q_1}{q_2}}(6-x) = \sqrt{\dfrac{4\ \mu C}{8\ \mu C}}(6-x)$; $x = 0.707(6-x)$

Solving for x, we obtain: $\boxed{x = 2.49\ cm \text{ from } 4\text{-}\mu C \text{ charge}}$

**23-30. A charge of +8 nC is placed 40 mm to the left of a −14 nC charge. Where should a third charge be placed if it is to experience a zero resultant force?

Considering the sign of the charges and their magnitudes, the charge must be to the left of the 8 nC charge as shown.

$F_1 = F_2$; $\dfrac{kq_3q_1}{x^2} = \dfrac{kq_3q_2}{(40+x)^2}$; $F_1 = F_2$; $\dfrac{q_1}{x^2} = \dfrac{q_2}{(40+x)^2}$; $x^2 = \left(\dfrac{q_1}{q_2}\right)(40+x)^2$

Take square root of both sides:

$x = \sqrt{\dfrac{q_1}{q_2}}(40+x) = \sqrt{\dfrac{8\ nC}{14\ nC}}(40+x)$; $x = 0.756(40+x)$

Solving for x, we obtain: $\boxed{x = 124\ mm \text{ left of } 8\ nC \text{ charge.}}$

**23-31. A +16-μC charge is 80 mm to the right of a +9 μC. Where should a third charge be placed so that the resultant force is zero?

$F_1 = F_2$; $\dfrac{kq_3q_1}{x^2} = \dfrac{kq_3q_2}{(80-x)^2}$; $F_1 = F_2$; $\dfrac{q_1}{x^2} = \dfrac{q_2}{(80-x)^2}$; $x^2 = \left(\dfrac{q_1}{q_2}\right)(80-x)^2$

Take square root of both sides: $x = \sqrt{\dfrac{q_1}{q_2}}(80-x) = \sqrt{\dfrac{9\ \mu C}{16\ \mu C}}(80-x)$; $x = 0.750(80-x)$

Solving for x, we obtain: $\boxed{x = 34.3\ mm \text{ from } 9\text{-}\mu C \text{ charge}}$

23-34. The total charge on two metal spheres 50 mm apart is 80 μC. If they repel each other with a force of 800 N, what is the charge on each sphere?

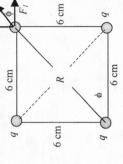

$q_1 + q_2 = 80$ μC; $\quad q_2 = 80$ μC $- q_1$

$F = \dfrac{kq_1q_2}{r^2} = \dfrac{kq_1(80\mu C - q_1)}{r^2}$; $\quad F = \dfrac{kq_1(80\mu C) - kq_1^2}{r^2}$; $\quad \dfrac{Fr^2}{k} = (80\,\mu C)q_1 - q_1^2$

$\dfrac{(800\text{ N})(50 \times 10^{-3}\text{ m})^2}{(9 \times 10^9\text{ N}\cdot\text{m}^2/\text{C}^2)} = (80\,\mu C)q_1 - q_1^2$; $\quad q_1^2 - (80 \times 10^{-6}\text{ C})q_1 + 222 \times 10^{-12}\text{ C}^2 = 0$

Solve the quadratic equation with $a = 1$, $b = -80 \times 10^{-6}$, and $c = 222 \times 10^{-12}$

$q_1 = 77.1$ μC $\quad$ and $\quad q_1 = 2.89$ μC

Now $q_2 = 80$ μC $- q_1$ yields the following : $q_2 = 2.89$ μC and $q_2 = 77.1$ μC

Thus, one charge is 77.1 μC and the other is 2.89 μC

23-35. Four small spheres are each given charges of q = +20 μC and placed at the corners of a square with sides of length 6 cm. Show that the resultant force on each charge has a magnitude equal to 1914 N. What is the direction of the force? What will change if the charges are each q = −20 μC? *(Like charges repel, so sign doesn't matter.)*

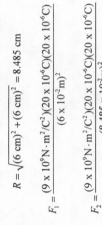

$R = \sqrt{(6\text{ cm})^2 + (6\text{ cm})^2} = 8.485$ cm

$F_1 = \dfrac{(9 \times 10^9\text{ N}\cdot\text{m}^2/\text{C}^2)(20 \times 10^{-6}\text{C})(20 \times 10^{-6}\text{C})}{(6 \times 10^{-2}\text{ m})^2}$

$F_2 = \dfrac{(9 \times 10^9\text{ N}\cdot\text{m}^2/\text{C}^2)(20 \times 10^{-6}\text{C})(20 \times 10^{-6}\text{C})}{(8.485 \times 10^{-2}\text{ m})^2}$

$F_1 = 1000$ N; $\quad F_2 = 500$ N; $\quad$ *For a square, the angle* φ = 45^0

$F_x = (1000\text{ N}) + (500\text{ N})\cos 45^0 + 0 = 1354$ N; $\quad F_y = 1000\text{ N} + (500\text{ N})\sin 45^0 = 1354$ N

$F = \sqrt{(1354\text{ N})^2 + (1354\text{ N})^2}$; $\quad \boxed{F = 1914\text{ N}, 45^0 \quad \text{away from center.}}$

23-32. Two 3-g spheres are suspended from a common point with two 80 mm light silk threads of negligible mass. What charge must be placed on each sphere if their final positions are 50 mm apart?

$\cos\phi = \dfrac{25\text{ mm}}{80\text{ mm}}$; $\quad \phi = 71.8^0 \quad T_y = T\sin\phi = mg$

$T = \dfrac{mg}{\sin\phi} = \dfrac{(3 \times 10^{-3}\text{kg})(9.8\text{ m/s}^2)}{\sin 71.8^0}$; $\quad T = 30.9$ mN

$T_x = T\cos 71.8^0 = (30.9\text{ mN})\cos 71.8^0$; $\quad T_x = 9.67$ mN;

$\Sigma F_x = 0$: $\quad F = T_x$

$F = \dfrac{kq^2}{r^2} = 9.67$ mN; $\quad q = \sqrt{\dfrac{Fr^2}{k}} = \sqrt{\dfrac{(9.67 \times 10^{-3}\text{ N})(50 \times 10^{-3}\text{ m})^2}{9 \times 10^9\text{ N}\cdot\text{m}^2/\text{C}^2}}$; $\quad \boxed{q = 51.8\text{ nC}}$

Critical Thinking Questions

*23-33. A small metal sphere is given a charge of +40 μC, and a second sphere 8 cm away is given a charge of −12 μC. What is the force of attraction between them? If the two spheres are allowed to touch and are then again placed 8 cm apart, what new electric force exists between them? Is it attraction or repulsion?

$F = \dfrac{(9 \times 10^9\text{ N}\cdot\text{m}^2/\text{C}^2)(12 \times 10^{-6}\text{C})(40 \times 10^{-6}\text{C})}{(0.080\text{ m})^2}$; $\quad \boxed{F = 675\text{ N, attraction}}$

When spheres touch, 6 μC of charge are neutralized, leaving 28 μC to be shared by two spheres, or +14 μC on each sphere. Now they are again separated:

$F = \dfrac{(9 \times 10^9\text{ N}\cdot\text{m}^2/\text{C}^2)(14 \times 10^{-6}\text{C})(14 \times 10^{-6}\text{C})}{(0.080\text{ m})^2}$;

$\boxed{F = 276\text{ N, repulsion}}$

Chapter 24. The Electric Field

The Electric Field Intensity

24-1. A charge of +2 μC placed at a point P in an electric field experiences a downward force of 8 x 10⁻⁴ N. What is the electric field intensity at that point?

$$E = \frac{F}{q} = \frac{8 \times 10^{-4} \text{ N}}{2 \times 10^{-6} \text{ C}};\qquad \boxed{E = 400 \text{ N/C, } downward}$$

24-2. A –5 nC charge is placed at point P in Problem 24-1. What are the magnitude and direction of the force on the –5 nC charge? (*Direction of force F is opposite field E*)

$$F = qE = (-5 \times 10^{-9} \text{ C})(-400 \text{ N/C});\qquad \boxed{F = 2.00 \times 10^{-6} \text{ N, } upward}$$

24-3. A charge of –3 μC placed at point A experiences a downward force of 6 x 10⁻⁵ N. What is the electric field intensity at point A?

A negative charge will experience a force opposite to the field.

*Thus, if the –3 μC charge has a downward force, the **E** is upward.*

$$E = \frac{F}{q} = \frac{-6 \times 10^{-5} \text{ N}}{-3 \times 10^{-6} \text{ C}};\qquad \boxed{E = 20 \text{ N/C, } upward}$$

24-4. At a certain point, the electric field intensity is 40 N/C, due east. An unknown charge receives a westward force of 5 x 10⁻⁵ N. What is the nature and magnitude of the charge?

If the force on the charge is opposite the field E, it must be a negative charge.

$$E = \frac{F}{q};\qquad q = \frac{F}{E} = \frac{-5 \times 10^{-5} \text{ N}}{40 \text{ N/C}};\qquad \boxed{q = -1.25 \text{ μC}}$$

23-36. Two charges q_1 and q_2 are separated by a distance r. They experience a force F at this distance. If the initial separation is decreased by only 40 mm, the force between the two charges is doubled. What was the initial separation?

$$\frac{2kq_1q_2}{x^2} = \frac{kq_1q_2}{(x-40 \text{ mm})^2};\qquad \frac{2}{x^2} = \frac{1}{(x-40 \text{ mm})^2}$$

$$x^2 = 2(x-40 \text{ mm})^2 \quad \textit{Take square root of both sides:}$$

$$x = 1.414(x - 40 \text{ mm});\qquad \boxed{x = 137 \text{ mm}}$$

23-37. Two 8-g pith balls are suspended from silk threads 60 cm long and attached to a common point. When the spheres are given equal amounts of negative charge, the balls come to rest 30 cm apart. Calculate the magnitude of the charge on each pith ball.

$$\cos\phi = \frac{0.15 \text{ m}}{0.60 \text{ m}};\qquad \phi = 75.5^0 \qquad T_y = T\sin\phi = mg$$

$$T = \frac{mg}{\sin\phi} = \frac{(8 \times 10^{-3} \text{ kg})(9.8 \text{ m/s}^2)}{\sin 75.5^0};\qquad T = 81.0 \text{ mN}$$

$$T_x = T\cos 71.8^0 = (81.0 \text{ mN})\cos 75.5^0;\qquad T_x = 20.25 \text{ mN};\qquad \Sigma F_x = 0:\quad F = T_x$$

$$F = \frac{kq^2}{r^2} = 20.25 \text{ mN};\qquad q = \sqrt{\frac{Fr^2}{k}} = \sqrt{\frac{(2.025 \times 10^{-4} \text{ N})(0.30 \text{ m})^2}{9 \times 10^9 \text{ N} \cdot \text{m}^2/\text{C}^2}};\qquad \boxed{q = -450 \text{ nC}}$$

24-5.
What are the magnitude and direction of the force that would act on an electron ($q = -1.6 \times 10^{-19}$ C) if it were placed at (a) point P in Problem 24-1? (b) point A in Problem 24-2?

The electric force on an electron will always be opposite the electric field.

(a) $F = qE = (-1.6 \times 10^{-19}$ C$)(-400$ N/C$)$; $\boxed{F = 6.40 \times 10^{-17} \text{ N, } upward}$

(a) $F = qE = (-1.6 \times 10^{-19}$ C$)(+20$ N/C$)$; $\boxed{F = -3.20 \times 10^{-18} \text{ N, } downward}$

24-6.
What must be the magnitude and direction of the electric field intensity between two horizontal plates if one wants to produce an upward force of 6×10^{-4} N on a +60-μC charge? *(The upward force on +q means E is also upward.)*

$$E = \frac{F}{q} = \frac{6 \times 10^{-4}\,\text{N}}{60 \times 10^{-6}\,\text{C}}; \qquad \boxed{E = 10.0 \text{ N/C, } up}$$

24-7.
The uniform electric field between two horizontal plates is 8×10^4 C. The top plate is positively charged and the lower plate has an equal negative charge. What are the magnitude and direction of the electric force acting on an electron as it passes horizontally through the plates? *(The electric field is from + to -, i.e., downward; force on e is up.)*

$F = qE = (-1.6 \times 10^{-19}$ C$)(8 \times 10^4$ N/C$)$; $\boxed{F = 1.28 \times 10^{-14} \text{ N, } upward}$

24-8.
Find the electric field intensity at a point P, located 6 mm to the left of an 8-μC charge. What are the magnitude and direction of the force on a -2-nC charge placed at point P?

$$E = \frac{kQ}{r^2} = \frac{(9 \times 10^9\,\text{N}\cdot\text{m}^2/\text{C}^2)(8 \times 10^{-6}\text{C})}{(6 \times 10^{-3}\text{mm})^2};$$

$\boxed{E = 2.00 \times 10^9 \text{ N/C, toward Q}}$

$F = qE = (-2 \times 10^{-9}$ C$)(2.00 \times 10^9$ N/C$)$

$\boxed{F = -4.00 \text{ N, away from Q}}$

24-9.
Determine the electric field intensity at a point P, located 4 cm above a -12-μC charge.

What are the magnitude and direction of the force on a +3-nC charge placed at point P?

Electric field will be downward, since that is the direction a positive charge would move.

$$E = \frac{kQ}{r^2} = \frac{(9 \times 10^9\,\text{N}\cdot\text{m}^2/\text{C}^2)(-12 \times 10^{-6}\text{C})}{(0.04\,\text{m})^2}; \qquad \boxed{E = -6.75 \times 10^7 \text{ N/C, } downward}$$

$F = qE = (3 \times 10^{-9}$ C$)(-6.75 \times 10^7$ N/C$)$; $\boxed{F = -0.202 \text{ N, } downward}$

Calculating the Resultant Electric Field Intensity

24-10.
Determine the electric field intensity at the midpoint of a 70 mm line joining a -60-μC charge with a +40-μC charge.

$$E_1 = \frac{kq_1}{r^2} = \frac{(9 \times 10^9\,\text{N}\cdot\text{m}^2/\text{C}^2)(-60 \times 10^{-6}\text{C})}{(0.035\,\text{m})^2};$$

$$E_2 = \frac{kq_2}{r^2} = \frac{(9 \times 10^9\,\text{N}\cdot\text{m}^2/\text{C}^2)(40 \times 10^{-6}\text{C})}{(0.035\,\text{m})^2};$$

$\mathbf{E_R} = \mathbf{E_1} + \mathbf{E_2}$ *(Both to left)*

$E_R = -4.41 \times 10^8$ N/C $- 2.94 \times 10^8$ N/C; $\boxed{\mathbf{E_R} = 7.35 \times 10^8 \text{ N/C, } toward\ -60\ \mu C}$

24-11.
An 8-nC charge is located 80 mm to the right of a +4-nC charge. Determine the field intensity at the midpoint of a line joining the two charges.

$$E_1 = \frac{kq_1}{r^2} = \frac{(9 \times 10^9\,\text{N}\cdot\text{m}^2/\text{C}^2)(4 \times 10^{-9}\text{C})}{(0.040\,\text{m})^2};$$

$$E_2 = \frac{kq_2}{r^2} = \frac{(9 \times 10^9\,\text{N}\cdot\text{m}^2/\text{C}^2)(8 \times 10^{-9}\text{C})}{(0.040\,\text{m})^2};$$

$\mathbf{E_R} = \mathbf{E_1} + \mathbf{E_2}$ *(E₁ right, E₂ left)*

$E_R = -4.50 \times 10^4$ N/C $+ 2.25 \times 10^4$ N/C; $\boxed{\mathbf{E_R} = -2.25 \times 10^4 \text{ N/C, } left}$

Note: The directions of the E field are based on how a test + charge would move.

*24-15. A charge of –20 μC is placed 50 mm to the right of a 49μC charge. What is the resultant field intensity at a point located 24 mm directly above the –20-μC charge?

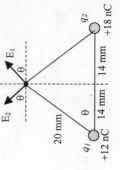

$$R = \sqrt{(50\ mm)^2 + (24\ mm)^2} = 55.5\ mm$$

$$\tan\theta = \frac{24\ mm}{50\ mm}; \qquad \theta = 25.6^0$$

$$E_1 = \frac{kq_1}{r^2} = \frac{(9 \times 10^9\,N \cdot m^2/C^2)(49 \times 10^{-6}\,C)}{(0.0555\ m)^2}; \qquad E_1 = 1.432 \times 10^8\ N/C\ at\ 25.6^0\ N\ of\ E$$

$$E_2 = \frac{kq_1}{r^2} = \frac{(9 \times 10^9\,N \cdot m^2/C^2)(20 \times 10^{-6}\,C)}{(0.024\ m)^2}; \qquad E_2 = 3.125 \times 10^8\ N/C,\ \textit{downward}$$

$$E_x = (1.432 \times 10^8\ N/C)\cos 25.6^0 + 0; \qquad E_x = 1.291 \times 10^8\ N/C$$

$$E_y = (1.432 \times 10^8\ N/C)\sin 25.6^0 - 3.125 \times 10^8\ N/C; \qquad E_y = -2.506 \times 10^8\ N/C$$

$$E_R = \sqrt{(1.29 \times 10^8)^2 + (-2.51 \times 10^8)^2}; \qquad E_R = 2.82 \times 10^8\ N/C$$

$$\tan\theta = \frac{-2.51 \times 10^8\,N/C}{1.29 \times 10^8\,N/C}; \qquad \theta = 62.7^0\ S\ of\ E; \qquad \boxed{E_R = 2.82 \times 10^8\ N/C,\ 297.3^0.}$$

*24-16. Two charges of +12 nC and +18 nC are separated horizontally by 28 mm. What is the resultant field intensity at a point 20 mm from each charge and above a line joining the two charges?

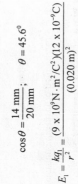

$$\cos\theta = \frac{14\ mm}{20\ mm}; \qquad \theta = 45.6^0$$

$$E_1 = \frac{kq_1}{r^2} = \frac{(9 \times 10^9\,N \cdot m^2/C^2)(12 \times 10^{-9}\,C)}{(0.020\ m)^2}$$

$$E_1 = 2.70 \times 10^5\ N/C,\ 45.6^0\ N\ of\ E$$

$$E_2 = \frac{kq_1}{r^2} = \frac{(9 \times 10^9\,N \cdot m^2/C^2)(18 \times 10^{-9}\,C)}{(0.020\ m)^2}$$

$$E_2 = 4.05 \times 10^5\ N/C,\ 45.6^0\ N\ of\ W$$

24-12. Find the electric field intensity at a point 30 mm to the right of a 16-nC charge and 40 mm to the left of a 9-nC charge.

$$E_1 = \frac{kq_1}{r^2} = \frac{(9 \times 10^9\,N \cdot m^2/C^2)(16 \times 10^{-9}\,C)}{(0.030\ m)^2}$$

$$E_2 = \frac{kq_2}{r^2} = \frac{(9 \times 10^9\,N \cdot m^2/C^2)(9 \times 10^{-9}\,C)}{(0.040\ m)^2}; \qquad E_R = E_1 + E_2\ \textit{(E$_1$ right, E$_2$ left)}$$

$$E_R = 16.0 \times 10^4\ N/C - 5.06 \times 10^4\ N/C; \qquad \boxed{E_R = 1.09 \times 10^5\ N/C,\ right}$$

24-13. Two equal charges of opposite signs are separated by a horizontal distance of 60 mm. The resultant electric field at the midpoint of the line is 4 x 10⁴ N/C. What is the magnitude of each charge?

Equal and opposite charges make field at center

equal to vector sum with both to left or both to right.. $E_R = E_1 + E_2 = E_1 + E_2$

$$E = \frac{2kq}{r^2} = 4 \times 10^4\ N/C; \qquad \frac{2(9 \times 10^9\,N \cdot m^2/C^2)q}{(0.030\ m)^2} = 4 \times 10^4\ N/C$$

$$\boxed{q = 2.00\ nC} \qquad \textit{(One positive and the other negative.)}$$

*24-14. A 20-μC charge is 4 cm above an unknown charge q. The resultant electric intensity at a point 1 cm above the 20-μC charge is 2.20 x 10⁹ N/C and is directed upward? What are the magnitude and sign of the unknown charge?

$$E_1 + E_2 = 2.20 \times 10^9\ N/C; \qquad \textit{First we find E$_1$ and E$_2$}$$

$$E_1 = \frac{kq_1}{r^2} = \frac{(9 \times 10^9\,N \cdot m^2/C^2)(20 \times 10^{-6}\,C)}{(0.010\ m)^2}; \qquad E_1 = 1.80 \times 10^9\ N/C$$

$$E_2 = E_R - E_1 = 2.20 \times 10^9\ N/C - 1.80 \times 10^9\ N/C; \qquad E_2 = 4 \times 10^8\ N/C,\ \textit{up}$$

$$E_2 = \frac{kq_2}{r^2}; \qquad q_2 = \frac{E_2 r^2}{k} = \frac{(4 \times 10^8\,N/C)(0.05\ m)^2}{(9 \times 10^9\,N \cdot m^2/C^2)}; \qquad \boxed{q = q_2 = 111\ \mu C}$$

*24-16. (Cont.) $E_x = (2.70 \times 10^5 \text{ N/C}) \cos 45.6^0 - (4.05 \times 10^5 \text{ N/C}) \cos 45.6^0 = -9.45 \times 10^4 \text{ N/C}$

$E_y = (2.70 \times 10^5 \text{ N/C}) \sin 45.6^0 - (4.05 \times 10^5 \text{ N/C}) \sin 45.6^0 = +4.82 \times 10^5 \text{ N/C}$

$E_R = \sqrt{(-9.45 \times 10^4)^2 + (4.82 \times 10^5)^2}$; $E_R = 4.91 \times 10^5 \text{ N/C}$

$\tan\theta = \dfrac{4.82 \times 10^5 \text{ N/C}}{-9.45 \times 10^4 \text{ N/C}}$; $\theta = 78.9^0$ N of W; $\boxed{E_R = 4.91 \times 10^5 \text{ N/C}, \ 101.1^0}$

*24-17. A +4 nC charge is placed at x = 0 and a +6 nC charge is placed at x = 4 cm on an x-axis.

Find the point where the resultant electric field intensity will be zero?

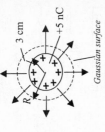

+4 nC   x   4 cm - x   +6 nC
q_1 $E_2 = E_1$ q_2
x = 0   x = 4 cm

$E_1 = E_2$; $\dfrac{kq_1}{x^2} = \dfrac{kq_2}{(4 \text{ cm} - x)^2}$;

$(4-x)^2 = \dfrac{q_2}{q_1}x^2$ or $4 - x = \sqrt{\dfrac{q_2 \, x}{q_1}}$

$4 \text{ cm} - x = \sqrt{\dfrac{6 \text{ nC}}{4 \text{ nC}}}x$; $4 \text{ cm} - x = 1.225 \, x$; $\boxed{x = 1.80 \text{ cm}}$

Applications of Gauss's Law

24-18. Use Gauss's law to show that the field outside a solid charged sphere at a distance r from its center is given by

$$E = \frac{Q}{4\pi\varepsilon_0 R^2}$$

where Q is the total charge on the sphere.

Construct a spherical gaussian surface around the charged sphere at the distance r from its center. Then, we have

Gaussian surface

$\Sigma\varepsilon_0 AE = \Sigma q$; $\varepsilon_0 E(4\pi R^2) = Q$

$$\boxed{E = \frac{Q}{4\pi\varepsilon_0 R^2}}$$

24-19. A charge of +5 nC is placed on the surface of a hollow metal sphere whose radius is 3 cm. Use Gauss's law to find the electric field intensity at a distance of 1 cm from the surface of the sphere? What is the electric field at a point 1 cm inside the surface?

Draw gaussian surface of radius R = 3 cm + 1 cm = 4 cm.

This surface encloses a net positive charge of +5 nC and has a surface area of $4\pi R^2$, so Gauss' law gives us:

(a) $\Sigma\varepsilon_0 AE = \Sigma q$; $\varepsilon_0(4\pi R^2)E = q$; $E = \dfrac{q}{4\pi\varepsilon_0 R^2}$

$E = \dfrac{5 \times 10^{-9} \text{C}}{4\pi(8.85 \times 10^{-12}\text{C}^2/\text{N}\cdot\text{m}^2)(0.04 \text{ m})^2}$; $\boxed{E = 2.81 \times 10^4 \text{ N/C, radially outward.}}$

(b) *Draw a gaussian surface just inside the sphere. Now, all charge resides on the surface of the sphere, so that zero net charge is enclosed, and $\Sigma\varepsilon_0 AE = \Sigma q = 0$.*

$$\boxed{E = 0, \ \text{inside sphere}}$$

24-20. Two parallel plates, each 2 cm wide and 4 cm long, are stacked vertically so that the field intensity between the two plates is 10,000 N/C directed upward. What is the charge on each plate? *First use Gauss' law to find E between plates.*

Draw gaussian cylinder of area A enclosing charge q.

$\Sigma\varepsilon_0 AE = \Sigma q$; $\varepsilon_0 AE = q$; $E = \dfrac{q}{\varepsilon_0 A}$

The charge density q/A enclosed is same as Q/A$_P$ for plate. First find q/A from E :

$\dfrac{q}{A} = \varepsilon_0 E = (8.85 \times 10^{-12}\text{C}^2/\text{N}\cdot\text{m}^2)(10,000 \text{ N/C})$; $\dfrac{q}{A} = 8.85 \times 10^{-8} \text{ C/m}^2$

$\dfrac{q}{A} = \dfrac{Q}{(0.02 \text{ m})(0.04 \text{ m})} = 8.85 \times 10^{-8} \text{ C/m}^2$; $\boxed{Q = 7.09 \times 10^{-11} \text{ C}}$

24-24. What are the magnitude and direction of the force on an alpha particle (q = +3.2 x 10^{-19} C) as it passes into an upward electric field of intensity 8 x 10^4 N/C? (Choose up as +)

$$F = qE = (3.2 \times 10^{-19} \text{ C})(+8 \times 10^4);\quad \boxed{F = 2.56 \times 10^{-14} \text{ N}}$$

24-25. What is the acceleration of an electron (e = -1.6 x 10^{-19} C) placed in a constant downward electric field of 4 x 10^5 N/C? What is the gravitational force on this charge if m_e = 9.11 x 10^{-31} kg. (Choose up as +, then E = -4 x 10^5 N/C.)

$$F = qE = (-1.6 \times 10^{-19} \text{ C})(-4 \times 10^5 \text{ N/C});\quad \boxed{F = 6.40 \times 10^{-14} \text{ N, upward}}$$

$$W = mg = (9.11 \times 10^{-31} \text{ kg})(9.8 \text{ m/s}^2);\quad \boxed{W = 8.93 \times 10^{-30} \text{ N, downward}}$$

The weight of an electron is often negligible in comparison with electric forces!

24-26. What is the electric field intensity at the midpoint of a 40 mm line between a 6-nC charge and a -9-nC charge? What force will act on a -2-nC charge placed at the midpoint?

$$E_1 = \frac{kq_1}{r^2} = \frac{(9 \times 10^9 \text{N} \cdot \text{m}^2/\text{C}^2)(6 \times 10^{-9}\text{C})}{(0.020 \text{ m})^2};$$

$$E_2 = \frac{kq_2}{r^2} = \frac{(9 \times 10^9 \text{N} \cdot \text{m}^2/\text{C}^2)(9 \times 10^{-9}\text{C})}{(0.020 \text{ m})^2};$$

$$\mathbf{E_R} = \mathbf{E_1} + \mathbf{E_2} \text{ (both to the right)}$$

$$E_R = 1.35 \times 10^5 \text{ N/C} + 2.025 \times 10^5 \text{ N/C};\quad \boxed{\mathbf{E_R} = 3.38 \times 10^5 \text{ N/C, right}}$$

*24-27. The charge density on each of two parallel plates is 4 μC/m². What is the electric field intensity between the plates? *Recall that σ = q/A, and see Prob.24-20:*

$$\Sigma \varepsilon_0 AE = \Sigma q; \quad \varepsilon_0 AE = q; \quad E = \frac{q}{\varepsilon_0 A} = \frac{\sigma}{\varepsilon_0}$$

$$E = \frac{\sigma}{\varepsilon_0} = \frac{4 \times 10^{-6} \text{ C/m}^2}{(8.85 \times 10^{-12}\text{C}^2/\text{N} \cdot \text{m}^2)};\quad \boxed{E = 4.52 \times 10^5 \text{ N/C}}$$

24-21. A sphere 8 cm in diameter has a charge of 4 μC placed on its surface. What is the electric field intensity at the surface, 2 cm outside the surface, and 2 cm inside the surface?

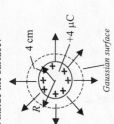

(a) *Draw gaussian surface just outside so that R = 4 cm and encloses the net charge of +4 uC. Then,*

$$E = \frac{q_{net}}{4\pi\varepsilon_0 R^2} = \frac{4 \times 10^{-6} \text{C}}{4\pi(8.85 \times 10^{-12}\text{C}^2/\text{N} \cdot \text{m}^2)(0.04 \text{ m})^2}$$

$$\boxed{E = 2.25 \times 10^7 \text{ N/C, radially outward}}$$

(b) *Draw gaussian surface of radius R = 4 cm + 2 cm = 6 cm. This surface encloses a net positive charge of +4 nC and Gauss law gives:*

$$E = \frac{4 \times 10^{-6} \text{C}}{4\pi(8.85 \times 10^{-12}\text{C}^2/\text{N} \cdot \text{m}^2)(0.06 \text{ m})^2};\quad \boxed{E = 9.99 \times 10^6 \text{ N/C, radially outward.}}$$

(b) *Since no net charge is inside the surface, $\Sigma\varepsilon_0 AE = \Sigma q = 0$.*

$$\boxed{E = 0, \text{ inside sphere}}$$

Supplementary Problems

24-22. How far from a point charge of 90 nC will the field intensity be 500 N/C?

$$E = \frac{kQ}{r^2}; \quad r = \sqrt{\frac{kQ}{E}} = \sqrt{\frac{(9 \times 10^9 \text{N} \cdot \text{m}^2/\text{C}^2)(90 \times 10^{-9}\text{C})}{500 \text{ N/C}}};\quad \boxed{r = 1.27 \text{ m}}$$

24-23. The electric field intensity at a point in space is found to be 5 x 10^5 N/C, directed due west. What are the magnitude and direction of the force on a -4-μC charge placed at that point?

Consider East positive: $F = qE = (-4 \text{ μC})(-5 \times 10^5 \text{ N/C});\quad \boxed{F = 2.00 \text{ N, East}}$

*24-28. A -2 nC charge is placed at x = 0 on the x-axis. A +8 nC charge is placed at x = 4 cm.

At what point will the electric field intensity be equal to zero?

The point can only be to the left of the -2 nC

$E_1 = E_2$; $\dfrac{kq_1}{x^2} = \dfrac{kq_2}{(x+4\,cm)^2}$

$(4+x)^2 = \dfrac{q_2}{q_1}x^2$ or $4 + x = \sqrt{\dfrac{q_2}{q_1}}\,x$

$4\,cm + x = \sqrt{\dfrac{8\,nC}{2\,nC}}\,x$; $4\,cm + x = 2x$; $x = 8.00\,cm,\ left,\ or$ $\boxed{x = -4.00\ cm}$

*24-29. Charges of -2 and +4 μC are placed at base corners of an equilateral triangle with 10-cm sides. What are the magnitude and direction of the electric field at the top corner?

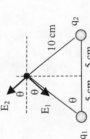

$\cos\theta = \dfrac{5\ mm}{10\ mm}$; $\theta = 60^0$

$E_1 = \dfrac{kq_1}{r^2} = \dfrac{(9\times10^9\,N\cdot m^2/C^2)(2\times10^{-6}C)}{(0.10\ m)^2}$

$E_1 = 1.80\times10^6\ N/C$, 60^0 of E

$E_2 = \dfrac{kq_1}{r^2} = \dfrac{(9\times10^9\,N\cdot m^2/C^2)(4\times10^{-6}C)}{(0.10\ m)^2}$; $E_2 = 3.60\times10^6\ N/C$, 60^0 N of W

$E_x = -\,(1.80\times10^6\ N/C)\cos60^0 - (3.60\times10^6\ N/C)\cos60^0 = -2.70\times10^6\ N/C$

$E_y = -\,(1.80\times10^6\ N/C)\sin60^0 + (3.60\times10^6\ N/C)\sin60^0 = +1.56\times10^6\ N/C$

$E_R = \sqrt{(-2.70\times10^6)^2 + (1.56\times10^6)^2}$; $E_R = 3.12\times10^6\ N/C$

$\tan\theta = \dfrac{1.56\times10^6\ N/C}{-2.70\times10^6\ N/C}$; $\theta = 30.0^0$ N of W; $\boxed{E_R = 3.12\times10^6\ N/C,\ 150.0^0}$

24-30. What are the magnitude and direction of the force that would act on a -2-μC charge placed at the apex of the triangle described by Problem 24-29?

First we find the magnitude: $F = qE = (2\times10^{-6}\,C)(3.12\times10^6\ N/C)$; $F = 6.24\ N$

Force is opposite field: $\theta = 180^0 + 150^0 = 330^0$ $\boxed{F = 6.24\ N,\ 330^0}$

*24-31. A 20-mg particle is placed in a uniform downward field of 2000 N/C. How many excess electrons must be placed on the particle for the electric and gravitational forces to balance? *(The gravitational force must balance the electric force.)*

$qE = mg$; $q = \dfrac{mg}{E} = \dfrac{(2\times10^{-5}\,kg)(9.8\ m/s^2)}{2000\ N/C}$

$q = 9.00\times10^{-8}\ C$; $1\,e = 1.6\times10^{-19}\ C$

$q_e = 9.8\times10^{-8}C\left(\dfrac{1\,e}{1.6\times10^{-19}C}\right)$; $\boxed{q_e = 6.12\times10^{11}\ \text{electrons}}$

*24-32. Use Gauss's law to show that the electric field intensity at a distance R from an infinite line of charge is given by

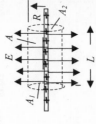

$E = \dfrac{\lambda}{2\pi\epsilon_0 R}$

where λ is the charge per unit length.

Gaussian surface area $A = [(2\pi R)L + A_1 + A_2]$

$\Sigma\epsilon_0 AE = \Sigma q$; $\epsilon_0 A_1 E_1 + \epsilon_0 A_2 E_2 + \epsilon_0(2\pi RL)E = q_{net}$

The fields E_1 *and* E_2 *are balanced through ends:* $\epsilon_0(2\pi RL)E = q_{net}$; *therefore:*

$E = \dfrac{q}{2\pi\epsilon_0 RL}$ *But the linear charge density is* $\lambda = q/L$, *therefore:*

$\boxed{E = \dfrac{\lambda}{2\pi\epsilon_0 R}}$

*24-33. Use Gauss's law to show that the field just outside any solid conductor is given by

$$E = \frac{\sigma}{\varepsilon_0}$$

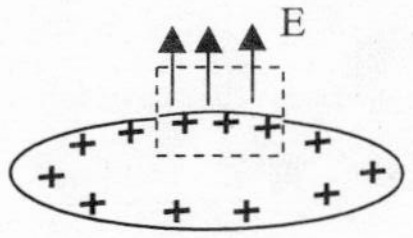

Draw a cylindrical pill box as gaussian surface.

The field lines through the sides are balanced and the field inside the surface is zero.

Thus, only one surface needs to be considered, the area A of the top of the pill box.

$\sum \varepsilon_0 AE = \sum q$; $\varepsilon_0 EA = q$; $E = \frac{q}{\varepsilon_0 A} = \frac{\sigma}{\varepsilon_0}$; $\boxed{E = \frac{\sigma}{\varepsilon_0}}$

---

*24-34. What is the electric field intensity 2 m from the surface of a sphere 20 cm in diameter having a surface charge density of +8 nC/m²? [$A = 4\pi R^2$; r = 2 m + 0.2 m = 2.2 m]

$q = \sigma A = (8 \times 10^{-9}\text{ C})(4\pi)(0.20\text{ m})^2$; $q = 2.01 \times 10^{-12}$ C

$E = \frac{kq}{r^2} = \frac{(9 \times 10^9 \text{N}\cdot\text{m}^2/\text{C}^2)(2.01 \times 10^{-12}\text{C})}{(2.20\text{ m})^2}$; $E = 3.74 \times 10^{-3}$ N/C

---

*24-35. A uniformly charged conducting sphere has a radius of 24 cm and a surface charge density of +16 μC/m². What is the total number of electric field lines leaving the sphere?

$q = \sigma A = (16 \times 10^{-6}\text{ C})(4\pi)(0.24\text{ m})^2$; $q = 1.16 \times 10^{-5}$ C

$N = \Sigma\varepsilon_0 AE = q$; $\boxed{N = 1.16 \times 10^{-5} \text{ lines}}$

---

*24-36. Two charges of +16 μC and +8 μC are 200 mm apart in air. At what point on a line joining the two charges will the electric field be zero? (200 mm = 20 cm)

$E_1 = E_2$; $\frac{kq_1}{x^2} = \frac{kq_2}{(20\text{ cm - x})^2}$

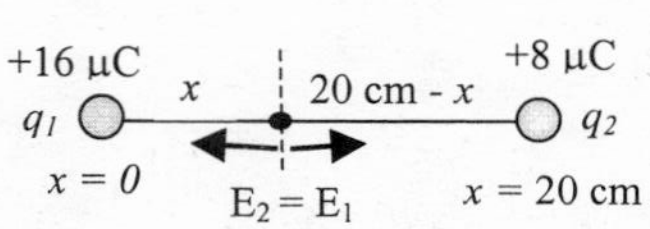

$(20 - x)^2 = \frac{q_2}{q_1}x^2$ or $20 - x = \sqrt{\frac{q_2}{q_1}}x$

*24-36 (Cont.) 20 cm - x = $\sqrt{\frac{8\ \mu C}{16\ \mu C}}x$; 20 cm - x = 0.707 x; $\boxed{x = 11.7 \text{ cm}}$

---

*24-37. Two charges of +8 nC and –5 nC are 40 mm apart in air. At what point on a line joining the two charges will the electric field intensity be zero?

The point can only be to right of –5 nC charge

$E_2 = E_1$; $\frac{kq_2}{x^2} = \frac{kq_1}{(x + 4\text{ cm})^2}$

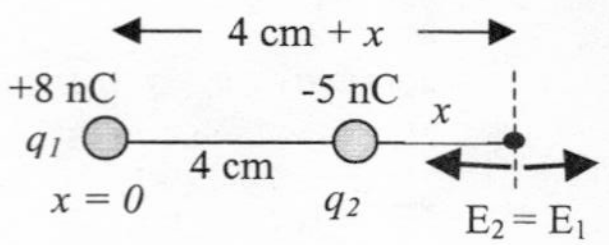

$(4 + x)^2 = \frac{q_1}{q_2}x^2$ or $4 + x = \sqrt{\frac{q_1}{q_2}}x$

4 cm + x = $\sqrt{\frac{8\text{ nC}}{5\text{ nC}}}x$; 4 cm + x = 1.265 x; $\boxed{x = 15.1 \text{ cm outside of } -5 \text{ nC charge.}}$

Critical Thinking Questions

*24-38. Two equal but opposite charges +*q* and –q are placed at the base corners of an equilateral triangle whose sides are of length *a*. Show that the magnitude of the electric field intensity at the apex is the same whether one of the charges is removed or not? What is the angle between the two fields so produced?

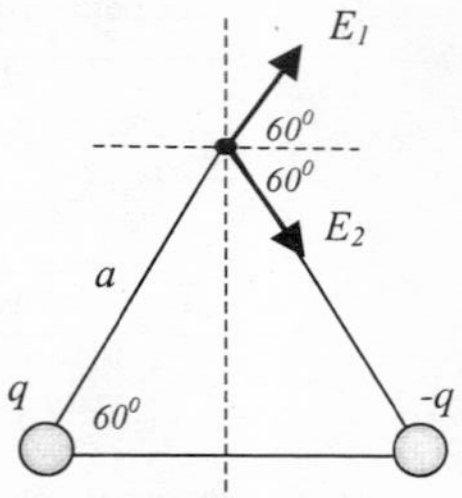

$E = kq/r^2$; $E_1 = E_2$ *since q and r are the same for each.*

$E_y = E_1 \sin 60^0 - E_2 \sin 60 = 0$, *(since $E_1 = E_2$)*

Let E be magnitude of either E_1 or E_2, then

$E_x = E \sin 60^0 + E \sin 60^0 = 2E \cos 60^0 = E$

Thus, for both charges in place $E = E_1 = E_2$

The field with both charges in place is at 0^0. The field produced by –q is at -60^0 and the field produced by +q is at $+60^0$. In either case the angle is 60^0 between the fields.

*24-39. What are the magnitude and direction of the electric field intensity at the center of the square of Fig. 24-16. Assume that q = 1 μC and that d = 4 cm. (d/2 = 2 cm).

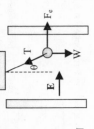

Rotate x and y-axes 45⁰ clockwise as shown to make calculating resultant easier. The distances r from each charge to center is:

$r = \sqrt{(2 \text{ cm})^2 + (2 \text{ cm})^2}$; $r = 2.83$ cm;

$E_1 = \dfrac{(9 \times 10^9\,\text{N}\cdot\text{m}^2/\text{C}^2)(1 \times 10^{-6}\,\text{C})}{(2.828 \times 10^{-2}\,\text{m})^2}$; $E_1 = 1.125 \times 10^7$ N/C   *(E₁ refers to E for −q)*

$E_2 = \dfrac{(9 \times 10^9\,\text{N}\cdot\text{m}^2/\text{C}^2)(2 \times 10^{-6}\,\text{C})}{(2.828 \times 10^{-2}\,\text{m})^2}$; $E_2 = 2.25 \times 10^7$ N/C,   *(E₂ refers to E for ±2q)*

$E_x = -E_1 - E_2 = -1.125 \times 10^7$ N/C $- 2.25 \times 10^7$ N/C; $E_x = -3.38 \times 10^7$ N/C

$E_y = E_1 - E_2 = 1.125 \times 10^7$ N/C $- 2.25 \times 10^7$ N/C; $E_y = -1.125 \times 10^7$ N/C

$E = \sqrt{(-3.38 \times 10^7\,\text{N/C})^2 + (-1.125 \times 10^7\,\text{N/C})^2}$; $E = 3.56 \times 10^7$ N/C

$\tan\theta = \dfrac{-1.125 \times 10^7\,\text{N/C}}{-3.38 \times 10^7\,\text{N/C}}$; $\theta = 18.4^0$ or 198.4^0 *from +x-axis*

It is better to give direction with respect to horizontal, instead of with diagonal.

Since we rotated axes 45⁰ clockwise, the true angle is: $\theta = 198.4^0 - 45^0 = 153.4^0$

Ans. $E = 3.56 \times 10^7$ N, 153.4⁰

---

*24-40. The electric field intensity between the plates in Fig. 24-17 is 4000 N/C. What is the magnitude of the charge on the suspended pith ball whose mass is 3 mg? (θ = 30⁰)

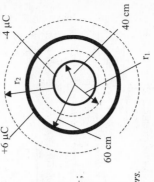

$W = mg$; $E = 4000$ N/C; $m = 3$ mg $= 3 \times 10^{-6}$ kg

$\Sigma F_x = 0$ *and* $\Sigma F_y = 0$ *(right = left; up = down)*

$T \sin 60^0 = (3 \times 10^{-6}\,\text{kg})(9.8\,\text{m/s}^2)$; $T = 3.39 \times 10^{-5}$ N

$F_e = T \cos 60^0 = (3.39 \times 10^{-5}\,\text{N})(0.500) = 1.70 \times 10^{-5}$ N

$E = \dfrac{F_e}{q}$; $q = \dfrac{F_e}{E} = \dfrac{1.70 \times 10^{-5}\,\text{N}}{4000\,\text{N/C}}$; $q = 1.27 \times 10^{-8}$ C;

$\boxed{q = 4.24 \text{ nC}}$

*24-41. Two concentric spheres have radii of 20 cm and 50 cm. The inner sphere has a negative charge of −4 μC and the outer sphere has a positive charge of +6 μC. Use Gauss's law to find the electric field intensity at distances of 40 cm and 60 cm from the center of the spheres.   *Draw concentric gaussian spheres.*

$\Sigma \varepsilon_0 AE = \Sigma q$; $\varepsilon_0 (4\pi r_2^2) E = -4\,\mu C + 6\,\mu C$

First find field at 60 cm from center:

$E = \dfrac{q_{net}}{4\pi\varepsilon_0 r^2} = \dfrac{+2 \times 10^{-6}\,\text{C}}{4\pi(8.85 \times 10^{-12}\,\text{C}^2/\text{N}\cdot\text{m}^2)(0.60\,\text{m})^2}$;

$\boxed{E = 5.00 \times 10^4 \text{ N/C, radially outward}}$

Now for field at 40 cm, only enclosed charge matters.

$E = \dfrac{q_{net}}{4\pi\varepsilon_0 r^2} = \dfrac{-4 \times 10^{-6}\,\text{C}}{4\pi(8.85 \times 10^{-12}\,\text{C}^2/\text{N}\cdot\text{m}^2)(0.40\,\text{m})^2}$;

$\boxed{E = 2.25 \times 10^5 \text{ N/C, radially inward}}$

Work and Electric Potential Energy

25-1. A positively charged plate is 30 mm above a negatively charged plate, and the electric field intensity has a magnitude of 6×10^4 N/C. How much work is done BY the electric field when a $+4$-μC charge is moved from the negative plate to the positive plate?

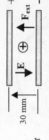

$Work = Fd = qEd;$ *F opposite to d makes work negative*

$Work = (4 \times 10^{-6} \text{ C})(6 \times 10^4 \text{ N/C})(0.030 \text{ m})$

$Work = -7.20 \times 10^{-3}$ J; $\boxed{Work = -7.20 \text{ mJ}}$

25-2. In Problem 25-1, how much work is done ON or against the electric field? What is the electric potential energy at the positive plate?

The displacement occurs against the electric force, so that work done ON the field due to outside UP force F_{ext} in same direction as the displacement.

Since the field is in a position to do positive work when at the positive, plate, the electric potential energy is positive at that point: $\boxed{E_p = +7.20 \text{ mJ}}$

25-3. The electric field intensity between two parallel plates, separated by 25 mm is 8000 N/C. How much work is done BY the electric field in moving a -2-μC charge from the negative plate to the positive plate? What is the work done BY the field in moving the same charge back to the positive plate? *(Electric force with motion)*

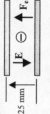

Work done BY field is positive, F_e with displacement.

$Work = qEd = (2 \times 10^{-6} \text{ C})(8000 \text{ N/C})(0.025 \text{ m})$ *Work done BY = Loss of electric energy.*

$\boxed{Work = 4.00 \times 10^{-4} \text{ J}}$ Now, in coming back electric force opposes motion.

Work done BY field is negative: $\boxed{Work = -4.00 \times 10^{-4} \text{ J.}}$

**24-42. The electric field intensity between the two plates in Fig. 24-4 is 2000 N/C. The length of the plates is 4 cm, and their separation is 1 cm. An electron is projected into the field from the left with horizontal velocity of 2×10^7 m/s. What is the upward deflection of the electron at the instant it leaves the plates?

We may neglect the weight of the electron.

$F = qE = ma_y;$ $a_y = \dfrac{qE}{g};$ $x = v_0 t$

$y = \tfrac{1}{2} a_y t^2$ and $t = \dfrac{x}{v_0};$ $t^2 = \dfrac{x^2}{v_0^2}$

$y = \dfrac{1}{2}\left(\dfrac{qE}{m}\right)\left(\dfrac{x^2}{v_0^2}\right) = \dfrac{1}{2}\left[\dfrac{(1.6 \times 10^{-19}\text{C})(2000 \text{ N/C})(0.04 \text{ m})^2}{(9.11 \times 10^{-31}\text{kg})(2 \times 10^7 \text{m/s})^2}\right],$

$y = 0.0704$ cm   *or* $\boxed{y = 0.70 \text{ mm}}$

25-4. In Problem 25-3, what is the potential energy when the charge is at (a) the positive plate and (b) the negative plate?

Remember, potential energy represents the work that the

electric field can do when electric forces are free to act. When the −2 μC charge is at the

positive plate, the E field can do no work, thus with reference to that point, $E_p = 0$.

(a) At + plate: $E_p = 0$ *No work can be done by the electric field.*

(b) At − plate, the field can do +work: $E_p = +4.00 \times 10^{-4}$ J

25-5. What is the potential energy of a +6 nC charge located 50 mm away from a +80-μC charge? What is the potential energy if the same charge is 50 mm from a −80-μC charge?

$$P.E. = \frac{kQq}{r} = \frac{(9 \times 10^9 \text{N} \cdot \text{m}^2/\text{C}^2)(+80 \times 10^{-6}\text{C})(6 \times 10^{-9}\text{C})}{0.050 \text{ m}}$$

$P.E. = 86.4$ mJ

$$P.E. = \frac{kQq}{r} = \frac{(9 \times 10^9 \text{N} \cdot \text{m}^2/\text{C}^2)(-80 \times 10^{-6}\text{C})(6 \times 10^{-9}\text{C})}{0.050 \text{ m}} \; ;$$

$P.E. = -86.4$ mJ

25-6. At what distance from a −7-μC charge will a −3-nC charge have a potential energy of 60 mJ? What initial force will the −3-nC charge experience?

$$P.E. = \frac{kQq}{r} \; ; \quad r = \frac{kQq}{P.E.}$$

$$r = \frac{(9 \times 10^9 \text{N} \cdot \text{m}^2/\text{C}^2)(-7 \times 10^{-6}\text{C})(-3 \times 10^{-6}\text{C})}{0.060 \text{ J}} \; ;$$

$r = 3.15$ mm

$$F = \frac{kQq}{r^2} = \frac{(9 \times 10^9 \text{N} \cdot \text{m}^2/\text{C}^2)(-7 \times 10^{-6}\text{C})(-3 \times 10^{-9}\text{C})}{(3.15 \times 10^{-3})^2} \; ;$$

$F = 19.0$ N, repulsion

Note: This value can also be obtained from: $F = \dfrac{P.E.}{r}$

25-7. A +8-nC charge is placed at a point P, 40 mm from a +12-μC charge. What is the potential energy per unit charge at point P in joules per coulomb? Will this change if the 8-nC charge is removed?

$$P.E. = \frac{kQq}{r} = \frac{(9 \times 10^9 \text{N} \cdot \text{m}^2/\text{C}^2)(+12 \times 10^{-6}\text{C})(8 \times 10^{-9}\text{C})}{0.040 \text{ m}}$$

$P.E. = 0.0216$ J;

$$V = \frac{P.E.}{q} = \frac{0.0270 \text{ J}}{8 \times 10^{-9}\text{C}} \; ; \quad V = 2.70 \times 10^6 \text{ J/C}; \quad \boxed{\text{No}} \quad \textit{The P.E./q is a property of space.}$$

If another charge were placed there or if no charge were there, the P.E./q is the same.

25-8. A charge of +6 μC is 30 mm away from another charge of 16 μC. What is the potential energy of the system?

$$P.E. = \frac{kQq}{r} = \frac{(9 \times 10^9 \text{N} \cdot \text{m}^2/\text{C}^2)(+6 \times 10^{-6}\text{C})(16 \times 10^{-6}\text{C})}{0.030 \text{ m}} \; ; \quad \boxed{P.E. = 28.8 \text{ J}}$$

25-9. In Problem 25-8, what is the change in potential energy if the 6-μC charge is moved to a distance of only 5 mm? Is this an increase or decrease in potential energy?

$(P.E.)_{30} = 28.8$ J *from previous example. Now assume charge is moved.*

$$(P.E.)_5 = \frac{kQq}{r} = \frac{(9 \times 10^9 \text{N} \cdot \text{m}^2/\text{C}^2)(+6 \times 10^{-6}\text{C})(16 \times 10^{-6}\text{C})}{0.005 \text{ m}} \; ; \quad (P.E.)_5 = 173 \text{ J}$$

Change in P.E. = 172 J − 28.8 J; $\boxed{\text{Change} = 144 \text{ J, increase}}$

25-10. A −3-μC charge is placed 6 mm away from a −9-μC charge. What is the potential energy? Is it negative or positive?

$$P.E. = \frac{kQq}{r} = \frac{(9 \times 10^9 \text{N} \cdot \text{m}^2/\text{C}^2)(-3 \times 10^{-6}\text{C})(-9 \times 10^{-6}\text{C})}{0.006 \text{ m}} \; ; \quad \boxed{P.E. = +40.5 \text{ J}}$$

25-15. Calculate the potential at point *A* that is 50 mm from a −40-μC charge. What is the potential energy if a +3-μC charge is placed at point A?

$$V = \frac{kQ}{r} = \frac{(9 \times 10^9 \text{N} \cdot \text{m}^2/\text{C}^2)(-40 \times 10^{-6}\text{C})}{0.050 \text{ m}}; \quad \boxed{V = -7.20 \times 10^6 \text{ V}}$$

$$\text{P.E.} = qV = (3 \times 10^{-6}\text{C})(-7.2 \times 10^6); \quad \boxed{\text{P.E.} = -21.6 \text{ J}}$$

25-16. What is the potential at the midpoint of a line joining a −12-μC charge with a +3-μC charge located 80 mm away from the first charge?

−12 μC   +3 μC
40 mm   40 mm

$$V = \sum \frac{kQ}{r} \quad \textit{(Net potential is algebraic sum)}$$

$$V = \sum \frac{kQ}{r} = \frac{(9 \times 10^9 \text{N} \cdot \text{m}^2/\text{C}^2)(-12 \times 10^{-6}\text{C})}{0.040 \text{ m}} + \frac{(9 \times 10^9 \text{N} \cdot \text{m}^2/\text{C}^2)(+3 \times 10^{-6}\text{C})}{0.040 \text{ m}}$$

$$V = -2.70 \times 10^6 \text{ V} + 0.675 \times 10^6 \text{ V}; \quad V = -2.025 \times 10^6 \text{ V}; \quad \boxed{V = -2.02 \text{ MV}}$$

25-17. A +45-nC charge is 68 mm to the left of a −9-nC charge. What is the potential at a point located 40 mm to the left of the −9-nC charge?

+45 nC   −9 nC
28 mm   40 mm

Find potential due to each charge, then add:

$$V = \sum \frac{kQ}{r} = \frac{(9 \times 10^9 \text{N} \cdot \text{m}^2/\text{C}^2)(45 \times 10^{-9}\text{C})}{0.028 \text{ m}} + \frac{(9 \times 10^9 \text{N} \cdot \text{m}^2/\text{C}^2)(-9 \times 10^{-9}\text{C})}{0.040 \text{ m}}$$

$$V = +14.5 \times 10^3 \text{ V} + (-2.025 \times 10^3 \text{ V}); \quad \boxed{V = +12.4 \text{ kV}}$$

*25-18. Points A and B are 68 mm and 26 mm away from a 90-μC charge. Calculate the potential difference between points A and B? How much work is done BY the electric field as a −5-μC charge moves from A to B?

A
68 mm
B
26 mm   90 μC

$$V_B = \frac{(9 \times 10^9 \text{N} \cdot \text{m}^2/\text{C}^2)(90 \times 10^{-6}\text{C})}{0.026 \text{ m}}; \quad V_B = 3.115 \times 10^7 \text{ V}$$

Chapter 25   Electric Potential   **351**

25-11. What is the change in potential energy when a 3-nC charge is moved from a point 8 cm away from a −6-μC charge to a point that is 20 cm away? Is this an increase or decrease of potential energy? (*Moves from A to B on figure.*)

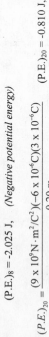

B
20 cm
A
8 cm   −6 μC

$$(P.E.)_8 = \frac{kQq}{r} = \frac{(9 \times 10^9 \text{N} \cdot \text{m}^2/\text{C}^2)(-6 \times 10^{-6}\text{C})(3 \times 10^{-6}\text{C})}{0.08 \text{ m}}$$

$$(P.E.)_8 = -2.025 \text{ J}, \quad \textit{(Negative potential energy)}$$

$$(P.E.)_{20} = \frac{(9 \times 10^9 \text{N} \cdot \text{m}^2/\text{C}^2)(-6 \times 10^{-6}\text{C})(3 \times 10^{-6}\text{C})}{0.20 \text{ m}} \quad (P.E.)_{20} = -0.810 \text{ J},$$

$$\textit{Change} = \textit{final} - \textit{initial} = -0.810 \text{ J} - (-2.025 \text{ J}); \quad \boxed{\text{Change in P.E.} = +1.22 \text{ J, } \textit{increase}}$$

25-12. At what distance from a −7-μC charge must a charge of −12 nC be placed if the potential energy is to be 9×10^{-5} J?

$$P.E. = \frac{kQq}{r}; \quad r = \frac{kQq}{P.E.}$$

$$r = \frac{(9 \times 10^9 \text{N} \cdot \text{m}^2/\text{C}^2)(-7 \times 10^{-6}\text{C})(-12 \times 10^{-9}\text{C})}{9 \times 10^{-5} \text{ J}}; \quad \boxed{r = 8.40 \text{ m}}$$

25-13. The potential energy of a system consisting of two identical charges is 4.50 mJ when their separation is 38 mm. What is the magnitude of each charge?

$$P.E. = \frac{kQq}{r} = \frac{kq^2}{r}; \quad q = \sqrt{\frac{r(P.E.)}{k}} = \sqrt{\frac{(0.038 \text{ m})(0.0045 \text{ J})}{(9 \times 10^9 \text{N} \cdot \text{m}^2/\text{C}^2)}}; \quad \boxed{q = 138 \text{ nC}}$$

Electric Potential and Potential Difference

25-14. What is the electric potential at a point that is 6 cm from a 8.40-μC charge? What is the potential energy of a 2 nC charge placed at that point?

$$V = \frac{kQ}{r} = \frac{(9 \times 10^9 \text{N} \cdot \text{m}^2/\text{C}^2)(8.40 \times 10^{-6}\text{C})}{0.06 \text{ m}}; \quad V = 1.26 \times 10^6 \text{ V}$$

$$\text{P.E.} = qV = (2 \times 10^{-9} \text{C})(1.26 \times 10^6 \text{ V}); \quad \boxed{\text{P.E.} = 2.52 \text{ mJ}}$$

350 Unit A   Solutions Manual

*25-18. (Cont.)

$$V_A = \frac{(9 \times 10^9 \text{N} \cdot \text{m}^2/\text{C}^2)(90 \times 10^{-6}\text{C})}{0.068 \text{ m}} ;$$

$$V_A = 1.19 \times 10^7 \text{ V}; \qquad V_B = 3.115 \times 10^7 \text{ V}$$

$$V_B - V_A = 3.115 \times 10^7 \text{ V} - 1.19 \times 10^7 \text{ V}; \quad \boxed{\Delta V = 1.92 \times 10^7 \text{ V}}$$

Note that the potential INCREASES because B is at a higher potential than A

Now for the field: $(Work)_{AB} = q(V_A - V_B) = (-5 \times 10^{-6} \text{ C})(1.19 \times 10^7 \text{ V} - 3.119 \times 10^7 \text{ V})$;

$\boxed{Work_{AB} = +96.2 \text{ mJ}}$;   The field does positive work on a negative charge.

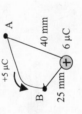

*25-19. Points A and B are 40 mm and 25 mm away from a +6-μC charge. How much work must be done against the electric field (by external forces) in moving a +5-μC charge from point A to point B?

$$V_A = \frac{(9 \times 10^9 \text{N} \cdot \text{m}^2/\text{C}^2)(6 \times 10^{-6}\text{C})}{0.040 \text{ m}} ; \quad V_A = 1.35 \times 10^6 \text{ V}$$

$$V_B = \frac{(9 \times 10^9 \text{N} \cdot \text{m}^2/\text{C}^2)(6 \times 10^{-6}\text{C})}{0.025 \text{ m}} ; \quad V_B = 2.16 \times 10^6 \text{ V}$$

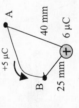

$(Work)_{AB} = q(V_A - V_B) = (+5 \times 10^{-6} \text{ C})(1.35 \times 10^6 \text{ V} - 2.16 \times 10^6 \text{ V})$; $\boxed{Work_{AB} = +4.05 \text{ J}}$

Note: The work BY the field is negative, because the motion is against the field forces.

*25-20. A +6 μC charge is located at x = 0 on the x-axis, and a -2-μC charge is located at x = 8 cm. How much work is done BY the electric field in moving a -3-μC charge from the point x = 10 cm to the point x = 3 cm?

$$V_A = \Sigma \frac{kQ}{r}; \qquad V_B = \Sigma \frac{kQ}{r}$$

$$V_A = \frac{(9 \times 10^9 \text{N} \cdot \text{m}^2/\text{C}^2)(6 \times 10^{-6}\text{C})}{0.10 \text{ m}} + \frac{(9 \times 10^9 \text{N} \cdot \text{m}^2/\text{C}^2)(-2 \times 10^{-6}\text{C})}{0.020 \text{ m}} ; \quad V_A = -360 \text{ kV}$$

---

*25-20. (Cont.) $V_A = -360$ V

$$V_B = \Sigma \frac{kQ}{r}$$

$$V_B = \frac{(9 \times 10^9 \text{N} \cdot \text{m}^2/\text{C}^2)(6 \times 10^{-6}\text{C})}{0.030 \text{ m}} + \frac{(9 \times 10^9 \text{N} \cdot \text{m}^2/\text{C}^2)(-2 \times 10^{-6}\text{C})}{0.050 \text{ m}} ; \quad V_B = 1440 \text{ kV}$$

$(Work)_{AB} = q(V_A - V_B) = (-3 \times 10^{-6} \text{ C})(-360 \text{ kV} - 1440 \text{ kV})$; $\boxed{Work_{AB} = +5.40 \text{ J}}$

Supplementary Problems

25-21. Point A is 40 mm above a -9-μC charge and point B is located 60 mm below the same charge. A -3-nC charge is moved from point B to point A. What is the change in potential energy?

$$(P.E.)_A = \frac{kQq}{r} = \frac{(9 \times 10^9 \text{N} \cdot \text{m}^2/\text{C}^2)(-9 \times 10^{-6}\text{C})(-3 \times 10^{-9}\text{C})}{0.040 \text{ m}}$$

$$(P.E.)_B = \frac{kQq}{r} = \frac{(9 \times 10^9 \text{N} \cdot \text{m}^2/\text{C}^2)(-9 \times 10^{-6}\text{C})(-3 \times 10^{-9}\text{C})}{0.060 \text{ m}}$$

$(P.E.)_A = 6.075 \times 10^{-3}$ J; $(P.E.)_B = 4.05 \times 10^{-3}$ J; $\Delta E_P = 6.075 \text{ mJ} - 4.05 \text{ mJ}$

$\boxed{\Delta E_P = 2.02 \text{ mJ}}$;   The potential energy increases.

25-22. Two parallel plates are separated by 50 mm in air. If the electric field intensity between the plates is 2 x 10⁴ N/C, what is the potential difference between the plates?

$$E = \frac{V}{d}; \quad V = Ed = (2 \times 10^4 \text{ N/C})(0.05 \text{ m})$$

$$\boxed{V = 1000 \text{ V}}$$

25-23. The potential difference between two parallel plates 60 mm apart is 4000 volts. What is the electric field intensity between the plates?

$$E = \frac{V}{d} = \frac{4000 \text{ V}}{0.060 \text{ m}} \; ; \quad \boxed{E = 66.7 \text{ kV/m}}$$

25-24. If an electron is located at the plate of lower potential in Problem 25-23, what will be its kinetic energy when it reaches the plate of higher potential. What is the energy expressed in electronvolts? (*Work done on electron equals its change in kinetic energy.*)

$$\tfrac{1}{2}mv^2 = qEd = (1.6 \times 10^{-19} \text{ J})(66{,}700 \text{ V/m})(0.060 \text{ m}) = 6.40 \times 10^{-16} \text{ J}$$

$$\tfrac{1}{2}(9.11 \times 10^{-31} \text{ kg})v^2 = 6.40 \times 10^{-16} \text{ J}; \quad \boxed{v = 3.75 \times 10^{7} \text{ m/s}}$$

25-25. Show that the potential gradient V/m is equivalent to the unit N/C for electric field.

$$1\frac{\text{V}}{\text{m}}\left(\frac{1\,\text{J/C}}{1\,\text{V}}\right)\left(\frac{1\,\text{N m}}{1\,\text{J}}\right) = 1\frac{\text{N}}{\text{C}}$$

25-26. What is the difference in potential between two points 30 and 60 cm away from a −50-μC charge? $\Delta E_p = V_A - V_B$

$$V_{AB} = \frac{(9 \times 10^9 \,\text{N}\cdot\text{m}^2/\text{C}^2)(-50 \times 10^{-6})}{0.030 \text{ m}} - \frac{(9 \times 10^9 \,\text{N}\cdot\text{m}^2/\text{C}^2)(-50 \times 10^{-6})}{0.060 \text{ m}}$$

$$V_{AB} = -1.50 \times 10^7 \text{ V} - (-7.50 \times 10^6 \text{ J}); \quad \boxed{\Delta V_{AB} = -7.50 \times 10^6 \text{ J}}$$

25-27. The potential gradient between two parallel plates 4 mm apart is 6000 V/m. What is the potential difference between the plates?

$$V = Ed = (6000 \text{ V/m})(0.004 \text{ m}); \quad \boxed{V = 24.0 \text{ V}}$$

25-28. The electric field between two plates separated by 50 mm is 6 x 10⁵ V/m. What is the potential difference between the plates?

$$V = Ed = (600{,}000 \text{ V/m})(0.005 \text{ m}); \quad \boxed{V = 3 \text{ kV}}$$

25-29. What must be the separation of two parallel plates if the field intensity is 5 x 10⁴ V/m and the potential difference is 400 V?

$$V = Ed; \quad d = \frac{V}{E} = \frac{400 \text{ V}}{50{,}000 \text{ V/m}}; \quad \boxed{d = 8.00 \text{ mm}}$$

25-30. The potential difference between two parallel plates is 600 V. A 6-μC charge is accelerated through the entire potential difference. What is the kinetic energy given to the charge?

$$\Delta E_k = Work = qV; \quad \Delta E_k = (6 \times 10^{-6} \text{ C})(600 \text{ V}); \quad \boxed{\Delta E_k = 3.60 \text{ mJ}}$$

25-31. Determine the kinetic energy of an alpha particle (+2e) that is accelerated through a potential difference of 800 kV. Give the answer in both electronvolts and joules.

$$\Delta E_k = Work = qV; \quad \Delta E_k = (2e)(8 \times 10^5 \text{ V}); \quad \boxed{\Delta E_p = 1.60 \text{ MeV}}$$

$$\Delta E_k = Work = qV; \quad \Delta E_k = 2(1.6 \times 10^{-19} \text{ C})(8 \times 10^5 \text{ V}); \quad \boxed{\Delta E_p = 2.56 \times 10^{-13} \text{ J}}$$

25-32. A linear accelerator accelerates an electron through a potential difference of 4 MV. What is the energy of an emergent electron in electronvolts and in joules?

$$\Delta E_k = qV = (1 \text{ e})(4 \times 10^6 \text{ V}); \quad \boxed{\Delta E_k = 4.00 \text{ MeV}}$$

$$\Delta E_k = qV = (1.6 \times 10^{-19} \text{ J})(4 \times 10^6 \text{ V}); \quad \boxed{\Delta E_k = 6.40 \times 10^{-13} \text{ J}}$$

25-33. An electron acquires an energy of 2.8 x 10⁻¹⁵ J as it passes from point A to point B. What is the potential difference between these points in volts?

$$\Delta E_k = qV; \quad (1.6 \times 10^{-19} \text{ C})V = 2.8 \times 10^{-15} \text{ J}; \quad \boxed{V = 17.5 \text{ kV}}$$

*25-34. Show that the total potential energy of the three charges placed at the corners of the equilateral triangle shown in Fig. 25-11 is given by:

$$\frac{-kq^2}{d}$$

First find the work required to bring the two +q's together.

Then add the extra work to bring the −2q charge to each q:

$$P.E. = \sum \frac{kQq}{r} = \frac{kqq}{d} + \frac{k(-2q)q}{d} + \frac{k(-2q)q}{d} \; ; \quad P.E. = \frac{kq^2}{d} - \frac{2kq^2}{d} - \frac{2kq^2}{d} = \frac{-3kq^2}{d}$$

$$\boxed{P.E. = \frac{-3q^2}{d}}$$

*25-35. Assume that q = 1 μC and d = 20 mm. What is the potential energy of the system of charges in Fig. 25-11.

$$P.E. = \frac{-3q^2}{d} = \frac{-3(1 \times 10^{-6}C)^2}{0.020 \text{ m}} \; ; \quad \boxed{P.E. = 1.50 \times 10^{-10} \text{ J}}$$

*25-36. The potential at a certain distance from a point charge is 1200 V and the electric field intensity at that point is 400 N/C. What is the distance to the charge, and what is the magnitude of the charge?

$$V = \frac{kQ}{r} = 1200 \text{ V}; \quad r = \frac{kQ}{1200 \text{ V}}; \quad E = \frac{kQ}{r^2} = 400 \text{N/C}$$

$$E = \frac{kQ}{(k^2Q^2/(1200 \text{ V})^2)} = \frac{(1200 \text{ V})^2}{kQ}; \quad \frac{1.44 \times 10^6 V^2}{(9 \times 10^9 N \cdot m^2/C^2)Q} = 400 \text{ N/C}$$

$$Q = \frac{1.44 \times 10^6 N/C}{(9 \times 10^9 N \cdot m^2/C^2)(400 N/C)}; \quad \boxed{Q = 400 \text{ nC}}$$

$$r = \frac{kQ}{1200 \text{ V}} = \frac{(9 \times 10^9 N \cdot m^2/C^2)(4.00 \times 10^{-9}C)}{1200 \text{ V}}; \quad \boxed{r = 3.00 \text{ m}}$$

356 Unit A Solutions Manual

---

*25-37. Two large plates are 80 mm apart and have a potential difference of 800 kV. What is the magnitude of the force that would act on an electron placed at the midpoint between these plates? What would be the kinetic energy of the electron moving from low potential plate to the high potential plate?

$$F = qE = \frac{qV}{d} = \frac{(1.6 \times 10^{-19} J)(8 \times 10^5 V)}{0.080 \text{ m}}; \quad \boxed{F = 1.6 \times 10^{-12} \text{ N}}$$

$$Work = qV = \tfrac{1}{2}mv^2; \quad E_k = (1.6 \times 10^{-19} C)(8 \times 10^5 V)$$

$$\boxed{\Delta E_k = 1.28 \times 10^{-13} \text{ J}}$$

Critical Thinking Problems

25-38. Plate A has a potential that is 600 V higher than Plate B which is 50 mm below A. A +2-μC charge moves from plate A to plate B? What is the electric field intensity between the plates? What are the sign and magnitude of the work done by the electric field? Does the potential energy increase or decrease? Now answer the same questions if a −2-μC charge is moved from A to B?

First find the field E between the plates:

$$E = \frac{V}{d} = \frac{600 \text{ V}}{0.050 \text{ m}}; \quad \boxed{E = 12,000 \text{ V/m, } downward.}$$

When a positive charge moves with the field, the work is positive, since F and d are same.

When a negative charge moves with E, the work is negative, since F and d are opposite

(a) $Work = q \, \Delta V = (2 \times 10^{-6} C)(600 \text{ V} - 0 \text{ V})$; $\boxed{Work = 1.20 \text{ mJ, } positive \ work}$

The field does work, so the +2-μC charge loses energy; $\boxed{P.E. \ decreases}$

(b) $Work = q \, \Delta V = (-2 \times 10^{-6} C)(600 \text{ V} - 0 \text{ V})$; $\boxed{Work = -1.20 \text{ mJ, } negative \ work}$

The field does negative work, so the −2-μC charge gains energy; $\boxed{P.E. \ increases}$

Chapter 25 Electric Potential **357**

179

25-39. Point A is a distance $x = +a$ to the right of a +4-μC charge. The rightward electric field at point A is 4000 N/C. What is the distance a? What is the potential at point A? What are the electric field and the potential at the point $x = -a$. Find the electric force and the electric potential energy when a -2-nC charge is placed at each point?

$$E_A = \frac{kq}{a^2}; \quad a^2 = \frac{kq}{E_A} = \frac{(9\times10^9 N\cdot m^2/C^2)(4\times10^{-6}C)}{4000 N/C}$$

$$a = \sqrt{9.00\ m^2} \quad \boxed{a = 3.0\ m}$$

$$V_A = \frac{kQ}{a} = \frac{(9\times10^9 N\cdot m^2/C^2)(4\times10^{-6}C)}{3.00\ m}; \quad \boxed{V_A = 12.0\ kV}$$

$$E_B = \frac{kq}{a^2} = \frac{(9\times10^9 N\cdot m^2/C^2)(4\times10^{-6}C)}{(3.00\ m)^2}; \quad \boxed{E_B = 4000\ N,\ to\ the\ left}$$

$$V_B = \frac{kQ}{a} = \frac{(9\times10^9 N\cdot m^2/C^2)(4\times10^{-6}C)}{3.00\ m}; \quad \boxed{V_A = 12.0\ kV}$$

$$F_A = qE_A = (-2\times10^{-9}C)(+4000\ N/C); \quad \boxed{F_A = -8\times10^{-6}\ N,\ leftward}$$

$$(P.E.)_A = qV_A = (-2\times10^{-9}C)(12{,}000\ V); \quad \boxed{(P.E.)_A = 8.00\times10^{-6}\ J}$$

$$F_B = qE_B = (-2\times10^{-9}C)(-4000\ N/C); \quad \boxed{F_A = +8\times10^{-6}\ N,\ rightward}$$

$$(P.E.)_B = qV_B = (-2\times10^{-9}C)(12{,}000\ V); \quad \boxed{(P.E.)_A = 8.00\times10^{-6}\ J}$$

---

*25-40. Points A, B, and C are at the corners of an equilateral triangle that is 100 mm on each side. At the base of the triangle, a +8-μC charge is 100 mm to the left of a -8-μC charge.

What is the potential at the apex C? What is the potential

at a point D that is 20 mm to the left of the -8-μC charge?

How much work is done by the electric field in moving a

+2-μC charge from point C to point D?

$$V_C = \frac{(9\times10^9 N\cdot m^2/C^2)(8\times10^{-6}C)}{0.10\ m} + \frac{(9\times10^9 N\cdot m^2/C^2)(-8\times10^{-6}C)}{0.10\ m}; \quad \boxed{V_C = 0}$$

$$V_D = \frac{(9\times10^9 N\cdot m^2/C^2)(8\times10^{-6}C)}{0.08\ m} + \frac{(9\times10^9 N\cdot m^2/C^2)(-8\times10^{-6}C)}{0.02\ m}; \quad \boxed{V_D = -2.70\ MV}$$

$$(Work)_{CD} = qV_{CD} = (+2\times10^{-6}C)[0 - (-2.70\times10^6\ V)] \quad \boxed{(Work)_{CD} = 5.40\ J}$$

*25-41. Two charges of +12 and -6-μC are separated by 160 mm. What is the potential at the

midpoint A of a line joining the two charges? At what point B is the electric potential equal

to zero?

$$V_A = \frac{(9\times10^9 N\cdot m^2/C^2)(12\times10^{-6}C)}{0.08\ m} + \frac{(9\times10^9 N\cdot m^2/C^2)(-6\times10^{-6}C)}{0.08\ m}; \quad \boxed{V_A = 675\ kV}$$

$$V_B = \frac{(9\times10^9 N\cdot m^2/C^2)(12\times10^{-6}C)}{x} + \frac{(9\times10^9 N\cdot m^2/C^2)(-6\times10^{-6}C)}{16\ cm - x} = 0$$

$$\frac{12\times10^{-6}C}{x} = \frac{6\times10^{-6}C}{(16\ cm - x)}$$

$$2(16\ cm - x) = x;$$

$$\boxed{x = 10.7\ cm\ from\ the\ +12\text{-}μC\ charge}$$

*25-42. For the charges and distances shown in Fig. 25-12, find the potential at points A, B, and C? How much work is done BY the electric field in moving a +2-μC charge from C to A?

How much work is done in moving a −2-μC charge from B to A?

$V_A = \frac{(9 \times 10^9 \text{N} \cdot \text{m}^2/\text{C}^2)(-6 \times 10^{-9}\text{C})}{0.03 \text{ m}} + \frac{(9 \times 10^9 \text{N} \cdot \text{m}^2/\text{C}^2)(+4 \times 10^{-9}\text{C})}{0.03 \text{ m}}$; $\boxed{V_A = -600 \text{ V}}$

$V_B = \frac{(9 \times 10^9 \text{N} \cdot \text{m}^2/\text{C}^2)(-6 \times 10^{-9}\text{C})}{0.09 \text{ m}} + \frac{(9 \times 10^9 \text{N} \cdot \text{m}^2/\text{C}^2)(+4 \times 10^{-9}\text{C})}{0.03 \text{ m}}$; $\boxed{V_B = +600 \text{ V}}$

$V_B = \frac{(9 \times 10^9 \text{N} \cdot \text{m}^2/\text{C}^2)(-6 \times 10^{-9}\text{C})}{0.06 \text{ m}} + \frac{(9 \times 10^9 \text{N} \cdot \text{m}^2/\text{C}^2)(+4 \times 10^{-9}\text{C})}{0.06 \text{ m}}$; $\boxed{V_C = -300 \text{ V}}$

$(Work)_{CA} = q(V_A - V_C) = (2 \times 10^{-6} \text{ C})[-300 \text{ V} - (-600 \text{ V})]$

$\boxed{Work = +6 \times 10^{-4} \text{ J}}$

$(Work)_{CA} = (-2 \times 10^{-6} \text{ C})[600 \text{ V} - (-600 \text{ V})]$

$\boxed{Work = -2.4 \times 10^{-3} \text{ J}}$

(Figure: C connected to −6 nC and +4 nC; 6 cm, 6 cm sides; 3 cm, 3 cm, A, 3 cm, 3 cm, B)

**25-43. The horizontal plates in Millikan's oil-drop experiment are 20 mm apart. The diameter of a particular drop of oil is 4 μm, and the density of oil is 900 kg/m³. Assuming that two electrons attach themselves to the droplet, what potential difference must exist between the plates to establish equilibrium? [Volume of a sphere = 4πR³/3]

$Vol. = \frac{4\pi(0.02 \text{ m})^3}{3} = 33.5 \times 10^{-18} \text{m}^3$; $\rho = \frac{m}{V}$; $m = \rho V$

$m = (900 \text{ kg/m}^3)(33.5 \times 10^{-18} \text{ m}^3) = 3.016 \times 10^{-14}$ kg;

$qE = mg$; $q\left(\frac{V}{d}\right) = mg$; $V = \frac{mgd}{q}$

$V = \frac{(3.016 \times 10^{-14} \text{kg})(9.8 \text{ m/s}^2)(0.02 \text{ m})}{2(1.6 \times 10^{-19}\text{C})}$; $\boxed{V = 18.5 \text{ kV}}$

Chapter 26. Capacitance

Capacitance

26-1. What is the maximum charge that can be placed on a metal sphere 30 mm in diameter and surrounded by air?

$E = \frac{kQ}{r^2} = 3 \times 10^6$ N/C; $Q = \frac{Er^2}{k} = \frac{(3 \times 10^6 \text{N/C})(0.015 \text{ m})^2}{(9 \times 10^9 \text{N} \cdot \text{m}^2/\text{C}^2)}$; $\boxed{Q = 75.0 \text{ nC}}$

26-2. How much charge can be placed on a metal sphere of radius 40 mm if it is immersed in transformer oil whose dielectric strength is 16 MV/m?

$E = \frac{kQ}{r^2} = 16 \times 10^6$ N/C; $Q = \frac{Er^2}{k} = \frac{(16 \times 10^6 \text{N/C})(0.040 \text{ m})^2}{(9 \times 10^9 \text{N} \cdot \text{m}^2/\text{C}^2)}$; $\boxed{Q = 2.48 \text{ μC}}$

26-3. What would be the radius of a metal sphere in air such that it could theoretically hold a charge of one coulomb?

$E = \frac{kQ}{r^2}$; $r = \sqrt{\frac{(9 \times 10^9 \text{N} \cdot \text{m}^2/\text{C}^2)(1 \text{ C})}{3 \times 10^6 \text{ N/C}}}$; $\boxed{r = 54.8 \text{ m}}$

26-4. A 28-μF parallel-plate capacitor is connected to a 120-V source of potential difference. How much charge will be stored on this capacitor?

$Q = CV = (28 \text{ μF})(120 \text{ V})$; $\boxed{Q = 3.36 \text{ mC}}$

26-5. A potential difference of 110 V is applied across the plates of a parallel-plate capacitor. If the total charge on each plate is 1200 μC, what is the capacitance?

$C = \frac{Q}{V} = \frac{1200 \text{ μC}}{110 \text{ V}}$; $\boxed{C = 10.9 \text{ μF}}$

26-6. Find the capacitance of a parallel-plate capacitor if 1600 µC of charge is on each plate when the potential difference is 80 V.

$$C = \frac{Q}{V} = \frac{1600\ \mu C}{80\ V}; \qquad \boxed{C = 20.0\ \mu F}$$

26-7. What potential difference is required to store a charge of 800 µC on a 40-µF capacitor?

$$V = \frac{Q}{C} = \frac{800\ \mu C}{40\ \mu F}; \qquad \boxed{V = 20.0\ V}$$

26-8. Write an equation for the potential at the surface of a sphere of radius r in terms of the permittivity of the surrounding medium. Show that the capacitance of such a sphere is given by $C = 4\pi\varepsilon_0 r$.

$$V = \frac{kQ}{r} = \frac{Q}{4\pi\varepsilon_0 r}; \quad Q = CV; \quad \cancel{V} = \frac{C\cancel{V}}{4\pi\varepsilon_0 r}; \qquad \boxed{C = 4\pi\varepsilon_0 r}$$

*26-9. A spherical capacitor has a radius of 50 mm and is surrounded by a medium whose permittivity is 3 x 10⁻¹¹ C²/N m². How much charge can be transferred to this sphere by a potential difference of 400 V?

We must replace ε_o *with* ε *for permittivity of surrounding medium, then*

$$V = \frac{kQ}{r} = \frac{Q}{4\pi\varepsilon r}; \quad Q = CV; \quad \cancel{V} = \frac{C\cancel{V}}{4\pi\varepsilon r}; \qquad \boxed{C = 4\pi\varepsilon r}$$

$$C = 4\pi\varepsilon r; \quad Q = \frac{C}{V} = \frac{4\pi\varepsilon r}{V}$$

$$Q = \frac{4\pi(3 \times 10^{-11}\ C^2/N \cdot m^2)(0.05\ m)}{400\ V}; \qquad \boxed{Q = 4.71 \times 10^{-14}\ C}$$

Calculating Capacitance

26-10. A 5-µF capacitor has a plate separation of 0.3 mm of air. What will be the charge on each plate for a potential difference of 400 V? What is the area of each plate?

$$Q = CV = (5\ \mu F)(400\ V); \qquad \boxed{Q = 2000\ \mu C}$$

26-11. The plates of a certain capacitor are 3 mm apart and have an area of 0.04 m². What is the capacitance if air is the dielectric?

$$C = \varepsilon_0 \frac{E}{A} = \frac{(8.85 \times 10^{-12}\ C^2/N \cdot m^2)(0.04\ m^2)}{0.003\ m}; \qquad \boxed{C = 118\ pF}$$

26-12. A capacitor has plates of area 0.034 m² and a separation of 2 mm in air. The potential difference between the plates is 200 V. What is the capacitance, and what is the electric field intensity between the plates? How much charge is on each plate?

$$C = \varepsilon_0 \frac{E}{A} = \frac{(8.85 \times 10^{-12}\ C^2/N \cdot m^2)(0.034\ m^2)}{0.002\ m}; \qquad \boxed{C = 150\ pF}$$

$$E = \frac{V}{d} = \frac{400\ V}{0.002\ m}; \qquad \boxed{E = 2.00 \times 10^5\ N/C}$$

$$Q = CV = (150\ pF)(400\ V); \qquad \boxed{Q = 30.1\ \mu C}$$

26-13. A capacitor of plate area 0.06 m² and plate separation 4 mm has a potential difference of 300 V when air is the dielectric. What is the capacitance for dielectrics of air (K = 1) and mica (K = 5)?

$$C = K\varepsilon_0 \frac{E}{A} = \frac{(1)(8.85 \times 10^{-12}\ C^2/N \cdot m^2)(0.06\ m^2)}{0.004\ m}; \qquad \boxed{C = 133\ pF}$$

$$C = K\varepsilon_0 \frac{E}{A} = \frac{(5)(8.85 \times 10^{-12}\ C^2/N \cdot m^2)(0.06\ m^2)}{0.004\ m}; \qquad \boxed{C = 664\ pF}$$

26-14. What is the electric field intensity for mica and for air in Problem 26-13?

$$E_0 = \frac{V_0}{d}; \quad E_0 = \frac{V_0}{d} = \frac{300 \text{ V}}{0.004 \text{ m}}; \quad \boxed{E_0 = 7.50 \times 10^4 \text{ V/m}}$$

$$K = \frac{E_0}{E}; \quad E = \frac{E_0}{K} = \frac{7.50 \times 10^4}{5}; \quad \boxed{E = 1.50 \times 10^4 \text{ V/m}}$$

26-15. Find the capacitance of a parallel-plate capacitor if the area of each plate is 0.08 m², and the dielectric is (a) air, (b) paraffined paper (K = 2)? separation of the plates is 4 mm, and the dielectric is (a) air, (b) paraffined paper (K = 2)?

$$C = K\varepsilon_0 \frac{E}{A} = \frac{(1)(8.85 \times 10^{-12}\text{C}^2/\text{N}\cdot\text{m}^2)(0.08 \text{ m}^2)}{0.004 \text{ m}}; \quad \boxed{C = 177 \text{ pF}}$$

$$C = K\varepsilon_0 \frac{E}{A} = \frac{(2)(8.85 \times 10^{-12}\text{C}^2/\text{N}\cdot\text{m}^2)(0.08 \text{ m}^2)}{0.004 \text{ m}}; \quad \boxed{C = 354 \text{ pF}}$$

26-16. Two parallel plates of a capacitor are 4.0 mm apart and the plate area is 0.03 m². Glass (K = 7.5) is the dielectric, and the plate voltage is 800 V. What is the charge on each plate, and what is the electric field intensity between the plates?

$$C = K\varepsilon_0 \frac{E}{A} = \frac{(7.5)(8.85 \times 10^{-12}\text{C}^2/\text{N}\cdot\text{m}^2)(0.03 \text{ m}^2)}{0.004 \text{ m}}; \quad \boxed{C = 498 \text{ pF}}$$

$$Q = CV = (498 \times 10^{-12} \text{ F})(800 \text{ V}); \quad \boxed{Q = 398 \text{ nC}}$$

*26-17. A parallel-plate capacitor with a capacitance of 2.0 nF is to be constructed with mica (K = 5) as the dielectric, and it must be able to withstand a maximum potential difference of 3000 V. The dielectric strength of mica is 200 MV/m. What is the minimum area the plates of the capacitor can have?

$$Q = CV = (2 \times 10^{-9}\text{F})(3000 \text{ V}); \quad Q = 6 \ \mu\text{C}; \quad d = \frac{V}{E} = \frac{3000 \text{ V}}{200 \times 10^6 \text{V/m}}$$

*26-17. (Cont.) d = 1.50 x 10⁻⁵ m; C = 2 nF; K = 5

$$C = K\varepsilon_0 \frac{A}{d}; \quad A = \frac{Cd}{K\varepsilon_0} = \frac{(2 \times 10^{-9}\text{F})(1.5 \times 10^{-5}\text{m})}{5(8.85 \times 10^{-12}\text{C}^2/\text{N}\cdot\text{m}^2)}; \quad \boxed{A = 6.78 \times 10^{-4} \text{ m}^2}$$

Capacitors in Series and in Parallel

26-18. Find the equivalent capacitance of a 6-μF capacitor and a 12-μF capacitor connected (a) in series, (b) in parallel.

Capacitors in series: $C_e = \dfrac{C_1 C_2}{C_1 + C_2} = \dfrac{(6 \ \mu\text{F})(12 \ \mu\text{F})}{6 \ \mu\text{F} + 12 \ \mu\text{F}}$; $\boxed{C_e = 4.00 \ \mu\text{F}}$

Capacitors in parallel: $C_e = C_1 + C_2 = 6 \ \mu\text{F} + 12 \ \mu\text{F}$; $\boxed{C_e = 18 \ \mu\text{F}}$

26-19. Find the effective capacitance of a 6-μF capacitor and a 15-μF capacitor connected (a) in series, (b) in parallel?

Capacitors in series: $C_e = \dfrac{C_1 C_2}{C_1 + C_2} = \dfrac{(6 \ \mu\text{F})(15 \ \mu\text{F})}{6 \ \mu\text{F} + 15 \ \mu\text{F}}$; $\boxed{C_e = 4.29 \ \mu\text{F}}$

Capacitors in parallel: $C_e = C_1 + C_2 = 6 \ \mu\text{F} + 12 \ \mu\text{F}$; $\boxed{C_e = 21.0 \ \mu\text{F}}$

26-20. What is the equivalent capacitance for capacitors of 4, 7, and 12 μF connected (a) in series, (b) in parallel?

Series: $\dfrac{1}{C_e} = \dfrac{1}{C_1} + \dfrac{1}{C_2} + \dfrac{1}{C_3} = \dfrac{1}{4 \ \mu\text{F}} + \dfrac{1}{7 \ \mu\text{F}} + \dfrac{1}{12 \ \mu\text{F}}$; $\boxed{C_e = 2.10 \ \mu\text{F}}$

Parallel: $C_e = \Sigma C_i = 4 \ \mu\text{F} + 7 \ \mu\text{C} + 12 \ \mu\text{C}$; $\boxed{C_e = 23.0 \ \mu\text{C}}$

*26-24. Find the equivalent capacitance of a circuit in which a 6-μF capacitor is connected in series with two parallel capacitors whose capacitances are 5 and 4 μF.

$C' = 5\ \mu F + 4\ \mu F = 9\ \mu F$;

$C_e = \dfrac{C'C_{40}}{C'+C_{40}} = \dfrac{(9\,\mu F)(6\,\mu F)}{9\,\mu F + 6\,\mu F}$; $\boxed{C_e = 3.60\ \mu F}$

*26-25. What is the equivalent capacitance for the circuit drawn in Fig. 26-15?

$C' = \dfrac{C_6 C_3}{C_6 + C_3} = \dfrac{(6\,\mu F)(3\,\mu F)}{6\,\mu F + 3\,\mu F}$; $C' = 2.40\ \mu F$;

$C_e = 2\ \mu F + 4\ \mu F$; $\boxed{C_e = 6.00\ \mu F}$

*26-26. What is the charge on the 4-μF capacitor in Fig. 26-15? What is the voltage across the 6-μF capacitor?

Total charge $Q_T = C_eV = (6.00\ \mu F)(200\ V)$; $Q_T = 1200\ \mu C$

$Q_4 = C_4V_4 = (4\ \mu C)(200\ V)$; $Q_4 = 800\ \mu C$

The rest of the charge is across EACH of other capacitors:

$Q_3 = Q_6 = 1200\ \mu C - 800\ \mu C$; $Q_6 = 400\ \mu C$

$V_6 = \dfrac{Q_6}{C_6} = \dfrac{400\ \mu C}{6\ \mu F}$; $\boxed{V_6 = 66.7\ V}$

You should show that $V_3 = 133.3$ V, so that $V_3 + V_6 = 200$ V.

26-21. Find the equivalent capacitance for capacitors of 2, 6, and 8 μF connected (a) in series, (b) in parallel?

Series: $\dfrac{1}{C_e} = \dfrac{1}{C_1} + \dfrac{1}{C_2} + \dfrac{1}{C_3} = \dfrac{1}{2\ \mu F} + \dfrac{1}{6\ \mu F} + \dfrac{1}{8\ \mu F}$; $\boxed{C_e = 1.26\ \mu F}$

Parallel: $C_e = \Sigma C_i = 2\ \mu F + 6\ \mu C + 8\ \mu C$; $\boxed{C_e = 16.0\ \mu C}$

26-22. A 20-μF and a 60-μF capacitor are connected in parallel. Then the pair are connected in series with a 40-μF capacitor. What is the equivalent capacitance?

$C' = 20\ \mu F + 60\ \mu F = 80\ \mu F$;

$C_e = \dfrac{C'C_{40}}{C'+C_{40}} = \dfrac{(80\,\mu F)(40\,\mu F)}{(80\,\mu F + 40\,\mu F)}$; $\boxed{C_e = 26.7\ \mu F}$

*26-23. If a potential difference of 80 V is placed across the group of capacitors in Problem 26-22, what is the charge on the 40-μF capacitor? What is the charge on the 20-μF capacitor? (*First find total charge, then find charge and voltage on each capacitor.*)

$Q_T = C_eV = (26.7\ \mu F)(80\ V)$; $Q_T = 2133\ \mu C$; $\boxed{Q_{40} = 2133\ \mu C}$

Note: 2133 μC are on each of the combination C' and the 40-μF capacitor. To find the charge across the 20 μF, we need to know the voltage across C':

$V_C = \dfrac{2133\ \mu C}{80\ \mu F} = 26.7\ V$;   *This is V across each of 20 and 60-μF capacitors*

Thus, charge on 20-μF capacitor is: $Q_{20} = (20\ \mu F)(26.7\ V)$; $\boxed{Q_{20} = 533\ \mu C}$

Note that $V_{40} = 2133\ \mu C/26.7\ \mu C$ *or 53.3 V. Also 53.3 V + 26.7 V = 80 V !*

Also, the charge on the 60-μC capacitor is 1600 μC and 1600 μC + 533 μC = Q_T

*26-27. A 6-μF and a 3-μF capacitor are connected in series with a 24-V battery. If they are connected in series, what are the charge and voltage across each capacitor?

$$C = \frac{C_6 C_3}{C_6 + C_3} = \frac{(6\,\mu F)(3\,\mu F)}{6\,\mu F + 3\,\mu F}; \quad C_e = 2.00\ \mu F$$

$$Q_T = C_e V = (2\,\mu F)(24\ V) = 48\ \mu F; \quad Q_3 = Q_6 = Q_T = 48\ \mu C$$

$$V_3 = \frac{Q_3}{C_3} = \frac{48\ \mu C}{3\ \mu F}; \quad \boxed{V_3 = 16.0\ V, \quad Q_3 = 48.0\ \mu C}$$

$$V_6 = \frac{Q_6}{C_6} = \frac{48\ \mu C}{6\ \mu F}; \quad \boxed{V_3 = 8.00\ V, \quad Q_3 = 48.0\ \mu C}$$

*26-28. If the 6 and 3-μF capacitors of Problem 26-27 are reconnected in parallel with a 24-V battery, what are the charge and voltage across each capacitor?

$$C_e = 3\ \mu F + 6\ \mu F; \quad C_e = 9\ \mu F$$

$$Q_T = (9\ \mu F)(24\ V) = 216\ \mu C; \quad \boxed{V_3 = V_6 = 24\ V}$$

$$Q_3 = (3\ \mu F)(24\ V); \quad \boxed{Q_3 = 72\ \mu C; \quad Q_6 = 144\ \mu C}$$

*26-29. Compute the equivalent capacitance for the entire circuit shown in Fig. 26-16. What is the total charge on the equivalent capacitance?

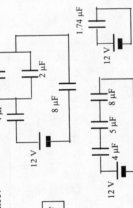

$$C_{2,3} = 2\ \mu F + 3\ \mu F = 5\ \mu F$$

$$\frac{1}{C_e} = \frac{1}{4\ \mu F} + \frac{1}{5\ \mu F} + \frac{1}{8\ \mu F}; \quad \boxed{C_e = 1.74\ \mu F}$$

$$\boxed{Q_T = C_e V = 20.9\ \mu C}$$

Also: $Q_4 = Q_5 = Q_8 = 20.9\ \mu C$

*26-30. What are the charge and voltage across each capacitor of Fig. 26-16? (See Prob. 26-29.)

$$Q_4 = Q_5 = Q_8 = 20.9\ \mu C; \quad V_4 = \frac{Q_4}{C_4} = \frac{20.9\ \mu C}{4\ \mu F} = 5.22\ V; \quad V_8 = \frac{Q_8}{C_8} = \frac{20.9\ \mu C}{8\ \mu F} = 2.61\ V$$

$$V_5 = V_3 = V_2 = \frac{Q_5}{C_5} = \frac{20.9\ \mu C}{5\ \mu F} = 4.17\ V; \quad Q_3 = C_3 V_3 = (3\ \mu F)(4.17\ V) = 12.5\ \mu C$$

$$Q_2 = (2\ \mu F)(4.17\ V) = 8.35\ \mu C; \quad \textit{Note that } Q_2 + Q_3 = Q_5 = Q_T = 20.9\ \mu C$$

Answer summary: $\boxed{Q_2 = 8.35\ \mu C; \quad Q_3 = 12.5\ C; \quad Q_4 = Q_8 = 20.9\ C}$

$$\boxed{V_2 = V_3 = 4.17\ V; \quad V_4 = 5.22\ V; \quad V_8 = 2.61\ V}$$

The Energy of a Charged Capacitor

26-31. What is the potential energy stored in the electric field of a 200-μF capacitor when it is charged to a voltage of 2400 V?

$$P.E. = \tfrac{1}{2} C V^2 = \tfrac{1}{2}(200 \times 10^{-6}\ F)(2400\ V)^2; \quad P.E. = 576\ J$$

26-32. What is the energy stored on a 25-μF capacitor when the charge on each plate is 2400 μF? What is the voltage across the capacitor?

$$P.E. = \frac{Q^2}{2C} = \frac{(2400 \times 10^{-6}\ C)^2}{2(25 \times 10^{-6}\ F)}; \quad \boxed{P.E. = 115\ mJ}$$

$$V = \frac{Q}{C} = \frac{2400\ \mu C}{25\ \mu F}; \quad \boxed{V = 96.0\ V}$$

26-33. How much work is required to charge a capacitor to a potential difference of 30 kV if 800 μC are on each plate?

$$Work = P.E. = \tfrac{1}{2} QV; \quad Work = \tfrac{1}{2}(800 \times 10^{-6}\ C)(30 \times 10^3\ V)$$

$$\boxed{Work = 12.0\ J}$$

*26-34. A parallel plate capacitor has a plate area of 4 cm² and a separation of 2 mm. A dielectric of constant K = 4.3 is placed between the plates, and the capacitor is connected to a 100-V battery. How much energy is stored in the capacitor?

$$C = K\varepsilon_0 \frac{A}{d} = \frac{(4.3)(8.85 \times 10^{-12} C^2/N \cdot m^2)(4 \times 10^{-4} m^2)}{0.002\ m}; \quad C = 7.61\ pF$$

$$P.E. = \tfrac{1}{2}CV^2 = \tfrac{1}{2}(7.61 \times 10^{-12}\ F)(100\ V)^2; \quad \boxed{P.E. = 3.81 \times 10^{-8}\ J}$$

Supplementary Problems

26-35. What is the break-down voltage for a capacitor with a dielectric of glass (K = 7.5) if the plate separation is 4 mm? The average dielectric strength is 118 MV/m.

$$V = E_m d = (118 \times 10^6\ V)(0.004\ m); \quad \boxed{V = 472\ kV}$$

26-36. A capacitor has a potential difference of 240 V, a plate area of 5 cm² and a plate separation of 3 mm. What is the capacitance and the electric field between the plates? What is the charge on each plate?

$$C = \varepsilon_0 \frac{A}{d} = \frac{(8.85 \times 10^{-12} C^2/N \cdot m^2)(5 \times 10^{-4} m^2)}{0.003\ m}; \quad \boxed{C = 1.48\ pF}$$

$$E = \frac{240\ V}{0.003\ m}; \quad \boxed{E = 8.00 \times 10^4\ V/m}; \quad Q = (1.48 \times 10^{-12}\ F)(240\ V); \quad \boxed{Q = 0.355\ nC}$$

26-37. Suppose the capacitor of Problem 26-36 is disconnected from the 240-V battery and then mica (K = 5) is inserted between the plates? What are the new voltage and electric field? If the 240-battery is reconnected, what charge will be on the plates?

$$K = \frac{V_0}{V} = \frac{E_0}{E}; \quad V = \frac{240\ V}{5}; \quad \boxed{V = 48.0\ V}; \quad E = -E = \frac{80{,}000\ V/m}{5} = \boxed{1.60 \times 10^4\ V/m}$$

$$C = KC_0 = 5(1.48\ pF) = 7.40\ pF; \quad Q = CV = (7.40\ pF)(240\ V); \quad \boxed{Q = 1.78\ nC}$$

26-38. A 6-μF capacitor is charged with a 24-V battery and then disconnected. When a dielectric is inserted, the voltage drops to 6 V. What is the total charge on the capacitor after the battery has been reconnected?

$$K = \frac{V_o}{V} = \frac{24\ V}{6\ V} = 4; \quad C = KC_o = 4(6\ \mu F) = 24\ \mu F;$$

$$Q = CV = (24\ \mu F)(24\ V); \quad \boxed{Q = 576\ \mu C}$$

26-39. A capacitor is formed from 30 parallel plates 20 x 20 cm. If each plate is separated by 2 mm of dry air, what is the total capacitance?

Thirty stacked plates means that there are 29 spaces, which make for 29 capacitors:

$$C = 29\varepsilon_0 \frac{A}{d} = \frac{(29)(8.85 \times 10^{-12} C^2/N \cdot m^2)(0.2\ m)^2}{0.002\ m}; \quad \boxed{C = 5.13\ nF}$$

*26-40. Four capacitors A, B, C, and D have capacitances of 12, 16, 20, and 26 μF, respectively. Capacitors A and B are connected in parallel. The combination is then connected in series with C and D. What is the effective capacitance?

$$C_1 = 12\ \mu F + 16\ \mu F = 26\ F; \quad C_2 = 28\ \mu F + 26\ \mu F = 46\ \mu F;$$

$$C_e = \frac{C_1 C_2}{C_1 + C_2} = \frac{(28\ \mu F)(46\ \mu F)}{28\ \mu F + 46\ \mu F};$$

$$\boxed{C_e = 17.4\ \mu F}$$

*26-41. Consider the circuit drawn in Fig. 26-17. What is the equivalent capacitance of the circuit? What are the charge and voltage across the 2-μF capacitor? (*Redraw Fig.*)

$$\frac{1}{C_{6,2}} = \frac{1}{2\ \mu F} + \frac{1}{6\ \mu F}; \quad C_{6,2} = 1.50\ \mu F$$

$$C_{6,2} = 1.5\ \mu F + 4.5\ \mu F = 6\ \mu F$$

*26-44. Suppose the capacitors of Problem 26-43 are reconnected in parallel with the 800-V source. What is the equivalent capacitance? What are the charge and voltage across the 4-μF capacitor?

$C_e = 2\,\mu F + 4\,\mu F + 6\,\mu F$; $\boxed{C_e = 12\,\mu F}$

$Q_T = C_e V = (12\,\mu F)(12\,V) = 144\,\mu C$

$V_T = V_2 = V_3 = V_4 = 12\,V$; $Q_4 = C_4 V_4 = (4\,\mu F)(12\,V)$; $\boxed{Q_4 = 48\,\mu C;\ V_4 = 12\,V}$

*26-45. Show that the total capacitance of a multiple-plate capacitor containing N plates separated by air is given by:

$$C_0 = \frac{(N-1)\varepsilon_0 A}{d}$$

where A is the area of each plate and d is the separation of each plate.

For a multiplate capacitor, if there are a total of N plates, we have the equivalent of (N – 1) capacitors each of area A and separation d. Hence, the above equation.

*26-46. The energy density, u, of a capacitor is defined as the energy (P.E.) per unit volume (Ad) of the space between the plates. Using this definition and several formulas from this chapter, derive the following relationship for finding the energy density, u:

$$u = \frac{1}{2}\varepsilon_0 E^2$$

where E is the electric field intensity between the plates?

$P.E. = \tfrac{1}{2}CV^2$; $V = Ed$; $C = \varepsilon_0 \dfrac{A}{d}$; $u = \dfrac{P.E.}{Ad}$

$u = \dfrac{\tfrac{1}{2}CV^2}{Ad} = \dfrac{\tfrac{1}{2}\left(\varepsilon_0\dfrac{A}{d}\right)\left(E^2 d^2\right)}{Ad}$; $\boxed{u = \tfrac{1}{2}\varepsilon_0 E^2}$

---

*26-41. (Cont.)

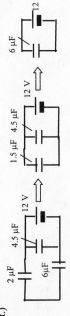

$Q_T = (6\,\mu F)(12\,V) = 72\,\mu C$; $Q_{1.5} = Q_2 = Q_3 = (1.5\,\mu F)(12\,V) = 18\,\mu C$

$V_2 = \dfrac{Q_2}{C_2} = \dfrac{18\,\mu C}{2\,\mu F} = 9.00\,V$; $\boxed{C_e = 6.00\,\mu F;\ V_2 = 9.00\,V;\ Q_2 = 18\,\mu C}$

*26-42. Two identical 20-μF capacitors A and B are connected in parallel with a 12-V battery. What is the charge on each capacitor if a sheet of porcelain (K = 6) is inserted between the plates of capacitor B and the battery remains connected?

$C_A = 20\,\mu F$; $C_B = 6(20\,\mu F) = 120\,\mu F$

$C_e = 120\,\mu F + 20\,\mu F$; $C_e = 140\,\mu F$

$Q_B = (120\,\mu F)(12\,V) = \boxed{1440\,\mu C}$; $Q_A = (20\,\mu F)(12\,V) = \boxed{240\,\mu C}$

Show that BEFORE insertion of dielectric, the charge on EACH was 240 μC!

*26-43. Three capacitors A, B, and C have respective capacitances of 2, 4, and 6 μF. Compute the equivalent capacitance if they are connected in series with an 800-V source. What are the charge and voltage across the 4-μF capacitor?

$\dfrac{1}{C_e} = \dfrac{1}{2\,\mu F} + \dfrac{1}{4\,\mu F} + \dfrac{1}{6\,\mu F}$; $\boxed{C_e = 1.09\,\mu F}$

$Q_T = C_e V = (1.09\,\mu F)(800\,V)$; $Q_T = 873\,\mu C$; $Q_2 = Q_4 = Q_6 = 873\,\mu C$

$Q_4 = 873\,\mu C$; $\boxed{Q_4 = 873\,\mu C;\ V_4 = 218\,V}$

Also:; $V_4 = \dfrac{873\,\mu C}{4\,\mu F} = 218\,V$; $V_4 = 218\,V$

*26-47. A capacitor with a plate separation of 3.4 mm is connected to a 500-V battery. Use the relation derived in Problem 26-46 to calculate the energy density between the plates?

$$E = \frac{V}{d} = \frac{500\ V}{0.0034\ m} = 1.47 \times 10^5\ V/m\ ; \qquad u = \frac{1}{2}\varepsilon_0 E^2$$

$$u = \frac{1}{2}(8.85 \times 10^{-12}\ C^2/N\cdot m^2)(1.47 \times 10^4\ V/m)^2\ ; \qquad \boxed{u = 95.7\ mJ/m^3}$$

Critical Thinking Problems

26-48. A certain capacitor has a capacitance of 12 µF when its plates are separated by 0.3 mm of vacant space. A 400-V battery charges the plates and is then disconnected from the capacitor. (a) What is the potential difference across the plates if a sheet of Bakelite (K = 7) is inserted between the plates? (b) What is the total charge on the plates? (c) What is the capacitance with the dielectric inserted? (d) What is the permittivity of Bakelite? (e) How much additional charge can be placed on the capacitor if the 400-V battery is reconnected?

400 V 400 V (Battery disconnected)

$$E_0 = \frac{V_0}{d} = \frac{400\ V}{0.0003\ m}\ ; \qquad E_0 = 1.33 \times 10^6\ V/m$$

$$C = KC_0 = (7)(12\ \mu F) = 84\ \mu F$$

(a) $K = \frac{V_0}{V}$; $V = \frac{400\ V}{7}$; $\boxed{V = 57.1\ V}$

(b) $Q_0 = C_0 V_0 = (12\ \mu F)(400\ V)$; $\boxed{Q_0 = 4800\ \mu C}$ (Battery disconnected)

(c) 40 µF

(d) $\varepsilon = K\varepsilon_0 = (7)(8.85 \times 10^{-12}\ N\ m^2/C^2)$; $\boxed{\varepsilon = 6.20 \times 10^{-11}\ N\ m^2/C^2}$;

(e) $Q = CV = (84\ \mu F)(400\ V)$; $Q = 33.6$ mC (400-V Battery reconnected)

The added charge is: $Q - Q_0 = 33.6$ mC - 4.8 mC; $\boxed{\Delta Q = 28.8\ mC}$

---

*26-49. A medical defibrillator uses a capacitor to revive heart attack victims. Assume that a 65-µF capacitor in such a device is charged to 5000 V. What is the total energy stored?

If 25 percent of this energy passes through a victim in 3 ms, what power is delivered?

$$P.E. = \frac{1}{2}CV^2 = \frac{1}{2}(65 \times 10^{-6}\ F)(5000\ V)\ ; \qquad \boxed{P.E. = 162\ mJ}$$

$$Power = \frac{0.25(0.162\ J)}{0.003\ s} = 13.5\ W\ ; \qquad \boxed{Power = 13.5\ W}$$

*26-50. Consider three capacitors of 10, 20, and 30 µF. Show how these might be connected to produce the maximum and minimum equivalent capacitances and list the values. Draw a diagram of a connection that would result in an equivalent capacitance of 27.5 µF.

Show a connection that will result in a combined capacitance of 22.0 µF.

The maximum is for a parallel connection: $C = 10\ \mu F + 20\ \mu F + 30\ \mu F$; $\boxed{C_{max} = 60\ \mu F}$

Minimum is for series: $\frac{1}{C_e} = \frac{1}{10\ \mu F} + \frac{1}{20\ \mu F} + \frac{1}{30\ \mu F}$; $\boxed{C_{min} = 5.45\ \mu F}$

Case 1: $\frac{1}{C_1} = \frac{1}{20\ \mu F} + \frac{1}{30\ \mu F}$; $C_1 = 7.5\ \mu F$

$C_e = C_1 + 20\ \mu F = 12\ \mu F + 20 \mu F$; $\boxed{C_e = 22.0\ \mu F}$

Case 2: $\frac{1}{C_2} = \frac{1}{20\ \mu F} + \frac{1}{30\ \mu F}$; $C_1 = 12\ \mu F$

$C_e = C_1 + 20\ \mu F = 12\ \mu F + 20 \mu F$; $\boxed{C_e = 22.0\ \mu F}$

30 µF — 10 µF — 20 µF

30 µF — 20 µF — 10 µF

*26-51. A 4-μF air capacitor is connected to a 500-V source of potential difference. The capacitor is then disconnected from the source and a sheet of mica (K = 5) is inserted between the plates. What is the new voltage on the capacitor? Now reconnect the 500-V battery and calculate the final charge on the capacitor. By what percentage did the total energy on the capacitor increase due to the dielectric?

(a) $K = \dfrac{V_0}{V}$; $V = \dfrac{500 \text{ V}}{5}$; $\boxed{V = 100 \text{ V}}$

(b) $Q_0 = C_0 V_0 = (4\ \mu\text{F})(500 \text{ V})$; $\boxed{Q_0 = 2000\ \mu\text{C}}$

(c) $(P.E.)_0 = \tfrac{1}{2}C_0 V^2 = \tfrac{1}{2}(4 \times 10^{-6}\text{ F})(500 \text{ V})^2$; $(P.E.)_0 = 0.500 \text{ J}$; $C = 5(4\ \mu\text{F}) = 20\ \mu\text{F}$

$(P.E.) = \tfrac{1}{2}CV^2 = \tfrac{1}{2}(20 \times 10^{-6}\text{ F})(500 \text{ V})^2$; $(P.E.)_0 = 2.50 \text{ J}$

$Percent\ increase = \dfrac{2.50 \text{ J} - 0.50 \text{ J}}{0.500 \text{ J}}$; $\boxed{Percent\ increase = 400\%}$

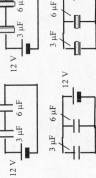

*26-52. A 3-μF capacitor and a 6-μF capacitor are connected in series with a 12-V battery. What is the total stored energy of the system? What is the total energy if they are connected in parallel? What is the total energy for each of these connections if mica (K = 5) is used as a dielectric for each capacitor?

Series: $C_e = \dfrac{(3\ \mu\text{F})(6\ \mu\text{F})}{3\ \mu\text{F} + 6\ \mu\text{F}} = 2.00\ \mu\text{F}$

$P.E. = \tfrac{1}{2}(2 \times 10^{-6}\text{ F})(12 \text{ V})^2 = \boxed{0.144 \text{ mJ}}$

Parallel: $C_e = 3\ \mu\text{F} + 6\ \mu\text{F} = 9\ \mu\text{F}$

$P.E. = \tfrac{1}{2}(9 \times 10^{-6}\text{ F})(12 \text{ V})^2 = \boxed{0.648 \text{ mJ}}$

$C_3 = 5(3\ \mu\text{F}) = 15\ \mu\text{F}$; $C_6 = 5(6\ \mu\text{F}) = 30\ \mu\text{F}$

Series: $C_e = \dfrac{(15\ \mu\text{F})(30\ \mu\text{F})}{15\ \mu\text{F} + 30\ \mu\text{F}} = 10.00\ \mu\text{F}$; Parallel: $C = 15\ \mu\text{F} + 30\ \mu\text{F} = 45\ \mu\text{F}$

$P.E. = \tfrac{1}{2}(10 \times 10^{-6}\text{ F})(12 \text{ V})^2 = \boxed{0.720 \text{ mJ}}$; $P.E. = \tfrac{1}{2}(45 \times 10^{-6}\text{ F})(12 \text{ V})^2 = \boxed{3.24 \text{ mJ}}$

Chapter 27. Current and Resistance

Electric Current and Ohm's Law

27-1. How many electrons pass a point every second in a wire carrying a current of 20 A? How much time is needed to transport 40 C of charge past this point?

$Q = It = (20 \text{ C/s})(1\text{ s})$; $Q = 20\ \dfrac{\text{C}}{\text{s}}\left(\dfrac{1e}{1.6 \times 10^{-19}\text{C}}\right)$; $\boxed{Q = 1.25 \times 10^{20} \text{ electrons/s}}$

$I = \dfrac{Q}{t}$; $t = \dfrac{Q}{I} = \dfrac{40 \text{ C}}{20 \text{ A}} = 2.00 \text{ s}$; $\boxed{t = 2.00 \text{ s}}$

27-2. If 600 C of charge pass a given point in 3 s, what is the electric current in amperes?

$I = \dfrac{Q}{t} = \dfrac{600 \text{ C}}{3 \text{ s}}$; $\boxed{I = 20 \text{ A}}$

27-3. Find the current in amperes when 690 C of charge pass a given point in 2 min.

$I = \dfrac{Q}{t} = \dfrac{690 \text{ C}}{120 \text{ s}}$; $\boxed{I = 5.75 \text{ A}}$

27-4. If a current of 24 A exists for 50 s, how many coulombs of charge have passed through the wire?

$Q = It = (24 \text{ A})(50 \text{ s})$; $\boxed{Q = 1200 \text{ C}}$

27-5. What is the potential drop across a 4-Ω resistor with a current of 8 A passing through it?

$V = IR = (8 \text{ A})(4\ \Omega)$; $\boxed{V = 32.0 \text{ V}}$

27-6. Find the resistance of a rheostat if the drop in potential is 48 V and the current is 4 A.

$R = \dfrac{V}{I} = \dfrac{48 \text{ V}}{4 \text{ A}}$; $\boxed{R = 12.0\ \Omega}$

27-7. Determine the current through a 5-Ω resistor that has a 40-V drop in potential across it?

$$I = \frac{V}{R} = \frac{40\ V}{5\ \Omega}; \quad \boxed{I = 8.00\ A}$$

27-8. A 2-A fuse is placed in a circuit with a battery having a terminal voltage of 12 V. What is the minimum resistance for a circuit containing this fuse?

$$R = \frac{V}{I} = \frac{12\ V}{2\ A}; \quad \boxed{R = 6.00\ \Omega}$$

27-9. What emf is required to pass 60 mA through a resistance of 20 kΩ? If this same emf is applied to a resistance of 300 Ω, what will be the new current?

$$\varepsilon = IR = 60 \times 10^{-3}\ A)(20 \times 10^3\ \Omega); \quad \varepsilon = 1200\ V$$

$$I = \frac{\varepsilon}{R} = \frac{1200\ V}{300\ \Omega}; \quad \boxed{I = 4.00\ A}$$

Electric Power and Heat Loss

27-10. A soldering iron draws 0.75 A at 120 V. How much energy will it use in 15 min?

$$P = IV = (0.75\ A)(120\ V); \quad P = 90.0\ W; \quad t = 15\ min = 900\ s$$

$$P = \frac{Work}{t}; \quad Energy = Pt = (90\ W)(900\ s); \quad \boxed{E = 81,000\ J}$$

27-11. An electric lamp has an 80-Ω filament connected to a 110-V direct-current line. What is the current through the filament? What is the power loss in watts?

$$I = \frac{V}{R} = \frac{110\ V}{80\ \Omega}; \quad \boxed{I = 1.38\ A}$$

$$P = \frac{V^2}{R} = \frac{(110\ V)^2}{80\ \Omega}; \quad \boxed{P = 151\ W}$$

27-12. Assume that the cost of energy in a home is 8 cents per kilowatt-hour. A family goes on a 2-week vacation leaving a single 80-W light bulb burning. What is the cost?

$$E = Pt = (80\ W)(2\ wk)(7\ day/wk)(24\ h/day)(3600\ s/h) = 26.9\ kW\ h$$

$$E = (26.9\ kW\ h)(0.08\ c/kw\ h) = \boxed{\$2.15} \quad (Rates\ vary)$$

27-13. A 120-V, direct-current generator delivers 2.4 kW to an electric furnace. What current is supplied? What is the resistance?

$$I = \frac{P}{V} = \frac{2400W}{120\ V}; \quad \boxed{I = 20\ A}; \quad R = \frac{V}{I} = \frac{120\ V}{20\ A}; \quad \boxed{R = 6.00\ \Omega}$$

27-14. A resistor develops heat at the rate of 250 W when the potential difference across its ends is 120 V. What is its resistance?

$$P = \frac{V^2}{R}; \quad R = \frac{V^2}{P} = \frac{(120\ V)^2}{250\ W}; \quad \boxed{R = 57.6\ \Omega}$$

27-15. A 120-V motor draws a current of 4.0 A. How many joules of electrical energy is used in one hour? How many kilowatt-hours?

$$P = VI = (120\ V)(4.0\ A) = 480\ W$$

$$P = \frac{E}{t}; \quad E = Pt = (480\ W)(3600\ s); \quad \boxed{E = 1.73\ MJ}$$

$$E = 1.73 \times 10^6\ J \left(\frac{1\ kW \cdot h}{3.60 \times 10^6\ J} \right) \quad \boxed{E = 0.480\ kW\ h}$$

27-16. A household hair dryer is rated at 2000 W and is designed to operate on a 120-V outlet. What is the resistance of the device?

$$P = \frac{V^2}{R}; \quad R = \frac{V^2}{P} = \frac{(120\ V)^2}{2000\ W}; \quad \boxed{R = 7.20\ \Omega}$$

Resistivity

27-17. What length of copper wire 1/16 in. in diameter is required to construct a 20-Ω resistor at 20°C? What length of nichrome wire is needed?

Copper: $\rho = 1.78 \times 10^{-8} \ \Omega \cdot m$; nichrome: $\rho = 100 \times 10^{-8} \ \Omega \cdot m$

$\tfrac{1}{16}$ ft = 0.0625 in. = 62.5 mil; $A = (62.5 \text{ mil})^2 = 3906 \text{ cmil}$

$R = \frac{\rho l}{A}$; $l = \frac{RA}{\rho} = \frac{(20\,\Omega)(3906\,\text{cmil})}{10.4\,\Omega\cdot\text{cmil/ft}}$; $\boxed{l = 7510 \text{ ft}}$

$R = \frac{\rho l}{A}$; $l = \frac{RA}{\rho} = \frac{(20\,\Omega)(3906\,\text{cmil})}{600\,\Omega\cdot\text{cmil/ft}}$; $\boxed{l = 130 \text{ ft}}$

27-18. A 3.0-m length of copper wire ($\rho = 1.78 \times 10^{-8} \ \Omega \cdot m$) at 20°C has a cross section of 4 mm². What is the electrical resistance of this wire?   [A = 4 mm² = 4 x 10⁻⁶ m²]

$R = \frac{\rho l}{A} = \frac{(1.72 \times 10^{-8}\,\Omega\cdot m)(3.0\ m)}{4.00 \times 10^{-6}\ m^2}$; $\boxed{R = 12.9 \text{ m}\Omega}$

27-19. Find the resistance of 40 m of tungsten ($\rho = 5.5 \times 10^{-8} \ \Omega \cdot m$) wire having a diameter of 0.8 mm at 20°C?

$A = \frac{\pi D^2}{4} = \frac{\pi(0.0008\ m)^2}{4}$; $A = 5.03 \times 10^{-7} \ m^2$

$R = \frac{\rho l}{A} = \frac{(5.5 \times 10^{-8}\,\Omega\cdot m)(40.0\ m)}{5.03 \times 10^{-7}\ m^2}$; $\boxed{R = 4.37\ \Omega}$

27-20. A certain wire has a diameter of 3 mm and a length of 150 m. It has a resistance of 3.00 Ω at 20°C. What is the resistivity?   [A = πD²/4 = 7.07 x 10⁻⁷ m².]

$R = \frac{\rho l}{A}$; $\rho = \frac{RA}{l} = \frac{(3\,\Omega)(7.07 \times 10^{-7}\ m^2)}{150\ m}$; $\boxed{\rho = 1.41 \times 10^{-8} \ \Omega \cdot m}$

27-21. What is the resistance of 200 ft of iron ($\rho = 9.5 \times 10^{-8} \ \Omega \cdot m$) wire with a diameter of 0.002 in. at 20°C? ($\rho = 9.5 \times 10^{-8} \ \Omega \cdot m$).   [200 ft = 61.0 m;   0.002 in. = 5.08 x 10⁻⁵ m]

$A = \frac{\pi D^2}{4} = \frac{\pi(5.08 \times 10^{-5}\ m)^2}{4}$; $A = 2.03 \times 10^{-9} \ m^2$

$R = \frac{\rho l}{A} = \frac{(9.5 \times 10^{-8}\,\Omega\cdot m)(61.0\ m)}{5.08 \times 10^{-5}\ m^2}$; $R = 2860\ \Omega$

*27-22. A nichrome wire ($\rho = 100 \times 10^{-8} \ \Omega \cdot m$) has a length of 40 at 20°C What is the diameter if the total resistance is 5 Ω?

$R = \frac{\rho l}{A}$; $A = \frac{\rho l}{R} = \frac{(100 \times 10^{-8}\,\Omega\cdot m)(40\ m)}{5.00\ \Omega}$; $A = 8 \times 10^{-6} \ m^2$

$A = \frac{\pi D^2}{4}$; $D = \sqrt{\frac{4A}{\pi}} = \sqrt{\frac{2(8 \times 10^{-6}\ m^2)}{\pi}}$; $\boxed{D = 2.26 \text{ mm}}$

*27-23. A 115-V source of emf is attached to a heating element which is a coil of nichrome wire ($\rho = 100 \times 10^{-8} \ \Omega \cdot m$) of cross section 1.20 mm² What must be the length of the wire if the resistive power loss is to be 800 W?   [A = 1.20 mm² = 1.20 x 10⁻⁶ m²]

$P = \frac{V^2}{R}$; $R = \frac{V^2}{P} = \frac{(115\ V)^2}{800\ W} = 16.5\ \Omega$; $R = 16.5\ \Omega$

$R = \frac{\rho l}{A}$; $l = \frac{RA}{\rho} = \frac{(16.5\,\Omega)(1.20 \times 10^{-6}\ m^2)}{100 \times 10^{-8}\ \Omega\cdot m}$; $\boxed{l = 19.8 \text{ m}}$

Temperature Coefficient of Resistance

27-24. The resistance of a length of wire ($\alpha = 0.0065/C^0$) is 4.00 Ω at 20°C. What is the resistance at 80°C?   [Δt = 80°C − 20°C = 60 C⁰]

$\Delta R = \alpha R_o \Delta t = (0.0065/C^0)(4\ \Omega)(60\ C^0) = 1.56\ \Omega$; $R = 4.00\ \Omega + 1.56\ \Omega = \boxed{5.56\ \Omega}$

27-30. A 110-V radiant heater draws a current of 6.0 A. How much heat energy in joules is delivered in one hour?

$$P = \frac{E}{t} = VI; \qquad E = VIt = (110\ V)(6\ A)(3600\ s); \qquad \boxed{E = 2.38\ MJ}$$

27-31. A power line has a total resistance of 4 kΩ. What is the power loss through the wire if the current is reduced to 6.0 mA?

$$P = I^2 R = (0.006\ A)^2 (4000\ Ω); \qquad \boxed{P = 144\ mW}$$

27-32. A certain wire has a resistivity of 2×10^{-8} Ω·m at 20°C. If its length is 200 m and its cross section is 4 mm², what will be its electrical resistance at 100°C. Assume that $\alpha = 0.005/C^0$ for this material. $[\ \Delta t = 100^0 C - 20^0 C = 80\ C^0\ ]$

$$R_0 = \frac{\rho l}{A} = \frac{(2 \times 10^{-8}\ Ω \cdot m)(200\ m)}{4 \times 10^{-6}\ m^2}; \qquad R_0 = 1.00\ Ω \quad at\ 20^0 C$$

$$R = R_0 + \alpha R_0 \Delta t = 1.00\ Ω + (0.005/C^0)(1\ Ω)(80\ C^0); \qquad \boxed{R = 1.40\ Ω}$$

27-33. Determine the resistivity of a wire made of an unknown alloy if its diameter is 0.007 in. and 100 ft of the wire is found to have a resistance of 4.0 Ω. $[\ D = 0.007\ in. = 7\ mil\ ]$

$$A = (7\ mil)^2 = 49\ cmil; \qquad R = \frac{\rho l}{A}; \qquad \rho = \frac{RA}{l}$$

$$\Delta = \frac{RA}{l} = \frac{(4\ Ω)(49\ cmil)}{100\ ft}; \qquad \boxed{\rho = 1.96\ Ω\ cmil/ft}$$

27-34. The resistivity of a certain wire is 1.72×10^{-8} Ω·m at 20°C. A 6-V battery is connected to a 20-m coil of this wire having a diameter of 0.8 mm. What is the current in the wire?

$$A = \frac{\pi D^2}{4} = \frac{\pi (0.0008\ m)^2}{4} = 5.03 \times 10^{-7}\ m^2; \qquad R = \frac{\rho l}{A}$$

27-25. If the resistance of a conductor is 100 Ω at 20°C, and 116 Ω at 60°C, what is its temperature coefficient of resistivity? $[\ \Delta t = 60^0 C - 20^0 C = 40\ C^0\ ]$

$$\alpha = \frac{\Delta R}{R_0 \Delta t} = \frac{116\ Ω - 100\ Ω}{(100\ Ω)(40\ C^0)}; \qquad \boxed{\alpha = 0.00400/C^0}$$

27-26. A length of copper ($\alpha = 0.0043/C^0$) wire has a resistance of 8 Ω at 20°C. What is the resistance at 90°C? At -30°C?

$$\Delta R = (0.0043/C^0)(8\ Ω)(70\ C^0) = 2.41\ Ω; \qquad R = 8.00\ Ω + 2.41\ Ω = \boxed{10.41\ Ω}$$

$$\Delta R = (0.0043/C^0)(8\ Ω)(-30^0 C - 20^0 C) = -1.72\ Ω; \qquad R = 8.00\ Ω - 1.72\ Ω = \boxed{6.28\ Ω}$$

*27-27. The copper windings ($\alpha = 0.0043/C^0$) of a motor experience a 20 percent increase in resistance over their value at 20°C. What is the operating temperature?

$$\frac{\Delta R}{R} = 0.2; \qquad \Delta t = \frac{\Delta R}{R_0 \alpha} = \frac{0.2}{0.0043/C^0} = 46.5\ C^0; \qquad t = 20^0 C + 46.5\ C^0 = \boxed{66.5\ ^0 C}$$

*27-28. The resistivity of copper at 20°C is 1.78×10^{-8} Ω·m. What change in temperature will produce a 25 percent increase in resistivity?

Supplementary Problems

27-29. A water turbine delivers 2000 kW to an electric generator which is 80 percent efficient and has an output terminal voltage of 1200 V. What current is delivered and what is the electrical resistance? $[\ P_{out} = (0.80)(2000\ kW) = 1600\ kW\ ]$

$$P = VI; \qquad I = \frac{P}{V} = \frac{1600 \times 10^3\ W}{1200\ V}; \qquad I = 1330\ A$$

$$R = \frac{V}{I} = \frac{1200\ V}{1300\ A}; \qquad \boxed{R = 0.900\ Ω}$$

Critical Thinking Problems

27-38. A 150-Ω resistor at 20⁰C is rated at 2.0 W maximum power. What is the maximum voltage that can be applied across the resistor with exceeding the maximum allowable power? What is the current at this voltage?

$$P = \frac{V^2}{R}; \quad V = \sqrt{PR} = \sqrt{(2.00\ W)(150\ \Omega)}; \quad \boxed{V = 17.3\ V}$$

27-39. The current in a home is alternating current, but the same formulas apply. Suppose a fan motor operating a home cooling system is rated at 10 A for a 120-V line. How much energy is required to operate the fan for a 24-h period? At a cost of 9 cents per kilowatt-hour, what is the cost of operating this fan continuously for 30 days?

$$P = VI = (110\ V)((10\ A) = 1100\ W; \quad E = Pt = (1100\ W)(24\ h) = 26.4\ kW\cdot h$$

$$E = (26.4\ kW\cdot h)(3600\ s/h)(1000\ W/kW); \quad \boxed{E = 95.0\ MJ}$$

$$Cost = 26.4\ \frac{kW\cdot h}{day}\left(\frac{\$0.08}{kW\cdot h}\right)(30\ days); \quad \boxed{Cost = \$53.36}$$

*27-40. The power consumed in an electrical wire (α = 0.004/C⁰) is 40 W at 20⁰C. If all other factors are held constant, what is the power consumption when (a) the length is doubled, (b) the diameter is doubled, (c) the resistivity is doubled, and (d) the absolute temperature is doubled? (Power loss is proportional to resistance R)

$$R = \frac{\rho l}{A}; \quad P \propto l; \quad P \propto \frac{1}{A}; \quad P \propto \Delta R \propto \Delta T$$

(a) Double length and double power loss; Loss = 2(40 W) = $\boxed{80\ W}$

(b) doubling diameter gives 4A₀ and one-fourth power loss: Loss = ¼(40 W) = $\boxed{10\ W}$

(c) Doubling resistivity doubles resistance, and also doubles power loss. Loss = $\boxed{80\ W}$

27-34. (Cont.)

$$R = \frac{\rho l}{A} = \frac{(1.72 \times 10^{-8}\ \Omega\cdot m)(20\ m)}{5.03 \times 10^{-7}\ m^2}; \quad R = 0.684\ \Omega$$

$$I = \frac{V}{R} = \frac{6.00\ V}{0.684\ \Omega}; \quad \boxed{I = 8.77\ A}$$

27-35. A certain resistor is used as a thermometer. Its resistance at 20⁰C is 26.00 Ω, and its resistance at 40⁰C is 26.20 Ω. What is the temperature coefficient of resistance for this material?

$$\alpha = \frac{\Delta R}{R_0 \Delta t} = \frac{(26.20\ \Omega - 26.00\ \Omega)}{(26.00\ \Omega)(40^0C - 20^0C)}; \quad \boxed{\alpha = 3.85 \times 10^{-4}/C^0}$$

*27-36. What length of copper wire at 20⁰C has the same resistance as 200 m of iron wire at 20⁰C? Assume the same cross section for each wire. [Product RA doesn't change.]

$$R = \frac{\rho l}{A}; \quad RA = \rho l; \quad \rho_1 R_1 = \rho l_2; \quad l_2 = \frac{\rho l_1}{\rho_2}$$

$$l_2 = \frac{\rho_1 l_1}{\rho_2} = \frac{(9.5 \times 10^{-8}\ \Omega\cdot m)(200\ m)}{1.72 \times 10^{-8}\ \Omega\cdot m}; \quad \boxed{l_2 = 1100\ m}$$

*27-37. The power loss in a certain wire at 20⁰C is 400 W. If α = 0.0036/C⁰, by what percentage will the power loss increase when the operating temperature is 68⁰C?

$$\Delta R = \alpha R_0 \Delta t; \quad \frac{\Delta R}{R} = (0.0036/C^0)(68^0 C - 20^0 C) = 0.173$$

Since P = I²R, the power loss increases by same percentage: $\boxed{17.3\ \%}$

*27-40. (Cont.) (d) $T = (20^0 + 273^0) = 293\,K;$ $\Delta T = 2T - T = T;$ $\Delta T = 293\,K = 293\,C^0$

If absolute temperature doubles, the new resistance is given by:

$$R = R_0(1 + \alpha\Delta T); \qquad \frac{R}{R_0} = 1 + (0.004/C^0)(293\,C^0) = 2.172;$$

$$\frac{P}{P_0} = \frac{R}{R_0} = 2.172; \qquad Loss = 2.172(40\,W); \qquad \boxed{Loss = 86.9\,W}$$

This of course presumes that resistivity remains linear, which is not likely.

*27-41. What must be the diameter of an aluminum wire if it is to have the same resistance as an equal length of copper wire of diameter 2.0 mm? What length of nichrome wire is needed to have the same resistance as 2 m of iron wire of the same cross section?

$$R = \frac{\rho l}{A}; \quad \frac{R}{l} = \frac{\rho}{A} = const.; \quad \frac{\rho_c}{A_c} = \frac{\rho_a}{A_a}; \quad A = \frac{\pi D^2}{4}; \quad \frac{\rho_c}{(D_c)^2} = \frac{\rho_a}{(D_c)^2}$$

$$D_a^2 = \frac{\rho_a D_c^2}{\rho_c}; \quad D_a = D_c\sqrt{\frac{\rho_c}{\rho_a}} = (2\,mm)\sqrt{\frac{1.72 \times 10^{-8}\Omega\cdot m}{2.80 \times 10^{-8}\Omega\cdot m}}; \quad \boxed{D_a = 1.57\,mm}$$

$$R = \frac{\rho l}{A}; \quad RA = \rho l = const.; \quad \rho_n l_n = \rho_i l_i; \quad l_n = \frac{\rho_i l_i}{\rho_n}$$

$$l_n = \frac{\rho_i l_i}{\rho_n} = \frac{(1.72 \times 10^{-8}\Omega\cdot m)}{(100 \times 10^{-8}\Omega\cdot m)}; \quad \boxed{l_n = 1.72\,cm}$$

*27-42. An iron wire ($\alpha = 0.0065/C^0$) has a resistance of 6.00 Ω at 20^0C and a copper wire ($\alpha = 0.0043/C^0$) has a resistance of 5.40 Ω at 20^0C. At what temperature will the two wires have the same resistance? [Conditions: $\alpha_i R_{oi}\Delta t_i - \alpha_c R_{0c}\Delta t_c = 6\,\Omega - 5.4\,\Omega = -0.60.\Omega.$]

$$\Delta t = \frac{-0.600\,\Omega}{\alpha_i R_{oi} - \alpha_c R_{oc}} = \frac{-0.600\,\Omega}{(0.0065/C^0)(6.0\,\Omega) - (0.0043/C^0)(5.4\,\Omega)}; \qquad \Delta t = -38.0\,C^0$$

$$\Delta t = t_f - 20^0 = -38.0\,C^0; \qquad \boxed{t_f = -18.0^0C}$$

Chapter 28. Direct-Current Circuits

Resistors in Series and Parallel (Ignore internal resistances for batteries in this section.)

28-1. A 5-Ω resistor is connected in series with a 3-Ω resistor and a 16-V battery. What is the effective resistance and what is the current in the circuit?

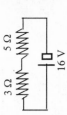

$$R_e = R_1 + R_2 = 3\,\Omega + 5\,\Omega; \qquad \boxed{R_e = 8.00\,\Omega}$$

$$I = \frac{V}{R} = \frac{16\,V}{8\,\Omega} \qquad \boxed{I = 2.00\,A}$$

28-2. A 15-Ω resistor is connected in parallel with a 30-Ω resistor and a 30-V source of emf. What is the effective resistance and what total current is delivered?

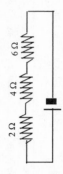

$$R_e = \frac{R_1 R_2}{R_1 + R_2} = \frac{(15\,\Omega)(30\,\Omega)}{15\,\Omega + 30\,\Omega}; \qquad \boxed{R_e = 10.0\,\Omega}$$

$$I = \frac{V}{R} = \frac{30\,V}{10\,\Omega}; \qquad \boxed{I = 3.00\,A}$$

28-3. In Problem 28-2, what is the current in 15 and 30-Ω resistors?

For Parallel: $V_{15} = V_{30} = 30\,V;$ $I_{15} = \frac{30\,V}{15\,\Omega};$ $\boxed{I_{15} = 2.00\,A}$

$$I_{30} = \frac{30\,V}{30\,\Omega}; \qquad \boxed{I_{30} = 1.00\,A} \qquad \text{Note: } I_{15} + I_{30} = I_T = 3.00\,A$$

28-4. What is the equivalent resistance of 2, 4, and 6-Ω resistors connected in parallel?

$$R_e = 2 + 4 + 6\,\Omega; \qquad \boxed{R_e = 12.0\,\Omega}$$

28-8. Given three resistors of 80, 60, and 40 Ω, find their effective resistance when connected in series and when connected in parallel.

Series: $R_e = 80 + 60 + 40\ \Omega$; $\boxed{R_e = 180\ \Omega}$

Parallel: $\dfrac{1}{R_e} = \sum \dfrac{1}{R_i} = \dfrac{1}{80\ \Omega} + \dfrac{1}{60\ \Omega} + \dfrac{1}{40\ \Omega}$; $\boxed{R_e = 18.5\ \Omega}$

28-9. Three resistances of 4, 9, and 11 Ω are connected first in series and then in parallel. Find the effective resistance for each connection.

Series: $R_e = 4\ \Omega + 9\ \Omega + 11\ \Omega$; $\boxed{R_e = 24.0\ \Omega}$

Parallel: $\dfrac{1}{R_e} = \sum \dfrac{1}{R_i} = \dfrac{1}{4\ \Omega} + \dfrac{1}{9\ \Omega} + \dfrac{1}{11\ \Omega}$; $\boxed{R_e = 2.21\ \Omega}$

*28-10. A 9-Ω resistor is connected in series with two parallel resistors of 6 and 12 Ω. What is the terminal potential difference if the total current from the battery is 4 A?

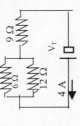

$R_e = \dfrac{(6\ \Omega)(12\ \Omega)}{6\ \Omega + 12\ \Omega} = 4\ \Omega$; $R_e = 4\ \Omega + 9\ \Omega = 13\ \Omega$

$V_T = IR = (4\ A)(13\ \Omega)$; $\boxed{V_T = 52.0\ V}$

*28-11. For the circuit described in Problem 28-10, what is the voltage across the 9-Ω resistor and what is the current through the 6-Ω resistor?

$V_9 = (4\ A)(9\ \Omega) = 36\ V$; $\boxed{V_9 = 36.0\ V}$

The rest of the 52 V drops across each of the parallel resistors:

$V_6 = V_7 = 52\ V - 36\ V$; $V_6 = 16\ V$

$I_6 = \dfrac{V_6}{R_6} = \dfrac{16\ V}{6\ \Omega}$; $\boxed{I_6 = 2.67\ A}$

28-5. An 18-Ω resistor and a 9-Ω resistor are first connected in parallel and then in series with a 24-V battery. What is the effective resistance for each connection? Neglecting internal resistance, what is the total current delivered by the battery in each case?

$R_e = \dfrac{R_1 R_2}{R_1 + R_2} = \dfrac{(18\ \Omega)(9\ \Omega)}{18\ \Omega + 9\ \Omega}$; $\boxed{R_e = 6.00\ \Omega}$

$I = \dfrac{V}{R} = \dfrac{24\ V}{6.00\ \Omega}$; $\boxed{I = 4.00\ A}$

$R_e = R_1 + R_2 = 18\ \Omega + 9\ \Omega$; $\boxed{R_e = 27.0\ \Omega}$

$I = \dfrac{V}{R} = \dfrac{24\ V}{27\ \Omega}$; $\boxed{I = 0.889\ A}$

28-6. A 12-Ω resistor and an 8-Ω resistor are first connected in parallel and then in series with a 28-V source of emf. What is the effective resistance and total current in each case?

$R_e = \dfrac{R_1 R_2}{R_1 + R_2} = \dfrac{(12\ \Omega)(8\ \Omega)}{12\ \Omega + 8\ \Omega}$; $\boxed{R_e = 4.80\ \Omega}$

$I = \dfrac{V}{R} = \dfrac{28\ V}{4.80\ \Omega}$; $\boxed{I = 5.83\ A}$

$R_e = R_1 + R_2 = 12\ \Omega + 8\ \Omega$; $\boxed{R_e = 20.0\ \Omega}$

$I = \dfrac{V}{R} = \dfrac{28\ V}{20\ \Omega}$; $\boxed{I = 1.40\ A}$

28-7. An 8-Ω resistor and a 3-Ω resistor are first connected in parallel and then in series with a 12-V source. Find the effective resistance and total current for each connection.

$R_e = \dfrac{(3\ \Omega)(8\ \Omega)}{3\ \Omega + 8\ \Omega}$; $\boxed{R_e = 2.18\ \Omega}$

$I = \dfrac{V}{R} = \dfrac{12\ V}{2.18\ \Omega}$; $\boxed{I = 5.50\ A}$

$R_e = R_1 + R_2 = 3\ \Omega + 8\ \Omega$; $\boxed{R_e = 11.0\ \Omega}$

$I = \dfrac{V}{R} = \dfrac{12\ V}{11\ \Omega}$; $\boxed{I = 1.09\ A}$

*28-12. Find the equivalent resistance of the circuit drawn in Fig. 28-19.

Start at far right and reduce circuit in steps: $R' = 1\,\Omega + 3\,\Omega + 2\,\Omega = 6\,\Omega$;

$$R'' = \frac{(6\,\Omega)(3\,\Omega)}{6\,\Omega+3\,\Omega} = 2\,\Omega; \quad R_e = 2\,\Omega+4\,\Omega+2\,\Omega; \quad \boxed{R_e = 8\,\Omega}$$

*28-13. Find the equivalent resistance of the circuit shown in Fig. 28-20.

Start at far right and reduce circuit in steps: $R = 1\,\Omega + 2\,\Omega = 3\,\Omega$;

$$R' = \frac{(6\,\Omega)(3\,\Omega)}{6\,\Omega+3\,\Omega} = 2\,\Omega; \quad R'' = 2\,\Omega+3\,\Omega = 5\,\Omega$$

$$R_e = \frac{(5\,\Omega)(4\,\Omega)}{5\,\Omega+4\,\Omega} = 2.22\,\Omega; \quad \boxed{R_e = 2.22\,\Omega}$$

*28-14. If a potential difference of 24 V is applied to the circuit drawn in Fig. 28-19, what is the current and voltage across the 1-Ω resistor?

$R_e = 8.00\,\Omega$; $\quad I = \dfrac{24\text{ V}}{8\,\Omega} = 3.00$ A;

The voltage across the 3 and 6-Ω parallel connection is found from I_1 and the 2-Ω combination resistance:

$V_3 = V_6 = (2\,\Omega)(3.00\text{ A}); \quad V_6 = 6.00\text{ V}; \quad I_6 = \dfrac{6\text{ V}}{6\,\Omega} = 1$ A

Thus, $I_1 = I_6 = 1.00$ A, *and* $V_1 = (1\text{ A})(1\,\Omega) = 1\text{ V};$ $\quad \boxed{V_1 = 1\text{ V}; \quad I_1 = 1\text{ A}}$

---

*28-15. If a potential difference of 12-V is applied to the free ends in Fig. 28-20, what is the current and voltage across the 2-Ω resistor?

$R_e = 2.22\,\Omega$; $\quad I = \dfrac{12\text{ V}}{2.22\,\Omega} = 5.40$ A;

Note that $V_5 = 12$ V; $\quad I_5 = \dfrac{12\text{ V}}{5\,\Omega} = 2.40$ A

$V_{3,6} = (2.4\text{ A})(2\,\Omega) = 4.80$ V; $\quad I_3 = \dfrac{4.8\text{ V}}{3\,\Omega} = 1.6$ A

$I_2 = I_1 = 1.60$ A; $\quad V_2 = (1.6\text{ A})(2\,\Omega) = 3.20$ V

$$\boxed{I_2 = 1.60\text{ A}; \quad V_2 = 3.20\text{ V}}$$

EMF and Terminal Potential Difference

28-16. A load resistance of 8 Ω is connected in series with a 18-V battery whose internal resistance is 1.0 Ω. What current is delivered and what is the terminal voltage?

$$I = \frac{E}{r+R_L} = \frac{18\text{ V}}{1.0\,\Omega+8\,\Omega}; \quad \boxed{I = 2.00\text{ A}}$$

28-17. A resistance of 6 Ω is placed across a 12-V battery whose internal resistance is 0.3 Ω. What is the current delivered to the circuit? What is the terminal potential difference?

$$I = \frac{E}{r+R_L} = \frac{12\text{ V}}{0.3\,\Omega+6\,\Omega}; \quad \boxed{I = 1.90\text{ A}}$$

$$V_T = E - Ir = 12\text{ V} - (1.90\text{ A})(0.3\,\Omega); \quad \boxed{V_T = 11.4\text{ V}}$$

28-18. Two resistors of 7 and 14 Ω are connected in parallel with a 16-V battery whose internal resistance is 0.25 Ω. What is the terminal potential difference and the current delivered to the circuit?

$R' = \frac{(7\,\Omega)(14\,\Omega)}{7\,\Omega + 14\,\Omega} = 4.67\,\Omega$; $R_e = 0.25\,\Omega + 4.67\,\Omega$

$I = \frac{E}{r+R'} = \frac{16\,V}{4.917\,\Omega}$; $I = 3.25\,A$ $V_T = E - Ir = 16\,V - (3.25\,A)(0.25\,\Omega)$;

$\boxed{V_T = 15.2\,V; \quad I = 3.25\,A}$

28-19. The open-circuit potential difference of a battery is 6 V. The current delivered to a 4-Ω resistor is 1.40 A. What is the internal resistance?

$E = IR_L + Ir$; $Ir = E - IR_L$

$r = \frac{E - IR_L}{I} = \frac{6\,V - (1.40\,A)(4\,\Omega)}{1.40\,A}$; $\boxed{r = 0.286\,\Omega}$

28-20. A dc motor draws 20 A from a 120-V dc line. If the internal resistance is 0.2 Ω, what is the terminal voltage of the motor?

$V_T = E - Ir = 120\,V - (20A)(0.2\,\Omega)$; $\boxed{V_T = 116\,V}$

28-21. For the motor in Problem 28-20, what is the electric power drawn from the line? What portion of this power is dissipated because of heat losses? What power is delivered by the motor?

$P_i = EI = (120\,V)(20\,A)$; $\boxed{P_i = 2400\,W}$

$P_L = I^2 r = (20\,A)^2(0.2)$; $\boxed{P_L = 80\,W}$

$P_o = V_T I = (116\,V)(20\,A)$; $\boxed{P_o = 2320\,W}$;

Note: $P_i = P_L + P_o$; $2400\,W = 80\,W + 2320\,W$

28-22. A 2-Ω and a 6-Ω resistor are connected in series with a 24-V battery of internal resistance 0.5 Ω. What is the terminal voltage and the power lost to internal resistance?

$R_e = 2\,\Omega + 6\,\Omega + 0.5\,\Omega = 8.50\,\Omega$; $I = \frac{E}{R_e} = \frac{24\,V}{8.5\,\Omega} = 2.82\,A$

$V_T = E - Ir = 24\,V - (2.82\,A)(0.5\,\Omega)$; $\boxed{V_T = 22.6\,V}$

$P_L = I^2 r = (2.82\,A)^2 (0.5\,\Omega)$; $\boxed{P_L = 3.99\,W}$

*28-23. Determine the total current and the current through each resistor for Fig. 28-21 when

E = 24 V, $R_1 = 6\,\Omega$, $R_2 = 3\,\Omega$, $R_3 = 1\,\Omega$, $R_4 = 2\,\Omega$, and r = 0.4 Ω.

$R_{1,2} = \frac{(3\,\Omega)(6\,\Omega)}{3\,\Omega + 6\,\Omega} = 2\,\Omega$; $R_{1,2,3} = 2\,\Omega + 1\,\Omega = 3\,\Omega$

$R_e = \frac{(3\,\Omega)(2\,\Omega)}{3\,\Omega + 2\,\Omega} = 1.20\,\Omega$;

$R_e = 1.20\,\Omega + 0.4\,\Omega = 1.60\,\Omega$

$I_T = \frac{24\,V}{1.60\,\Omega}$; $I_T = 15.0\,A$

$V_4 = V_{1,2} = (1.2\,\Omega)(15\,A) = 18\,V$ $I_4 = \frac{18\,V}{2\,\Omega}$

$I_4 = 9.0\,A$; $I_3 = 15\,A - 9\,A = 6\,A$; $V_3 = (6\,A)(1\,\Omega) = 6\,V$; $V_1 = V_2 = 18\,V - 6\,V$;

$V_1 = V_2 = 12\,V$; $I_2 = \frac{12\,V}{3\,\Omega} = 4\,A$; $I_1 = \frac{12\,V}{6\,\Omega} = 2\,A$;

$\boxed{I_T = 15\,A, \ I_1 = 2\,A, I_2 = 4\,A, I_3 = 6\,A, I_4 = 9\,A.}$

The solution is easier using Kirchhoff's laws, developed later in this chapter.

*28-24. Find the total current and the current through each resistor for Fig. 28-21 when E = 50 V, R_1 = 12 Ω, R_2 = 6 Ω, R_3 = 6 Ω, R_4 = 8 Ω, and r = 0.4 Ω.

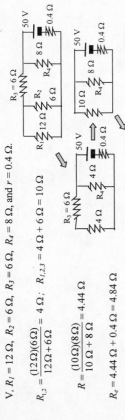

$$R_{1,2} = \frac{(12\,\Omega)(6\,\Omega)}{12\,\Omega+6\,\Omega} = 4\,\Omega; \quad R_{1,2,3} = 4\,\Omega + 6\,\Omega = 10\,\Omega$$

$$R = \frac{(10\,\Omega)(8\,\Omega)}{10\,\Omega + 8\,\Omega} = 4.44\,\Omega$$

$$R_e = 4.44\,\Omega + 0.4\,\Omega = 4.84\,\Omega$$

$$I_T = \frac{50\,V}{4.84\,\Omega}; \quad I_T = 10.3\,A$$

$$V_4 = V_p = (4.44\,\Omega)(10.3\,A) = 45.9\,V \quad I_4 = \frac{45.9\,V}{8\,\Omega}$$

$I_4 = 5.73$ A; $I_3 = 10.3$ A – 5.73 A = 4.59 A; $V_3 = (4.59\,A)(6\,\Omega) = 27.5$ V;

$V_1 = V_2 = 45.9$ V – 27.5 V = 18.4 V; $I_2 = \frac{18.4\,V}{6\,\Omega} = 3.06$ A; $I_1 = \frac{18.4\,V}{12\,\Omega} = 1.53$ A;

$$\boxed{I_T = 10.3\ A,\ I_1 = 1.53\ A,\ I_2 = 3.06\ A,\ I_3 = 4.59\ A,\ I_4 = 5.73\ A.}$$

Kirchhoff's Laws

28-25. Apply Kirchhoff's second rule to the current loop in Fig. 28-22. What is the net voltage around the loop? What is the net IR drop? What is the current in the loop?

Indicate output directions of emf's, assume direction of current, and trace in a clockwise direction for loop rule:

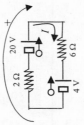

$$\Sigma E = \Sigma IR; \quad 20\,V - 4\,V = I(6\,\Omega) + I(2\,\Omega);$$

$$(8\,\Omega)I = 16\,V; \quad I = \frac{16\,V}{8\,\Omega}; \quad \boxed{I = 2.00\ A}$$

Net voltage drop = ΣE = $\boxed{16\ V}$ $\Sigma IR = (8\,\Omega)(2\,A) = \boxed{16\ V}$

28-26. Answer the same questions for Problem 28-25 where the polarity of the 20-V battery is changed, that is, its output direction is now to the left? (*Refer to Fig. in Prob. 28-25.*)

$$\Sigma\ E = -20\,V - 4\,V = \boxed{-24\ V}; \quad \Sigma IR = I(2\,\Omega) + I(6\,\Omega) = (8\Omega)I$$

$$\Sigma E = \Sigma IR; \quad -24\,V = (8\,\Omega)I; \quad \boxed{I = -4.00\ A}; \quad \Sigma IR = (8\,\Omega)(-4\,A) = \boxed{-24\ V}$$

The minus sign means the current is counterclockwise (against the assume direction)

*28-27. Use Kirchhoff's laws to solve for the currents through the circuit shown as Fig. 28-23.

First law at point P: $I_1 + I_2 = I_3$ *Current rule*

Loop A (2nd law): $\Sigma E = \Sigma IR$ *Loop rule*

$$5\,V - 4\,V = (4\,\Omega)I_1 + (2\,\Omega)I_1 - (6\,\Omega)I_2$$

Simplifying we obtain: (1) $6I_1 - 6I_2 = 1$ A

Loop B: $4\,V - 3\,V = (6\,\Omega)I_2 + (3\,\Omega)I_3 + (1\,\Omega)I_3$

Simplifying: (2) $6I_2 + 4I_3 = 1$ A, *but* $I_3 = I_1 + I_2$

Substituting we have: $6I_2 + 4(I_1 + I_2) = 1$ A *or* (3) $4I_1 + 10I_2 = 1$ A;

From which, $I_1 = 0.25\ A - 2.5\,I_2$; *Substituting into* (1): $6(0.25\ A - 2.5I_2) - 6\,I_2 = 1$ A

$1.5\ A - 15I_2 - 6I_2 = 1$ A; $-21I_2 = -0.5$ A; $I_2 = 0.00238$ A; $\boxed{I_2 = 23.8\ mA}$

Putting this into (1)*, we have:* $6I_1 - 6(0.0238\ A) = 1$ A, *and* $\boxed{I_1 = 190\ mA}$

Now, $I_1 + I_2 = I_3$ *so that* $I_3 = 23.8\ mA + 190\ mA$ *or* $\boxed{I_3 = 214\ mA}$

*28-28. Use Kirchhoff's laws to solve for the currents in Fig. 28-24.

Current rule: $I_1 + I_3 = I_2$ *or* (1) $I_3 = I_2 - I_1$

Loop A: $20\,V = (3\,\Omega)I_1 + (4\,\Omega)I_2$; (2) $3I_1 + 4I_2 = 20$ A

Loop B: $8\,V = (6\,\Omega)I_3 + (4\,\Omega)I_2$; (3) $3I_3 + 2I_2 = 4$ A

Outside Loop: $20\,V - 8\,V = (3\,\Omega)I_1 - (6\,\Omega)I_3$ *or* $I_1 - 2 I_3 = 4$ A

The Wheatstone Bridge

28-30. A Wheatstone bridge is used to measure the resistance R_x of a coil of wire. The resistance box is adjusted for 6 Ω, and the contact key is positioned at the 45 cm mark when measured from point A of Fig. 28-13. Find R_x. (Note: $l_1 + l_2 = 100$ cm)

$$R_x = \frac{R_3 l_2}{l_1} = \frac{(6\ \Omega)(55\ cm)}{(45\ cm)}; \quad R_x = 7.33\ \Omega$$

28-31. Commercially available Wheatstone bridges are portable and have a self-contained galvanometer. The ratio R_2/R_1 can be set at any integral power of ten between 0.001 and 1000 by a single dual switch. When this ratio is set to 100 and the known resistance R is adjusted to 46.7 Ω, the galvanometer current is zero. What is the unknown resistance?

$$R_x = R_3 \frac{R_2}{R_1} = (46.7\ \Omega)(100); \quad \boxed{R_x = 4670\ \Omega}$$

28-32. In a commercial Wheatstone bridge, R_1 and R_2 have the resistances of 20 and 40 Ω, respectively. If the resistance R_x is 14 Ω, what must be the known resistance R_3 for zero galvanometer deflection?

$$R_x = R_3 \frac{R_2}{R_1} = (14\ \Omega)\frac{20\ \Omega}{40\ \Omega}; \quad \boxed{R_x = 7.00\ \Omega}$$

Supplementary Problems:

28-33. Resistances of 3, 6, and 9 Ω are first connected in series and then in parallel with an 36-V source of potential difference. Neglecting internal resistance, what is the current leaving the positive terminal of the battery?

$$R_e = \Sigma R_i = 3\ \Omega + 6\ \Omega + 9\ \Omega = 18\ \Omega; \quad I = \frac{36\ V}{18\ \Omega}; \quad I = 2.00\ A$$

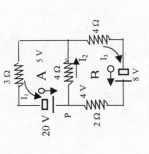

*28-28. (Cont.) (3) $3I_3 + 2I_2 = 4$ A and $I_3 = I_2 - I_1$

$3(I_2 - I_1) + 2I_2 = 4$ A; $3I_1 = 5I_2 - 4$ A

(2) $3I_1 + 4I_2 = 20$ A; $(5I_2 - 4$ A$) + 4I_2 = 20$;

$I_2 = 2.67$ A; $3I_1 = 5(2.67$ A$) - 4$ A; $I_1 = 3.11$ A

$I_3 = I_2 - I_1 = 2.67$ A $- 3.11$ A $= -0.444$ A

Note: I_3 goes in opposite direction to that assumed.

$\boxed{I_1 = 3.11\ \text{A},\ I_2 = 2.67\ \text{A},\ I_3 = 0.444\ \text{A}}$

**28-29. Apply Kirchhoff's laws to the circuit of Fig. 28-25. Find the currents in each branch.

Current rule: (1) $I_1 + I_4 = I_2 + I_3$

Applying loop rule gives six possible equations:

(2) $1.5I_1 + 3I_2 = 3$ A;   (3) $3I_2 - 5I_3 = 0$

(4) $5I_3 + 6I_4 = 6A$;   (5) $1.5I_1 - 6I_4 = -3A$

(6) $6I_4 + 3I_2 = 6$ A   (7) $1.5I_1 + 5I_3 = 3A$

Put $I_4 = I_2 + I_3 - I_1$; into (4): $5I_3 + 6(I_2 + I_3 - I_1) = 6$ A → $-6I_1 + 6I_2 + 11I_3 = 6$ A

Now, solving (2) for I_1 gives: $I_1 = 2$ A $- 2I_2$, which gives:

$-6(2$ A$- 2I_2) + 6I_2 + 11I_3 = 6$ A, which gives: $18I_2 + 11I_3 = 18$ A

But, from (3), we put $I_2 = \frac{5}{3}I_3$ into above equation to find that: $I_3 = 0.439$ A

From (2): $1.5I_1 + 3(0.439$ A$) = 3$ A;   and $I_1 = 0.536$ A

From (3): $3I_2 - 5(0.439$ A$) = 0$;   and $I_2 = 0.736$ A

From (4): $5(0.439$ A$) + 6I_4 = 6$ A;   and $I_4 = 0.634$ A

Currents in each branch are: $\boxed{I_1 = 536\ \text{mA},\ I_2 = 732\ \text{mA},\ I_3 = 439\ \text{mA},\ I_4 = 634\ \text{mA}}$

Note: Not all of the equations are independent. Elimination of two may yield another.

It is best to start with the current rule, and use it to eliminate one of the currents quickly.

396 Unit A   Solutions Manual

28-33. (Cont.) $\dfrac{1}{R_e} = \sum \dfrac{1}{R_i} = \dfrac{1}{3\,\Omega} + \dfrac{1}{6\,\Omega} + \dfrac{1}{9\,\Omega}$; $R_e = 1.64\,\Omega$; $I = \dfrac{36\,V}{1.64\,\Omega}$; $I = 22.0\,A$

28-34. Three 3-Ω resistors are connected in parallel. This combination is then placed in series with another 3-Ω resistor. What is the equivalent resistance?

$\dfrac{1}{R'} = \dfrac{1}{3\,\Omega} + \dfrac{1}{3\,\Omega} + \dfrac{1}{3\,\Omega} = 1\,\Omega$; $R_e = R' + 3\,\Omega$

$R_e = 1\,\Omega + 3\,\Omega$; $R_e = 4\,\Omega$

*28-35. Three resistors of 4, 8, and 12 Ω are connected in series with a battery. A switch allows the battery to be connected or disconnected from the circuit? When the switch is open, a voltmeter across the terminals of the battery reads 50 V. When the switch is closed, the voltmeter reads 48 V. What is the internal resistance in the battery?

$R_L = 4\,\Omega + 8\,\Omega + 12\,\Omega = 24\,\Omega$; E = 50 V; $V_T = 48\,V = IR_L$

$I = \dfrac{48\,V}{24\,\Omega} = 2.00\,A$; $E - V_T = Ir$; $50\,V - 48\,V = Ir$

$r = \dfrac{50\,V - 48\,V}{2.00\,A}$; $r = 1.00\,\Omega$

*28-36. The generator in Fig. 28-26 develops an emf of $E_1 = 24\,V$ and has an internal resistance of 0.2 Ω. The generator is used to charge a battery $E_2 = 12\,V$ whose internal resistance is 0.3 Ω. Assume that $R_1 = 4\,\Omega$ and $R_2 = 6\,\Omega$. What is the terminal voltage across the generator? What is the terminal voltage across the battery?

$I = \dfrac{24\,V - 12\,V}{6\,\Omega + 4\,\Omega + 0.2\,\Omega + 0.3\,\Omega} = 1.14\,A$

$V_1 = E_1 - Ir = 24\,V - (1.14\,A)(0.2\,\Omega) = 23.8\,V$;

$V_2 = 12\,V + (1.14\,A)(0.3\,\Omega) = 12.3\,V$

'28-37. What is the power consumed in charging the battery for Problem 28-36? Show that the power delivered by the generator is equal to the power losses due to resistance and the power consumed in charging the battery.

$P = EI = (24\,V)(1.143\,A)$ $P_e = 27.43\,W$

$P_R = I^2 R_e = (1.143\,A)^2 (10.5\,\Omega)$; $P_R = 13.69\,W$

$P_V = (12\,V)(1.143\,A) = 13.72\,W$; $P_e = P_R + P_V$;

$27.4\,W = 13.7\,W + 13.7\,W$

*28-38. Assume the following values for the parameters of the circuit illustrated in Fig. 28-8: $E_1 = 100\,V$, $E_2 = 20\,V$, $r_1 = 0.3\,\Omega$. $r_2 = 0.4\,\Omega$, and $R = 4\,\Omega$. What are the terminal voltages V_1 and V_2? What is the power lost through the 4-Ω resistor?

$I = \dfrac{100\,V - 20\,V}{4\,\Omega + 0.3\,\Omega + 0.4\,\Omega} = 17.0\,A$

$V_1 = E_1 - Ir = 100\,V - (17.0\,A)(0.3\,\Omega) = 94.9\,V$;

$V_2 = 20\,V + (17.0\,A)(0.4\,\Omega) = 26.8\,V$; $P = I^2 R = (17\,A)^2(4\,\Omega) = 1160\,W$

*28-39. Solve for the currents in each branch for Fig. 28-27.

Current rule: $I_1 = I_2 + I_3$;   *Loops:* $\Sigma E = \Sigma IR's$

(1) $5I_1 + 10I_2 = 12\,A$;   (2) $-10I_2 + 20I_3 = 6\,A$

(2) $-5I_2 + 10I_3 = 3\,A$;   (3) $5I_1 + 20I_3 = 18\,A$

From (1): $5(I_2 + I_3) + 10I_2 = 12\,A \rightarrow 15I_2 + 5I_3 = 12\,A$

Multiplying this equation by -2: $-30I_2 - 10I_3 = -24\,A$

Now add this to (2): $-35I_2 + 0 = -21\,A$ and $I_2 = 0.600\,A$

Now, from (1) and from (2): $I_1 = 1.20\,A$ and $I_3 = 0.600\,A$

*28-39. (Cont.)

Now add this to (2): $-35I_2 + 0 = -21$ A and $I_2 = 0.600$ A

Now, from (1) and from (2): $I_1 = 1.20$ A and $I_3 = 0.600$ A

*28-40. If the current in the 6-Ω resistor of Fig. 28-28 is 2 A, what is the emf of the battery? Neglect internal resistance. What is the power loss through the 1-Ω resistor?

$V_6 = (2\ A)(6\ \Omega) = 12$ V; $V_3 = 12$ V $= I_3(3\ \Omega)$

$I_3 = \dfrac{12\ V}{3\ \Omega} = 4$ A; $I_T = 2\ A + 4\ A = 6$ A;

$V_1 = (1\ \Omega)(6\ A) = 6$ V; $E = 6\ V + 12\ V = 18$ V; $P = I_T^2 R = (6\ A)^2(1\ \Omega) = 36$ W

Critical Thinking Problems

*28-41. A three-way light bulb uses two resistors, a 50-W filament and a 100-W filament. A three-way switch allows each to be connected in series and provides a third possibility by connecting the two filaments in parallel. Draw a possible arrangement of switches that will accomplish these tasks. Assume that the household voltage is 120 V. What are the resistances of each filament? What is the power of the parallel combination?

Switch can be set at A, B, or C to give three possibilities:

$P = \dfrac{V^2}{R}$; $R_1 = \dfrac{(120\ V)^2}{50\ W} = 288\ \Omega$; $R_2 = \dfrac{(120\ V)^2}{100\ W} = 144\ \Omega$

For Parallel: $R_e = \dfrac{(288\ \Omega)(144\ \Omega)}{288\ \Omega + 144\ \Omega} = 96\ \Omega$

$P = \dfrac{V^2}{R} = \dfrac{(120\ V)^2}{96\ \Omega}$; $P = 150$ W

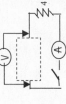

*28-42. The circuit illustrated in Fig. 28-7 consists of a 12-V battery, a 4-Ω resistor, and a switch. When new, the internal resistance of the battery is 0.4 Ω, and a voltmeter is placed across the terminals of the battery. What will be the reading of the voltmeter when the switch is open and when it is closed? After a long period of time, the experiment is repeated and it is noted that open circuit reading is unchanged, but the terminal voltage has reduced by 10 percent. How do you explain the lower terminal voltage? What is the internal resistance of the old battery?

When new: $I = \dfrac{E}{R+r} = \dfrac{12\ V}{4\ \Omega + 0.4\ \Omega}$; $I = 2.73$ A

$V_T = E - Ir = 12\ V - (2.73\ A)(0.4\ \Omega)$; $V_T = 10.9$ V

V_T reduced by 10% due to increase of r_{int}. $V' = 10.9\ V - 0.1(10.9\ V)$; $V' = 9.81$ V

$V' = IR_L = 9.81$ V; $I = \dfrac{9.81\ V}{4\ \Omega} = 2.45$ A; $V' = E - Ir$; $r = \dfrac{E - V'}{I}$

$r = \dfrac{E - V'}{I} = \dfrac{12\ V - 9.81\ V}{2.45\ A}$;

$r = 0.893\ \Omega$

*28-43. Given three resistors of 3, 9, and 18 Ω, list all the possible equivalent resistances that can be obtained through various connections?

All in parallel: $\dfrac{1}{R_e} = \dfrac{1}{3\ \Omega} + \dfrac{1}{9\ \Omega} + \dfrac{1}{18\ \Omega}$; $R_e = 2\ \Omega$

All in series: $R_e = R_1 + R_2 + R_3 = 3\ \Omega + 9\ \Omega + 18\ \Omega$; $R_e = 30\ \Omega$

Parallel (3,9) in series with (18): $R_e = \dfrac{(3\ \Omega)(9\ \Omega)}{3\ \Omega + 9\ \Omega} + 18\ \Omega$; $R_e = 20.2\ \Omega$

Parallel (3,18) in series with (9): $R_e = \dfrac{(3\ \Omega)(18\ \Omega)}{3\ \Omega + 18\ \Omega} + 9\ \Omega$; $R_e = 11.6\ \Omega$

Parallel (9,18) in series with (3): $R_e = \dfrac{(9\ \Omega)(18\ \Omega)}{9\ \Omega + 18\ \Omega} + 3\ \Omega$; $R_e = 9.00\ \Omega$

*28-45. What is the effective resistance of the external circuit for Fig. 28-29 if internal resistance is neglected. What is the current through the 1-Ω resistor?

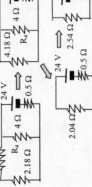

$$R_{4,5} = \frac{(3\,\Omega)(8\,\Omega)}{3\,\Omega + 8\,\Omega} = 2.18\,\Omega; \qquad R_{3,4,5} = 2.18\,\Omega + 1\,\Omega = 3.18\,\Omega;$$

$$R_{1,2,3,4} = \frac{(3.18\,\Omega)(6\,\Omega)}{3.18\,\Omega + 6\,\Omega}; \qquad R_{1,2,3,4} = 2.08\,\Omega$$

$$R_e = 2.08\,\Omega + 4\,\Omega; \qquad \boxed{R_e = 6.08\,\Omega}$$

I_3 in the 1-Ω resistor is same as I in $R_{3,4,5}$

$$I_T = \frac{24\,\text{V}}{6.08\,\Omega} = 3.95\,\text{A}$$

$$V_{2,3,4,5} = (3.95\,\text{A})(2.08\,\Omega) = 8.21\,\text{V}; \qquad Also \quad V_{3,4,5} = 8.21\,\text{V}$$

$$I_{3,4,5} = \frac{8.21\,\text{V}}{3.18\,\Omega} = 2.58\,\text{A}; \qquad Therefore \quad I_3 = 2.58\,\text{A} \; in \; 1\text{-}\Omega \; resistor$$

$$\boxed{R_e = 6.08\,\Omega; \quad I_3 = 2.58\,\text{A}}$$

---

*28-43 (Cont.) Series (3 + 9) in parallel with (18):

$$R_e = \frac{(12\,\Omega)(18\,\Omega)}{12\,\Omega + 18\,\Omega}; \qquad \boxed{R_e = 20.2\,\Omega}$$

Series (3 + 18) in parallel with (9):

$$R_e = \frac{(9\,\Omega)(21\,\Omega)}{9\,\Omega + 21\,\Omega}; \qquad \boxed{R_e = 6.30\,\Omega}$$

Series (9 + 18) in parallel with (3):

$$R_e = \frac{(3\,\Omega)(27\,\Omega)}{3\,\Omega + 27\,\Omega}; \qquad \boxed{R_e = 2.70\,\Omega}$$

*28-44. Referring to Fig. 28-21, assume that $E = 24\,\text{V}$, $R_1 = 8\,\Omega$, $R_2 = 3\,\Omega$, $R_3 = 2\,\Omega$, $R_4 = 4\,\Omega$, and $r = 0.5\,\Omega$. What current is delivered to the circuit by the 24-V battery? What are the voltage and current for the 8-Ω resistor?

$$R_{1,2} = \frac{(3\,\Omega)(8\,\Omega)}{3\,\Omega + 8\,\Omega} = 2.18\,\Omega; \qquad R_{1,2,3} = 2.18\,\Omega + 2\,\Omega = 4.18\,\Omega$$

$$R_e = \frac{(4.18\,\Omega)(4\,\Omega)}{4.18\,\Omega + 4\,\Omega} = 2.04\,\Omega;$$

$$R_e = 2.04\,\Omega + 0.5\,\Omega = 2.54\,\Omega$$

$$I_T = \frac{24\,\text{V}}{2.54\,\Omega}; \qquad I_T = 9.43\,\text{A}$$

$$V_4 = V_{1,2,3} = (9.43\,\text{A})\,(2.04\,\Omega) = 19.3\,\text{V}$$

$$I_4 = \frac{19.3\,\text{V}}{4\,\Omega} = 4.82\,\text{A}; \quad I_3 = 9.43\,\text{A} - 4.82\,\text{A} = 4.61\,\text{A}; \quad V_3 = (4.61\,\text{A})(2\,\Omega) = 9.23\,\text{V}$$

$$V_1 = V_2 = 19.3\,\text{V} - 9.23\,\text{V}; \quad V_1 = V_2 = 10.1\,\text{V}; \quad I_1 = \frac{10.1\,\text{V}}{8\,\Omega} = 1.26\,\text{A};$$

Finally, for the 8-Ω resistor: $\boxed{V_1 = 10.1\,\text{V} \; and \; I_1 = 1.26\,\text{A}}$

Chapter 29. Magnetism and the Electric Field

Magnetic Fields

29-1. The area of a rectangular loop is 200 cm² and the plane of the loop makes an angle of 41^0 with a 0.28-T magnetic field. What is the magnetic flux penetrating the loop?

$A = 200$ cm² $= 0.0200$ m²; $\theta = 41^0$; $B = 0.280$ T

$\phi = BA \sin \theta = (0.280$ T$)(0.0200$ m²$) \sin 41^0$; $\boxed{\phi = 3.67 \text{ mWb}}$

29-2. A coil of wire 30 cm in diameter is perpendicular to a 0.6-T magnetic field. If the coil turns so that it makes an angle of 60^0 with the field, what is the change in flux?

$A = \dfrac{\pi D^2}{4} = \dfrac{\pi (0.30 \text{ m})^2}{4}$; $A = 7.07 \times 10^{-2}$ m²; $\Delta\phi = \phi_f - \phi_o$

$\phi_o = BA \sin 90^0 = (0.6$ T$)(0.0707$ m²$)(1)$; $\phi_o = 42.4$ mWb

$\phi_f = BA \sin 60^0 = (0.6$ T$)(0.0707$ m²$)(1)$; $\phi_f = 36.7$ mWb

$\Delta\phi = \phi_f - \phi_o = 36.7$ mWb $- 42.4$ mWb; $\boxed{\Delta\phi = -5.68 \text{ mWb}}$

29-3. A constant horizontal field of 0.5 T pierces a rectangular loop 120 mm long and 70 mm wide. Determine the magnetic flux through the loop when its plane makes the following angles with the **B** field: 0^0, 30^0, 60^0, and 90^0. [Area $= 0.12$ m$)(0.07$ m$) = 8.40 \times 10^{-3}$ m²]

$\phi = BA \sin \theta$; $BA = (0.5$ T$)(8.4 \times 10^{-3}$ m²$) = 4.2 \times 10^{-3}$ T m²

$\phi_1 = (4.2 \times 10^{-3}$ T m²$) \sin 0^0 = $ $\boxed{0 \text{ Wb}}$; $\phi_2 = (4.2 \times 10^{-3}$ T m²$) \sin 30^0 = $ $\boxed{2.10 \text{ mWb}}$;

$\phi_3 = (4.2 \times 10^{-3}$ T m²$) \sin 60^0 = $ $\boxed{3.64 \text{ mWb}}$; $\phi_1 = (4.2 \times 10^{-3}$ T m²$) \sin 90^0 = $ $\boxed{4.20 \text{ mWb}}$

29-4. A flux of 13.6 mWb penetrates a coil of wire 240 mm in diameter. Find the magnitude of the magnetic flux density if the plane of the coil is perpendicular to the field.

$A = \dfrac{\pi D^2}{4} = \dfrac{\pi (0.240 \text{ m})^2}{4}$; $A = 4.52 \times 10^{-2}$ m²; $\phi = BA \sin \theta$

$B = \dfrac{\phi}{A \sin \theta} = \dfrac{0.0136 \text{ Wb}}{(4.52 \times 10^{-2} \text{m}^2)(1)}$; $\boxed{B = 0.300 \text{ T}}$

29-5. A magnetic flux of 50 μWb passes through a perpendicular loop of wire having an area of 0.78 m². What is the magnetic flux density?

$B = \dfrac{\phi}{A \sin \theta} = \dfrac{50 \times 10^{-6} \text{ Wb}}{(0.78 \text{ m}^2)(1)}$; $\boxed{B = 64.1 \text{ μT}}$

29-6. A rectangular loop 25 x 15 cm is oriented so that its plane makes an angle θ with a 0.6-T **B** field. What is the angle θ if the magnetic flux linking the loop is 0.015 Wb?

$A = (0.25$ m$)(0.15$ m$) = 0.0375$ m²; $\phi = 0.015$ Wb

$\phi = BA \sin \theta$; $\sin \theta = \dfrac{\phi}{BA} = \dfrac{0.015 \text{ Wb}}{(0.6 \text{ T})(0.0375 \text{ m}^2)}$; $\boxed{\theta = 41.8^0}$

The Force on Moving Charge

29-7. A proton ($q = +1.6 \times 10^{-19}$ C) is injected to the right into a **B** field of 0.4 T directed upward. If the velocity of the proton is 2×10^6 m/s, what are the magnitude and direction of the magnetic force on the proton?

$F = qvB_\perp = (1.6 \times 10^{-19}$ C$)(2 \times 10^6$ m/s$)(0.4$ T$)$

$\boxed{F = 1.28 \times 10^{-13} \text{ N, into paper}}$

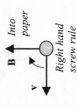

B *Into paper* **v** *Right hand screw rule*

29-8. An alpha particle (+2e) is projected with a velocity of 3.6 x 10⁶ m/s into a 0.12-T magnetic field. What is the magnetic force on the charge at the instant its velocity is directed at an angle of 35⁰ with the magnetic flux? [$q = 2 (1.6 \times 10^{-19}$ C) $= 3.2 \times 10^{-19}$ C]

$F = qvB \sin\theta = (3.2 \times 10^{-19}$ C$)(3.6 \times 10^6$ m/s$)(0.12$ T$) \sin 35^0$; $\boxed{F = 7.93 \times 10^{-14} \text{ N}}$

29-9. An electron moves with a velocity of 5 x 10⁵ m/s at an angle of 60⁰ with an eastward B field. The electron experiences an force of 3.2 x 10⁻¹⁸ N directed into the paper. What are the magnitude of B and the direction the velocity v?

In order for the force to be INTO the paper for a NEGATIVE charge, the 60⁰ angle must be S of E. $\boxed{\theta = 60^0 \text{ S of E.}}$

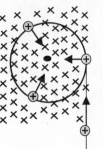

$B = \dfrac{F}{qv \sin\theta} = \dfrac{3.2 \times 10^{-18} \text{N}}{(1.6 \times 10^{-19} \text{C})(5 \times 10^5 \text{ m/s})}$; $\boxed{B = 46.3 \ \mu\text{T}}$

29-10. A proton (+1e) is moving vertically upward with a velocity of 4 x 10⁶ m/s. It passes through a 0.4-T magnetic field directed to the right. What are the magnitude and direction of the magnetic force?

$F = qvB_\perp = (1.6 \times 10^{-19}$ C$)(4 \times 10^6$ m/s$)(0.4$ T$)$;

$\boxed{F = 2.56 \times 10^{-13} \text{ N, directed into paper.}}$

Force is into paper.

29-11. What if an electron replaces the proton in Problem 29-10. What is the magnitude and direction of the magnetic force?

The direction of the magnetic force on an electron is opposite to that of the proton, but the magnitude of the force is unchanged since the magnitude of the charge is the same.

$\boxed{F_e = 2.56 \times 10^{-13} \text{ N, out of paper.}}$

*29-12. A particle having a charge q and a mass m is projected into a **B** field directed into the paper. If the particle has a velocity v, show that it will be deflected into a circular path of radius:

$$R = \frac{mv}{qB}$$

Draw a diagram of the motion, assuming a positive charge entering the **B** field from left to right. Hint: The magnetic force provides the necessary centripetal force for the circular motion.

$F_C = \dfrac{mv^2}{R}$; $F_B = qvB$; $\dfrac{mv^2}{R} = qvB$

From which: $R = \dfrac{mv}{qB}$

The diagram shows that the magnetic force is a centripetal force that acts toward the center causing the charge to move in a counterclockwise circle of radius R.

*29-13. A deuteron is a nuclear particle consisting of a proton and a neutron bound together by nuclear forces. The mass of a deuteron is 3.347 x 10⁻²⁷ kg, and its charge is +1e. A deuteron projected into a magnetic field of flux density 1.2 T is observed to travel in a circular path of radius 300 mm. What is the velocity of the deuteron? See Problem 29-12.

$F_C = \dfrac{mv^2}{R}$; $F_B = qvB$; $\dfrac{mv^2}{R} = qvB$; $v = \dfrac{qRB}{m}$

$v = \dfrac{qRB}{m} = \dfrac{(1.6 \times 10^{-19} \text{C})(0.3 \text{ m})(1.2 \text{ T})}{3.347 \times 10^{-27} \text{ kg}}$; $v = 1.72 \times 10^7$ m/s

Note: This speed which is about 6% of the speed of light is still not fast enough to cause significant effects due to relativity (see Chapter 38.)

Force on a Current-Carrying Conductor

29-14. A wire 1 m in length supports a current of 5.00 A and is perpendicular to a **B** field of 0.034 T. What is the magnetic force on the wire?

$$F = I B_\perp l = (5 \text{ A})(0.034 \text{ T})(1 \text{ m}); \quad \boxed{F = 0.170 \text{ N}}$$

29-15. A long wire carries a current of 6 A in a direction 35° north of an easterly 40-mT magnetic field. What are the magnitude and direction of the force on each centimeter of wire?

$$F = Il B \sin\theta = (6 \text{ A})(0.040 \text{ T})(0.01 \text{ m})\sin 35°$$

$$\boxed{F = 1.38 \times 10^{-3} \text{ N}, \text{ into paper}}$$

The force is into paper as can be seen by turning I into B to advance a screw inward.

29-16. A 12-cm segment of wire carries a current of 4.0 A directed at an angle of 41° north of an easterly **B** field. What must be the magnitude of the **B** field if it is to produce a 5 N force on this segment of wire? What is the direction of the force?

$$B = \frac{F}{Il\sin\theta} = \frac{5.00 \text{ N}}{(4.0 \text{ A})(0.12 \text{ m})\sin 41°}; \quad \boxed{B = 15.9 \text{ T}}$$

The force is directed inward according to the right-hand rule.

29-17. An 80 mm segment of wire is at an angle of 53° south of a westward, 2.3-T **B** field. What are the magnitude and direction of the current in this wire if it experiences a force of 2 N directed out of the paper?

$B = 2.30$ T; $l = 0.080$ m; $\theta = 53°$; $F = 2.00$ N

$$I = \frac{F}{Bl\sin\theta} = \frac{2.00 \text{ N}}{(2.3 \text{ T})(0.080 \text{ m})\sin 53°}; \quad \boxed{I = 13.6 \text{ A}}$$

The current must be directed 53° N of E if I turned into B produces outward force.

---

*29-18. The linear density of a certain wire is 50.0 g/m. A segment of this wire carries a current of 30 A in a direction perpendicular to the **B** field. What must be the magnitude of the magnetic field required to suspend the wire by balancing its weight?

$$\lambda = \frac{m}{l}; \quad m = \lambda l; \quad W = mg = \lambda lg; \quad F_B = W = \lambda lg \quad F_B = IlB$$

$$\lambda lg = IlB; \quad B = \frac{\lambda g}{I} = \frac{(0.050 \text{ kg/m})(9.8 \text{ m/s}^2)}{30 \text{ A}}; \quad \boxed{B = 16.3 \text{ mT}}$$

Calculating Magnetic Fields

29-19. What is the magnetic induction **B** in air at a point 4 cm from a long wire carrying a current of 6 A?

$$B = \frac{\mu_0 I}{2\pi l} = \frac{(4\pi \times 10^{-7} \text{T} \cdot \text{m/A})(6 \text{ A})}{2\pi(0.04 \text{ m})}; \quad \boxed{B = 30.0 \text{ μT}}$$

29-20. Find the magnetic induction in air 8 mm from a long wire carrying a current of 14.0 A.

$$B = \frac{\mu_0 I}{2\pi l} = \frac{(4\pi \times 10^{-7} \text{T} \cdot \text{m/A})(14 \text{ A})}{2\pi(0.008 \text{ m})}; \quad \boxed{B = 350 \text{ μT}}$$

29-21. A circular coil having 40 turns of wire in air has a radius of 6 cm and is in the plane of the paper. What current must exist in the coil to produce a flux density of 2 mT at its center?

$$B = \frac{\mu_0 NI}{2r}; \quad I = \frac{2rB}{\mu_0 N};$$

$$I = \frac{2(0.06 \text{ m})(0.002 \text{ T})}{(4\pi \times 10^{-7} \text{T} \cdot \text{m/A})(40)}; \quad \boxed{I = 4.77 \text{ A}}$$

29-22. If the direction of the current in the coil of Problem 29-21 is clockwise, what is the direction of the magnetic field at the center of the loop?

If you grasp the loop with your right hand so that the thumb points in the direction of the current, it is seen that the B field will be directed OUT of the paper at the center of the loop.

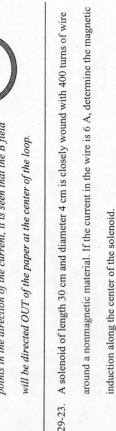

29-23. A solenoid of length 30 cm and diameter 4 cm is closely wound with 400 turns of wire around a nonmagnetic material. If the current in the wire is 6 A, determine the magnetic induction along the center of the solenoid.

$$B = \frac{\mu_0 NI}{l} = \frac{(4\pi \times 10^{-7}\,T \cdot m/A)(400)(6\ A)}{0.300\ m} ; \quad \boxed{B = 10.1\ \text{mT}}$$

29-24. A circular coil having 60 turns has a radius of 75 mm. What current must exist in the coil to produce a flux density of 300 μT at the center of the coil?

$$I = \frac{2rB}{\mu_0 N} = \frac{2(0.075\ m)(300 \times 10^{-6}\,T)}{(4\pi \times 10^{-7}\,T \cdot m/A)(60)}; \quad \boxed{I = 0.597\ \text{A}}$$

*29-25. A circular loop 240 mm in diameter supports a current of 7.8 A. If it is submerged in a medium of relative permeability 2.0, what is the magnetic induction at the center?

$$r = \tfrac{1}{2}(240\ mm) = 120\ mm; \quad \mu = 2\mu_0 = 8\pi \times 10^{-7}\ T\ m/A$$

$$B = \frac{\mu NI}{2r} = \frac{(8\pi \times 10^{-7}\,T \cdot m/A)(1)(7.8\ A)}{2(0.120\ m)}; \quad \boxed{B = 81.7\ \mu T}$$

---

*29-26. A circular loop of radius 50 mm in the plane of the paper carries a counterclockwise current of 15 A. It is submerged in a medium whose relative permeability is 3.0. What are the magnitude and direction of the magnetic induction at the center of the loop?

$$B = \frac{\mu NI}{2r} = \frac{3(4\pi \times 10^{-7}\,T \cdot m/A)(1)(15\ A)}{2(0.050\ m)}; \quad \boxed{B = 565\ \mu T}$$

Supplementary Problems

29-27. A +3-μC charge is projected with a velocity of 5 x 10⁵ m/s along the positive x axis perpendicular to a **B** field. If the charge experiences an upward force of 6.0×10^{-3} N, what must be the magnitude and direction of the **B** field?

v = 5 x 10⁵ m/s

$$F = qvB \sin\theta; \quad B = \frac{F}{qv} = \frac{6 \times 10^{-3}\,N}{(3 \times 10^{-6}\,C)(5 \times 10^5\,m/s)}$$

$$\boxed{B = 4.00\ \text{mT, directed into paper.}} \qquad \textit{Direction from right-hand rule.}$$

29-28. An unknown charge is projected with a velocity of 4 x 10⁵ m/s from right to left into a 0.4-T **B** field directed out of the paper. The perpendicular force of 5×10^{-3} N causes the particle to move in a clockwise circle. What are the magnitude and sign of the charge?

If the charge were positive, the force should be downward by the right-hand rule. Since in is upward, the charge must be negative. We find the magnitude as follows:

$$F = qvB \sin\theta; \quad q = \frac{F}{vB} = \frac{5 \times 10^{-3}\,N}{(4 \times 10^5\,m/s)(0.4\ T)}; \quad q = 31.2\ nC$$

The charge is therefore: $\boxed{q = -31.2\ \text{nC}}$

*29-32. A velocity selector is a device (Fig. 29-26) that utilizes crossed E and B fields to select ions of only one velocity v. Positive ions of charge q are projected into the perpendicular fields at varying speeds. Ions with velocities sufficient to make the magnetic force equal and opposite to the electric force pass through the bottom of the slit undeflected. Show that the speed of these ions can be found from

$$v = \frac{E}{B}$$

The electric force (qE) must balance the magnetic force (qvB) for zero deflection:

$$qE = qvB; \qquad \boxed{v = \frac{E}{B}}$$

29-33. What is the velocity of protons (+1e) injected through a velocity selector (see Problem 29-32) if E = 3 x 10⁵ V/m and B = 0.25 T?

$$v = \frac{E}{B} = \frac{3 \times 10^5\ V/m}{0.25\ T}; \qquad \boxed{v = 1.20 \times 10^6\ m/s}$$

*29-34. A singly charged Li⁷ ion (+1e) is accelerated through a potential difference of 500 V and then enters at right angles to a magnetic field of 0.4 T. The radius of the resulting circular path is 2.13 cm. What is the mass of the lithium ion?

First we find the entrance velocity from energy considerations: *Work = $\Delta(K.E.)$*

$$qV = \tfrac{1}{2}mv^2; \qquad v = \sqrt{\frac{2qV}{m}}; \quad and \quad \frac{mv^2}{R} = qvB; \qquad v = \frac{qBR}{m} \qquad set\ v = v$$

$$\sqrt{\frac{2qV}{m}} = \frac{qBR}{m} \quad or \quad \frac{2qV}{m} = \frac{q^2B^2R^2}{m^2} \quad and \quad m = \frac{qB^2R^2}{2V}$$

$$m = \frac{qB^2R^2}{2V} = \frac{(1.6 \times 10^{-19}C)(0.4\ T)^2(0.0213\ m)^2}{2(500\ V)}; \qquad \boxed{m = 1.16 \times 10^{-26}\ kg}$$

29-29. A –8-nC charge is projected upward at 4 x 10⁵ m/s into a 0.60-T B field directed into the paper. The field produces a force (F = qvB) that is also a centripetal force (mv²/R). What is the mass of the charge and does it move clockwise or counterclockwise?

$$\frac{mv^2}{R} = qvB; \qquad m = \frac{qBR}{v} = \frac{(8 \times 10^{-9})(0.6\ T)(0.20\ m)}{4 \times 10^5\ m/s}$$

$$\boxed{m = 2.40 \times 10^{-15}\ kg}$$

Since the charge is negative, the magnetic force is to the left and the motion is clockwise.

29-30. What is the magnitude and direction of the B field 6 cm above a long segment of wire carrying a 9-A current directed out of the paper? What is the magnitude and direction of the B field 6 cm below the segment?

Wrapping the fingers around the wire with thumb pointing outward

shows that the direction of the B field is counterclockwise around wire.

$$B_1 = \frac{\mu_0 I}{2\pi I_1} = \frac{(4\pi \times 10^{-7}\,T\cdot m/A)(9\ A)}{2\pi(0.06\ m)}; \qquad \boxed{B_1 = 30\ \mu T,\ to\ left}$$

$$B_2 = \frac{\mu_0 I}{2\pi I_2} = \frac{(4\pi \times 10^{-7}\,T\cdot m/A)(9\ A)}{2\pi(0.06\ m)}; \qquad \boxed{B_1 = 30\ \mu T,\ to\ right}$$

29-31. A 24 cm length of wire makes an angle of 32⁰ above a horizontal B field of 0.44 T along the positive x axis. What are the magnitude and direction of the current required to produce a force of 4 mN directed out of the paper?

The current must be 32⁰ downward and to the left.

$$I = \frac{F}{lB\sin\theta} = \frac{4 \times 10^{-3}N}{(0.24\ m)(0.44\ T)\sin 32^0}; \qquad \boxed{I = 71.5\ mA}$$

*29-38. Two parallel wires carrying currents I_1 and I_2 are separated by a distance d. Show that the force per unit length F/l each wire exerts on the other is given by

$$\frac{F}{\ell} = \frac{\mu I_1 I_2}{2\pi d}$$

Wire 1 finds itself in a magnetic field created by the current in wire 2. Thus, the force on wire 1 due to its own current can be calculated:

$$F_1 = I_1 B_2 l_1 \quad and \quad B_2 = \frac{\mu I_2}{2\pi d}; \qquad F_1 = I_1\!\left(\frac{\mu I_2}{2\pi d}\right)l_1 \quad (Force\ on\ wire\ 1\ due\ to\ B_2)$$

Same result would be obtained by considering force on wire 2 due to B_1, Thus,

$$\boxed{\frac{F}{l} = \frac{\mu I_1 I_2}{2\pi d}}$$

*29-39. Two wires lying in a horizontal plane carry parallel currents of 15 A each and are 200 mm apart in air. If both currents are directed to the right, what are the magnitude and direction of the flux density at a point midway between the wires?

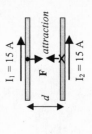

The magnitudes of the B fields at the midpoint are the same, but B_{upper} is inward and B_{lower} is outward, so that $B_{net} = 0$.

$$\boxed{B_{midpoint} = 0}$$

*29-40. What is the force per unit length that each wire in Problem 29-39 exerts on the other? Is it attraction or repulsion?

$$\frac{F}{l} = \frac{\mu_0 I_1 I_2}{2\pi d} = \frac{(4\pi \times 10^{-7}\,T\cdot m/A)(15\,A)(15\,A)}{2\pi(0.200\,m)}$$

$$\boxed{\frac{F}{l} = 2.25 \times 10^{-4}\ N/m,\ attraction}$$

The force on upper wire due to B_{lower} is downward; The force on lower wire is upward.

---

*29-35. A singly charged sodium ion (+1e) moves through a B field with a velocity of 4×10^4 m/s. What must be the magnitude of the B field if the ion is to follow a circular path of radius 200 mm? (The mass of the sodium ion is 3.818×10^{-27} kg).

$$\frac{mv^2}{R} = qvB; \quad B = \frac{mv}{qR} = \frac{(3.818 \times 10^{-27}\,kg)(4 \times 10^4\,m/s)}{(1.6 \times 10^{-19}\,C)(0.200\,m)}; \quad \boxed{B = 4.77\ mT}$$

*29-36. The cross sections of two parallel wires are located 8 cm apart in air. The left wire carries a current of 6 A out of the paper and the right wire carries a current of 4 A into the paper. What is the resultant magnetic induction at the midpoint A due to both wires?

Applying right thumb rule, both fields are UP.

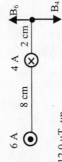

$$B_6 = \frac{(4\pi \times 10^{-7}\,T\cdot m/A)(6\,A)}{2\pi(0.04\,m)} = 30.0\,\mu T,\ up$$

$$B_4 = \frac{(4\pi \times 10^{-7}\,T\cdot m/A)(4\,A)}{2\pi(0.04\,m)} = 20.0\,\mu T,\ up; \quad B_R = 30\,\mu T + 20\,\mu T; \quad \boxed{B_R = 50\,\mu T,\ up}$$

*29-37. What is the resultant magnetic field at point B located 2 cm to the right of the 4-A wire?

Find the fields due to each wire, and then add them as vectors at the point 2 cm to the right.

$$B_6 = \frac{(4\pi \times 10^{-7}\,T\cdot m/A)(6\,A)}{2\pi(0.10\,m)} = 12.0\,\mu T,\ up$$

$$B_4 = \frac{(4\pi \times 10^{-7}\,T\cdot m/A)(4\,A)}{2\pi(0.04\,m)} = 40.0\,\mu T,\ down$$

$$B_R = 12\,\mu T - 40\,\mu T; \quad \boxed{B_R = 28\,\mu T,\ downward}$$

*29-41.

A solenoid of length 20 cm and 220 turns carries a coil current of 5 A. What should be the relative permeability of the core to produce a magnetic induction of 0.2 T at the center of the coil?

$$B = \frac{\mu N I}{L}; \quad \mu = \frac{BL}{NI} = \frac{(0.2\ \text{T})(0.20\ \text{m})}{(220)(5\ \text{A})}; \quad \mu = 3.64 \times 10^{-5}\ \text{T}\cdot\text{m/A}$$

$$\mu_r = \frac{\mu}{\mu_0} = \frac{3.64 \times 10^{-5}\ \text{T}\cdot\text{m/A}}{4\pi \times 10^{-7}\ \text{T}\cdot\text{m/A}}; \quad \boxed{\mu_r = 28.9}$$

*29-42.

A one meter segment of wire is fixed so that it cannot move, and it carries a current of 6 A directed north. Another 1-m wire segment is located 2 cm above the fixed wire. If the upper wire has a mass of 0.40 g, what must be the magnitude and direction of the current in the upper wire if its weight is to be balanced by the magnetic force due to the field of the fixed wire?

$$F = mg = (0.04\ \text{kg})(9.8\ \text{m/s}^2) = 0.00392\ \text{N}; \quad \frac{F}{l} = \frac{\mu_0 I_1 I_2}{2\pi d}$$

$$I_1 = \frac{2\pi d F}{\mu_0 I_2 l} = \frac{2\pi (0.02\ \text{m})(0.00392\ \text{N})}{(4\pi \times 10^{-7}\ \text{T}\cdot\text{m/A})(6\ \text{A})(1\ \text{m})}; \quad I_1 = 65.3\ \text{A}$$

The direction of I_1 must be south (left) in order to produce an upward force.

$$\boxed{I_1 = 65.3\ \text{A, south}}$$

*29-43.

What is the resultant magnetic field at point C in Fig. 29-27.

$$B_4 = \frac{\mu_0 I_4}{2\pi d} = \frac{(4\pi \times 10^{-7}\ \text{T}\cdot\text{m/A})(4\ \text{A})}{2\pi(0.08\ \text{m})} = 10.0\ \mu\text{T}$$

$$B_6 = \frac{\mu_0 I_4}{2\pi d} = \frac{(4\pi \times 10^{-7}\ \text{T}\cdot\text{m/A})(6\ \text{A})}{2\pi(0.08\ \text{m})} = 15.0\ \mu\text{T}$$

Right hand rules, give directions of B_4 and B_6 as shown.

---

*29-43. (Cont.);

$B_4 = 15\ \mu\text{T}$, 60^0 N of E; $B_6 = 10\ \mu\text{T}$, 60^0 N of W.

$$B_x = (10\ \mu\text{T})\cos 60^0 - (15\ \mu\text{T})\cos 60^0 = -2.50\ \mu\text{T}$$

$$B_y = (10\ \mu\text{T})\sin 60^0 + (15\ \mu\text{T})\sin 60^0 = 21.65\ \mu\text{T}$$

$$B = \sqrt{(-2.5)^2 + (21.65)^2} \quad \boxed{B = 21.8\ \mu\text{T}}$$

$$\tan\theta = \frac{21.65\ \mu\text{T}}{-2.5\ \mu\text{T}}; \quad \boxed{\theta = 96.6^0}$$

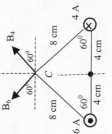

Critical Thinking Problems

*29-44.

A magnetic field of 0.4 T is directed into the paper. Three particles are injected into the field in an upward direction, each with a velocity of 5×10^5 m/s. Particle 1 is observed to move in a clockwise circle of radius 30 cm; particle 2 continues to travel in a straight line; and particle 3 is observed to move counterclockwise in a circle of radius 40 cm. What are the magnitude and sign of the charge per unit mass (q/m) for each of the particles? (Apply right-hand rule to each.)

Particle 1 has a rightward force on entering.

It's charge is therefore negative; Particle 3 has a leftward force and is therefore positive.

Particle 3 has zero charge (undeviated.)

$$\frac{mv^2}{R} = qvB; \quad \frac{q}{m} = \frac{v}{RB} \quad \text{in each instance.}$$

Particle 1: $\dfrac{q}{m} = \dfrac{v}{RB} = \dfrac{5 \times 10^5\ \text{m/s}}{(0.30\ \text{m})(0.4\ \text{T})};$ $\boxed{\dfrac{q}{m} = -4.17 \times 10^6\ \text{C/kg}}$

Particle 3: $\dfrac{q}{m} = \dfrac{v}{RB} = \dfrac{5 \times 10^5\ \text{m/s}}{(0.40\ \text{m})(0.4\ \text{T})};$ $\boxed{\dfrac{q}{m} = +3.12 \times 10^6\ \text{C/kg}}$

$\boxed{\text{Particle 2 has zero charge and zero q/m. (No deviation.)}}$

*29-45. A 4.0 A current flows through the circular coils of a solenoid in a counterclockwise direction as viewed along the positive x axis which is aligned with the air core of the solenoid. What is the direction of the B field along the central axis? How many turns per meter of length is required to produce a B field of 0.28 T? If the air core is replaced by a material whose relative permeability is 150, what current would be needed to produce the same 0.28-T field as before?

Grasping the coil from the near side with the thumb pointing upward, shows the field at the center to be directed to the left (negative).

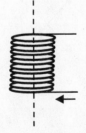

$$B = \frac{\mu N I}{L} = \mu n I, \quad \text{where} \quad n = \frac{N}{L}, \quad n = \frac{B}{\mu L} = \frac{0.28\ \text{T}}{(4\pi \times 10^{-7}\,\text{T}\cdot\text{m/A})(4\ \text{A})}$$

$$\boxed{n = 55{,}000\ \text{turns/m}}$$

$$\mu = \mu_r \mu_0 = 150(4\pi x \times 10^{-7}\,\text{T}\cdot\text{m/A}) = 1.88 \times 10^{-4}\ \text{T m/A}$$

$$I = \frac{B}{\mu n} = \frac{0.28\ \text{T}}{(1.88 \times 10^{-4}\,\text{T}\cdot\text{m/A})(55{,}000\ \text{turns/m})};$$

$$\boxed{I = 27.0\ \text{mA}}$$

*29-46. The plane of a current loop 50 cm long and 25 cm wide is parallel to a 0.3 T **B** field directed along the positive x axis. The 50 cm segments are parallel with the field and the 25 cm segments are perpendicular to the field. When looking down from the top, the 6-A current is clockwise around the loop. Draw a sketch to show the directions of the **B** field and the directions of the currents in each wire segment. (a) What are the magnitude and direction of the magnetic force acting on each wire segment? (b) What is the resultant torque on the current loop?

The top view is shown to the right:

Forces on segments AB and CD are each equal to zero, since I is parallel to B.

*29-46. (Cont.) *Forces on AC and BD are equal and opposite, as shown in front view, but form a torque couple. Resultant is sum of each.*

$$F_{AC} = BiL_{AC} = (0.3\ \text{T})(6\ \text{A})(0.25\ \text{m}) = 0.450\ \text{N}$$

$$\boxed{F_{AC} = 0.450\ \text{N, down}; \quad F_{BD} = 0.450\ \text{N, up}}$$

$$\tau_R = F_{AC}\frac{l_{CD}}{2} + F_{BD}\frac{l_{CD}}{2} = (0.450\ \text{N})(0.25\ \text{m}) + (0.450\ \text{N})(0.25\ \text{m})$$

$$\boxed{\tau_R = 0.225\ \text{N·m, counterclockwise about z axis.}}$$

*29-47. Consider the two wires in Fig. 29-29 where the dot indicates current out of the page and the cross indicates current into the page. What is the resultant flux density at points A, B, and C? *First consider point A. The field due to 5 A is directed downward at A, and the field due to 8 A is directed upward.*

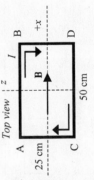

$$B_5 = \frac{-(4\pi \times 10^{-7}\,\text{T}\cdot\text{m/A})(5\ \text{A})}{2\pi(0.02\ \text{m})} = -50\ \mu\text{T}$$

$$B_8 = \frac{(4\pi \times 10^{-7}\,\text{T}\cdot\text{m/A})(8\ \text{A})}{2\pi(0.10\ \text{m})} = +16\ \mu\text{T}$$

$$B_A = -50\ \mu\text{T} + 16\ \mu\text{T}; \quad \boxed{B_A = -34\ \mu\text{T, downward}}$$

Next consider field at point B:

$$B_B = \frac{(4\pi \times 10^{-7}\,\text{T}\cdot\text{m/A})(5\ \text{A})}{2\pi(0.06\ \text{m})} + \frac{(4\pi \times 10^{-7}\,\text{T}\cdot\text{m/A})(8\ \text{A})}{2\pi(0.02\ \text{m})};$$

$$\boxed{B_B = +96.7\ \mu\text{T, upward}}$$

$$\tan\theta = \frac{6\ \text{cm}}{8\ \text{cm}}; \quad \theta = 36.9^\circ; \quad R = \sqrt{(8\ \text{cm})^2 + (6\ \text{cm})^2} = 10\ \text{cm}$$

At C: $B_x = B_5 \cos\theta + B_8$ and $B_y = + B_5 \sin\theta$

$$B_x = \frac{-(4\pi \times 10^{-7}\,\text{T}\cdot\text{m/A})(5\ \text{A})}{2\pi(0.10\ \text{m})}\cos 36.9^\circ + \frac{(4\pi \times 10^{-7}\,\text{T}\cdot\text{m/A})(8\ \text{A})}{2\pi(0.06\ \text{m})};$$

$$B_x = 20.7\ \mu\text{T}$$

$$B_x = \frac{(4\pi \times 10^{-7}\,\text{T}\cdot\text{m/A})(5\ \text{A})}{2\pi(0.10\ \text{m})}\sin 36.9^\circ = 8.00\ \mu\text{T};$$

$$\boxed{B_R = 22.2\ \mu\text{T}, 21.2^0}$$

Chapter 30. Forces and Torques in a Magnetic Field

Magnetic Torque on a Loop (α is angle that *plane* of loop makes with **B** field.)

30-1. A rectangular loop of wire has an area of 30 cm^2 and is placed with its plane parallel to a 0.56-T magnetic field. What is the magnitude of the resultant torque if the loop carries a current of 15 A? (1 cm^2 = 1 x 10^{-4} m^2)

$\tau = NBIA\cos\alpha = (1)(0.56$ T$)(15$ A$)(30 \times 10^{-4}$ m$^2)\cos 0^0$; $\boxed{\tau = 0.0252 \text{ N·m}}$

30-2. A coil of wire has 100 turns, each of area 20 cm^2. The coil is free to turn in a 4.0 T field. What current is required to produce a maximum torque of 2.30 N·m?

$I = \dfrac{\tau}{NBA\cos\alpha} = \dfrac{2.30 \text{ N·m}}{(100)(4.0 \text{ T})(20 \times 10^{-4} \text{ m}^2)(1)}$; $\boxed{I = 2.88 \text{ A}}$

30-3. A rectangular loop of wire 6 cm wide and 10 cm long is placed with its plane parallel to a magnetic field of 0.08 T. What is the magnitude of the resultant torque on the loop if it carries a current of 14.0 A. [A = (0.10 m)(0.06 m) = 6 x 10^{-3} m^2]

$\tau = NBIA\cos\alpha = (1)(0.08$ T$)(14$ A$)(6 \times 10^{-3}$ m$^2)\cos 0^0$; $\boxed{\tau = 6.72 \times 10^{-3} \text{ N·m}}$

30-4. A rectangular loop of wire has an area of 0.30 m^2. The plane of the loop makes an angle of 30^0 with a 0.75-T magnetic field. What is torque on the loop if the current is 7.0 A?

$\tau = NBIA\cos\alpha = (1)(0.75$ T$)(7.0$ A$)(0.30$ m$^2)\cos 30^0$; $\boxed{\tau = 1.36 \text{ N·m}}$

30-5. Calculate the B field required to give a 100-turn coil a torque of 0.5 N m when its plane is parallel to the field. The dimensions of each turn is 84 cm^2 and the current is 9.0 A.

$B = \dfrac{\tau}{NIA\cos\alpha} = \dfrac{0.500 \text{ N·m}}{(100)(9.0 \text{ A})(84 \times 10^{-4} \text{ m}^2)\cos 0^0}$; $\boxed{B = 66.1 \text{ mT}}$

---

*29-48. Two long, fixed, parallel wires A and B are 10 cm apart in air and carry currents of 6 A and 4 A, respectively, in opposite directions. (a) Determine the net flux density at a point midway between the wires. (b) What is the magnetic force per unit length on a third wire placed midway between A and B and carrying a current of 2 A in the same direction as A?

Applying right thumb rule, both fields are UP.

$B_6 = \dfrac{(4\pi \times 10^{-7} \text{T·m/A})(6 \text{ A})}{2\pi(0.05 \text{ m})} = 24.0 \text{ μT, } up$

$B_4 = \dfrac{(4\pi \times 10^{-7} \text{T·m/A})(4 \text{ A})}{2\pi(0.05 \text{ m})} = 16.0 \text{ μT, } up$; $B_R = 24 \text{ μT} + 16 \text{ μT}$; $\boxed{B_R = 40 \text{ μT, } up}$

Currents in same direction attract each other; Currents in opposite directions repel:

$\dfrac{F}{l} = \dfrac{\mu_0 I_1 I_2}{2\pi d} = \dfrac{(4\pi \times 10^{-7} \text{T·m/A})(6 \text{ A})(2 \text{ A})}{2\pi(0.05 \text{ m})}$

$\dfrac{F_{AC}}{l} = 48 \text{ μN/m, } toward A$

$\dfrac{F}{l} = \dfrac{\mu_0 I_1 I_2}{2\pi d} = \dfrac{(4\pi \times 10^{-7} \text{T·m/A})(4 \text{ A})(2 \text{ A})}{2\pi(0.05 \text{ m})}$

$\dfrac{F_{BC}}{l} = 32 \text{ μN/m, } toward A$

Therefore, the resultant force per unit length on the 2 A wire is: 48 μN/m + 32μN/m

$\boxed{Resultant\ F/l = 80 \text{ μN/m, } toward A}$

30-6. What current is required to produce a maximum torque of 0.8 N·m on a solenoid having 800 turns of area 0.4 m²? The flux density is 3.0 mT. What is the position of the solenoid in the field? (*For solenoid, θ is the angle that coil axis makes with B field*).

The torque is a maximum when: $\boxed{\theta = 90}$

$$I = \frac{\tau}{NBA\sin\theta} = \frac{0.80 \text{ N·m}}{(800)(0.003 \text{ T})(0.4 \text{ m}^2)\sin 90^0}; \quad \boxed{I = 833 \text{ mA}}$$

30-7. The axis of a solenoid, having 750 turns of wire, makes an angle of 34⁰ with a 5-mT field. What is the current if the torque is 4.0 N at that angle. The area of each turn of wire is 0.25 m².

$$I = \frac{\tau}{NBA\sin\theta} = \frac{4.00 \text{ N·m}}{(750)(0.005 \text{ T})(0.25 \text{ m}^2)\sin 34^0}; \quad \boxed{I = 7.63 \text{ A}}$$

Galvanometers, Voltmeters, and Ammeters

30-8. A galvanometer coil 50 mm x 120 mm is mounted in a constant radial 0.2-T B field. If the coil has 600 turns, what current is required to develop a torque of 3.6 x 10⁻⁵ N m?

$A = (0.05 \text{ m})(0.120 \text{ m}) = 6 \times 10^{-3} \text{ m}^2; \quad \theta = 90^0; \quad B = 0.200 \text{ T}; \quad \tau = 3 \times 10^{-5} \text{ N·m}$

$$I = \frac{\tau}{NBA\sin\theta} = \frac{3.60 \times 10^{-5} \text{ N·m}}{(600)(0.2 \text{ T})(6 \times 10^{-3} \text{ m}^2)\sin 90^0}; \quad \boxed{I = 50.0 \text{ µA}}$$

30-9. A galvanometer has a sensitivity of 20 µA per scale division. What current is required to give full-scale deflection with 25 divisions on either side of the central equilibrium position?

$$I = 25 \text{ div}(20 \text{ µA/div}); \quad \boxed{I = 500 \text{ µA}}$$

30-10. A galvanometer has a sensitivity of 15 µA per scale division. How many scale divisions will be covered by the deflecting needle when the current is 60 µA?

$$Number = \frac{60 \text{ µA}}{15 \text{ µA/div}}; \quad \boxed{Number = 15 \text{ div}}$$

30-11. A certain voltmeter draws 0.02 mA for full-scale deflection at 50 V. (a) What is the resistance of the voltmeter? (b) What is the resistance per volt?

$$R_v = \frac{50 \text{ V}}{2 \times 10^{-5} \text{ A}} = 2.5 \times 10^6 \text{ Ω}; \quad \boxed{R_v = 2.5 \text{ MΩ}}$$

$$\frac{R}{V} = \frac{2.5 \times 10^6 \text{ Ω}}{50 \text{ V}}; \quad \boxed{\frac{R}{V} = 50.0 \text{ kΩ/V}}$$

*30-12. For the voltmeter in Problem 30-11, what multiplier resistance must be used to convert this voltmeter to an instrument that reads 100 mV full scale?

$$R_m = \frac{V_B - V_g}{I_f} = \frac{150 \text{ V} - 50 \text{ V}}{2 \times 10^{-5} \text{ A}}; \quad \boxed{R_m = 5.00 \text{ MΩ}}$$

*30-13. The coil of a galvanometer will burn out if a current of more than 40 mA is sent through it. If the coil resistance is 0.5 Ω, what shunt resistance should be added to permit the measurement of 4.00 A?

$$R_s = \frac{I_g R_g}{I - I_g} = \frac{(40 \times 10^{-3} \text{ A})(0.500 \text{ Ω})}{4 \text{ A} - 0.04 \text{ A}}; \quad \boxed{R_s = 5.05 \text{ Ω}}$$

*30-14. A current of only 90 μA will produce full-scale deflection of a voltmeter that is designed to read 50 mV full scale. (a) What is the resistance of the meter? (b) What multiplier resistance is required to permit the measurement of 100 mV full scale?

(a) $R_v = \dfrac{50 \times 10^{-3}\,\text{V}}{90 \times 10^{-6}\,\text{A}}$; $\boxed{R_v = 555\,\Omega}$ (b) $R_m = \dfrac{0.100\,\text{V} - 0.050\,\text{V}}{90 \times 10^{-6}\,\text{A}}$; $\boxed{R_m = 555\,\Omega}$

Adding the same resistance as voltmeter resistance doubles the range of the meter.

*30-15. An ammeter that has a resistance of 0.10 Ω is connected in a circuit and indicates a current of 10 A at full scale. A shunt having a resistance of 0.01 Ω is then connected across the terminals of the meter. What new circuit current is needed to produce full-scale deflection of the ammeter?

$I_s R_s = I_g R_g$; $I_s = I - I_g$; $(I - I_g)\,R_s = I_g R_g$

$I R_s - I_g R_s = I_g R_g$; $I R_s = I_g R_s + I_g R_g$ *Solve for I*

$I = \dfrac{I_g(R_g + R_s)}{R_s} = \dfrac{(10\,\text{A})(0.1\,\Omega + 0.01\,\Omega)}{0.01\,\Omega}$; $\boxed{I = 110\,\text{A}}$

Supplementary Problems

30-16. A wire of length 12 cm is made in to a loop and placed into a 3.0-T magnetic field. What is the largest torque the wire can experience for a current of 6 A? $C = 2\pi R$

$R = \dfrac{C}{2\pi}\,\dfrac{0.12\,\text{m}}{2\pi}$; $R = 0.0191\,\text{m}$; $A = \pi R^2 = \pi (0.0191\,\text{m})^2$; $A = 1.16 \times 10^{-4}\,\text{m}^2$

$\tau = NBIA\cos\alpha = (1)(3\,\text{T})(6\,\text{A})(1.16 \times 10^{-4}\,\text{m}^2)\cos 0^0$; $\boxed{\tau = 2.09 \times 10^{-3}\,\text{N}\cdot\text{m}}$

---

*30-17. A solenoid has 600 turns of area 20 cm^2 and carries a current of 3.8 A. The axis of the solenoid makes an angle of 30^0 with an unknown magnetic field. If the resultant torque on the solenoid is 1.25 N·m, what is the magnetic flux density?

$B = \dfrac{\tau}{NAI\sin\theta} = \dfrac{1.25\,\text{N}\cdot\text{m}}{(600)(20 \times 10^{-4}\,\text{m}^2)(3.8\,\text{A})\sin 30^0}$; $\boxed{B = 548\,\text{mT}}$

30-18. A flat coil of wire has 150 turns of radius 4.0 cm, and the current is 5.0 A. What angle does the plane of the coil make with a 1.2-T B field if the resultant torque is 0.60 N·m?

$A = \pi R^2 = \pi(0.04\,\text{m})^2$; $A = 5.03 \times 10^{-3}\,\text{m}^2$; $I = 5\,A$; $\tau = 0.6\,N\cdot m$

$\cos\alpha = \dfrac{\tau}{NBIA}$ $\dfrac{0.600\,\text{N}\cdot\text{m}}{(150)(1.2\,\text{T})(5\,\text{A})(5.03 \times 10^{-3}\,\text{m}^2)}$; $\boxed{\alpha = 82.4^0}$

30-19. A circular loop consisting of 500 turns carries a current of 10 A in a 0.25-T magnetic field. The area of each turn is 0.2 m^2. Calculate the torque when the plane of the loop makes the following angles with the field: 0^0, 30^0, 45^0, 60^0, and 90^0.

(a) $\tau = NBIA\cos\alpha = (500)(0.25\,\text{T})(10.0\,\text{A})(0.20\,\text{m}^2)\cos 0^0$; $\boxed{\tau = 250\,\text{N}\cdot\text{m}}$

(b) $\tau = (250\,\text{N}\cdot\text{m})\cos 30^0$; $\boxed{\tau = 217\,\text{N}\cdot\text{m}}$; (c) $\tau = (250\,\text{N}\cdot\text{m})\cos 45^0$; $\boxed{\tau = 177\,\text{N}\cdot\text{m}}$

(d) $\tau = (250\,\text{N}\cdot\text{m})\cos 30^0$; $\boxed{\tau = 125\,\text{N}\cdot\text{m}}$; (e) $\tau = (250\,\text{N}\cdot\text{m})\cos 0^0$; $\boxed{\tau = 0\,\text{N}\cdot\text{m}}$

30-20. A solenoid of 100 turns has a cross-sectional area of 0.25 m^2 and carries a current of 10 A. What torque is required to hold the solenoid at an angle of 30^0 with a 40-mT magnetic field? (*The angle of the solenoid axis is $\theta = 30^0$*)

$\tau = NBIA\sin\theta = (100)(0.04\,\text{T})(10.0\,\text{A})(0.25\,\text{m}^2)\sin 30^0$; $\boxed{\tau = 5.00\,\text{N}\cdot\text{m}}$

214

30-21. A solenoid consists of 400 turns of wire, each of radius 60 mm. What angle does the axis of the solenoid make with the magnetic flux if the current through the wire is 6 A, the flux density is 46 mT, and the resulting torque is 0.80 N·m?

$A = \pi R^2 = \pi(0.06 \text{ m})^2 = 0.0113 \text{ m}^2$; $\tau = 0.80$ N·m; $B = 46$ mT; $I = 6$ A; $\theta = ?$

$$\sin\theta = \frac{\tau}{NBIA} = \frac{0.800 \text{ N·m}}{(400)(0.046 \text{ T})(6 \text{ A})(0.0113 \text{ m}^2)}; \quad \boxed{\theta = 39.8^0}$$

*30-22. A galvanometer having an internal resistance of 35 Ω requires 1.0 mA for full-scale deflection for a current of 10 mA. What multiplier resistance is needed to convert this device to a voltmeter that reads a maximum of 30 V?

$$R_m = \frac{V_R}{I_g} - R_g = \frac{30 \text{ V}}{0.001 \text{ A}} - 35 \Omega; \quad \boxed{R_m = 29,965 \ \Omega}$$

*30-23. The internal resistance of a galvanometer is 20 Ω and it reads full scale for a current of 10 mA. Calculate the multiplier resistance required to convert this galvanometer into a voltmeter whose range is 50 V. What is the total resistance of the resulting meter?

$$R_m = \frac{V_R}{I_g} - R_g = \frac{50 \text{ V}}{0.01 \text{ A}} - 20 \Omega; \quad \boxed{R_m = 4980 \ \Omega}$$

$$R_v = R_m + R_g = 4980 \ \Omega + 20 \ \Omega; \quad \boxed{R_v = 5000 \ \Omega}$$

*30-24. What shunt resistance is needed to convert the galvanometer of Problem 30-22 to an ammeter reading 10 mA full scale?

$$R_s = \frac{I_g R_g}{I - I_g} = \frac{(0.0001A)(35 \ \Omega)}{0.01 \text{ A} - 0.001 \text{ A}}; \quad \boxed{R_s = 3.89 \ \Omega}$$

*30-25. A certain voltmeter reads 150 V full scale. The galvanometer coil has a resistance of 50 Ω and produces a full-scale deflection on 20 mV. Find the multiplier resistance of the voltmeter.

$$R_m = \frac{V_R}{I_g} - R_g; \quad I_g = \frac{V_g}{R_g} = \frac{0.020 \text{ V}}{50.0 \ \Omega} = 4 \times 10^{-4} \text{A}$$

$$R_m = \frac{V_R}{I_g} - R_g = \frac{150 \text{ V}}{4 \times 10^{-4} \text{ A}} - 50 \ \Omega; \quad \boxed{R_m = 374,950 \ \Omega}$$

*30-26. A galvanometer has a coil resistance of 50 Ω and a current sensitivity of 1 mA (full scale). What shunt resistance is needed to convert this galvanometer to an ammeter reading 2.0 A full scale?

$$R_s = \frac{I_g R_g}{I - I_g} = \frac{(0.001A)(50 \ \Omega)}{2 \text{ A} - 0.001 \text{ A}}; \quad \boxed{R_s = 0.025 \ \Omega}$$

*30-27. A laboratory ammeter has a resistance of 0.01 Ω and reads 5.0 A full scale. What shunt resistance is needed to increase the range of the ammeter tenfold?

$$\frac{I}{I_g} = 10; \quad R_s = \frac{I_g R_g}{I - I_g}; \quad IR_s - I_g R_s = I_g R_g; \quad IR_s = I_g(R_s + R_g);$$

$$\frac{I}{I_g} = \frac{R_s + R_g}{R_s} = 10; \quad R_s + R_g = 10R_s; \quad R_s(10-1) = R_g$$

$$R_s = \frac{R_g}{9} = \frac{0.01 \ \Omega}{9}; \quad R_s = 1.11 \text{ m}\Omega$$

Thus, by adding 1.11 μΩ in parallel, the meter range will extend to 50 A full scale.

*30-28. A commercial 3-V voltmeter requires a current of 0.02 mA to produce full-scale deflection. How can it be converted to an instrument with a range of 150 V?

$$R_m = \frac{V_B - V_g}{I_g} = \frac{150\ V - 3\ V}{0.02 \times 10^{-3}\ A}; \qquad \boxed{R_m = 7.35\ \Omega}$$

Adding $R_m = 7.35\ \Omega$ in series will increase the range to 150 V.

Critical Thinking Problems

30-29. Consider the rectangular, 4 cm by 6 cm loop of 60 turns of wire in Fig. 30-11. The plane of the loop makes an angle of 40^0 with a 1.6-T magnetic field **B** directed along the x-axis. The loop is free to rotate about the y-axis and the clockwise current in the coil is 6.0 A. What is the torque and will it turn toward the x axis or toward the z axis?

$A = (0.06\ m)(0.04\ m) = 2.4 \times 10^{-3}\ m^2; \qquad \alpha = 40^0$

$\tau = NBIA \cos \alpha = (60)(1.6\ T)(6\ A)(0.0024\ m^2)\cos 40^0$

$\tau = 1.06\ N\cdot m$, *The downward direction of the current in the near segment means that the force producing the torque will cause the loop to rotate AWAY from x axis.*

$$\boxed{\tau = 1.06\ N\cdot m,\ \text{toward z axis}}$$

*30-30. A voltmeter of range 150 V and total resistance 15,000 Ω is connected in series with another voltmeter of range 100 V and total resistance 20,000 Ω. What will each meter read when they are connected across a 120-V battery of negligible internal resistance?

To determine what the readings will be we need to know the galvanometer currents I_g required for full-scale deflection of the galvanometer in each voltmeter. These are found by dividing the full-scale voltages by their galvanometer resistances (Ohm's law).

*30-30. (Cont.) For A: $I_{gf} = \frac{150\ V}{15,000\ \Omega} = 0.010\ A$; For B: $I_{gf} = \frac{100\ V}{20,000\ \Omega} = 0.005\ A$

150-V meter A   100-V meter B

120-V source C

Since voltmeters are in series: $I_v = I_g$

$$I_v = \frac{120\ V}{15\ k\Omega + 20\ k\Omega} = 3.43\ mA; \qquad I_g = 3.43\ mA$$

Consider reading of Voltmeter A (150-V full):

$V_A = I_v(R_{mA} + R_{gA}) = (3.43\ mA)(15\ k\Omega)$

$V_A = I_v(R_{mA} + R_{gA}) = (3.43\ mA)(20\ k\Omega)$

$$\boxed{V_A = 51.5\ V; \qquad V_B = 68.6\ \Omega}$$

*30-31. The magnetic moment μ is a vector quantity whose magnitude for a coil of N turns of area A is given by NIA, where I is the current in the coil. The direction of the magnetic moment is perpendicular to the plane of the coil in the direction given by the right hand thumb rule (see Fig. 29-19). If such a coil is placed into a uniform B field, show that the torque has a magnitude given by:

$$\tau = \mu B \sin \theta$$

This is sometimes written as a vector (cross) product $\tau = \mu \ \times\ \textbf{B}$.

For a coil or loop: $\tau = NBIA \cos \alpha$ [$\cos\alpha = \sin\theta$]

Recall that the angle θ is the complement of the angle α that the plane of the loop makes with the B field, thus the magnetic moment is perpendicular to the plane of the loop.

Simply substitute $\mu = NIA$ into $\tau = (NIA)B \sin \theta$, then write:

$$\boxed{\tau = \mu B \sin \theta}$$

Induced Electromotive Force

31-1. A coil of wire 8 cm in diameter has 50 turns and is placed in a B field of 1.8 T. If the B field in reduced to 0.6 T in 0.002 s, what is the induced emf?

$$A = \frac{\pi D^2}{4} = \frac{\pi (0.08 \text{ m})^2}{4} = 5.03 \times 10^{-3} \text{ m}^2; \quad \Delta B = 1.8 \text{ T} - 0.6 \text{ T} = 1.20 \text{ T}$$

$$\varepsilon = -N \frac{\Delta \phi}{\Delta t} = -\frac{NA\Delta B}{\Delta t}; \quad \varepsilon = -\frac{(50)(5.03 \times 10^{-3} \text{ m}^2)(1.20 \text{ T})}{0.002 \text{ s}}; \quad \boxed{\varepsilon = -151 \text{ V}}$$

31-2. A square coil of wire having 100 turns of area 0.044 m² is placed with its plane perpendicular to a constant B field of 4 mT. The coil is flipped to a position parallel with the field in a time of 0.3 s. What is the induced emf?

$$\varepsilon = -N \frac{\Delta \phi}{\Delta t} = -\frac{NB\Delta A}{\Delta t}; \quad \varepsilon = -\frac{(100)(0.004 \text{ T})(0.044 \text{ m}^2 - 0)}{0.3 \text{ s}}; \quad \boxed{\varepsilon = -58.7 \text{ mV}}$$

31-3 A coil of 300 turns moving perpendicular to the flux in a uniform magnetic field experiences a flux linkage of 0.23 mWb in 0.002 s. What is the induced emf?

$$\varepsilon = -N \frac{\Delta \phi}{\Delta t} = -(300)\frac{0.23 \times 10^{-3} \text{ Wb}}{0.002 \text{ s}}; \quad \varepsilon = -34.5 \text{ V}.$$

31-4. The magnetic flux linking a loop of wire changes from 5 mWb to 2 mWb in 0.1 s. What is the average induced emf?

$$\varepsilon = -N \frac{\Delta \phi}{\Delta t} = -(1)\frac{5 \times 10^{-3} \text{ Wb} - 2 \times 10^{-3} \text{ Wb}}{0.100 \text{ s}}; \quad \boxed{\varepsilon = -30.0 \text{ mV}}$$

---

*30-32. Verify the answer obtained for Problem 30-19 by applying the formula derived in the previous problem. Do not confuse the angle θ with the angle α that the plane of the loop makes with the B field. [*Recall that* $\theta + \alpha = 90^0$ *and* $\cos \alpha = \sin \theta$]

Thus angles change from: $\alpha = 0^0, 30^0, 45^0, 60^0,$ and 90^0 to $\theta = 90^0, 60^0, 45^0, 30^0,$ and 0^0

The maximum torque is still 250 N·m, from $\tau = NBIA \cos \alpha$ or from $\tau = NBIA \sin \theta$:

$$\mu = NIA = (500)(10.0 \text{ A})(0.20 \text{ m}^2) = 1000 \text{ A·m}^2 \quad directed \ at \ angle \ \theta$$

Applying $\tau = \mu B \sin\theta = (1000 \text{ A·m}^2)(0.25 \text{ T}) \sin \theta$ for each angle gives:

$$\boxed{\text{(a) } 250 \text{ N·m; (b) } 217 \text{ N·m; (c) } 177 \text{ N·m; (d) } 125 \text{ N·m; and (e) } 0 \text{ N·m}}$$

*30-33. The internal wiring of a three-scale voltmeter is shown in Fig. 30-12. The galvanometer has an internal resistance of 40 Ω and a current of 1.00 mA will produce full-scale deflection. Find the resistances R₁, R₂, and R₃ for the use of the voltmeter for 10, 50, and 100 V. (*Multiplier resistances* R_m)

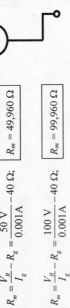

$$R_m = \frac{V_R}{I_g} - R_g = \frac{10 \text{ V}}{0.001 \text{ A}} - 40 \text{ Ω}; \quad \boxed{R_m = 9960 \text{ Ω}}$$

$$R_m = \frac{V_R}{I_g} - R_g = \frac{50 \text{ V}}{0.001 \text{ A}} - 40 \text{ Ω}; \quad \boxed{R_m = 49,960 \text{ Ω}}$$

$$R_m = \frac{V_R}{I_g} - R_g = \frac{100 \text{ V}}{0.001 \text{ A}} - 40 \text{ Ω}; \quad \boxed{R_m = 99,960 \text{ Ω}}$$

Generators

31-9. The magnetic field in the air gap between the magnetic poles and the armature of an electric generator has a flux density of 0.7 T. The length of the wires on the armature is 0.5 m. How fast must these wires move to generate a maximum emf of 1.00 V in each armature wire?

$$v = \frac{E}{Bl \sin 90^0} = \frac{1.00 \text{ V}}{(0.7 \text{ T})(0.5 \text{ m})(1)} ; \quad \boxed{v = 2.86 \text{ m/s}}$$

31-10. A single loop of wire has a diameter of 60 mm and makes 200 rpm in a constant 4-mT magnetic field. What is the maximum emf generated?

$$A = \frac{\pi D^2}{4} = \frac{\pi (0.06 \text{ m})^2}{4} = 2.83 \times 10^{-3} \text{m}^2; \quad f = 200 \text{ rpm} = 3.33 \text{ rev/s}$$

$$E_{max} = 2\pi fNBA = 2\pi(3.33 \text{ rev/s})(1)(0.004 \text{ T})(2.83 \times 10^{-3}\text{T}); \quad \boxed{E = 237 \text{ } \mu V}$$

31-11. The armature of a simple generator has 300 loops of diameter 20 cm in a constant 6-mT magnetic field. What must be the frequency of rotation in revolutions per second in order to induce a maximum emf of 7.00 V? [$A = \pi R^2 = \pi(0.10 \text{ m})^2 = 0.314 \text{ m}^2$]

$$f = \frac{E_{max}}{2\pi NBA} = \frac{7.00 \text{ V}}{2\pi(300)(0.006 \text{ T})(0.314 \text{ m}^2)}; \quad \boxed{f = 19.7 \text{ rev/s}}$$

31-12. An armature in an ac generator consists of 500 turns, each of area 60 cm². The armature is rotated at a frequency of 3600 rpm in a uniform 2-mT magnetic field. What is the frequency of the alternating emf? What is the maximum emf generated?

$$f = 3600 \frac{\text{rev}}{\text{min}} \left(\frac{1 \text{ min}}{60 \text{ s}} \right) = 60 \text{ rev/s}; \quad f = 60.0 \text{ Hz}$$

$$E_{max} = 2\pi fNBA = 2\pi(60 \text{ Hz})(500)(0.002 \text{ T})(60 \times 10^{-4} \text{ m}^2); \quad \boxed{E_{max} = 2.26 \text{ V}}$$

31-5. A coil of 120 turns is 90 mm in diameter and has its plane perpendicular to a 60-mT magnetic field produced by a nearby electromagnet. The current in the electromagnet is cut off, and as the field collapses, an emf of 6 V is induced in the coil. How long does it take for the field to disappear? [$A = \pi R^2 = \pi(0.045 \text{ m})^2 = 6.36 \times 10^{-3} \text{ m}^2$]

$$E = -N \frac{\Delta \phi}{\Delta t} = -\frac{NA \Delta B}{\Delta t} ; \quad \Delta t = \frac{-NA \Delta B}{E} = \frac{-(120)(6.36 \times 10^{-3} \text{ m}^2)(0.06 \text{ T})}{-6.00 \text{ V}}$$

$$\boxed{\Delta t = 7.63 \text{ ms.}}$$

31-6. A coil of 56 turns has an area of 0.3 m². Its plane is perpendicular to a 7-mT magnetic field. If this field collapses to zero in 6 ms, what is the induced emf?

$$E = -N \frac{\Delta \phi}{\Delta t} = - \frac{NA \Delta B}{\Delta t} = \frac{-56(0.3 \text{ m}^2)(0.007 \text{ T} - 0)}{0.006 \text{ s}} ; \quad \boxed{E = -19.6 \text{ V}}$$

31-7. A wire 0.15 m long moves at a constant velocity of 4 m/s in a direction that is 36° with respect to a 0.4-T magnetic field. The axis of the wire is perpendicular to the magnetic flux lines. What is the induced emf?

$$E = Blv \sin \theta = (0.4 \text{ T})(0.15 \text{ m})(4 \text{ m/s}) \sin 36^0 ; \quad \boxed{E = 141 \text{ mV}}$$

31-8. A 0.2-m wire moves at an angle of 28° with an 8-mT magnetic field. The wire length is perpendicular to the flux. What velocity v is required to induce an emf of 60 mV?

$$E = Blv \sin \theta; \quad v = \frac{E}{Bl \sin \theta}$$

$$v = \frac{E}{Bl \sin \theta} = \frac{60 \times 10^{-3} \text{V}}{(0.7 \text{ T})(0.2 \text{ m}) \sin 28^0}$$

$$\boxed{v = 79.9 \text{ m/s}}$$

31-13. In Problem 31-12, what is the instantaneous emf at the time when the plane of the coil makes an angle of 60° with the magnetic flux? [Note $\theta = 90° - 60° = 30°$]

$$\mathcal{E}_{inst} = \mathcal{E}_{max}\sin 30° = (2.26 \text{ V})(0.500); \qquad \mathcal{E}_{inst} = 1.13 \text{ V}$$

31-14. The armature of a simple ac generator has 100 turns of wire, each having a radius of 5.00 cm. The armature turns in a constant 0.06-T magnetic field. What must be the rotational frequency in rpm to generate a maximum voltage of 2.00 V?

$$A = \pi R^2 = \pi(0.05 \text{ m})^2 = 7.85 \times 10^{-3}\,\text{m}^2;$$

$$f = \frac{\mathcal{E}_{max}}{2\pi NBA} = \frac{2.00 \text{ V}}{2\pi(100)(0.06 \text{ T})(7.85 \times 10^{-3}\,\text{m}^2)}; \qquad f = 6.75 \text{ rev/s}$$

$$f = 6.75\,\frac{\text{rev}}{\text{s}}\left(\frac{60 \text{ s}}{\text{min}}\right); \qquad f = 405 \text{ rpm}$$

31-15. A circular coil has 70 turns, each 50 mm in diameter. Assume that the coil rotates about an axis that is perpendicular to a magnetic field of 0.8 T. How many revolutions per second must the coil make to generate a maximum emf of 110 V?

$$A = \frac{\pi D^2}{4} = \frac{\pi(0.05 \text{ m})^2}{4} = 1.96 \times 10^{-3}\,\text{m}^2;$$

$$f = \frac{\mathcal{E}_{max}}{2\pi NBA} = \frac{110 \text{ V}}{2\pi(70)(0.8 \text{ T})(1.96 \times 10^{-3}\,\text{m}^2)}; \qquad f = 159 \text{ rev/s}$$

*31-16. The armature of an ac generator has 800 turns, each of area 0.25 m². The coil rotates at a constant 600 rpm in a 3-mT field. What is the maximum induced emf? What is the instantaneous emf 0.43 s after the coil passes a position of zero emf? [600 rpm = 10 rev/s]

$$\mathcal{E}_{max} = 2\pi fNBA = 2\pi(10 \text{ Hz})(800)(0.003 \text{ T})(0.25 \text{ m}^2); \qquad \mathcal{E}_{max} = 37.7 \text{ V}$$

$$\mathcal{E}_{inst} = \mathcal{E}_{max}\sin(2\pi ft) = (37.7 \text{ V})\sin[2\pi(10 \text{ Hz})(0.43 \text{ s})]; \qquad \mathcal{E}_{inst} = 35.9 \text{ V}$$

*31-17. A 300-Ω resistor is connected in series with an ac generator of negligible internal resistance. The armature of the generator has 200 turns of wire 30 cm in diameter and it turns at 300 rpm in a constant 5-mT field. What is the instantaneous current through the resistor 0.377 s after the coil passes a position of zero emf? [300 rpm = 5.00 rev/s]

$$A = \frac{\pi D^2}{4} = \frac{\pi(0.3 \text{ m})^2}{4} = 0.0707 \text{ m}^2; \qquad \mathcal{E}_{inst} = 2\pi fNBA\sin(2\pi ft)$$

$$\mathcal{E}_{inst} = 2\pi(5 \text{ Hz})(200)(0.005 \text{ T})(0.0707 \text{ m}^2)\sin[2\pi(5 \text{ Hz})(0.377 \text{ s})]$$

$$\mathcal{E}_{inst} = (2.22 \text{ V})\sin(0.118 \text{ rad}); \qquad \mathcal{E}_{inst} = 1.47 \text{ V}$$

$$I_{inst} = \frac{1.47 \text{ V}}{300 \text{ Ω}}; \qquad I_{inst} = 4.90 \text{ mA}$$

DC Motors and Back EMF

31-18. A 120-V dc motor draws a current of 3.00 A in operation and has a resistance of 8.00 Ω. What is the back emf when the motor is operating and what is the starting current?

$$V - \mathcal{E}_b = IR; \qquad \mathcal{E}_b = V - IR = 120 \text{ V} - (3.00 \text{ A})(8.00 \text{ Ω}); \qquad \mathcal{E}_b = 96.0 \text{ V}$$

$$I_0 = \frac{120 \text{ V}}{8 \text{ Ω}}; \qquad I_0 = 15.0 \text{ A}$$

31-19. The armature coil of the starting motor in an automobile has a resistance of 0.05 Ω. The motor is driven by a 12-V battery, and the back emf at operating speed is 6.00 V. What is the starting current? What is the current at full speed?

$$I_0 = \frac{12.0 \text{ V}}{0.05 \text{ Ω}} = 240 \text{ A}; \qquad I_0 = 240 \text{ A}$$

$$I = \frac{V - \mathcal{E}_b}{R} = \frac{12 \text{ V} - 6 \text{ V}}{0.05 \text{ Ω}}; \qquad I = 120 \text{ A}$$

31-24. A step-down transformer is used to drop an alternating voltage from 10,000 to 500 V. What must be the ratio of secondary turns to primary turns? If the input current is 1.00 A and the transformer is 100 percent efficient, what is the output current?

$$\frac{N_p}{N_s} = \frac{E_p}{E_s} = \frac{500 \text{V}}{10,000 \text{ V}} = \frac{1}{20}; \qquad \boxed{Ratio = 1:20}$$

$$P_{out} = P_{in}; \quad I_p E_p = I_s E_s; \quad I_s = \frac{(1 \text{ A})(10,000 \text{ V})}{(500 \text{ V})}; \qquad \boxed{I_s = 20 \text{ A}}$$

31-25. A step-up transformer is 95 percent efficient and has 80 primary turns and 720 secondary turns. If the primary draws a current of 20 A at 120 V, what are the current and voltage for the secondary?

$$\frac{E_p}{E_s} = \frac{N_p}{N_s}; \quad E_s = \frac{E_p N_s}{N_p} = \frac{(120 \text{ V})(720)}{(80)}; \qquad \boxed{E_s = 1080 \text{ V}}$$

$$E = \frac{P_{out}}{P_{in}} = \frac{E_s I_s}{E_p I_p} = 0.95; \quad I_s = \frac{0.95(20 \text{ A})(120 \text{ V})}{1080 \text{ V}}; \qquad \boxed{I_s = 2.11 \text{ A}}$$

31-26. A 25-W light bulb has a resistance of 8.0 Ω while burning. The light is powered from the secondary of a small transformer connected to a 120-V circuit. What must be the ratio of secondary turns to primary turns in this application? Assume 100 percent efficiency.

$$P_{out} = \frac{V_{out}^2}{R}; \quad V_{out} = \sqrt{P_{out} R} = \sqrt{(25 \text{ W})(8 \text{ Ω})}; \quad V_{out} = 14.1 \text{ V}$$

$$\frac{N_s}{N_p} = \frac{E_s}{E_p} = \frac{14.1 \text{ V}}{120 \text{ V}}; \qquad \boxed{\frac{N_s}{N_p} = 0.118}$$

31-20. A 220-V dc motor draws a current of 10 A in operation and has an armature resistance of 0.4 Ω. What is the back emf when the motor is operating and what is the starting current?

$$E_b = V - IR = 220 \text{ V} - (10 \text{A})(0.4 \text{ Ω}); \qquad \boxed{E_b = 216 \text{ V}}$$

$$I_0 = \frac{220 \text{ V}}{0.4 \text{ Ω}}; \qquad \boxed{I_0 = 550 \text{ A}}$$

*31-21. A 120-V series-wound dc motor has a field resistance of 90 Ω and an armature resistance of 10 Ω. When operating at full speed, a back emf of 80 V is generated. What is the total resistance of the motor? What is the starting current? What is the operating current?

(a) $R_T = 90 \text{ Ω} + 10 \text{ Ω} = \boxed{100 \text{ Ω}}$; (b) $I_0 = \frac{120 \text{ V}}{100 \text{ Ω}}$; $\boxed{I_0 = 1.20 \text{ A}}$

(c) $I = \frac{120 \text{ V} - 80 \text{ V}}{100 \text{ Ω}}$; $\boxed{I = 0.400 \text{ A}}$

*31-22. The efficiency of the motor in Problem 31-21 is the ratio of the power output to the power input. Determine the efficiency based on the known data.

$$E = \frac{P_{out}}{P_{in}} = \frac{P_{in} - P_{out}}{P_{in}}; \quad P_{out} = I^2 R = (0.4A)^2 (100 \text{ Ω}); \quad P_{out} = 16.0 \text{ W}$$

$$P_{in} = IV = (0.4 \text{ A})(120 \text{ V}) = 48.0 \text{ W}; \quad E = \frac{48 \text{ W} - 16 \text{ W}}{48 \text{ W}}; \quad E = 66.7\%$$

Transformers

31-23. A step-up transformer has 400 secondary turns and only 100 primary turns. A 120-V alternating voltage is connected to the primary coil. What is the output voltage?

$$\frac{E_p}{E_s} = \frac{N_p}{N_s}; \quad E_s = \frac{E_p N_s}{N_p} = \frac{(120 \text{ V})(400)}{(100)}; \qquad \boxed{E_s = 480 \text{ V}}$$

Supplementary Problems

31-27. A 70-turn coil of wire has an area of 0.06 m² and is placed perpendicular to a constant 8-mT magnetic field. Calculate the induced emf if the coil flips 90° in 0.02 s.

$E = -N\dfrac{\Delta\phi}{\Delta t} = -\dfrac{NB\Delta A}{\Delta t}$; $E = -\dfrac{(70)(0.008\ T)(0.06\ m^2 - 0)}{0.02\ s}$; $\boxed{E = -1.68\ mV}$

31-28. A coil of area 0.2 m² has 80 turns of wire and is suspended with its plane perpendicular to a uniform magnetic field. What must be the flux density to produce an average emf of 2 V as the coil is flipped parallel to the field in 0.5 s?

$E = -N\dfrac{\Delta\phi}{\Delta t} = -\dfrac{NB\Delta A}{\Delta t}$; $B = -\dfrac{(-2\ V)(0.5\ s)}{(80)(0.2\ m^2 - 0)}$; $\boxed{B = 62.5\ mT}$

31-29. The flux through a 200-turn coil changes from 0.06 to 0.025 Wb in 0.5 s. The coil is connected to an electric light, and the combined resistance is 2 Ω. What is the average induced emf and what average current is delivered to the light filament?

$E = -N\dfrac{\Delta\phi}{\Delta t} = -\dfrac{200(0.06\ Wb - 0.025\ Wb)}{0.5\ s}$; $\boxed{E = -14.0\ V}$

$I = \dfrac{14.0\ V}{2\ \Omega}$; $\boxed{I = 7.00\ A}$

31-30. A 90-mm length of wire moves with an upward velocity of 35 m/s between the poles of a magnet. The magnetic field is 80 mT directed to the right. If the resistance in the wire is 5.00 mΩ, what are the magnitude and direction of the induced current?

$E = Blv\sin\theta = (80 \times 10^{-3}\ T)(0.09\ m)(35\ m/s)(1)$; $\boxed{E = 0.252\ V}$

$I = \dfrac{0.252\ V}{0.005\ \Omega}$; $\boxed{I = 50.4\ A,\ into\ paper}$

31-31. A generator develops an emf of 120 V and has a terminal potential difference of 115 V when the armature current is 25.0 A. What is the resistance of the armature?

$E - V_T = I_A R_A$; $120\ V - 115\ V = (25\ A)R_A$; $\boxed{R_A = 0.200\ \Omega}$

31-32. The coil of an ac generator rotates at a frequency of 60 Hz and develops a maximum emf of 170 V. The coil has 500 turns, each of area $4 \times 10^{-3}\ m^2$. What is the magnitude of the magnetic field in which the coil rotates?

$E_{max} = 2\pi fNBA$; $B = \dfrac{E_{max}}{2\pi fNA} = \dfrac{170\ V}{2\pi(60\ Hz)(500)(0.004\ m^2)}$; $\boxed{B = 225\ mT}$

31-33. A generator produces a maximum emf of 24 V when the armature rotates at 600 rpm. Assuming nothing else changes, what is the maximum emf when the armature rotates at 1800 rpm? (*Maximum emf is proportional to the frequency*)

$\dfrac{E_2}{E_1} = \dfrac{f_2}{f_1}$; $E_2 = \dfrac{(1800\ rpm)(24\ V)}{600\ rpm}$; $\boxed{E_2 = 72.0\ V}$

*31-34. A shunt-wound motor connected across a 117-V line generates a back emf of 112 V when the armature current is 10 A. What is the armature resistance?

Loop rule for first loop: $\Sigma E = \Sigma IR : E - E_b = I_A R_A$

$117\ V - 112\ V = (10\ A)R_A$; $R_A = \dfrac{5\ V}{10\ A} = \boxed{0.500\ \Omega}$

*31-37. (Cont.) $E - Ir = 120$ V; $P_0 = (120 \text{ V})I$; $I = \frac{P_0}{V} = \frac{4000 \text{ W}}{120 \text{ V}} = 33.3$ A;

$$E = 120 \text{ V} - (33.3 \text{ A})(1.99 \ \Omega); \qquad \boxed{E = 187 \text{ V}}$$

Critical Thinking Problems

31-38. A coil of wire has 10 loops, each of diameter D, placed inside a B field that varies at the rate of 2.5 mWb/s. If the induced emf is 4 mV, what is the diameter of the coil? What will the induced emf be if the diameter is doubled? What is the induced emf if the rate of change in the B field is doubled?

$$E = -N\frac{\Delta\phi}{\Delta t} = -\frac{NA\Delta B}{\Delta t}; \qquad A = \frac{-E}{N\left(\Delta B / \Delta t\right)} = \frac{-(-0.004 \text{ V})}{(10)(2.5 \times 10^{-3} \text{ wb/s})}; \qquad A = 0.160 \text{ m}^2$$

$$A = \frac{\pi D^2}{4}; \qquad D = \sqrt{\frac{4A}{\pi}} = \sqrt{\frac{4(0.160 \text{ m}^2)}{\pi}}; \qquad \boxed{D = 0.451 \text{ m} = 45.1 \text{ cm}}$$

Doubling D quadruples the area A and thus increases the emf by factor of four:

$$E_{2D} = 4(-0.004 \text{ V}); \qquad \boxed{E_{2D} = -16.0 \text{ mV}} \qquad (Doubling \ the \ diameter)$$

The emf varies directly with $\Delta B/\Delta t$, therefore emf is doubled when it doubles:

$$E_{2B} = 2(-0.004 \text{ V}); \qquad \boxed{E_{2B} = -8.00 \text{ mV}} \qquad (Doubling \ the \ diameter)$$

Chapter 31   Electromagnetic Induction   **441**

---

*31-35. A 110-V shunt-wound motor has a field resistance of 200 Ω connected in parallel with an armature resistance of 10 Ω. When the motor is operating at full speed, the back emf is 90 V. What is the starting current and what is the operating current?

$$R_T = \frac{R_A R_F}{R_A + R_F} = \frac{(10 \ \Omega)(200 \ \Omega)}{10 \ \Omega + 200 \ \Omega}; \qquad R_T = 9.524 \ \Omega$$

At start $E_b = 0$: $I_0 = \frac{110 \text{ V}}{9.524 \ \Omega}$; $\boxed{I_0 = 11.6 \text{ A}}$

Loop rule for first loop $\Sigma E = \Sigma IR$: $110 \text{ V} - 90 \text{ V} = I_A(10 \ \Omega)$; $I_A = 2.00$ A

Loop rule for outside loop: $110 \text{ V} = I_F R_F$; $I_F = \frac{110 \text{ V}}{200 \ \Omega} = 0.550$ A

Current rule: $I_T = I_F + I_A = 0.550 \ \Omega + 2.00 \ \Omega$; $\boxed{I_T = 2.55 \text{ A}}$

*31-36. A 120-V shunt motor has a field resistance of 160 Ω and an armature resistance of 1.00 Ω. When the motor is operating at full speed, it draws a current of 8.00 A. Find the starting current. What series resistance must be added to reduce the starting current to 30 A?

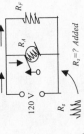

$$R_T = \frac{R_A R_F}{R_A + R_F} = \frac{(1.0 \ \Omega)(160 \ \Omega)}{1.0 \ \Omega + 160 \ \Omega}; \qquad R_T = 0.994 \ \Omega$$

At start $E_b = 0$: $I_0 = \frac{120 \text{ V}}{0.994 \ \Omega}$; $\boxed{I_0 = 120.75 \text{ A}}$

Added R_s: $I_0 = \frac{120 \text{ V}}{R_s + 0.994 \ \Omega} = 30$ A; $\boxed{R_s = 3.01 \ \Omega}$

*31-37. A shunt generator has a field resistance of 400 Ω and an armature resistance of 2.00 Ω. The generator delivers a power of 4000 W to an external line at 120 V. What is the emf of the generator?

$$R_T = \frac{R_A R_F}{R_A + R_F} = \frac{(2.0 \ \Omega)(400 \ \Omega)}{2.0 \ \Omega + 400 \ \Omega}; \qquad R_T = 1.99 \ \Omega$$

440 Unit A   Solutions Manual

31-39. In Fig. 31-18a, the single loop of area 0.024 m² is connected to a 4 mΩ resistor. The magnet moves to the left through the center of the loop causing the magnetic flux to increase at the rate of 2 mWb/s. (a) What are the magnitude and direction of the current through the resistor? What if the magnet is then pulled back out of the loop with the same speed? *First let's reason the direction from Lenz's Law:*

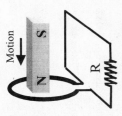

(a) The flux lines are increasing to the left, which means that the induced emf must generate a B field to the right which opposes the cause that gave rise to it. The current must be counterclockwise viewed from the magnet side.

$$E = -N\frac{\Delta\phi}{\Delta t} = -(1)(0.002\ Wb/s); \quad E = -2.00\ mV; \quad I = \frac{-0.002\ V}{0.004\ \Omega}; \quad \boxed{I = 0.500\ A}$$

(b) When magnet moves out to the right, the flux lines are decreasing, so the induced emf in the coil must be such as to oppose that motion, i.e., to the right. The induced current must be clockwise viewed from the magnet side. Magnitude is unchanged:

$$\boxed{I = 0.500\ A}$$

31-40. In Fig. 31-18b a changing B field is produced first by an increasing current through the loops and then by a decreasing current through the loops. In each case will the induced current be downward or upward on the near side of the single loop?

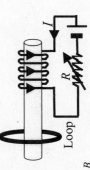

(a) Grasping near wires of coil with thumb down shows field increasing to right. Induced B must be left, so induced current is upward in near loop.

(b) Reverse reasoning for decreasing current shows B will be down in near loop. Ans. *(a) Up; (b) Down*

*31-41. A coil of 50 turns is rotated clockwise with a frequency of 60 Hz in a constant 3.0-mT magnetic field. The direction of the B field is along the positive x-axis and the coil of area 0.070 m² rotates clockwise in the x-y plane. When the plane of the loop is parallel to the field, what is the direction of the current as viewed from the top (clockwise or counter-clockwise)? What is the maximum induced emf? Starting time t = 0 when the emf is zero, at what later time will its emf first rise to 2.00 V?

The right edge of the loop moves downward causing the induced current to be out at that point. Thus, the current in the coil is <u>clockwise</u> viewed from the top.

Note also from Lenz's law that as the loop rotates, the "back" field induced inside the loop is directed left, or opposite to the B field from the magnets.

$$E_{max} = 2\pi f N B A = 2\pi (60\ Hz)(50)(0.003\ T)(0.07\ m^2); \quad \boxed{E_{max} = 3.96\ V}$$

$$E_{inst} = E_{max} \sin(2\pi f t); \quad \sin(2\pi f t) = \frac{E_{inst}}{E_{max}} = \frac{2\ V}{3.96\ V}; \quad 2\pi f t = \sin^{-1}(0.505);$$

$$2\pi f t = 0.5294\ rad; \quad t = \frac{0.5294\ rad}{2\pi(60\ Hz)}; \quad \boxed{t = 1.40\ ms}$$

*31-42. When the motor on a heat pump is first turned on, it momentarily draws 40.0 A. The current then immediately drops to a steady value of 12.0 A. If the motor operates on a 120-V power source, what is the back emf generated while the motor is running?

At start: $I_0 = \dfrac{120\ V}{R_A} = 40.0\ A$; $R_A = \dfrac{120\ V}{40\ A} = 3.0\ \Omega$;

Operating: $120\ V - E_b = (12\ A)(3.0\ \Omega)$; $\boxed{E_b = 84.0\ V}$

Chapter 32. Alternating-Current Circuits

The Capacitor

32-1. A series dc circuit consists of a 4-μF capacitor, a 5000-Ω resistor, and a 12-V battery.

What is the time constant for this circuit?

$$\tau = RC = (5000\ \Omega)(4 \times 10^{-6}\text{F}) ; \qquad \boxed{\tau = 20\ \text{ms}}$$

32-2. What is the time constant for a series dc circuit containing a 6-μF capacitor and a 400-Ω resistor connected to a 20-V battery?

$$\tau = RC = (400\ \Omega)(6 \times 10^{-6}\text{F}) ; \qquad \boxed{\tau = 2.40\ \text{ms}}$$

32-3. For the circuit described in Problem 32-1, what is the initial current and the final current? How much time is needed to be assured that the capacitor is fully charged?

The initial current I_0 (before charge builds on capacitor) is determined by Ohm's law:

$$I_0 = \frac{V}{R} = \frac{12\ \text{V}}{5000\ \Omega} ; \qquad \boxed{I_0 = 2.40\ \text{mA}}$$

It is assumed that a capacitor is fully charged after five time constants.

$$t = 5\tau = 5(20\ \text{ms}); \qquad \boxed{t = 100\ \text{ms}}$$

The current is zero when the capacitor is fully charged; $\boxed{I_f = 0\ A}$

32-4. For the circuit in Problem 32-2, what is the maximum charge for the capacitor and how much time is required to fully charge the capacitor?

$$Q_{max} = CV_B = (6 \times 10^{-6}\ \text{F})(20\ \text{V}); \qquad Q_{max} = 120\ \mu\text{F}$$

$$t = 5RC = 5(2.40\ \text{ms}); \qquad \boxed{t = 12.0\ \text{ms}}$$

---

*32-5. An 8-μF capacitor is connected in series with a 600-Ω resistor and a 24-V battery. After one time constant, what are the charge on the capacitor and the current in the circuit?

$$Q = CV_B(1 - e^{-t/RC}) = CV_B\left(1 - \frac{1}{e}\right) = CV_B(0.632);$$

$$Q = (8\ \mu F)(24\ \text{V})(0.632); \qquad \boxed{Q = 121\ \mu\text{C}}$$

$$I = \frac{V_B}{R}\,e^{-t/RC} = \frac{24\ \text{V}}{600\ \Omega}\left(\frac{1}{e}\right); \qquad \boxed{I = 14.7\ \text{mA}}$$

*32-6. Assume that the fully charged capacitor of Problem 32-5 is allowed to discharge. After one time constant, what are the current in the circuit and the charge on the capacitor?

$$I = \frac{-V_B}{R}\,e^{-t/RC} = \frac{-24\ \text{V}}{600\ \Omega}\left(\frac{1}{e}\right); \qquad \boxed{I = \text{-14.7 mA, } decreasing}$$

$$Q = CV_B\,e^{-t/RC} = (8\ \mu F)(24\ \text{V})\left(\frac{1}{e}\right); \qquad \boxed{Q = 70.6\ \mu\text{C}}$$

**32-7. Assume that the 8-μF capacitor in Problem 32-5 is fully charged and is then allowed to decay. Find the time when the current in the circuit will have decayed to 20 percent of its initial value? [*Procedure: Let $x = t/RC$, solve for x, and then find t.*]

$$I = \frac{-V_B}{R}\,e^{-t/RC} = I_{max}e^{-x}; \qquad \frac{I}{I_{max}} = e^{-x}; \qquad e^{-x} = 0.20; \qquad e^{+x} = \frac{1}{0.2} = 5.0$$

Take ln of both sides: $x = \ln(5.0) = 1.61$ *Now,* $x = \frac{t}{RC} = 1.61; \qquad t = 1.61RC$

$$t = 1.61(600\ \Omega)(24\ \text{V}); \qquad \boxed{t = 7.73\ \text{ms}}$$

Chapter 32   Alternating-Current Circuits **445**

**32-8. A 5-μF capacitor is connected in series with a 12-V source of emf and a 4000 Ω resistor. How much time is required to place 40 μC of charge on the capacitor? [*Let x = t/RC*]

$Q = CV_B(1 - e^{-t/RC})$; $\quad 40\ \mu C = (5\ \mu F)(12\ V)(1 - e^{-x})$; $\quad 0.667 = (1 - e^{-x})$

$e^{-x} = 1 - 0.667$; $\quad e^{-x} = 0.333$; $\quad e^{+x} = \dfrac{1}{0.333} = 3.0$

$x = \ln(3)$; $\quad \dfrac{t}{RC} = 1.10$; $\quad t = 1.10RC$; $\quad \boxed{t = 22.2\ ms}$

The Inductor

32-9. A series dc circuit contains a 4-mH inductor and an 80-Ω resistor in series with a 12-V battery. What is the time constant for the circuit? What are the initial and final currents?

$\tau = \dfrac{L}{R} = \dfrac{0.004\ H}{80\ \Omega}$; $\quad \boxed{\tau = 50.0\ \mu s}$

When t = 0, $\quad i = \dfrac{V_B}{R}(1 - e^{-(R/L)t}) = \dfrac{V_B}{R}(1-1) = 0$; $\quad \boxed{i_o = 0}$

When t = ∞, $\quad i = \dfrac{V_B}{R}(1 - e^{-(R/L)t}) = \dfrac{V_B}{R}(1-0)$; $\quad i = \dfrac{12\ V}{80\ \Omega}$; $\quad \boxed{i_f = 150\ mA}$

32-10. A 5-mH inductor, a 160-Ω resistor and a 50-V battery are connected in series. What time is required for the current in the inductor to reach 63 percent of its steady state value? What is the current at that instant? *(Current reaches 63% in one time constant.)*

$\tau = \dfrac{L}{R} = \dfrac{0.005\ H}{160\ \Omega}$; $\quad \boxed{\tau = 31.2\ \mu s}$

32-11. What is the current in Problem 32-9 after a time of one time constant?

$i = \dfrac{V_B}{R}(1 - e^{-(R/L)t}) = \dfrac{12\ V}{80\ \Omega}\left(1 - \dfrac{1}{e}\right)$; $\quad i = (0.15\ A)(0.632)$; $\quad \boxed{i = 94.8\ mA}$

32-12. Assume that the inductor in Problem 32-10 has reached its steady state value. If the circuit is broken how much time must pass before we can be sure the current in the inductor is zero? *(After 5 time constants: t = 5τ)*

$t = 5\tau = 5(31.2\ ms)$; $\quad \boxed{t = 156\ \mu s}$

32-13 The current in a 25-mH solenoid increases from 0 to 2 A in a time of 0.1 s. What is the magnitude of the self-induced emf?

$\varepsilon = -L\dfrac{\Delta i}{\Delta t} = -(0.025\ H)\dfrac{(2\ A - 0)}{0.1\ s}$; $\quad \boxed{\varepsilon = -500\ mV}$

32-14. A series dc circuit contains a 0.05-H inductor and a 40-Ω resistor in series with a 90-V source of emf. What are the maximum current in the circuit and the time constant?

$i_{max} = \dfrac{V_B}{R} = \dfrac{90\ V}{40\ \Omega}$; $\quad \boxed{i_{max} = 2.25\ A}$

$\tau = \dfrac{L}{R} = \dfrac{0.05\ H}{40\ \Omega}$; $\quad \boxed{\tau = 1.25\ ms}$

*32-15. What is the instantaneous current in the inductor of Problem 32-14 after a decay time of 1.0 ms? *(Assume the current decays from it's maximum value of 2.25 A.)*

Let x = (R/L)t: $\quad x = \left(\dfrac{40\ \Omega}{0.05\ H}\right)(0.001\ s)$; $\quad x = 0.80$; $\quad e^{-x} = \dfrac{1}{e^x} = \dfrac{1}{e^{0.8}} = 0.449$

$i = \dfrac{V_B}{R}e^{-(R/L)t} = \dfrac{V_B}{R}e^{-x}$; $\quad i = \dfrac{90\ V}{40\ \Omega}(0.449)$; $\quad i = 1.01\ A$

You should show that the current after a rise time of 1 ms is 1.24 A.

32-16. A 6-mH inductor, a 50-Ω resistor, and a 38-V battery are connected in series. At what time after the connection will the current reach an instantaneous value of 600 mA?

Procedure: Let x = (R/L)t; then solve for x and substitute to find the time t:

$i = \frac{V_B}{R}(1 - e^{-x})$; $\frac{iR}{V_B} = 1 - e^{-x}$; $e^{-x} = 1 - \frac{iR}{V_B} = 1 - \frac{(0.6 \text{ A})(50 \text{ }\Omega)}{38 \text{ V}}$; $e^{-x} = 0.211$

$e^{+x} = \frac{1}{0.211} = 4.75$; *Take ln of both sides:* $x = \ln(4.75) = 1.56$

$x = 1.56 = \frac{Rt}{L}$; $t = \frac{1.56L}{R} = \frac{1.56(0.006 \text{ H})}{50 \text{ }\Omega}$; $\boxed{x = 187 \text{ }\mu s}$

Alternating Currents

32-17. An ac voltmeter, when placed across a 12-Ω resistor, reads 117 V. What are the maximum values for the voltage and current?

$V_{max} = \sqrt{2}V_{eff} = 1.414(117 \text{ V})$; $\boxed{V_{max} = 165 \text{ V}}$

$I_{max} = \sqrt{2}I_{eff} = 1.414\left(\frac{117 \text{ V}}{12 \text{ }\Omega}\right)$; $\boxed{I_{max} = 13.8 \text{ A}}$

32-18. In an ac circuit, the voltage and current reach maximum values of 120 V and 6.00 A. What are the effective ac values?

$I_{eff} = \frac{I_{max}}{\sqrt{2}} = \frac{6 \text{ A}}{1.414}$; $\boxed{I_{eff} = 4.24 \text{ A}}$; $V_{eff} = \frac{V_{max}}{\sqrt{2}} = \frac{120 \text{ V}}{1.414}$; $\boxed{V_{eff} = 84.9 \text{ V}}$

32-19. A capacitor has a maximum voltage rating of 500 V. What is the highest effective ac voltage that can be supplied to it without breakdown?

$V_{eff} = \frac{V_{max}}{\sqrt{2}} = \frac{500 \text{ V}}{1.414}$; $\boxed{V_{eff} = 354 \text{ V}}$

32-20. A certain appliance is supplied with an effective voltage of 220 V under an effective current of 20 A. What are the maximum and minimum values?

$V_{max} = \sqrt{2}V_{eff} = 1.414(220 \text{ V})$; $\boxed{V_{max} = \pm 311 \text{ V}}$

$I_{max} = \sqrt{2}I_{eff} = 1.414(20 \text{ A})$; $\boxed{I_{max} = \pm 28.3 \text{ A}}$

Reactance

32-21. A 6-μF capacitor is connected to a 40-V, 60 Hz ac line. What is the effective ac current in the circuit containing pure capacitance?

$X_C = \frac{1}{2\pi fC} = \frac{1}{2\pi(60 \text{ Hz})(6 \times 10^{-6}\text{F})}$; $\boxed{X_C = 442 \text{ }\Omega}$

$I_{eff} = \frac{V_{eff}}{X_C} = \frac{40 \text{ V}}{442 \text{ }\Omega}$; $\boxed{I_{eff} = 90.5 \text{ mA}}$

32-22. A 2-H inductor of negligible resistance is connected to a 50-V, 50 Hz ac line. What is the reactance? What is the effective ac current in the coil?

$X_L = 2\pi fL = 2\pi(50 \text{ Hz})(2 \text{ H}) = 628 \text{ }\Omega$; $\boxed{X_L = 628 \text{ }\Omega}$

$I_{eff} = \frac{V_{eff}}{X_L} = \frac{50 \text{ V}}{628 \text{ }\Omega}$; $\boxed{I_{eff} = 79.6 \text{ mA}}$

32-23. A 50-mH inductor of negligible resistance is connected to a 120-V, 60-Hz ac line. What is the inductive reactance? What is the effective ac current in the circuit?

$X_L = 2\pi fL = 2\pi(60 \text{ Hz})(0.050 \text{ H}) = 18.85 \text{ }\Omega$

$I_{eff} = \frac{V_{eff}}{X_L} = \frac{120 \text{ V}}{18.85 \text{ }\Omega}$; $\boxed{I_{eff} = 6.37 \text{ A}}$

32-24. A 6-μF capacitor is connected to a 24-V, 50-Hz ac source. What is the current in the circuit?

$$X_c = \frac{1}{2\pi fC} = \frac{1}{2\pi(50\text{ Hz})(6 \times 10^{-6}\text{F})};\quad \boxed{X_C = 531\ \Omega}$$

$$I_{eff} = \frac{V_{eff}}{X_c} = \frac{24\text{ V}}{531\ \Omega};\quad \boxed{I_{eff} = 45.2\text{ mA}}$$

32-25. A 3-μF capacitor connected to a 120-V, ac line draws an effective current of 0.5 A. What is the frequency of the source?

$$X_c = \frac{V_{eff}}{I_{eff}} = \frac{120\text{ V}}{0.5\text{ A}};\quad X_c = 240\ \Omega$$

$$X_c = \frac{1}{2\pi fC};\quad f = \frac{1}{2\pi C X_c} = \frac{1}{2\pi(3 \times 10^{-6}\text{F})(240\ \Omega)};\quad \boxed{f = 221\text{ Hz}}$$

32-26. Find the reactance of a 60-μF capacitor in a 600-Hz ac circuit. What is the reactance if the frequency is reduced to 200 Hz?

$$X_c = \frac{1}{2\pi fC} = \frac{1}{2\pi(600\text{ Hz})(60 \times 10^{-6}\text{F})};\quad \boxed{X_C = 4.42\ \Omega}$$

$$X_c = \frac{1}{2\pi fC} = \frac{1}{2\pi(200\text{ Hz})(60 \times 10^{-6}\text{F})};\quad \boxed{X_C = 13.3\ \Omega}$$

32-27. The frequency of an alternating current is 200 Hz and the inductive reactance for a single inductor is 100 Ω. What is the inductance?

$$X_L = 2\pi fL;\quad L = \frac{X_L}{2\pi f} = \frac{100\ \Omega}{2\pi(200\text{ Hz})};\quad \boxed{L = 79.6\text{ mH.}}$$

32-28. A 20-Ω resistor, a 2-μF capacitor, and a 0.70-H inductor are available. Each of these, in turn, is connected to a 120-V, 60 Hz ac source as the only circuit element. What is the effective ac current in each case?

Resistance only: $\quad i = \frac{V}{R} = \frac{120\text{ V}}{20\ \Omega};\quad \boxed{i = 6.00\text{ A}}$

Capacitor only: $\quad X_C = \frac{1}{2\pi(60\text{ Hz})(2 \times 10^{-6}\text{F})} = 1326\ \Omega;\quad i = \frac{120\text{ V}}{1326\ \Omega};\quad \boxed{i = 90.5\text{ mA}}$

Inductor only: $\quad X_L = 2\pi fL = 2\pi(60\text{ Hz})(0.7\text{ H}) = 264\ \Omega;\quad i = \frac{120\text{ V}}{264\ \Omega};\quad \boxed{i = 455\text{ mA}}$

Series AC Circuits

*32-29. A 300-Ω resistor, a 3-μF capacitor, and a 4-H inductor are connected in series with a 90-V, 50 Hz ac source. What is the net reactance of the circuit? What is the impedance?

$$X_c = \frac{1}{2\pi(50\text{ Hz})(3 \times 10^{-6}\text{F})} = 1061\ \Omega;\quad X_L = 2\pi(50\text{ Hz})(4\text{ H}) = 1257\ \Omega;$$

Net Reactance: $\quad \boxed{X_L - X_C = 196\ \Omega}$

$$Z = \sqrt{R^2 + (X_L - X_C)^2} = \sqrt{(300\ \Omega)^2 + (1257\ \Omega - 1061\ \Omega)^2};\quad \boxed{Z = 358\ \Omega}$$

*32-30. What is the effective ac current delivered to the ac series circuit described in Problem 32-29? What is the peak value for this current?

$$i = \frac{V}{Z} = \frac{90\text{ V}}{300\ \Omega};\quad \boxed{i = 300\text{ mA}}$$

$$i_{max} = \sqrt{2}(300\text{ mA});\quad \boxed{i = 424\text{ mA}}$$

*32-31. A series ac circuit consists of a 100-Ω resistor, a 0.2-H inductor, and a 3-μF capacitor connected to a 110-V, 60 Hz ac source. What is the inductive reactance, the capacitative reactance, and the impedance for the circuit?

$$X_c = \frac{1}{2\pi(60\ Hz)(3\times10^{-6}F)} = \boxed{884\ \Omega}; \quad X_L = 2\pi(60\ Hz)(0.2\ H) = \boxed{75.4\ \Omega}$$

$$Z = \sqrt{R^2 + (X_L - X_C)^2} = \sqrt{(100\ \Omega)^2 + (75.4\ \Omega - 884\ \Omega)^2}; \quad \boxed{Z = 815\ \Omega}$$

*32-32. What are the phase angle and the power factor for the circuit described in Problem 32-31?

$$\tan\phi = \frac{X_L - X_C}{R} = \frac{75.4\ \Omega - 884\ \Omega}{100\ \Omega}; \quad \boxed{\phi = -83.0^0}$$

$$Power\ Factor = \cos\phi = \cos(-83.0^0); \quad Power\ Factor = 0.123 \quad or \quad \boxed{12.3\%}$$

*32-33. Assume that all the elements of Problem 32-28 above are connected in series with the given source. What is the effective current delivered to the circuit?

From Problem 32-28: $R = 20\ \Omega$, $X_C = 1326$, and $X_L = 264\ \Omega$, $V = 120\ V$, $f = 60\ Hz$

$$Z = \sqrt{R^2 + (X_L - X_C)^2} = \sqrt{(20\ \Omega)^2 + (264\ \Omega - 1326\ \Omega)^2}; \quad Z = 1062\ \Omega$$

$$i = \frac{V}{Z} = \frac{120\ V}{1062\ \Omega}; \quad \boxed{i = 113\ mA}$$

*32-34. A series ac circuit contains a 12-mH inductor, an 8-μF capacitor, and a 40-Ω resistor connected to a 110-V, 200 Hz ac line. What is the effective ac current in the circuit?

$$X_C = \frac{1}{2\pi(200\ Hz)(8\times10^{-6}F)} = \boxed{99.5\ \Omega}; \quad X_L = 2\pi(200\ Hz)(0.012\ H) = \boxed{15.1\ \Omega}$$

$$Z = \sqrt{R^2 + (X_L - X_C)^2} = \sqrt{(40\ \Omega)^2 + (15.1\ \Omega - 99.5\ \Omega)^2}; \quad \boxed{Z = 93.4\ \Omega}$$

*32-34. (Cont.)

$$\tan\phi = \frac{X_L - X_C}{R} = \frac{15.1\ \Omega - 99.5\ \Omega}{40\ \Omega}; \quad \boxed{\phi = -64.6^0}$$

$$Power\ Factor = \cos\phi = \cos(-64.6^0);$$

$$Power\ Factor = 0.428 \quad or \quad \boxed{42.8\%}$$

*32-35. When a 6-Ω resistor and a pure inductor are connected to a 100-V, 60 Hz ac line, the effective current is 10 A. What is the inductance ? What is the power loss through the resistor and what is the power loss through the inductor?

$$Z = \frac{110\ V}{10\ A} = 11.0\ \Omega; \quad X_L = \sqrt{Z^2 - R^2} = \sqrt{(11.0)^2 - (6\ \Omega)^2};$$

$$X_L = 9.22\ \Omega; \quad L = \frac{X_L}{2\pi f} = \frac{(9.22\ \Omega)}{2\pi(60\ Hz)}; \quad \boxed{L = 24.5\ mH}$$

$$P = I^2R = (10\ A)^2(6.00\ \Omega); \quad \boxed{P = 600\ W};$$

No Power lost in inductor: $\boxed{0}$

*32-36. A capacitor is in series with a resistance of 35 Ω and connected to a 220-V, ac line. The reactance of the capacitor is 45 Ω. What is the effective ac current? What is the phase angle? What is the power factor?

$$Z = \sqrt{R^2 + (0 - X_C)^2} = \sqrt{(35\ \Omega)^2 + (45\ \Omega)^2} = 57.0\ \Omega;$$

$$i = \frac{220\ V}{57.0\ \Omega} = 3.89\ A; \quad \boxed{i = 3.89\ A}$$

$$\tan\phi = \frac{X_L - X_C}{R} = \frac{-45\ \Omega}{35\ \Omega}; \quad \boxed{\phi = -52.1^0};$$

$$Power\ Factor = \cos 52.1^0 = \boxed{61.4\%}$$

Circuits 453
Copyright © by Glencoe/McGraw-Hill.

452 Unit A Solutions Manual

Copyright © by Glencoe/McGraw-Hill.

227

*32-37. A coil having an inductance of 0.15 H and a resistance of 12 Ω is connected to a 110-V, 25 Hz line. What is the effective current in the circuit? What is the power factor? What power is lost in the circuit? ($X_C = 0$)

$$X_L = 2\pi fL = 2\pi(25\,Hz)(0.15\,H) = 23.56\,\Omega; \quad Z = \sqrt{R^2 + X_L^2}$$

$$Z = \sqrt{(12)^2 + (23.56)^2} = 26.44\,\Omega; \quad i = \frac{110\,V}{26.44\,\Omega}; \quad \boxed{i = 4.16\,A}$$

$$\tan\phi = \frac{X_L - X_C}{R} = \frac{23.56\,\Omega}{12.0\,\Omega}; \quad \phi = 63^0; \quad Power\ Factor = \cos 63^0 = \boxed{45.4\%}$$

Power is lost only through resistance: $\quad P = I^2R = (4.16\,A)^2(12\,\Omega) = \boxed{208\,W}$

*32-38. What is the resonant frequency for the circuit described by Problem 32-29?

$$f_r = \frac{1}{2\pi\sqrt{LC}} = \frac{1}{2\pi\sqrt{(0.2\,H)(3\times10^{-6}F)}}; \quad \boxed{f_r = 205\,Hz}$$

*32-39. What is the resonant frequency for the circuit described by Problem 32-34?

$$f_r = \frac{1}{2\pi\sqrt{LC}} = \frac{1}{2\pi\sqrt{(0.012\,H)(8\times10^{-6}F)}}; \quad \boxed{f_r = 514\,Hz}$$

Supplementary Problems

32-40. A 100-V battery is connected to a dc series circuit with a 60-mH inductor and a 50-Ω resistor. Calculate the maximum current in the circuit and the time constant.

When $t = \infty$, $i = \frac{V_B}{R}(1-e^{-(R/L)t}) = \frac{V_B}{R}(1-0)$; $i = \frac{100\,V}{50\,\Omega}$; $\boxed{i_{max} = 2.00\,A}$

$$\tau = \frac{L}{R} = \frac{0.060\,H}{50\,\Omega}; \quad \boxed{\tau = 1.20\,ms}$$

32-41. If the circuit of Problem 32-40 reaches a steady state condition and is then broken, what will be the instantaneous current after one time constant? *(Decay of an inductor.)*

$$i = \frac{V_B}{R}e^{-(R/L)t} = \frac{100\,V}{50\,\Omega}\left(\frac{1}{e}\right); \quad \boxed{i = 736\,mA}$$

32-42. A resonant circuit has an inductance of 400 µH and a capacitance of 100 pF. What is the resonant frequency?

$$f_r = \frac{1}{2\pi\sqrt{LC}} = \frac{1}{2\pi\sqrt{(4\times10^{-4}H)(1\times10^{-10}F)}}; \quad \boxed{f_r = 796\,kHz}$$

32-43. An LR dc circuit has a time constant of 2 ms. What is the inductance if the resistance is 2 kΩ? Find the instantaneous current 2 ms after the circuit is connected to a 12-V battery.

$$\tau = \frac{L}{R}; \quad L = \tau R = (0.002\,s)(2000\,\Omega); \quad \boxed{L = 4.00\,H}$$

$$i = \frac{V_B}{R}(1-e^{-(R/L)t}) = \frac{12\,V}{2000\,\Omega}\left(1-\frac{1}{e}\right); \quad \boxed{i = 3.79\,mA}$$

32-44. A series dc circuit consists of a 12-V battery, a 20-Ω resistor, and an unknown capacitor. The time constant is 40 ms. What is the capacitance? What is the maximum charge on the capacitor?

$$\tau = RC; \quad C = \frac{\tau}{R} = \frac{0.040\,s}{20\,\Omega}; \quad \boxed{C = 2.00\,mF;}$$

$$Q = CV = (2\,mF)(12\,V) = \boxed{24\,mC}$$

*32-45. A 2-H inductor having a resistance of 120 Ω is connected to a 30-V battery. How much time is required for the current to reach 63 percent of its maximum value? What is the initial rate of current increase in amperes per second? What is the final current?

The current reaches 63% of its maximum value in a time equal to one time constant:

$$\tau = \frac{L}{R} = \frac{2\,H}{120\,\Omega}; \qquad \boxed{\tau = 16.7\,ms}$$

For Loop: $\Sigma E = \Sigma IR$ or $V_B - L\dfrac{\Delta i}{\Delta t} = iR$

Solving for $\Delta i/\Delta t$ with initial $i = 0$, we have: $\quad V_B - iR = L\dfrac{\Delta i}{\Delta t}; \qquad \dfrac{\Delta i}{\Delta t} = \dfrac{V_B}{L};$

$$\frac{\Delta i}{\Delta t} = \frac{V_B}{L} = \frac{30\,V}{2\,H}; \qquad \boxed{\frac{\Delta i}{\Delta t} = 15\,A/s}$$

The final current is the maximum: $\quad i_{max} = \dfrac{V_B}{R} = \dfrac{30\,V}{120\,\Omega}; \qquad \boxed{i_{max} = 250\,mA}$

---

*32-46. Consider the circuit shown in Fig. 32-13. What is the impedance? What is the power loss in the circuit? What is the effective current?

$L = 4\,mH;\quad C = 10\,\mu F;\quad R = 20\,\Omega;$

Source: 50 V, 600 Hz

$X_L = 2\pi f L = 2\pi(600\,Hz)(0.004\,H) = 15.1\,\Omega$

$X_C = \dfrac{1}{2\pi(600\,Hz)(10 \times 10^{-6}\,F)} = 26.5\,\Omega; \qquad Z = \sqrt{(20\,\Omega)^2 + (15.1\,\Omega - 26.5\,\Omega)^2};$

Impedance: $\boxed{Z = 23.0\,\Omega}$ $\qquad i = \dfrac{V}{Z} = \dfrac{50\,V}{23\,\Omega}; \qquad$ *Effective current:* $\boxed{i = 2.17\,A};$

Power loss is entirely in resistance: $\quad P = i^2R = (2.17\,A)^2(20\,\Omega); \qquad \boxed{P = 94.2\,W}$

---

*32-47. A tuner circuit contains a 4-mH inductor and a variable capacitor. What must be the capacitance if the circuit is to resonate at a frequency of 800 Hz?

$$f_r = \frac{1}{2\pi\sqrt{LC}}; \qquad f_r^2 = \frac{1}{4\pi^2 LC}; \qquad C = \frac{1}{4\pi^2 L f_r^2}$$

$$C = \frac{1}{4\pi^2(0.004\,H)(800\,Hz)^2}; \qquad \boxed{C = 9.89\,\mu F}$$

---

*32-48. An 8-μF capacitor is in series with a 40-Ω resistor and connected to a 117-V, 60-Hz source. What is the impedance? What is the power factor? How much power is lost in the circuit? *(Note: $X_L = 0$, so that all reactance is due to the capacitor.)*

$$X_C = \frac{1}{2\pi(60\,Hz)(8 \times 10^{-6}\,F)} = 332\,\Omega$$

$Z = \sqrt{(40\,\Omega)^2 + (0 - 332)^2}; \qquad \boxed{Z = 334\,\Omega}$

$i = \dfrac{V}{Z} = \dfrac{117\,V}{334\,\Omega}; \qquad i = 350\,mA$

$\tan\phi = \dfrac{X_L - X_C}{R} = \dfrac{-332\,\Omega}{40\,\Omega}; \qquad \phi = -83.1^0; \qquad$ *Power Factor* $= \cos 83.1^0 = \boxed{12.0\%}$

Power is lost only through resistance: $\quad P = i^2R = (0.350\,A)^2(40\,\Omega) = \boxed{4.90\,W}$

Source: 117 V, 60 Hz

---

*32-49. Someone wants to construct a circuit whose resonant frequency is 950 kHz. If a coil in the circuit has an inductance of 3 mH, what capacitance should be added to the circuit?

$$f_r = \frac{1}{2\pi\sqrt{LC}}; \qquad f_r^2 = \frac{1}{4\pi^2 LC}; \qquad C = \frac{1}{4\pi^2 L f_r^2}$$

$$C = \frac{1}{4\pi^2(0.003\,H)(950,000\,Hz)^2}; \qquad \boxed{C = 9.36\,pF}$$

Critical Thinking Problems

*32-52. The resistance of an 8-H inductor is 200 Ω. If this inductor is suddenly connected across a potential difference of 50 V, what is the initial rate of increase of the current in A/s (see Eq. 32-15)? What is the final steady current? At what rate is the current increasing after one time constant. At what time after connecting the source of emf, does the current equal one-half of its final value? (Initially, the current is zero.)

L

R

$$\tau = \frac{L}{R} = \frac{8\ H}{200\ \Omega}; \qquad \tau = 40.0\ ms$$

For Loop: $\Sigma E = \Sigma IR$ or $V_B - L\frac{\Delta i}{\Delta t} = iR$

Solving for Δi/Δt with initial i = 0, we have: $V_B - iR = L\frac{\Delta i}{\Delta t}$; $\frac{\Delta i}{\Delta t} = \frac{V_B}{L}$;

$$\frac{\Delta i}{\Delta t} = \frac{V_B}{L} = \frac{50\ V}{8\ H}; \qquad \boxed{\frac{\Delta i}{\Delta t} = 6.25\ A/s}$$

The final current is the maximum: $i_{max} = \frac{V_B}{R} = \frac{50\ V}{200\ \Omega}$; $\boxed{i_{max} = 250\ mA}$

To find the rate of increase after one time constant, we need to know i at t = τ:

$$i = i_{max}(1 - e^{-t/\tau}) = (250\ mA)\left(1 - \frac{1}{e}\right); \qquad i = 158\ mA$$

$$V_B - L\frac{\Delta i}{\Delta t} = iR; \qquad L\frac{\Delta i}{\Delta t} = V_B - iR; \qquad \frac{\Delta i}{\Delta t} = \frac{V_B - iR}{L}$$

$$\frac{\Delta i}{\Delta t} = \frac{V_B - iR}{L} = \frac{50\ V - (0.158\ A)(200\ \Omega)}{8\ H}; \qquad \boxed{\frac{\Delta i}{\Delta t} = 2.30\ A/s}$$

Let $x = \frac{Rt}{L}$, then: $\frac{i}{i_{max}} = (1 - e^{-x}) = 0.50$; $e^{-x} = 0.5$; $e^{-x} = 2.0$

$$x = 0.693 = \frac{Rt}{L}; \qquad t = \frac{0.693(8\ H)}{200\ \Omega}; \qquad \boxed{t = 27.7\ ms}$$

---

*32-50. A 50-μF capacitor and a 70-Ω resistor are connected in series across a 120-V, 60 Hz ac line. Determine the current in the circuit, the phase angle, and the total power loss?

R   C

Source: 120 V, 60 Hz

$$X_C = \frac{1}{2\pi(60\ Hz)(50 \times 10^{-6}\ F)} = 53.05\ \Omega$$

$$Z = \sqrt{(70\ \Omega)^2 + (0 - 53.05)^2}; \qquad Z = 87.8\ \Omega$$

$$i = \frac{V}{Z} = \frac{120\ V}{87.8\ \Omega}; \qquad \boxed{i = 1.37\ A}$$

$$\tan\phi = \frac{X_L - X_C}{R} = \frac{-53.05\ \Omega}{70\ \Omega}; \qquad \phi = -37.2^0; \qquad Power\ Factor = \cos 37.2^0 = \boxed{79.8\%}$$

Power is lost only through resistance: $P = I^2R = (1.37\ A)^2(70\ \Omega) = \boxed{131\ W}$

*32-51. Refer to Problem 32-50. What is the voltage across the resistor? What is the voltage across the capacitor? What inductance should be added to the circuit to reach resonance?

$$V = iR = (1.37\ A)(70\ \Omega) = \boxed{95.6\ V} \qquad V_C = iX_C = (1.37\ A)(53.05\ \Omega) = \boxed{72.5\ V}$$

$$f_r = \frac{1}{2\pi\sqrt{LC}}; \qquad f_r^2 = \frac{1}{4\pi^2 LC}; \qquad L = \frac{1}{4\pi^2 Cf_r^2}$$

$$L = \frac{1}{4\pi^2(50 \times 10^{-6}\ F)(60\ Hz)^2}; \qquad \boxed{L = 141\ mH}$$

*32-53. In Chapter 29, we found that the magnetic flux density within a solenoid was given by:

$$(1) \quad B = \frac{\Phi}{A} = \frac{\mu_0 NI}{l}$$

Here we have used l for the length of the solenoid in order to avoid confusion with the symbol L used for inductance. We also know that induced emf is found in two ways:

$$(2) \quad \varepsilon = -N\frac{\Delta\Phi}{\Delta t} \quad \text{and} \quad (3) \quad \varepsilon = -L\frac{\Delta i}{\Delta t}$$

Prove the following relationships for a solenoid of length l having N turns of area A:

$$L = \frac{N\Phi}{I} \quad \text{and} \quad L = \frac{\mu N^2 A}{l}$$

Combining Eqs (2) and (3) above, we obtain: $\quad N\Delta\phi = L\Delta i$

Now, at maximum current I: $\quad N\phi = LI \quad$ or $\quad \boxed{L = \frac{N\phi}{I}}$

From (1): $\quad \phi = \frac{\mu_0 NIA}{l} \quad$ which gives: $\quad L = \frac{N\phi}{I} = \frac{N}{I}\left(\frac{\mu_0 NIA}{l}\right)$

And finally: $\quad \boxed{L = \frac{\mu_0 N^2 A}{l}} \qquad$ *Note: L is not dependent on current or voltage.*

*32-54. An inductor consists of a coil 30 cm long with 300 turns of area 0.004 m^2. Find the inductance (see previous problem). A battery is connected and the current builds from zero to 2.00 A in 0.001 s. What is the average induced emf in the coil?

$$L = \frac{\mu_0 N^2 A}{l} = \frac{(4\pi \times 10^{-7} \text{ T·m/A})(300)^2 (0.004 \text{ m}^2)}{0.300 \text{ m}}; \qquad \boxed{L = 1.51 \text{ mH}}$$

$$\varepsilon = -L\frac{\Delta i}{\Delta t} = -(1.51 \times 10^{-3} \text{ H})\left(\frac{2 \text{ A} - 0}{0.001 \text{ s}}\right); \qquad \varepsilon = -3.02 \text{ V}$$

---

*32-55. An inductor, resistor, and capacitor are connected in series with a 60-Hz ac line. A voltmeter connected to each element in the circuit gives the following readings:

$V_R = 60$ V, $V_L = 100$ V, and $V_C = 160$ V. What is the total voltage drop in the circuit? What is the phase angle?

$$V_T = \sqrt{V_R^2 + (V_L - V_C)^2} = \sqrt{(60 \text{ V})^2 + (100 \text{ V} - 160 \text{ V})^2}; \qquad \boxed{V_T = 84.6 \text{ V}}$$

$$\tan\phi = \frac{V_L - V_C}{V_R} = \frac{(100 \text{ V} - 160 \text{ V})}{60 \text{ V}}; \qquad \phi = -45.0^0$$

*32-56. The antenna circuit in a radio receiver consists of a variable capacitor and a 9-mH coil. The resistance of the circuit is 40 Ω. A 980-kHz radio wave produces a potential difference of 0.2 mV across the circuit. Determine the capacitance required for resonance. . What is the current at resonance?

$$f_r = \frac{1}{2\pi\sqrt{LC}}; \quad f_r^2 = \frac{1}{4\pi^2 LC}; \quad C = \frac{1}{4\pi^2 L f_r^2}$$

$$C = \frac{1}{4\pi^2 (0.009 \text{ H})(980,000 \text{ Hz})^2}; \qquad \boxed{C = 2.93 \text{ μF}}$$

At f_r, $X_C = X_L$ and: $Z = R = 40$ Ω; $\quad i = \frac{0.2 \text{ mV}}{40 \text{ Ω}}; \qquad \boxed{i = 5.00 \text{ mA}}$

Chapter 33. Light and Illumination

Light and the Electromagnetic Spectrum

33-1. An infrared spectrophotometer scans the wavelengths from 1 to 16 μm. Express this range in terms of the frequencies of the infrared rays.

$$f_1 = \frac{c}{\lambda_1} = \frac{3 \times 10^8 \text{m/s}}{1 \times 10^{-6}\text{m}} = 30.0 \times 10^{13}\text{Hz}; \quad f_2 = \frac{c}{\lambda_2} = \frac{3 \times 10^8 \text{m/s}}{16 \times 10^{-6}\text{m}} = 1.88 \times 10^{13}\text{Hz}$$

$$\boxed{\text{Range of frequencies: } 1.88 \times 10^{13}\text{ Hz to } 30 \times 10^{13}\text{ Hz}}$$

33-2. What is the frequency of violet light of wavelength 410 nm?

$$f = \frac{c}{\lambda} = \frac{3 \times 10^8 \text{m/s}}{410 \times 10^{-9}\text{m}} \qquad \boxed{f = 7.32 \times 10^{14}\text{ Hz}}$$

33-3. A microwave radiator used in measuring automobile speeds emits radiation of frequency 1.2×10^9 Hz. What is the wavelength?

$$\lambda = \frac{c}{f} = \frac{3 \times 10^8 \text{m/s}}{1.2 \times 10^9 \text{Hz}}; \qquad \boxed{\lambda = 250 \text{ mm}}$$

33-4. What is the range of frequencies for visible light? (*Range of λ:* 700 nm to 400 nm)

$$f_1 = \frac{c}{\lambda_1} = \frac{3 \times 10^8 \text{m/s}}{700 \times 10^{-9}\text{m}} = 4.29 \times 10^{14}\text{Hz}; \quad f_2 = \frac{c}{\lambda_2} = \frac{3 \times 10^8 \text{m/s}}{400 \times 10^{-9}\text{m}} = 7.50 \times 10^{14}\text{Hz}$$

$$\boxed{\text{Range of frequencies: } 4.29 \times 10^{14}\text{ Hz to } 7.50 \times 10^{14}\text{ Hz}}$$

33-5. If Planck's constant h is equal to 6.626×10^{-34} J s, what is the energy of light of wavelength 600 nm?

$$E = hf = \frac{hc}{\lambda} = \frac{(6.625 \times 10^{-34}\text{J}\cdot\text{s})(3 \times 10^8 \text{m/s})}{600 \times 10^{-9}\text{m}}; \qquad E = 3.31 \times 10^{-19}\text{ J}$$

Chapter 33   Light and Illumination   **463**

---

*32-57. A series RLC circuit has elements as follows: $L = 0.6$ H, $C = 3.5$ μF, and $R = 250$ Ω. The circuit is driven by a generator that produces a *maximum* emf of 150 V at 60 Hz. What is the effective ac current? What is the phase angle? What is the average power loss in the circuit? (*First find V_{eff}*)

Source: 150 V, 60 Hz

$$V_{eff} = \frac{V_{max}}{\sqrt{2}} = \frac{150 \text{ V}}{\sqrt{2}}; \quad V_{eff} = 106 \text{ V}$$

$L = 0.600$ H; $C = 3.5$ μF; $R = 250$ Ω;

$$X_L = 2\pi f L = 2\pi(60 \text{ Hz})(0.6 \text{ H}) = 226 \text{ Ω}$$

$$X_C = \frac{1}{2\pi(60 \text{ Hz})(3.5 \times 10^{-6}\text{F})} = 758 \text{ Ω}; \quad Z = \sqrt{(250 \text{ Ω})^2 + (226 \text{ Ω} - 758 \text{ Ω})^2};$$

Impedance: $\boxed{Z = 588 \text{ Ω}}$ $\qquad i = \frac{V}{Z} = \frac{106 \text{ V}}{588 \text{ Ω}};$ *Effective current:* $\boxed{i = 181 \text{ mA}}$

$$\tan\phi = \frac{X_L - X_C}{R} = \frac{226 \text{ Ω} - 768 \text{ Ω}}{250 \text{ Ω}}; \quad \boxed{\phi = 42.7^0}$$

Power loss is entirely in resistance: $\quad P = i^2 R = (0.181 \text{ A})^2 (250 \text{ Ω}); \quad \boxed{P = 8.19 \text{ W}}$

33-6. What is the frequency of light whose energy is 5×10^{-19} J?

$$f = \frac{E}{h} = \frac{5.00 \times 10^{-19} \text{ J}}{(6.625 \times 10^{-34} \text{ J} \cdot \text{s})}; \quad \boxed{f = 7.55 \times 10^{14} \text{ Hz}}$$

33-7. The frequency of yellow-green light is 5.41×10^{14} Hz. Express the wavelength of this light in nanometers and in angstroms?

$$\lambda = \frac{c}{f} = \frac{3 \times 10^8 \text{ m/s}}{5.41 \times 10^{14} \text{ Hz}}; \quad \boxed{\lambda = 555 \text{ nm}}$$

$$\lambda = 555 \times 10^{-9} \text{ m}(1 \times 10^{10} \text{ Å/m}); \quad \boxed{\lambda = 5550 \text{ Å}}$$

33-8. What is the wavelength of light whose energy is 7×10^{-19} J?

$$E = \frac{hc}{\lambda}; \quad \lambda = \frac{hc}{E} = \frac{(6.625 \times 10^{-34} \text{ J} \cdot \text{s})(3 \times 10^8 \text{ m/s})}{7 \times 10^{-19} \text{ J}}; \quad \boxed{\lambda = 284 \text{ nm}}$$

The Velocity of Light

33-9. The sun is approximately 93 million miles from the earth. How much time is required for the light emitted by the sun to reach us on earth?

$$t = \frac{93 \times 10^6 \text{ mi}}{186,000 \text{ mi/s}} = 500 \text{ s}; \quad \boxed{t = 8.33 \text{ min}}$$

33-10. If two experimenters in Galileo's experiment were separated by a distance of 5 km, how much time would have passed from the instant the lantern was opened until the light was observed?

$$t = \frac{s}{c} = \frac{5000 \text{ m}}{3 \times 10^8 \text{ m/s}}; \quad t = 17.0 \times 10^{-6} \text{ s or } \boxed{17.0 \ \mu\text{s}}$$

33-11. The light reaching us from the nearest star, Alpha Centauri, requires 4.3 years to reach us. How far is this in miles? In kilometers?

$$s = ct = (186,000 \text{ mi/s})(3.154 \times 10^7 \text{ s/yr})(4.30 \text{ yr}); \quad \boxed{s = 2.53 \times 10^{13} \text{ mi}}$$

$$s = ct = (3 \times 10^8 \text{ m/s})(3.154 \times 10^7 \text{ s/yr})(4.30 \text{ yr}); \quad \boxed{s = 4.07 \times 10^{13} \text{ km}}$$

33-12. A spacecraft circling the moon at a distance of 384,000 km from the earth communicates by radio with a base on earth. How much time elapses between the sending and receiving of a signal?

$$s = (384,000 \text{ km})(1000 \text{ m/km}) = 3.10 \times 10^8 \text{ m}; \quad t = \frac{3.84 \times 10^8 \text{ m}}{3 \times 10^8 \text{ m/s}} = \boxed{1.28 \text{ s}}$$

$$t = \frac{4 \times 10^{10} \text{ m}}{3 \times 10^8 \text{ m/s}} \quad \boxed{t = 133 \text{ s}}$$

33-13. A spacecraft sends a signal that requires 20 min to reach the earth. How far away is the spacecraft from earth?

$$s = ct = (3 \times 10^8 \text{ m/s})(20 \text{ min})(60 \text{ s/min}); \quad s = 3.60 \times 10^{11} \text{ m}$$

Light Rays and Shadows

33-14. The shadow formed on a screen 4 m away from a point source of light is 60 cm tall. What is the height of the object located 1 m from the source and 3 m from the shadow?

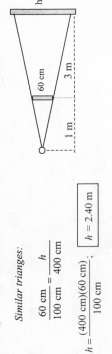

Similar triangles:

$$\frac{60 \text{ cm}}{100 \text{ cm}} = \frac{h}{400 \text{ cm}}$$

$$h = \frac{(400 \text{ cm})(60 \text{ cm})}{100 \text{ cm}}; \quad \boxed{h = 2.40 \text{ m}}$$

33-15. A point source of light is placed 15 cm from an upright 6-cm ruler. Calculate the length of the shadow formed by the ruler on a wall 40 cm from the ruler.

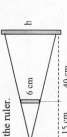

$$\frac{h}{55\ cm} = \frac{6\ cm}{15\ cm}; \qquad \boxed{h = 22.0\ cm}$$

33-16. How far must an 80-mm-diameter plate be placed in front of a point source of light if it is to form a shadow 400 mm in diameter at a distance of 2 m from the light source?

$$\frac{x}{80\ mm} = \frac{2000\ mm}{400\ mm}; \qquad \boxed{x = 400\ mm}$$

33-17. A source of light 40 mm in diameter shines through a pinhole in the tip of a cardboard box 2 m from the source. What is the diameter of the image formed on the bottom of the box if the height of the box is 60 mm?

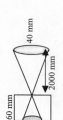
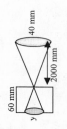

$$\frac{y}{40\ mm} = \frac{60\ mm}{2000\ mm}; \qquad \boxed{y = 1.20\ mm}$$

*33-18. A lamp is covered with a box, and a 20-mm-long narrow slit is cut in the box so that light shines through. An object 30 mm tall blocks the light from the slit at a distance of 500 mm. Calculate the length of the umbra and penumbra formed on a screen located 1.50 m from the slit. (Similar Δ's)

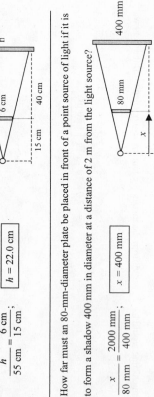

$$\frac{a}{20\ mm} = \frac{500+a}{30\ mm}; \qquad a = 1000\ mm$$

$$\frac{u}{1500+a} = \frac{20}{a}; \qquad \frac{u}{1500+1000} = \frac{20}{1000}; \qquad \boxed{u = 50\ mm}$$

$$\frac{b}{20} = \frac{500-b}{30}; \qquad b = 200\ mm; \qquad Now,\ \frac{p}{1500-b} = \frac{20}{b}\ from\ which\ \boxed{p = 130\ mm}$$

Illumination of Surfaces

33-19. What is the solid angle subtended at the center of a 3.20-m-diameter sphere by a 0.5-m² area on its surface?

$$\Omega = \frac{A}{R^2} = \frac{0.5\ m^2}{(1.6\ m)^2}; \qquad \boxed{\Omega = 0.195\ sr}$$

33-20. A solid angle of 0.080 sr is subtended at the center of a 9.00 cm diameter sphere by surface area A on the sphere. What is this area?

$$A = \Omega R^2 = (0.08\ sr)(0.09\ m)^2; \qquad \boxed{A = 6.48 \times 10^{-4}\ m^2}$$

33-21. An 8½ x 11 cm sheet of metal is illuminated by a source of light located 1.3 m directly above it. What is the luminous flux falling on the metal if the source has an intensity of 200 cd. What is the total luminous flux emitted by the light source?

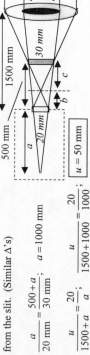

$$A = (0.085\ m)(0.11\ m); \qquad A = 9.35 \times 10^{-3}\ m^2$$

$$\Omega = \frac{A}{R^2} = \frac{9.35 \times 10^{-3}\ m^2}{(1.3\ m)^2} = 5.53 \times 10^{-3}\ sr$$

$$F = I\Omega = (200\ cd)(5.53 \times 10^{-3}\ sr); \qquad \boxed{F = 1.11\ lm}$$

$$Total\ Flux = 4\pi I = 4\pi(200\ cd); \qquad \boxed{Total\ Flux = 2510\ lm}$$

33-22. A 40-W monochromatic source of yellow-green light (555 nm) illuminates a 0.5-m² surface at a distance of 1.0 m. What is the luminous intensity of the source and how many lumens fall on the surface?

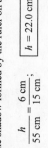

$$F = (680\ lm/W)(40\ W) = \boxed{27,200\ lm}; \qquad I = \frac{F}{\Omega}; \quad \Omega = \frac{A}{R^2}$$

$$I = \frac{FR^2}{A} = \frac{(27,200\ lm)(1\ m)^2}{0.5\ m^2}; \qquad \boxed{I = 54,400\ cd}$$

33-23. What is the illumination produced by a 200-cd source on a small surface 4.0 m away?

$$E = \frac{I}{R^2} = \frac{200\text{ cd}}{(4\text{ m})^2}; \qquad \boxed{E = 12.5\text{ lx}}$$

33-24. A lamp 2 m from a small surface produces an illumination of 100 lx on the surface. What is the intensity of the source?

$$I = ER^2 = (100\text{ lx})(2\text{ m})^2; \qquad \boxed{I = 400\text{ cd}}$$

33-25. A table top 1 m wide and 2 m long is located 4.0 m from a lamp. If 40 lm of flux fall on this surface, what is the illumination E of the surface?

$$E = \frac{F}{A} = \frac{40\text{ lm}}{(1\text{ m})(2\text{ m})}; \qquad E = 20\text{ lx}$$

33-26. What should be the location of the lamp in Problem 33-25 in order to produce twice the illumination? *(Illumination varies inversely with square of distance.)*

$$E_1R_1^2 = E_2R_2^2 = (2E_1)R_2^2; \qquad R_2 = \sqrt{\frac{R_1^2}{2}} = \sqrt{\frac{(4m)^2}{2}}; \qquad \boxed{R_2 = 2.83\text{ m}}$$

---

*33-27. A point source of light is placed at the center of a sphere 70 mm in diameter. A hole is cut in the surface of the sphere, allowing the flux to pass through a solid angle of 0.12 sr. What is the diameter of the opening? [R = D/2 = 35 mm]

$$A = \Omega R^2 = (0.12\text{ sr})(35\text{ mm})^2; \quad A = 147\text{ mm}^2$$

$$A = \frac{\pi D^2}{4}; \quad D = \sqrt{\frac{4A}{\pi}} = \sqrt{\frac{4(147\text{ mm}^2)}{\pi}}; \qquad \boxed{D = 13.7\text{ mm}}$$

Supplementary Problems

33-28. When light of wavelength 550 nm passes from air into a thin glass plate and out again into the air, the frequency remains constant, but the speed through the glass is reduced to 2 x 20^8 m/s. What is the wavelength inside the glass? *(f is same for both)*

$$f = \frac{v_{air}}{\lambda_{air}} = \frac{v_{glass}}{\lambda_{glass}}; \quad \lambda_{glass} = \frac{v_{glass}\lambda_{air}}{v_{air}} = \frac{(2\text{ x }10^8\text{m/s})(550\text{ nm})}{3\text{ x }10^8\text{m/s}}; \qquad \boxed{\lambda_{glass} = 367\text{ nm}}$$

33-29. A 30-cd standard light source is compared with a lamp of unknown intensity using a grease-spot photometer (refer to Fig. 33-21). The two light sources are placed 1 m apart, and the grease spot is moved toward the standard light. When the grease spot is 25 cm from the standard light source, the illumination is equal on both sides. Compute the unknown intensity? [*The illumination E is the same for each.*]

$$\frac{I_x}{r_x^2} = \frac{I_s}{r_s^2}; \quad I_x = \frac{I_s r_x^2}{r_s^2} = \frac{(30\text{ cd})(75\text{ cm})^2}{(25\text{ cm})^2}; \qquad \boxed{I_x = 270\text{ cd}}$$

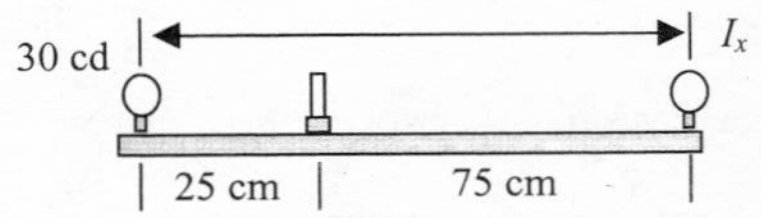

33-30. Where should the grease spot in Problem 33-29 be placed for the illumination by the unknown light source to be exactly twice the illumination of the standard source?

$$E_x = 2E_s; \quad \frac{I_x}{r_x^2} = \frac{2I_s}{r_s^2}; \quad \frac{270\text{ cd}}{(1-x)^2} = \frac{2(30\text{ cd})}{x^2};$$

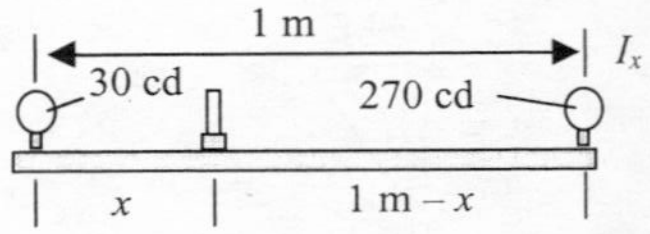

$$\frac{4.5}{(1-x)^2} = \frac{1}{x^2}; \quad 4.5x^2 = (1-x)^2; \quad 2.12x = 1 - x;$$

$$3.12x = 1; \quad x = \frac{1}{3.12} = 0.320\text{ m}; \qquad \boxed{x = 32.0\text{ cm } \textit{from standard}}$$

33-31. The illumination of a given surface is 80 lx when it is 3 m away from the light source. At what distance will the illumination be 20 lx? (*Recall that I = ER is constant*)

$$E_1 R_1^2 = E_2 R_2^2; \quad R_2 = \sqrt{\frac{E_1 R_1^2}{E_2}} = \sqrt{\frac{(80 \text{ lx})(3 \text{ m})^2}{(20 \text{ lx})}}; \quad \boxed{R_2 = 6.00 \text{ m}}$$

33-32. A light is suspended 9 m above a street and provides an illumination of 35 lx at a point directly below it. Determine the luminous intensity of the light.

$$E = \frac{I}{R^2}; \quad I = ER^2 = (36 \text{ lx})(9 \text{ m})^2; \quad \boxed{I = 2920 \text{ cd}}$$

*33-33. A 60-W monochromatic source of yellow-green light (555 nm) illuminates a 0.6 m^2 surface at a distance of 1.0 m. What is the solid angle subtended at the source? What is the luminous intensity of the source?

$$F = (680 \text{ lm/W})(60 \text{ W}) = 40{,}800 \text{ lm}; \quad \Omega = \frac{A}{R^2} = \frac{0.6 \text{ m}^2}{(1 \text{ m})^2} = \boxed{0.600 \text{ sr}}$$

$$I = \frac{F}{\Omega} = \frac{(40{,}800 \text{ lm})}{0.60 \text{ sr}}; \quad \boxed{I = 68{,}000 \text{ cd}}$$

*33-34. At what distance from a wall will a 35-cd lamp provide the same illumination as an 80-cd lamp located 4.0 m from the wall? [$E_1 = E_2$]

$$\frac{I_1}{r_1^2} = \frac{I_2}{r_2^2}; \quad r_2 = \sqrt{\frac{I_2 r_1^2}{I_1}} = \sqrt{\frac{(35 \text{ cd})(4 \text{ m})^2}{80 \text{ cd}}}; \quad \boxed{r_2 = 2.65 \text{ m}}$$

*33-35. How much must a small lamp be lowered to double the illumination on an object that is 80 cm directly under it? $E_2 = 2E_1$ *and* $E_1 R_1^2 = E_2 R_2^2$, *so that:* $E_1 R_1^2 = (2E_1)R_2^2$

$$R_2 = \sqrt{\frac{R_1^2}{2}} = \sqrt{\frac{(80 \text{ cm})^2}{2}}; \quad R_2 = 56.6 \text{ cm}; \quad y = 80 \text{ cm} - 56.6 \text{ cm} = \boxed{23.4 \text{ cm}}$$

*33-36. Compute the illumination of a given surface 140 cm from a 74-cd light source if the normal to the surface makes an angle of 38° with the flux.

$$E = \frac{I \cos\theta}{R^2} = \frac{(74 \text{ cd})(\cos 38°)}{(1.40 \text{ m})^2}; \quad \boxed{E = 29.8 \text{ lx}}$$

*33-37. A circular table top is located 4 m below and 3 m to the left of a lamp that emits 1800 lm. What illumination is provided on the surface of the table? What is the area of the table top if 3 lm of flux falls on its surface?

R=5 m   θ   4 m   3 m

$$\tan\theta = \frac{3 \text{ m}}{4 \text{ m}} \qquad \theta = 36.9° \qquad F = 4\pi I$$

$$I = \frac{F}{4\pi} = \frac{1800 \text{ lm}}{4\pi}; \qquad I = 143 \text{ lm/sr}$$

$$E = \frac{I \cos\theta}{R^2} = \frac{(143 \text{ lm/sr})\cos 36.9°}{(5 \text{ m})^2}; \qquad \boxed{E = 4.58 \text{ lx}}; \qquad A = \frac{F}{E} = \boxed{0.655 \text{ m}^2}$$

*33-38. What angle θ between the flux and a line drawn normal to a surface will cause the illumination of that surface to be reduced by one-half when the distance to the surface has not changed?

$$E_1 = \frac{I_1}{R_1^2}; \qquad E_2 = \frac{I \cos\theta}{R_2^2}; \qquad E_1 = 2E_2; \qquad I_1 = I_2 \quad \text{and} \quad R_1 = R_2$$

Substitution yields: $2I \cos\theta = I$ *and* $\cos\theta = 0.5$ or $\boxed{\theta = 60°}$

*33-39. In Michelson's measurements of the speed of light, as shown in Fig. 33-11, he obtained a value of 2.997×10^8 m/s. If the total light path was 35 km, what was the rotational frequency of the eight-sided mirror?

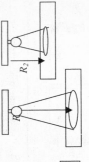

The time for light to reappear from edge 1 to edge 2 is:

$$t = \frac{s}{c} = \frac{35{,}000 \text{ m}}{3 \times 10^8 \text{ m/s}} = 1.167 \times 10^{-4}\text{s}$$

The time for one revolution is 8t: $T = 8(1.167 \times 10^{-4}\text{ s})$

$$f = \frac{1}{T} = \frac{1}{8(1.167 \times 10^{-4}\text{s})};\qquad \boxed{f = 1071 \text{ Hz}}$$

*33-40. All of the light from a spotlight is collected and focused on a screen of area 0.30 m². What must be the luminous intensity of the light in order that an illumination of 500 lx be achieved?

$$E = \frac{I}{A};\qquad I = EA = (500 \text{ lx})(0.30 \text{ m}^2) = 150 \text{ cd}\qquad \boxed{I = 150 \text{ cd}}$$

*33-41. A 300-cd light is suspended 5 m above the left edge of a table. Find the illumination of a small piece of paper located a horizontal distance of 2.5 m from the edge of the table?

$$R = \sqrt{(2.5 \text{ m})^2 + (5 \text{ m})^2} = 5.59 \text{ m}$$

$$\tan \theta = \frac{2.5 \text{ m}}{5 \text{ m}}\qquad \theta = 26.6^0$$

$$E = \frac{I\cos\theta}{R^2} = \frac{(300 \text{ cd})(\cos 26.6^0)}{(5.59 \text{ m})^2};\qquad \boxed{E = 8.59 \text{ lx}}$$

Critical Thinking Problems

33-42. A certain radio station broadcasts at a frequency of 1150 kHz; A red beam of light has a frequency of 4.70×10^{14} Hz; and an ultraviolet ray has a frequency of 2.4×10^{16} Hz.

Which has the highest wavelength? Which has the greatest energy? What are the wavelengths of each electromagnetic wave? [*Recall that* $h = 6.625 \times 10^{-34}$ J.]

$$\lambda = \frac{c}{f} = \frac{3 \times 10^8 \text{ m/s}}{1.150 \times 10^6 \text{Hz}};\qquad \boxed{\lambda = 261 \text{ m}}\qquad E = hf = \boxed{7.62 \times 10^{-28}\text{ J}}$$

$$\lambda = \frac{c}{f} = \frac{3 \times 10^8 \text{ m/s}}{4.70 \times 10^{14}\text{Hz}};\qquad \boxed{\lambda = 639 \text{ nm}}\qquad E = hf = \boxed{3.11 \times 10^{-19}\text{ J}}$$

$$\lambda = \frac{c}{f} = \frac{3 \times 10^8 \text{ m/s}}{2.40 \times 10^{16}\text{Hz}};\qquad \boxed{\lambda = 12.5 \text{ nm}}\qquad E = hf = \boxed{1.59 \times 10^{-17}\text{ J}}$$

The radio wave has highest wavelength; The ultraviolet ray has highest energy.

*33-43. An unknown light source A located 80 cm from a screen produces the same illumination as a standard 30-cd light source at point B located 30 cm from the screen. What is the luminous intensity of the unknown light source?

$$\frac{I_x}{r_x^2} = \frac{I_s}{r_s^2};\qquad I_x = \frac{I_s r_x^2}{r_s^2} = \frac{(30 \text{ cd})(80 \text{ cm})^2}{(30 \text{ cm})^2};\qquad \boxed{I_x = 213 \text{ cd}}$$

*33-44. The illumination of a surface 3.40 m directly below a light source is 20 lx. Find the intensity of the light source? At what distance below the light source will the illumination be doubled? Is the luminous flux also doubled at this location?

$$I = ER^2 = (20 \text{ lx})(3.40 \text{ m})^2;\qquad \boxed{I = 231 \text{ cd}}$$

$$E_2 = 2E_1 \quad and \quad E_1R_1^2 = E_2R_2^2 = (2E_1)R_2^2$$

$$R_2 = \sqrt{\frac{R_2^2}{2}} = \sqrt{\frac{(3.40 \text{ m})^2}{2}};\qquad \boxed{R_2 = 2.40 \text{ m}}\qquad \boxed{\Delta F = 0}$$

Chapter 34. Reflection and Mirrors

Reflection from Plane Mirrors

34-1. A man 1.80 m tall stands 1.2 m from a large plane mirror. How tall is his image? How far is he from his image? (*Image symmetric, reversed.*)

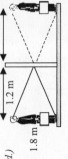

Image distance q = object distance p:

$$q = p = 1.2 \text{ m};$$ $$\boxed{y' = y = 1.8 \text{ m}}$$

34-2. What is the shortest mirror length required to enable a 1.68 m woman to see her entire image? (*Virtual image is behind the mirror. Rays show that only half length is needed.*)

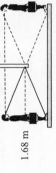

Mirror height = (1/2) object height

$$h = \frac{5 \text{ ft, 8 in.}}{2}$$ $$\boxed{h = 2 \text{ ft, 10 in.}}$$

It doesn't matter where she stands.

*34-3. A plane mirror moves at a speed of 30 km/h away from a stationary person. How fast does this person's image appear to be moving in the opposite direction?

Each time mirror moves, image also moves, so that speed is doubled: $\boxed{v_i = 60 \text{ km/h}}$

*33-4. The optical lever is a sensitive measuring device that utilizes minute rotations of a plane mirror to measure small deflections. The device is illustrated in Fig. 34-19. When the mirror is in position 1, the light ray follows the path IVR_1. If the mirror is rotated through an angle θ to position 2, the ray will follow the path IVR_2. Show that the reflected beam turns through an angle 2θ, which is twice the angle through which the mirror itself turns.

Remember the basic principles of ray tracing and that the angle of incidence always equals the angle of reflection. Refer to the figure drawn on the following page.

**33-45. The illumination of an isotropic source is E_A at a point A on a table 30 cm directly below the source. At what horizontal distance from A on the table top will the illumination be reduced by one half?

$$E_A = \frac{I}{R_A^2}; \quad E_B = \frac{I\cos\theta}{R_B^2}; \quad E_A = 2E_B; \quad I_A = I_B$$

$$\frac{I}{R_A^2} = \frac{2I\cos\theta}{R_B^2}; \quad \frac{R_A^2}{R_B^2} = \frac{1}{2\cos\theta}; \quad \text{but} \quad \frac{R_A}{R_B} = \cos\theta$$

So that: $(\cos\theta)^2 = \frac{1}{2\cos\theta}; \quad (\cos\theta)^3 = \frac{1}{2}; \quad \cos\theta = \sqrt[3]{0.5} = 0.794; \quad \text{and} \quad \theta = 37.5^0$

$$\tan\theta = \frac{x}{30 \text{ cm}}; \quad x = (30 \text{ cm}) \tan 37.5^0; \quad \boxed{x = 23.0 \text{ cm}}$$

33-46. In Fizeau's experiment to calculate the speed of light, the plane mirror was located at a distance of 8630 m. He used a wheel containing 720 teeth (and voids). Every time the rotational speed of the wheel was increased by 24.2 rev/s, the light came through to his eye. What value did he obtain for the speed of light?   **Ans. 3.01 x 10⁸ m/s.

An increase of $f = 24.2$ Hz is needed for light to reappear from Edge 1 to Edge 2. Thus, the time for one revolution of entire wheel is:

$$T = \frac{1}{f} = \frac{1}{24.2 \text{ Hz}} = 0.0413 \text{ s}$$

Now, the time for one tooth and one void between 1 and 2 is:

$$t = \frac{0.0413 \text{ s}}{720 \text{ teeth}} = 5.74 \times 10^{-5} \text{ s}; \quad \textit{Time for one round trip.}$$

$$c = \frac{2(8630 \text{ m})}{5.74 \times 10^{-5} \text{ s}}; \quad \boxed{c = 3.01 \times 10^8 \text{ m/s}}$$

*34-4. (Cont.) *Show that the deviated ray turns through twice the angle turned by mirror.*

In horizontal initial position, $\theta_i = \theta_r$. *Now from figure:*

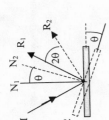

$$\theta_{i1} = \theta_{i\,l} + \theta; \qquad \theta_{r2} = \theta_{r1} + \theta$$

$$\theta_{i2} = (\theta_{i1} + \theta) + (\theta_{r1} + \theta)$$

$$\boxed{\angle R_1 R_2 = 2\,\theta}$$

Images Formed by Spherical Mirrors

34-5. A light bulb 3 cm high is placed 20 cm in front of a concave mirror with a radius of curvature of 15 cm. Determine the nature, size, and location of the image formed. Sketch the ray-tracing diagram. [$y = 3$ cm, $p = 20$ cm]

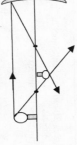

$$q = \frac{pf}{p - f} = \frac{(20\text{ cm})(7.5\text{ cm})}{20\text{ cm} - 7.5\text{ cm}}; \qquad q = 12\text{ cm, real}$$

$$M = \frac{y'}{y} = \frac{-q}{p}; \quad y' = \frac{-qy}{p} = \frac{-(12\text{ cm})(3\text{ cm})}{(20\text{ cm})}; \qquad y' = -1.80\text{ cm}$$

$$\boxed{q = 12.0\text{ cm}, \; y' = -1.80\text{ cm}; \; \textit{Real, inverted, and diminished.}}$$

34-6. A spherical concave mirror has a focal length of 20 cm. What are the nature, size, and location of the image formed when a 6 cm tall object is located 15 cm from this mirror?

$$q = \frac{pf}{p - f} = \frac{(15\text{ cm})(20\text{ cm})}{15\text{ cm} - 20\text{ cm}};$$

$$q = -60\text{ cm, virtual and enlarged}$$

$$M = \frac{y'}{y} = \frac{-q}{p}; \quad y' = \frac{-qy}{p} = \frac{-(-60\text{ cm})(6\text{ cm})}{(20\text{ cm})}; \qquad y' = +18\text{ cm}$$

$$\boxed{q = -60\text{ cm}, \; y' = 18.0\text{ cm}; \; \textit{virtual, erect, and enlarged.}}$$

34-7. A 8-cm pencil is placed 10 cm from a diverging mirror of radius 30 cm. Determine the nature, size, and location of the image formed. Sketch the ray-tracing diagram.

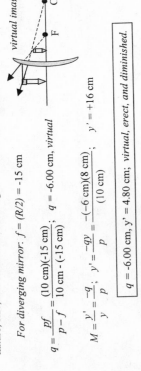

For diverging mirror: $f = (R/2) = -15$ cm

$$q = \frac{pf}{p - f} = \frac{(10\text{ cm})(-15\text{ cm})}{10\text{ cm} - (-15\text{ cm})}; \qquad q = -6.00\text{ cm, virtual}$$

$$M = \frac{y'}{y} = \frac{-q}{p}; \quad y' = \frac{-qy}{p} = \frac{-(-6\text{ cm})(8\text{ cm})}{(10\text{ cm})}; \qquad y' = +16\text{ cm}$$

$$\boxed{q = -6.00\text{ cm}, \; y' = 4.80\text{ cm}; \; \textit{virtual, erect, and diminished.}}$$

34-8. A spherical convex mirror has a focal length 25 cm. What are the nature, size, and location of the image formed of a 5-cm tall object located 30 cm from the mirror?

For diverging mirror: $f = -25$ cm

$$q = \frac{pf}{p - f} = \frac{(30\text{ cm})(-25\text{ cm})}{30\text{ cm} - (-25\text{ cm})}; \qquad q = -13.6\text{ cm, virtual}$$

$$M = \frac{y'}{y} = \frac{-q}{p}; \quad y' = \frac{-qy}{p} = \frac{-(-13.6\text{ cm})(5\text{ cm})}{(30\text{ cm})}; \qquad y' = +2.27\text{ cm}$$

$$\boxed{q = -13.6\text{ cm}, \; y' = 2.27\text{ cm}; \; \textit{virtual, erect, and diminished.}}$$

34-9. An object 5 cm tall is place halfway between the focal point and the center of curvature of a concave spherical mirror of radius 30 cm. Determine the location and magnification of the image? $f = (R/2) = 15$ cm. $p = 22.5$ cm

$$q = \frac{pf}{p - f} = \frac{(22.5\text{ cm})(15\text{ cm})}{22.5\text{ cm} - 15\text{ cm}}; \qquad q = 45\text{ cm, real}$$

$$M = \frac{y'}{y} = \frac{-q}{p}; \quad M = \frac{-(45\text{ cm})}{(22.5\text{ cm})}; \qquad M = -2.00$$

$$\boxed{q = 45.0\text{ cm}, \; M = -2.00; \; \textit{Real, inverted, and enlarged.}}$$

34-10. A 4-cm high source of light is placed in front of a spherical concave mirror whose radius is 40 cm. Determine the nature, size, and location of the images formed for the following object distances: (a) 60 cm, (b) 40 cm, (c) 30 cm, (d) 20 cm, and (e) 10 cm. Draw the appropriate ray-tracing diagrams. *(In the interest of space, diagrams are not drawn)*

Givens: $f = (40\ cm/2) = 20\ cm$; $y = 4\ cm$, $p = 60, 40, 30, 20, and\ 10\ cm$.

$$q = \frac{pf}{p-f}; \qquad M = \frac{y'}{y} = \frac{-q}{p}; \qquad y' = \frac{-qy}{p}$$

(a) $q = \dfrac{(60\ cm)(20\ cm)}{60\ cm - 20\ cm} = 30\ cm, real$ $\qquad y' = \dfrac{-(30\ cm)(4\ cm)}{(60\ cm)} = -2\ cm, inverted$

(b) $q = \dfrac{(40\ cm)(20\ cm)}{40\ cm - 20\ cm} = 40\ cm, real$ $\qquad y' = \dfrac{-(40\ cm)(4\ cm)}{(40\ cm)} = -4\ cm, inverted$

(c) $q = \dfrac{(30\ cm)(20\ cm)}{30\ cm - 20\ cm} = 60\ cm, real$ $\qquad y' = \dfrac{-(60\ cm)(4\ cm)}{(30\ cm)} = -8\ cm, inverted$

(d) $q = \dfrac{(20\ cm)(20\ cm)}{20\ cm - 20\ cm} = \infty, no\ image$ $\qquad y' = \dfrac{-(\infty)(4\ cm)}{(20\ cm)} = \infty, no\ image$

(e) $q = \dfrac{(10\ cm)(20\ cm)}{10\ cm - 20\ cm} = -20\ cm, virtual$ $\qquad y' = \dfrac{-(-20\ cm)(4\ cm)}{(10\ cm)} = 8\ cm, erect$

34-11. At what distance from a concave spherical mirror of radius 30 cm must an object be placed to form an enlarged, inverted image located 60 cm from the mirror?

Enlarged and inverted means object between F and C.

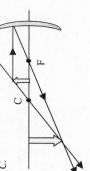

and the image is beyond the radius.

$f = (R/2) = (30\ cm/2)$; $f = +15\ cm$

$p = \dfrac{qf}{q-f} = \dfrac{(60\ cm)(15\ cm)}{60\ cm - 15\ cm}$; $\boxed{p = 20\ cm}$

$q = +60\ cm$, *positive since image is real.*

Magnification

34-12. What is the magnification of an object if it is located 10 cm from a mirror and its image is erect and seems to be located 40 cm behind the mirror? Is this mirror diverging or converging? *(Erect image means diverging mirror.)*

$q = -40\ cm$, $p = 10\ cm$

$M = \dfrac{-q}{p} = \dfrac{-(-40\ cm)}{10\ cm}$; $\boxed{M = -4.00}$

virtual image

34-13. A Christmas tree ornament has a silvered surface and a diameter of 3 in. What is the magnification of an object placed 6 in. from the surface of this ornament? [R = D/2]

$f = \dfrac{R}{2} = \dfrac{-1.5\ in.}{2}$; $f = -0.75\ in.$ (−) *since converging*

$q = \dfrac{(6\ in.)(-0.75\ in.)}{6\ in. - (-0.75\ in.)}$; $q = -0.667\ in$, *virtual*

$M = \dfrac{-q}{p} = \dfrac{-(-0.667\ in.)}{6.00\ in.}$; $\boxed{M = +0.111}$

34-14. What type of mirror is required to form an image on a screen 2 m away from the mirror when an object is placed 12 cm in front of the mirror? What is the magnification?

It must be a __converging__ mirror, since image is __real__.

Also, from position and size, it must be enlarged and inverted. Thus, $q = +2.00\ m$, $p = 12\ cm$.

$M = \dfrac{-q}{p} = \dfrac{-(2\ m)}{0.12\ m}$; $\boxed{M = -16.7}$

$f = \dfrac{pq}{p+q} = \dfrac{(0.12\ m)(2\ m)}{0.12\ m + 2\ m}$; $f = +11.3\ cm$; *Positive means it is* $\boxed{converging.}$

34-19. What are the nature, size, and location of the image formed when a 6-cm tall object is located 15 cm from a spherical concave mirror of focal length 20 cm?

$$q = \frac{(15 \text{ cm})(20 \text{ cm})}{15 \text{ cm} - 20 \text{ cm}} = -60 \text{ cm}, \text{ virtual}$$

$$y' = \frac{-(-60 \text{ cm})(6 \text{ cm})}{(15 \text{ cm})} = 24 \text{ cm}, \text{ erect}$$

$$q = -60.0 \text{ cm}, y' = 24.0 \text{ cm}; \; virtual, \; erect, \; and \; enlarged.$$

virtual image

34-20. An erect image has a magnification of +0.6. Is the mirror diverging or converging? What is the object distance if the image distance is −12 cm?

The mirror is *diverging* since image is *diminished, erect, and virtual.*

$$M = \frac{-q}{p} = 0.6; \quad p = \frac{-q}{0.6} = \frac{-(-12 \text{ cm})}{0.6}; \quad \boxed{p = 20 \text{ cm}}$$

34-21. An object is located 50 cm from a converging mirror whose radius is 40 cm. What is the image distance and the magnification?

$$q = \frac{pf}{p-f} = \frac{(50 \text{ cm})(20 \text{ cm})}{50 \text{ cm} - 20 \text{ cm}}; \quad q = 33.3 \text{ cm, real}$$

$$M = \frac{y'}{y} = \frac{-q}{p} = \frac{-(33.3 \text{ cm})}{(50 \text{ cm})}; \quad M = -0.667$$

$$\boxed{q = 33.3 \text{ cm}, M = -0.667; \; Real, \; inverted, \; and \; diminished.}$$

34-22. What is the focal length of a diverging mirror if the image of an object located 200 mm from the mirror appears to be a distance of 120 mm behind the mirror?

$$f = \frac{pq}{p+q} = \frac{(200 \text{ mm})(-120 \text{ mm})}{200 \text{ mm} - (-120 \text{ mm})}; \quad \boxed{f = -75.0 \text{ mm}}$$

---

*34-15. A concave shaving mirror has a focal length of 520 mm. How far away from it should an object be placed for the image to be erect and twice its actual size?

$$M = \frac{-q}{p} = +2; \quad q = -2p; \quad q = \frac{pf}{p-f};$$

$$-2p = \frac{pf}{p-f}; \quad -2(p-f) = f;$$

$$-2p + 2f = f; \quad p = \frac{f}{2} = \frac{520 \text{ mm}}{2}; \quad \boxed{p = 260 \text{ mm}}$$

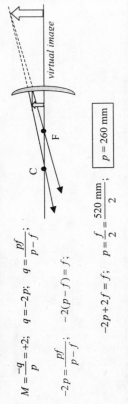

virtual image

*34-16. If a magnification of +3 is desired, how far should the mirror of Problem 34-15 be placed from the face?

$$M = \frac{-q}{p} = +3; \quad q = -3p; \quad q = \frac{pf}{p-f}; \quad -3p = \frac{pf}{p-f}; \quad -3(p-f) = f;$$

$$-3p + 3f = f; \quad p = \frac{2f}{3} = \frac{2(520 \text{ mm})}{3}; \quad \boxed{p = 357 \text{mm}}$$

*34-17. An object is placed 12 cm from the surface of a spherical mirror. If an erect image is formed that is one-third the size of the object, what is the radius of the mirror. Is it converging or diverging? (It is *diverging since image is erect and diminished.*)

$$M = \frac{-q}{p} = +\frac{1}{3}; \quad q = \frac{-p}{3} = \frac{-(12 \text{ cm})}{3}; \quad q = -4 \text{ cm}$$

$$f = \frac{pq}{p+q} = \frac{(12 \text{ cm})(-4 \text{ cm})}{12 \text{ cm} + (-4 \text{ cm})}; \quad \boxed{f = -6.00 \text{ cm, diverging}}$$

*34-18. A concave spherical mirror has a radius of 30 cm and forms an inverted image on a wall 90 cm away. What is the magnification? [$f = (30 \text{ cm}/2) = 15 \text{ cm}; \quad q = +90 \text{ cm}$]

$$p = \frac{(90 \text{ cm})(15 \text{ cm})}{90 \text{ cm} - 15 \text{ cm}} = 18 \text{ cm}; \quad M = \frac{-90 \text{ cm}}{18 \text{ cm}}; \quad \boxed{M = -5.00}$$

34-23. A silver ball is 4.0 cm in diameter. Locate the image of a 6-cm object located 9 cm from the surface of the ball. What is the magnification? [R = 4 cm/2 = 2 cm.]

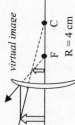

virtual image

F   C

R = 4 cm

$$f = (R/2) = (-2 \text{ cm}/2) = -1 \text{ cm}; \quad p = 9 \text{ cm};$$

$$q = \frac{pf}{p-f} = \frac{(9 \text{ cm})(-1 \text{ cm})}{9 \text{ cm} - (-1 \text{ cm})}; \quad \boxed{q = -0.9 \text{ cm}}$$

$$M = \frac{-q}{p} = \frac{-(-0.9 \text{ cm})}{9.00 \text{ cm}}; \quad \boxed{M = +0.100}$$

34-24. An object 80 mm tall is placed 400 mm in front of a diverging mirror of radius –600 mm. Determine the nature, size, and location of the image

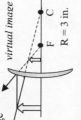

virtual image

F   C

R = 3 in.

$$f = (R/2) = (-600 \text{ mm}/2) = -300 \text{ mm}$$

$$q = \frac{pf}{p-f} = \frac{(400 \text{ mm})(-300 \text{ mm})}{400 \text{ mm} - (-300 \text{ mm})}; \quad \boxed{q = -171 \text{ cm}}$$

$$M = \frac{y'}{y} = \frac{-q}{p}; \quad y' = \frac{-(-171 \text{ mm})(80 \text{ mm})}{400 \text{ mm}}; \quad \boxed{y' = +34.3 \text{ mm}}$$

---

*34-25. An object 10 cm tall is located 20 cm from a spherical mirror. If an erect image 5-cm tall is formed, what is the focal length of the mirror?

$$M = \frac{y'}{y} = \frac{5 \text{ cm}}{10 \text{ cm}} = +0.5; \quad M = \frac{-q}{p}; \quad q = -Mp = -(0.5)(20 \text{ cm}); \quad q = -10 \text{ cm}$$

$$f = \frac{pq}{p+q} = \frac{(20 \text{ cm})(-10 \text{ cm})}{20 \text{ cm} + (-10 \text{ cm})}; \quad \boxed{f = -20 \text{ cm}}$$

---

*34-26. What is the magnification if the image of an object is located 15 cm from a diverging mirror of focal length –20 cm? [q = -15 cm; f = -20 cm]

$$p = \frac{qf}{q-f} = \frac{(-15 \text{ cm})(-20 \text{ cm})}{-15 \text{ cm} - (-20 \text{ cm})} = 60 \text{ cm}; \quad M = \frac{-q}{p} = \frac{-(-15 \text{ cm})}{60 \text{ cm}}; \quad \boxed{M = +0.250}$$

---

*34-27. An object is placed 200 mm from the vertex of a convex spherical mirror whose radius is 400 mm. What is the magnification of the mirror?

virtual image

C   F

p

R = 400 mm.

$$f = R/2 = -400 \text{ mm}/2 = -200 \text{ mm}; \quad p = 200 \text{ mm}$$

$$q = \frac{pf}{p-f} = \frac{(200 \text{ mm})(-200 \text{ mm})}{200 \text{ mm} - (-200 \text{ mm})}; \quad q = -100 \text{ mm}$$

Magnification: $M = \frac{-q}{p} = \frac{-(-100 \text{ mm})}{200 \text{ mm}}; \quad \boxed{M = +\frac{1}{2}}$

---

*34-28. A convex spherical mirror has a radius of –60 cm. How far away should an object be held if the image is to be one-third the size of the object?

virtual image

F   C

R = -60 cm

$$f = R/2 = -60m/2 = -30 \text{ mm}; \quad M = +1/3$$

$$M = \frac{-q}{p} = \frac{1}{3}; \quad q = -\frac{p}{3}; \quad q = \frac{pf}{p-f}$$

$$\frac{-p}{3} = \frac{pf}{p-f}; \quad (-1)(p-f) = 3f; \quad -p + f - 3f = 0;$$

$$p = -2f = -2(-30 \text{ cm}); \quad \boxed{p = 60 \text{ cm}}$$

---

*34-29. What should be the radius of curvature of a convex spherical mirror to produce an image one-fourth as large as the object which is located 40 in. from the mirror?

$$M = \frac{-q}{p} = \frac{1}{4}; \quad q = \frac{-p}{4}; \quad q = \frac{pf}{p-f}; \quad \frac{-1}{4} = \frac{f}{40 \text{ in.} - f};$$

$$-40 \text{ in.} + f = 4f \qquad f = \frac{-40 \text{ in.}}{3} \qquad \boxed{f = -26.7 \text{ in.}}$$

---

*34-30. A convex mirror has a focal length of –500 mm. If an object is placed 400 mm from the vertex, what is the magnification?

$$q = \frac{(400 \text{ mm})(-500 \text{ mm})}{400 \text{ mm} - (-500 \text{ mm})} = -222 \text{ mm}; \quad M = \frac{-q}{p} = \frac{-(-222 \text{ mm})}{400 \text{ mm}}; \quad \boxed{M = +0.556}$$

*34-31. A spherical mirror forms a real image 18 cm from the surface. The image is twice as large as the object. Find the location of the object and the focal length of the mirror.

Since the image is real and enlarged, we draw as shown:

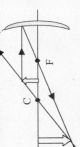

Note: $q = -18$ cm, $M = -2$ (inverted)

$M = \dfrac{-q}{p} = -2;\quad p = \dfrac{q}{2} = \dfrac{-(18\ \text{cm})}{2};\quad \boxed{p = 9.00\ \text{cm}}$

$f = \dfrac{pq}{p+q} = \dfrac{(9\ \text{cm})(-18\ \text{cm})}{9\ \text{cm} +(-18\ \text{cm})};\quad \boxed{f = 6.00\ \text{cm}}$

*34-32. A certain mirror placed 2 m from an object produces an erect image enlarged three times. Is the mirror diverging or converging? What is the radius of the mirror?

An erect, enlarged image is consistent only for converging mirrors.

virtual image

$M = \dfrac{-q}{p} = +3;\quad q = -3p = -3(2\ \text{m});\quad q = -6.00\ \text{m}$

$f = \dfrac{pq}{p+q} = \dfrac{(2\ \text{cm})(-6\ \text{cm})}{2\ \text{cm} +(-6\ \text{cm})};\quad \boxed{f = +3.00\ \text{cm, converging}}$

*34-33. The magnification of a mirror is -0.333. Where is the object located if its image is formed on a card 540 mm from the mirror? What is the focal length?

$M = \dfrac{-q}{p} = -0.333;\quad p = \dfrac{q}{0.333} = \dfrac{540\ \text{mm}}{0.333};\quad \boxed{p = 1.62\ \text{m}}$

$f = \dfrac{pq}{p+q} = \dfrac{(1.62\ \text{m})(0.540\ \text{m})}{1.62\ \text{m} + 0.540\ \text{m}};\quad \boxed{f = +405\ \text{mm}}$

---

*34-34. What should be the radius of curvature of a concave mirror to produce an image one-fourth as large as an object 50 cm away from the mirror?

The magnification must be negative if image is diminished by concave mirror:

$M = \dfrac{-q}{p} = -\dfrac{1}{4};\quad q = \dfrac{p}{4} = \dfrac{(50\ \text{cm})}{4};\quad \boxed{q = 12.5\ \text{cm}}$

$f = \dfrac{pq}{p+q} = \dfrac{(50\ \text{cm})(12.5\ \text{cm})}{50\ \text{cm} + 12.5\ \text{cm}};\quad \boxed{f = +10\ \text{cm}}$

*34-35. A spherical shaving mirror has a magnification of $+2.5$ when an object is located 15 cm from the surface. What is the focal length of the mirror?

virtual image

$M = \dfrac{-q}{p} = +2.5;\quad q = -2.5(15\ \text{cm});$

$q = -37.5\ \text{cm}$

$f = \dfrac{pq}{p+q} = \dfrac{(15\ \text{cm})(-37.5\ \text{cm})}{15\ \text{cm} +(-37.5\ \text{cm})};\quad \boxed{f = +25.0\ \text{cm, converging}}$

Critical Thinking Problems

34-36. A baseball player is 6 ft tall and stands 30 ft in front of a plane mirror. The distance from the top of his cap to his eyes is 8 in. Draw a diagram showing location of the images formed of his feet and of the top of his cap? What is the minimum length of mirror required for him to see his entire image. If he walks 10 m closer to the mirror what is the new separation of object and image?

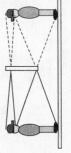

From the drawing of reflected rays, you see that:

$y = \tfrac{1}{2}(8\ \text{in.}) + \tfrac{1}{2}(72\ \text{in.} - 8\ \text{in.});\quad \boxed{y_{min} = 36\ \text{in.}}$

Moving 10 ft makes the object distance 20 ft. The image distance is also 20 ft. Thus the separation is 40 ft.

*34-37. The diameter of the moon is 3480 km and it is 3.84 × 10⁸ m away from the earth. A telescope on the earth utilizes a spherical mirror, whose radius is 8.00 m to form an image of the moon. What is the diameter of the image formed. What is the magnification of the mirror? ($y = 3.48 \times 10^6$ m, $p = 3.84 \times 10^8$ m.)

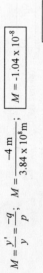

$$q = \frac{pf}{p-f} = \frac{(3.84 \times 10^6\text{ m})(4\text{ m})}{3.84 \times 10^8\text{ m} - 4\text{ m}} = 4.00 \text{ m } (at\ F)$$

$$M = \frac{y'}{y} = \frac{-q}{p}; \quad M = \frac{-4\text{ m}}{3.84 \times 10^8\text{m}}; \quad \boxed{M = -1.04 \times 10^{-8}}$$

$$y' = My = (-1.04 \times 10^{-8})(3.48 \times 10^6\text{ m}); \quad \boxed{y = 3.62 \text{ cm}}$$

---

*34-38. An image 60 mm long is formed on a wall located 2.3 m away from a source of light 20 mm high. What is the focal length of this mirror? Is it diverging or converging? What is the magnification? (*The image in inverted so that M is negative, image is inverted.*)

$$q = p + 2.3 \text{ m}; \quad M = \frac{-q}{p} = \frac{-(p+2.3\text{ m})}{p} = -3$$

$$p + 2.3 \text{ m} = 3p; \quad p = 1.15 \text{ m}; \quad q = p + 2.3 \text{ m} = 3.45 \text{ m}$$

$$f = \frac{pq}{p+q} = \frac{(1.15\text{ m})(3.45\text{ m})}{1.15\text{ m} + 3.45\text{ m}}; \quad \boxed{f = +0.862 \text{ m}}$$

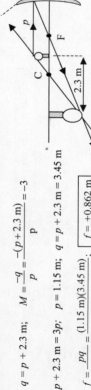

$$M = \frac{-q}{p} = \frac{-(3.45\text{ m})}{1.15\text{ m}}; \quad \boxed{M = -3.00}$$

The positive focal length indicates that the mirror is $\boxed{converging.}$

---

*34-39. Derive an expression for calculating the focal length of a mirror in terms of the object distance *p* and the magnification M. Apply it to Problem 34-35. Derive a similar relation for calculating the image distance *q* in terms of M and *p*. Apply it to Problem 34-33.

$$M = \frac{-q}{p}; \quad q = -Mp; \quad q = \frac{pf}{p-f}; \quad -Mp = \frac{pf}{p-f}$$

$$-Mp(p-f) = f; \quad -Mp + Mf = Mp; \quad Mf - f = Mp; \quad \boxed{f = \frac{Mp}{(M-1)}}$$

$$M = 2.5, \ p = 15 \text{ cm}; \quad f = \frac{Mp}{(M-1)} = \frac{(2.5)(15\text{ cm})}{(2.5-1)}; \quad \boxed{f = +25 \text{ cm}}$$

$$M = \frac{-q}{p}; \quad p = \frac{-q}{M}; \quad p = \frac{qf}{q-f}; \quad \frac{-q}{M} = \frac{qf}{q-f}$$

$$-(q-f) = Mf; \quad -q + f = Mf; \quad Mf - f = -q; \quad \boxed{f = \frac{-q}{(M-1)}}$$

$$M = -0.333, \ q = 540 \text{ mm}; \quad f = \frac{-q}{(M-1)} = \frac{-540\text{ mm}}{-0.333-1}; \quad \boxed{f = +405 \text{ mm}}$$

*34-40. A concave mirror of radius 800 mm is placed 600 mm from a plane mirror that faces it.

A source of light placed midway between the mirrors is shielded so that the light is first

reflected from the concave surface. What are the position and magnification of the image

formed after reflection from the plane mirror? (Hint: treat the image formed by the first

mirror as the object for the second mirror.)

$$p = \frac{0.600 \text{ m}}{2} = 0.300 \text{ m}; \quad f = \frac{R}{2} = 0.400 \text{ m}$$

First find q formed by spherical mirror.

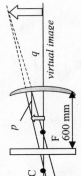

virtual image

$$q = \frac{pf}{p-f} = \frac{(0.300 \text{ m})(0.400 \text{ m})}{(0.300 \text{ m} - 0.400 \text{ m})}; \quad q = -1.20 \text{ m}; \quad (behind \ mirror)$$

Since plane mirror is 0.600 m in left of spherical mirror, the final image q' = p' is:

$$q' = 1.20 \text{ m} + 0.600 \text{ m} = 1.8 \text{ m}; \quad \boxed{q' = 1.8 \text{ m to left of plane mirror.}}$$

$$M_1 = \frac{-q}{p} = \frac{-(-1.2 \text{ m})}{0.300 \text{ m}} = +4; \quad M_2 = +1; \quad M_1 \times M_2 = (+4)(+1); \quad \boxed{M = +4}$$

Chapter 35. Refraction

The Index of Refraction (Refer to Table 35-1 for values of *n*.)

35-1. The speed of light through a certain medium is 1.6×10^8 m/s in a transparent medium.

What is the index of refraction in that medium?

$$n = \frac{c}{v} = \frac{3 \times 10^8 \text{ m/s}}{1.6 \times 10^8 \text{ m/s}}; \quad \boxed{n = 1.88}$$

35-2. If the speed of light is to be reduced by one-third, what must be the index of refraction for

the medium through which the light travels? *The speed c is reduced by a third, so that:*

$$v_x = (\tfrac{2}{3})c; \quad n = \frac{c}{v_x} = \frac{c}{(\tfrac{2}{3})c}; \quad n = \frac{3}{2} \quad and \quad \boxed{n = 1.50}$$

35-3. Compute the speed of light in (a) crown glass, (b) diamond, (c) water, and (d) ethyl

alcohol. *(Since n = c/v, we find that v = c/n for each of these media.)*

(a) $v_g = \dfrac{3 \times 10^8 \text{ m/s}}{1.50}$; $\boxed{v_g = 1.97 \times 10^8 \text{ m/s}}$;   (b) $v_d = \dfrac{3 \times 10^8 \text{ m/s}}{2.42}$; $\boxed{v_d = 1.24 \times 10^8 \text{ m/s}}$;

(a) $v_w = \dfrac{3 \times 10^8 \text{ m/s}}{1.33}$; $\boxed{v = 2.26 \text{x} 10^8 \text{ m/s}}$;   (b) $v_a = \dfrac{3 \times 10^8 \text{ m/s}}{1.36}$; $\boxed{v_a = 2.21 \times 10^8 \text{ m/s}}$

35-4 If light travels at 2.1×10^8 m/s in a transparent medium, what is the index of refraction?

$$n = \frac{(3 \times 10^8 \text{ m/s})}{2.1 \times 10^8 \text{ m/s}}; \quad \boxed{n = 1.43}$$

The Laws of Refraction

35-5. Light is incident at an angle of 37^0 from air to flint glass (n = 1.6). What is the angle of

refraction into the glass?

$$n_g \sin \theta_g = n_a \sin \theta_a; \quad \sin \theta_g = \frac{(1.0)\sin 37^0}{1.6}; \quad \boxed{\theta_g = 22.1^0}$$

35-6. A beam of light makes an angle of 60^0 with the surface of water. What is the angle of refraction into the water?

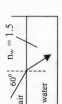

$n_a \sin\theta_a = n_w \sin\theta_w$; $\quad \sin\theta_w = \dfrac{n_a \sin\theta_a}{n_w}$

$\sin\theta_w = \dfrac{(1)\sin 60^0}{1.33} = 0.651$; $\quad \boxed{\theta_w = 40.6^0}$

35-7. Light passes from water (n = 1.33) to air. The beam emerges into air at an angle of 32^0. What is the angle of incidence inside the water? with the horizontal water surface?

$\theta = 90^0 - 32^0 = 58^0$; $\quad n_a \sin\theta_a = n_w \sin\theta_w$; $\quad \sin\theta_w = \dfrac{n_a \sin\theta_a}{n_w}$

$\sin\theta_w = \dfrac{(1)\sin 58^0}{1.33} = 638$; $\quad \boxed{\theta_w = 39.6^0}$

35-8. Light in air is incident at 60^0 and is refracted into an unknown medium at an angle of 40^0. What is the index of refraction for the unknown medium?

$n_x \sin\theta_x = n_a \sin\theta_a$; $\quad n_x = \dfrac{n_a \sin\theta_a}{\sin\theta_x} = \dfrac{(1)(\sin 60^0)}{\sin 40^0}$; $\quad \boxed{n = 1.35}$

35-9. Light strikes from medium A into medium B at an angle of 35^0 with the horizontal boundary. If the angle of refraction is also 35^0, what is the relative index of refraction between the two media? [$\theta_A = 90^0 - 35^0 = 55^0$.]

$n_A \sin\theta_A = n_B \sin\theta_B$; $\quad \dfrac{n_B}{n_A} = \dfrac{\sin\theta_A}{\sin\theta_B} = \dfrac{\sin 55^0}{\sin 35^0}$;

$\dfrac{n_B}{n_A} = \dfrac{\sin 55^0}{\sin 35^0} = 1.43$; $\quad \boxed{n_r = 1.43}$

35-10. Light incident from air at 45^0 is refracted into a transparent medium at an angle of 34^0.

What is the index of refraction for the material?

$n_A \sin\theta_A = n_m \sin\theta_m$; $\quad n_m = \dfrac{(1)\sin 45^0}{\sin 35^0}$; $\quad n_m = 1.23$

---

*35-11. A ray of light originating in air (Fig. 35-20) is incident on water (n = 1.33) at an angle of 60^0. It then passes through the water entering glass (n = 1.50) and finally emerging back into air again. Compute the angle of emergence.

The angle of refraction into one medium becomes the angle of incidence for the next, and so on . . .

$n_{air} \sin\theta_{air} = n_w \sin\theta_w = n_g \sin\theta_g = n_{air} \sin\theta_{air}$

Thus it is seen that a ray emerging into the same medium as that from which it originally entered has the same angle:

$\boxed{\theta_e = \theta_i = 60^0}$

---

*35-12. Prove that, no matter how many parallel layers of different media are traversed by light, the entrance angle and the final emergent angle will be equal as long as the initial and final media are the same. *The prove is the same as shown for Problem 35-11:*

$n_{air} \sin\theta_{air} = n_w \sin\theta_w = n_g \sin\theta_g = n_{air} \sin\theta_{air}$; $\quad \boxed{\theta_e = \theta_i = 60^0}$

Wavelength and Refraction

35-13. The wavelength of sodium light is 589 nm in air. Find its wavelength in glycerine.

From Table 28-1, the index for glycerin is: n = 1.47.

$\dfrac{\lambda_g}{\lambda_a} = \dfrac{n_a}{n_g}$; $\quad \lambda_g = \dfrac{\lambda_a n_a}{n_g} = \dfrac{(589 \text{ nm})(1)}{1.47}$; $\quad \boxed{\lambda_g = 401 \text{ nm}}$

35-19. The critical angle for a given medium relative to air is 40^0. What is the index of refraction for the medium?

$$\sin\theta_c = \frac{n_2}{n_1}; \quad n_x = \frac{n_{air}}{\sin 40^0} = \frac{1}{\sin 40^0}; \quad \boxed{n_x = 1.56}$$

35-20. If the critical angle of incidence for a liquid to air surface is 46^0, what is the index of refraction for the liquid?

$$\sin\theta_c = \frac{n_2}{n_1}; \quad n_x = \frac{n_{air}}{\sin 46^0} = \frac{1}{\sin 46^0}; \quad \boxed{n_x = 1.39}$$

35-21. What is the critical angle relative to air for (a) diamond, (b) water, and (c) ethyl alcohol.

Diamond: $\sin\theta_c = \frac{n_2}{n_1}; \quad \sin\theta_c = \frac{1.0}{2.42}; \quad \theta_c = 24.4^0$

Water: $\sin\theta_c = \frac{n_2}{n_1}; \quad \sin\theta_c = \frac{1.0}{1.33}; \quad \theta_c = 48.8^0$

Alcohol: $\sin\theta_c = \frac{n_2}{n_1}; \quad \sin\theta_c = \frac{1.0}{1.36}; \quad \theta_c = 47.3^0$

35-22. What is the critical angle for flint glass immersed in ethyl alcohol?

$$\sin\theta_c = \frac{n_2}{n_1} = \frac{1.36}{1.63}; \quad \boxed{\theta_c = 56.5^0}$$

*35-23. A right-angle prism like the one shown in Fig. 35-10a is submerged in water. What is the minimum index of refraction for the material to achieve total internal reflection?

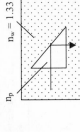

$$\theta_c < 45^0, \quad \sin\theta_c = \frac{n_w}{n_p} = \frac{1.33}{n_p}; \quad n_p = \frac{1.33}{\sin 45^0};$$

$\boxed{n_p = 1.88}$ (Minimum for total internal reflection.)

35-14. The wavelength decreases by 25 percent as it goes from air to an unknown medium. What is the index of refraction for that medium?

A decrease of 25% means λ_x is equal to ¾ of its air value:

$$\frac{\lambda_x}{\lambda_{air}} = 0.750; \quad \frac{n_{air}}{n_x} = \frac{\lambda_x}{\lambda_{air}} = 0.750; \quad n_{air} = \frac{n_{air}}{0.750}; \quad \boxed{n_x = 1.33}$$

35-15. A beam of light has a wavelength of 600 nm in air. What is the wavelength of this light as it passes into glass (n = 1.50)?

$$\frac{n_g}{n_{air}} = \frac{\lambda_{air}}{\lambda_g}; \quad \lambda_g = \frac{n_{air}\lambda_{air}}{n_g} = \frac{(1)(600 \text{ nm})}{1.5}; \quad \boxed{\lambda_g = 400 \text{ nm}}$$

35-16. Red light (620 nm) changes to blue light (478 nm) when it passes into a liquid. What is the index of refraction for the liquid? What is the velocity of the light in the liquid?

$$\frac{n_L}{n_{air}} = \frac{\lambda_r}{\lambda_b}; \quad n_L = \frac{n_{air}\lambda_r}{\lambda_b} = \frac{(1)(620 \text{ nm})}{478 \text{ nm}}; \quad \boxed{n_L = 1.30}$$

*35-17. A ray of monochromatic light of wavelength 400 nm in medium A is incident at 30^0 at the boundary of another medium B. If the ray is refracted at an angle of 50^0, what is its wavelength in medium B?

$$\frac{\sin\theta_A}{\sin\theta_B} = \frac{\lambda_A}{\lambda_B}; \quad \lambda_B = \frac{\lambda_A \sin\theta_B}{\sin\theta_A} = \frac{(400 \text{ nm})\sin 50^0}{\sin 30^0}; \quad \boxed{\lambda_B = 613 \text{ nm}}$$

Total Internal Reflection

35-18. What is the critical angle for light moving from quartz (n = 1.54) to water (n = 1.33).

$$\sin\theta_c = \frac{n_2}{n_1} = \frac{1.33}{1.54}; \quad \boxed{\theta_c = 59.7^0}$$

Supplementary Problems

35-24. The angle of incidence is 30^0 and the angle of refraction is 26.3^0. If the incident medium is water, what might the refractive medium be?

$$n_x \sin\theta_x = n_w \sin\theta_w; \quad n_x = \frac{n_w \sin\theta_w}{\sin\theta_x} = \frac{(1.33)(\sin 30^0)}{\sin 26.3^0}; \quad \boxed{n = 1.50, \text{ glass}}$$

35-25. The speed of light in an unknown medium is 2.40×10^8 m/s. If the wavelength of light in this unknown medium is 400 nm, what is the wavelength of light in air?

$$\frac{c}{v_x} = \frac{\lambda_{air}}{\lambda_x}; \quad \lambda_{air} = \frac{(400 \text{ nm})(3 \times 10^8 \text{ m/s})}{(2.40 \times 10^8 \text{ m/s})}; \quad \boxed{\lambda_x = 500 \text{ nm}}$$

35-26. A ray of light strikes a pane of glass at an angle of 30^0 with the glass surface. If the angle of refraction is also 30^0, what is the index of refraction for the glass?

$$n_A \sin\theta_A = n_g \sin\theta_g; \quad \frac{n_g}{n_A} = \frac{\sin\theta_A}{\sin\theta_g} = \frac{\sin 60^0}{\sin 30^0}; \quad \boxed{n_r = 1.73}$$

35-27. A beam of light is incident on a plane surface separating two media of indexes 1.6 and 1.4. The angle of incidence is 30^0 in the medium of higher index. What is the angle of refraction?

$$\frac{\sin\theta_2}{\sin\theta_1} = \frac{n_1}{n_2}; \quad \sin\theta_1 = \frac{n_2 \sin\theta_2}{n_1} = \frac{1.6\sin 30^0}{1.4}; \quad \theta_1 = 34.8^0$$

35-28. In going from glass (n = 1.50) to water (n = 1.33), what is the critical angle for total internal reflection?

$$\sin\theta_c = \frac{n_2}{n_1} = \frac{1.33}{1.50}; \quad \boxed{\theta_c = 62.5^0}$$

494 Unit A   Solutions Manual

35-29. Light of wavelength 650 nm in a particular glass has a speed of 1.7×10^8 m/s. What is the index of refraction for this glass? What is the wavelength of this light in air?

$$n = \frac{3 \times 10^8 \text{ m/s}}{1.7 \times 10^8 \text{ m/s}}; \quad \boxed{n = 1.76}$$

$$\frac{v_g}{v_{air}} = \frac{\lambda_g}{\lambda_a}; \quad \lambda_{air} = \frac{(3 \times 10^8 \text{ m/s})(650 \text{ nm})}{1.7 \times 10^8 \text{ m/s}}; \quad \boxed{\lambda_{air} = 1146 \text{ nm}}$$

35-30. The critical angle for a certain substance is 38^0 when it is surrounded by air. What is the index of refraction of the substance?

$$\sin\theta_c = \frac{n_2}{n_1}; \quad n_1 = \frac{1.0}{\sin 38^0}; \quad \boxed{n_1 = 1.62}$$

35-31. The water in a swimming pool is 2 m deep. How deep does it appear to a person looking vertically down?

$$\frac{q}{p} = \frac{n_{air}}{n_w} = \frac{1.00}{1.33}; \quad q = \frac{2 \text{ m}}{1.33}; \quad \boxed{q = 1.50 \text{ m}}$$

35-32. A plate of glass (n = 1.50) is placed over a coin on a table. The coin appears to be 3 cm below the top of the glass plate. What is the thickness of the glass plate?

$$\frac{q}{p} = \frac{n_{air}}{n_g} = \frac{1.00}{1.50}; \quad p = 1.50q = (1.50)(3 \text{ cm}); \quad \boxed{p = 4.50 \text{ cm}}$$

Critical Thinking Problems

*35-33. Consider a horizontal ray of light striking one edge of an equilateral prism of glass (n = 1.50) as shown in Fig. 35-21. At what angle θ will the ray emerge from the other side?

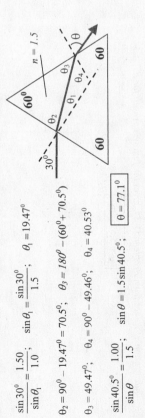

$\dfrac{\sin 30^0}{\sin \theta_1} = \dfrac{1.50}{1.0}$; $\sin \theta_1 = \dfrac{\sin 30^0}{1.5}$; $\theta_1 = 19.47^0$

$\theta_2 = 90^0 - 19.47^0 = 70.5^0$, $\theta_3 = 180^0 - (60^0 + 70.5^0)$

$\theta_3 = 49.47^0$, $\theta_4 = 90^0 - 49.46^0$, $\theta_4 = 40.53^0$

$\dfrac{\sin 40.5^0}{\sin \theta} = \dfrac{1.00}{1.5}$; $\sin \theta = 1.5 \sin 40.5^0$; $\boxed{\theta = 77.1^0}$

*35-34. What is the minimum angle of incidence at the first face of the prism in Fig. 35-21 such that the beam is refracted into air at the second face? (*Larger angles do not produce total internal reflection at the second face.*) [*First find critical angle for θ_4*]

$\sin \theta_{4c} = \dfrac{n_{air}}{n_g} = \dfrac{1}{1.5}$; $\theta_{4c} = 41.8^0$;   *Now find θ_1:* $\theta_3 = 90^0 - 41.8^0 = 48.2^0$

$\theta_2 = 180^0 - (48.2^0 + 60^0)$; $\theta_2 = 71.8$ and $\theta_1 = 90^0 - 71.8^0 = 18.2^0$

$\dfrac{\sin 18.2^0}{\sin \theta_{min}} = \dfrac{1.00}{1.50}$; $\sin \theta_{min} = 1.5 \sin 18.2^0$; $\boxed{\theta_{min} = 27.9^0}$

35-35. Light passing through a plate of transparent material of thickness t suffers a lateral displacement d, as shown in Fig. 35-22. Compute the lateral displacement if the light passes through glass surrounded by air. The angle of incidence θ_1 is 40^0 and the glass (n = 1.50) is 2 cm thick.

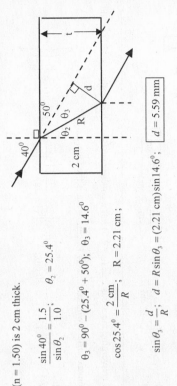

$\dfrac{\sin 40^0}{\sin \theta_2} = \dfrac{1.5}{1.0}$; $\theta_2 = 25.4^0$

$\theta_3 = 90^0 - (25.4^0 + 50^0)$; $\theta_3 = 14.6^0$

$\cos 25.4^0 = \dfrac{2 \text{ cm}}{R}$; $R = 2.21$ cm ;

$\sin \theta_3 = \dfrac{d}{R}$; $d = R \sin \theta_3 = (2.21 \text{ cm}) \sin 14.6^0$; $\boxed{d = 5.59 \text{ mm}}$

*35-36. A rectangular shaped block of glass (n = 1.54) is submerged completely in water (n = 1.33). A beam of light traveling in the water strikes a vertical side of the glass block at an angle of incidence θ_1 and is refracted into the glass where it continues to the top surface of the block. What is the minimum angle θ_1 at the side such that the light does not go out of the glass at the top? (*First find θ_c*)

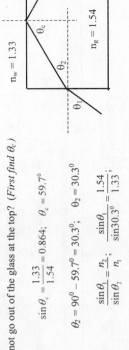

$\sin \theta_c = \dfrac{1.33}{1.54} = 0.864$; $\theta_c = 59.7^0$

$\theta_2 = 90^0 - 59.7^0 = 30.3^0$; $\theta_2 = 30.3^0$

$\dfrac{\sin \theta_1}{\sin \theta_2} = \dfrac{n_2}{n_1}$; $\dfrac{\sin \theta_1}{\sin 30.3^0} = \dfrac{1.54}{1.33}$;

$\sin \theta_1 = \dfrac{1.54 \sin 30.3^0}{1.33}$ $\boxed{\theta_1 = 35.7^0}$

For angles smaller than 35.7^0, the light will leave the glass at the top surface.

**35-37. Prove that the lateral displacement in Fig. 35-22 can be calculated from

$$d = t\sin\theta_1\left(1 - \frac{n_1\cos\theta_1}{n_2\cos\theta_2}\right)$$

Use this relationship to verify the answer to Critical Thinking Problem 35-35.

$$\cos\theta_1 = \frac{d}{p}; \quad p = \frac{d}{\cos\theta_1}$$

$$\tan\theta_1 = \frac{\sin\theta_1}{\cos\theta_1} = \frac{p+a}{t}; \quad \tan\theta_2 = \frac{a}{t};$$

$$a = t\tan\theta_2; \quad a = t\frac{\sin\theta_2}{\cos\theta_2}; \quad p = \frac{d}{\cos\theta_1}$$

$$\frac{\sin\theta_1}{\cos\theta_1} = \frac{p+a}{t} = \left(\frac{\dfrac{d}{\cos\theta_1} + t\dfrac{\sin\theta_2}{\cos\theta_2}}{t}\right)$$

Simplifying this expression and solving for d, we obtain: $d = t\sin\theta_1 - \dfrac{t\sin\theta_2\cos\theta_1}{\cos\theta_2}$

Now, $n_2\sin\theta_2 = n_1\sin\theta_1$ *or* $\sin\theta_2 = \dfrac{n_1}{n_2}\sin\theta_1$

Substitution and simplifying, we finally obtain the expression below:

$$d = t\sin\theta_1\left(1 - \frac{n_1\cos\theta_1}{n_2\cos\theta_2}\right)$$

Substitution of values from Problem 35-35, gives the following result for d:

$$\boxed{d = 5.59\text{ mm}}$$

Chapter 36. Lenses and Optical Instruments

Focal Length and the Lensmaker's Equation
(Assume n = 1.50 unless told otherwise.)

36-1. A plano-convex lens is to be constructed out of glass so that it has a focal length of 40 cm. What is the radius of curvature of the curved surface?

$R_2 = \infty$

$R_1 = ?$

$n = 1.5$

$$\frac{1}{f} = (n-1)\left(\frac{1}{R_1} + \frac{1}{R_2}\right) = (1.5-1)\left(\frac{1}{40\text{ cm}} + \frac{1}{\infty}\right);$$

$$\frac{1}{40\text{ cm}} = (0.5)\left(\frac{1}{R_1}\right); \quad R_1 = 0.5(40\text{ cm}); \quad \boxed{R_1 = 20.0\text{ cm}}$$

36-2. If one uses a glass, double-convex lens to obtain a focal length of 30 cm, what must be the curvature of each convex surface?   [$R_1 = R_2 = R$]

$$\frac{1}{f} = (n-1)\left(\frac{1}{R} + \frac{1}{R}\right) = (1.5-1)\left(\frac{2}{R}\right); \quad R = f; \quad \boxed{R = 30\text{ cm}}$$

36-3. The curved surface of a plano-concave lens has a radius of –12 cm.   What is the focal length if the lens is made from a material with a refractive index of 1.54.

R_1

$R_2 = \infty$

$$\frac{1}{f} = (n-1)\left(\frac{1}{R_1} + \frac{1}{R_2}\right) = (1.54-1)\left(\frac{1}{-12\text{ cm}} + \frac{1}{\infty}\right);$$

$$\frac{1}{f} = (1.54-1)\left(\frac{1}{-12\text{ cm}}\right); \quad \frac{1}{f} = \frac{0.540}{-12\text{ cm}}; \quad \boxed{f = -22.2\text{ cm}}$$

36-4. A converging meniscus lens (n = 1.5) has a concave surface whose radius is –20 cm and a convex surface whose radius is 12 cm.   What is the focal length?

$$\frac{1}{f} = (1.5-1)\left(\frac{1}{12\text{ cm}} + \frac{1}{-20\text{ cm}}\right) = (0.5)\left[\frac{-20\text{ cm} + 12\text{ cm}}{(12\text{ cm})(-20\text{ cm})}\right]; \quad \boxed{f = 30\text{ cm}}$$

36-5. A converging lens such as shown in Fig. 36-8a is made of glass. The first surface has a radius of 15 cm and the second surface has a radius of 10 cm. What is the focal length?

Both surfaces are convex, and therefore positive: ($R_1 = +15\ cm$, $R_2 = +10\ cm$, $n = 1.5$)

$$\frac{1}{f} = (1.5-1)\left(\frac{1}{15\text{ cm}} + \frac{1}{10\text{ cm}}\right) = (0.5)\left[\frac{10\text{ cm}+15\text{ cm}}{(10\text{ cm})(15\text{ cm})}\right]; \quad \boxed{f = 12\text{ cm}}$$

36-6. A meniscus lens has a convex surface whose radius is 20 cm and a concave surface whose radius is −30 cm. What is the focal length if the refractive index is 1.54.

Given: $R_1 = 20\ cm$, $R_2 = -30\ cm$, $n = 1.54$: Find: $f = ?$

$$\frac{1}{f} = (1.54-1)\left(\frac{1}{20\text{ cm}} + \frac{1}{-30\text{ cm}}\right) = (0.54)\left[\frac{-30\text{ cm}+20\text{ cm}}{(20\text{ cm})(-30\text{ cm})}\right]; \quad \boxed{f = 1.11\text{ m}}$$

36-7. A plano-convex lens is ground from crown glass (n = 1.52). What should be the radius of the curved surface if the desired focal length is to be 400 mm?

$R_2 = \infty$
$f = 400$ mm
$n = 1.52$

$$\frac{1}{f} = (n-1)\left(\frac{1}{R_1} + \frac{1}{R_2}\right); \quad \frac{1}{400\text{ mm}} = (1.52-1)\left(\frac{1}{R_1} + \frac{1}{\infty}\right);$$

$$\frac{1}{400\text{ mm}} = (0.52)\left(\frac{1}{R_1}\right); \quad R_1 = 0.52(400\text{ mm}); \quad \boxed{R_1 = 208\text{ mm}}$$

36-8. The magnitudes of the concave and convex surfaces of a glass lens are 200 and 600 mm, respectively. What is the focal length? Is it diverging or converging?

Given: $R_1 = -20\ cm$, $R_2 = +60\ cm$, $n = 1.5$: Find: $f = ?$

$$\frac{1}{f} = (1.5-1)\left(\frac{1}{-20\text{ cm}} + \frac{1}{60\text{ cm}}\right) = (0.5)\left[\frac{60\text{ cm}-20\text{ cm}}{(-20\text{ cm})(60\text{ cm})}\right]; \quad \boxed{f = -60\text{ cm}}$$

The lens is a diverging lens, since the focal length is negative.

36-9. A plastic lens (n = 1.54) has a convex surface of radius 25 cm and a concave surface of −70 cm. What is the focal length? Is it diverging or converging?

$$\frac{1}{f} = (1.54-1)\left(\frac{1}{25\text{ cm}} + \frac{1}{-70\text{ cm}}\right) = (0.54)\left[\frac{-70\text{ cm}+25\text{ cm}}{(25\text{ cm})(-70\text{ cm})}\right]; \quad \boxed{f = +72.0\text{ cm}}$$

The lens is a converging lens, since the focal length is positive.

Images Formed by Thin Lenses

36-10. A 7-cm tall pencil is placed 35 cm from a thin converging lens of focal length 25 cm. What are the nature, size, and location of the image formed?

$$q = \frac{pf}{p-f} = \frac{(35\text{ cm})(25\text{ cm})}{35\text{ cm} - 25\text{ cm}}; \quad q = 87.5\text{ cm}$$

$$M = \frac{-q}{p} = \frac{y'}{y}; \quad y' = \frac{-qy'}{p} = \frac{-(87.5\text{ cm})(7\text{ m})}{35\text{ cm}}$$

$$\boxed{q = +87.5\text{ cm}, \ y' = -17.5\text{ cm}, \ real,\ inverted,\ and\ enlarged.}$$

36-11. An object 8 cm high is placed 30 cm from a thin converging lens of focal length 12 cm. What are the nature, size, and location of the image formed?

$$q = \frac{pf}{p-f} = \frac{(30\text{ cm})(12\text{ cm})}{30\text{ cm} - 12\text{ cm}}; \quad q = 20\text{ cm}$$

$$M = \frac{-q}{p} = \frac{y'}{y}; \quad y' = \frac{-qy'}{p} = \frac{-(20\text{ cm})(8\text{ m})}{30\text{ cm}}$$

$$\boxed{q = +20.0\text{ cm}, \ y' = -5.33\text{ cm}, \ real,\ inverted,\ and\ diminished.}$$

36-12. A virtual, erect image appears to be located 40 cm in front of a lens of focal length 15 cm. What is the object distance? *The focal length must be positive (converging), since real objects cannot produce erect virtual images farther away from lens than the object.*

36-12. (Cont.). Find object distance for given values:

$$p = \frac{qf}{q-f} = \frac{(-40\ cm)(15\ cm)}{-40\ cm - 15\ cm}; \qquad \boxed{p = 10.9\ cm}$$

Note: You should show that the magnification is +2.67.

36-13. A 50 mm tall object is placed 12 cm from a converging lens of focal length 20 cm. What are the nature, size, and location of the image? (See drawing for Prob. 36-12 above.)

$$q = \frac{(12\ cm)(20\ cm)}{12\ cm - 20\ cm}; \quad q = -30\ cm; \quad M = \frac{-q}{p} = \frac{y'}{y}; \quad y' = \frac{-qy}{p} = \frac{-(-30\ cm)(50\ mm)}{12\ cm}$$

$$\boxed{q = -30.0\ cm, y' = +125\ mm, \textit{virtual, erect, and enlarged.}}$$

36-14. An object located 30 cm from a thin lens has a real, inverted image located a distance of 60 cm on the opposite side of the lens. What is the focal length of the lens?

$$f = \frac{pq}{p+q} = \frac{(30\ cm)(60\ cm)}{30\ cm + 60\ cm}; \qquad f = +20\ cm$$

The focal length is positive, so the lens is <u>*converging.*</u>

$$\boxed{f = +20\ cm, \textit{converging}}$$

36-15. A light source is 600 mm from a converging lens of focal length 180 mm. Construct the image using ray diagrams. What is the image distance? Is the image real or virtual?

$$q = \frac{pf}{p-f} = \frac{(60\ cm)(18\ cm)}{60\ cm - 18\ cm}; \qquad q = 25.7\ cm$$

$$\boxed{q = +25.7cm, \textit{real, inverted, and diminished.}}$$

Note: Show that the magnification of the image is M = - 0.428.

36-16. A plano-convex lens is held 40 mm from a 6-cm object. What are the nature and location of the image formed if the focal length is 60 mm?

$$q = \frac{(40\ mm)(60\ mm)}{40\ cm - 60\ cm}; \quad q = -120\ mm; \quad y' = \frac{-qy}{p} = \frac{-(-120\ mm)(6\ cm)}{40\ mm}$$

$$\boxed{q = -120\ mm, y' = +18.0\ cm, \textit{virtual, erect, and enlarged.}}$$

36-17. An object 6 cm high is held 4 cm from a diverging meniscus lens of focal length −24 cm.

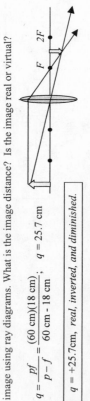

What are the nature, size, and location of the image?

$$q = \frac{pf}{p-f} = \frac{(4\ cm)(-24\ cm)}{4\ cm - (-24\ cm)}; \quad q = -3.43\ cm$$

$$M = \frac{-q}{p} = \frac{y'}{y}; \quad y' = \frac{-qy}{p} = \frac{-(-3.43\ cm)(6\ m)}{4\ cm}$$

$$\boxed{q = -3.43\ cm, y' = 5.14\ cm, \textit{virtual, erect, and diminished.}}$$

36-18. The focal length of a converging lens is 200 mm. An object 60 mm high is mounted on a movable track so that the distance from the lens can be varied. Calculate the nature, size, and location of the image formed for the following object distances: (a) 150 mm, (b) 200 mm, (c) 300 mm, (d) 400 mm, (e) 600 mm. *(Figures not drawn to conserve space.)*

$$p = 15\ cm, 20\ cm, 30\ cm, 40\ cm, \text{ and } 60\ cm; \qquad f = 20\ cm; \qquad y = 6\ cm$$

$$q = \frac{pf}{p-f}; \qquad M = \frac{y'}{y} = \frac{-q}{p}; \qquad y' = \frac{-qy}{p}$$

(a) $q = \frac{(15\ cm)(20\ cm)}{15\ cm - 20\ cm} = -60\ cm$, *virtual* $\quad y' = \frac{-(-60\ cm)(6\ cm)}{(15\ cm)} = 24\ cm$, *erect*

(b) $q = \frac{(20\ cm)(20\ cm)}{20\ cm - 20\ cm} = \infty$, *no image* $\quad y' = \frac{-(\infty)(6\ cm)}{(20\ cm)} = \infty$, *no image*

(c) $q = \frac{(30\ cm)(20\ cm)}{30\ cm - 20\ cm} = 60\ cm$, *real* $\quad y' = \frac{-(60\ cm)(6\ cm)}{(30\ cm)} = -12\ cm$, *inverted*

*36-23. A magnifying glass held 40 mm from a specimen produces an erect image that is twice the object size. What is the focal length of the lens?

$$M = \frac{-q}{p} = +2; \quad q = -2p; \quad q = \frac{pf}{p-f}; \quad -2p = \frac{pf}{p-f}$$

$$-2(p-f)=f; \quad -2p+2f=f; \quad f=2p=2(40\text{ mm}); \quad \boxed{f=80.0\text{ mm}}$$

*36-24. What is the magnification of a lens if the focal length is 40 cm and the object distance is 65 cm?

$$q = \frac{(65\text{ cm})(40\text{ cm})}{65\text{ cm}-40\text{ cm}}=104\text{ cm}; \quad M=\frac{-q}{p}=\frac{-(104\text{ cm})}{(65\text{ cm})}; \quad \boxed{M=-1.60}$$

Supplementary Problems

36-25. The radius of the curved surface in a plano-concave lens is 20 cm. What is the focal length if $n = 1.54$? [$R_1 = -20$ cm, $R_2 = \infty$]

$$\frac{1}{f}=(n-1)\left(\frac{1}{R_1}+\frac{1}{R_2}\right)=(1.54-1)\left(\frac{1}{-20\text{ cm}}+\frac{1}{\infty}\right);$$

$$\frac{1}{f}=(1.54-1)\left(\frac{1}{-20\text{ cm}}\right); \quad \frac{1}{f}=\frac{0.540}{-20\text{ cm}}; \quad \boxed{f=-37.4\text{ cm}}$$

36-26. A thin meniscus lens is formed with a concave surface of radius –40 cm and a convex surface of radius +30 cm. If the resulting focal length is 79.0 cm, what was the index of refraction of the transparent material?

$$\frac{1}{f}=(n-1)\left(\frac{1}{R_1}+\frac{1}{R_2}\right); \quad \frac{1}{79\text{ cm}}=(n-1)\left(\frac{1}{-40\text{ cm}}+\frac{1}{30\text{ cm}}\right);$$

$$\frac{1}{79\text{ cm}}=(n-1)\left(\frac{-10\text{ cm}}{-1200\text{ cm}^2}\right); \quad n-1=1.52; \quad \boxed{n=2.52}$$

36-18. (Cont.) *Images formed by converging mirror, f = 20 cm, y = 6 cm.*

(d) $q = \frac{(40\text{ cm})(20\text{ cm})}{40\text{ cm}-20\text{ cm}}=40\text{ cm}$, *real* $y' = \frac{-(40\text{ cm})(6\text{ cm})}{(40\text{ cm})}=-6\text{ cm}$, *inverted*

(e) $q = \frac{(60\text{ cm})(20\text{ cm})}{60\text{ cm}-20\text{ cm}}=30\text{ cm}$, *real* $y' = \frac{-(30\text{ cm})(6\text{ cm})}{(60\text{ cm})}=-3\text{ cm}$, *inverted*

36-19. An object 450 mm from a converging lens forms a real image 900 mm from the lens. What is the focal length of the lens?

$$f = \frac{pq}{p+q}=\frac{(45\text{ cm})(90\text{ cm})}{45\text{ cm}+90\text{ cm}}; \quad f=+30\text{ cm}$$

Magnification

*36-20. An object is located 20 cm from a converging lens. If the magnification is –2, what is the image distance?

$$M = \frac{-q}{p}=-2; \quad q=2p=2(20\text{ cm}); \quad \boxed{q=40\text{ cm}, real, inverted, and enlarged.}$$

*36-21. A pencil is held 20 cm from a diverging lens of focal length –10 cm. What is the magnification?

$$M = \frac{-q}{p}=\frac{-(-10\text{ cm})}{20\text{ cm}}; \quad M=+\tfrac{1}{2}$$

*36-22. A magnifying glass has a focal length of 27 cm. How close must this glass be held to an object to produce an erect image three times the size of the object?

$$M = \frac{-q}{p}=+3; \quad q=-3p; \quad q=\frac{pf}{p-f}; \quad -3p=\frac{pf}{p-f}$$

$$-3(p-f)=f; \quad -3p+3f=f; \quad p=\tfrac{2}{3}f=\tfrac{2}{3}(27\text{ cm}); \quad \boxed{p=18.0\text{ cm}}$$

36-27. A converging lens has a focal length of 20 cm. An object is placed 15.0 cm from the lens. find the image distance and the nature of the image. *The object is inside the focus.*

$q = \dfrac{pf}{p-f} = \dfrac{(15\text{ cm})(20\text{ cm})}{15\text{ cm} - 20\text{ cm}}$; $\boxed{q = -60 \text{ cm}}$

The image is erect, virtual, and enlarged.

36-28. How far from a source of light must a lens be placed if it is to form an image 800 mm from the lens? The focal length is 200 mm.

$p = \dfrac{qf}{q-f} = \dfrac{(80\text{ cm})(20\text{ cm})}{80\text{ cm} - 20\text{ cm}}$;

$\boxed{p = 26.7 \text{ cm}}$

36-29. A source of light 36 cm from a lens projects an image on a screen 18.0 cm from the lens. Is it converging or diverging.

What is the focal length of the lens? Is it converging or diverging.

$f = \dfrac{pq}{p+q} = \dfrac{(36\text{ cm})(18\text{ cm})}{36\text{ cm} + 18\text{ cm}}$; $\boxed{f = 12 \text{ cm, converging.}}$

36-30. What is the minimum film size needed to project the image of a student who is 2 m tall?

Assume that the student is located 2.5 m from the camera lens and that the focal length is

55.0 mm?

$q = \dfrac{pf}{p-f} = \dfrac{(2000\text{ mm})(55\text{ mm})}{2000\text{ mm} - 55\text{ mm}}$;

$\boxed{q = 56.6 \text{ mm}}$

---

*36-31. When parallel light strikes a lens, the light diverges, apparently coming from a point 80 mm behind the lens. How far from an object should this lens be held to form an image one-fourth the size of the object?

$M = \dfrac{-q}{p} = +\dfrac{1}{4}$; $p = -4q = -4(-80\text{ mm})$; $\boxed{p = 240 \text{ mm}}$

*36-32. How far from a diverging lens should an object be placed in order that its image be one-fourth the size of the object?   The focal length is -35 cm.

$M = \dfrac{-q}{p} = \dfrac{1}{4}$; $q = \dfrac{-p}{4}$; $q = \dfrac{pf}{p-f}$; $\dfrac{-p}{4} = \dfrac{pf}{p-f}$

$-(p-f) = 4f$; $-p + f = 4f$; $p = -3f = -3(-35\text{ cm})$; $\boxed{p = 105 \text{ cm}}$

*36-33. The first surface of a thin lens has a convex radius of 20 cm. What should be the radius of the second surface to produce a converging lens of focal length 8.00 cm?

$\dfrac{1}{f} = (n-1)\left(\dfrac{1}{R_1} + \dfrac{1}{R_2}\right)$; $\dfrac{1}{8\text{ cm}} = (1.5-1)\left(\dfrac{1}{20\text{ cm}} + \dfrac{1}{R_2}\right)$;

$\dfrac{1}{8\text{ cm}} = 0.5\left[\dfrac{R_2 + 20\text{ cm}}{(20\text{ cm})R_2}\right]$; $2.5R_2 = 0.5R_2 + 10\text{ cm}$; $\boxed{R_2 = +5.00 \text{ cm}}$

**36-34. Two thin converging lenses are placed 60 cm apart and have the same axis. The first lens has a focal length 10 cm, and the second has a focal length of 15.0 cm. If an object 6.0 cm high is placed 20 cm in front of the first lens, what are the location and size of the final image? Is it real or virtual?   (*See figure on following page.*)

$q_1 = \dfrac{(20\text{ cm})(10\text{ cm})}{20\text{ cm} - 10\text{ cm}} = 20\text{ cm}$; $p_2 = 60\text{ cm} - 20\text{ cm} = 40$ cm

$q_2 = \dfrac{(40\text{ cm})(15\text{ cm})}{40\text{ cm} - 15\text{ cm}} = 24\text{ cm}$; $\boxed{q = 24.0 \text{ cm, real image}}$

**36-34. (Cont.) $q_1 = 20$ cm; $q_2 = 24$ cm

$$M = M_1 \times M_2$$

$$M = \left(\frac{-q_1}{p_1}\right)\left(\frac{-q_2}{p_2}\right) = \frac{q_1 q_2}{p_1 p_2}$$

60 cm

$f_2 = 15$ cm

$f_1 = 10$ cm

$$M = \frac{(20\text{ cm})(24\text{ cm})}{(20\text{ cm})(40\text{ cm})} = +0.6; \quad y' = My = (0.6)(6\text{ cm}); \quad y' = 3.6 \text{ cm};$$

$q = 24$ cm beyond lens 2, $y' = 3.6$ cm, real, erect, and diminished.

**36-35. A converging lens of focal length 25 cm is placed 50 cm in front of a diverging lens whose focal length is −25 cm. If an object is placed 75 cm in front of the converging lens, what is the location of the final image? What is the total magnification. Is the image real or virtual? (*Take image of 1st as object for 2nd.*)

$$q_1 = \frac{(75\text{ cm})(25\text{ cm})}{75\text{ cm} - 25\text{ cm}} = 37.5 \text{ cm};$$

$$p_2 = 60\text{ cm} - 20\text{ cm} = 40 \text{ cm}$$

$$q_2 = \frac{(12.5\text{ cm})(-25\text{ cm})}{12.5\text{ cm} - (-25\text{ cm})} = -8.33 \text{ cm}; \quad M = M_1 \times M_2 = \frac{(-q_1)(-q_2)}{p_1 p_2}; \quad M = -0.333$$

$$M = \frac{q_1 q_2}{p_1 p_2} = \frac{(37.5\text{ cm})(-8.33\text{ cm})}{(75\text{ cm})(12.5\text{ cm})}; \quad M = -0.333$$

$q = -8.33$ cm left of lens 2; *virtual, inverted, diminished; M = -0.333*

255

Critical Thinking Problems

*36-36. A camera consists of a converging lens of focal length 50 mm mounted in front of a light-sensitive film as shown in Fig. 36-19. When photographing infinite objects, how far should the lens be from the film? What is the image distance when photographing object 500 mm from the lens? What is the magnification?

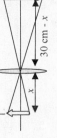

(a) $p = \infty$; $\dfrac{1}{\infty} + \dfrac{1}{q} = \dfrac{1}{f}$; $q = f = 50$ mm

(b) $q = \dfrac{pf}{p-f} = \dfrac{(500\text{ mm})(50\text{ mm})}{500\text{ mm} - 50\text{ mm}}$; $q = 55.6$ mm *for object at 500 mm.*

(c) $M = \dfrac{-q}{p} = \dfrac{-(55.6\text{ mm})}{500\text{ mm}}$; $M = -0.111$, inverted, real, and diminished.

*36-37. An object is placed 30 cm from a screen. At what points between the object and the screen can a lens of focal length 5 cm be placed to obtain an image on the screen?

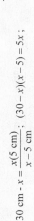

30 cm

x

30 cm − x

Let $p = x$ and $q = (30 - x)$; $q = \dfrac{pf}{p-f}$;

$30\text{ cm} - x = \dfrac{x(5\text{ cm})}{x - 5\text{ cm}}$; $(30 - x)(x - 5) = 5x$;

$30x - 150 - x^2 + 5x = 5x$; $x^2 - 30x + 150 = 0$; (*Solve the quadratic equation for x*)

Two positions are: $x = 6.34$ *and* 23.7 cm *from object.*

**36-38. A simple projector is illustrated in Fig. 36-20. The condenser provides even illumination of the film by the light source. The frame size of regular 8-mm film is 5 x 4 mm. An image is to be projected 600 x 480 mm on a screen located 6 m from the projection lens. What should be the focal length of the projection lens? How far should the film be from the lens?

$M = \frac{y'}{y} = \frac{(-60 \text{ cm})}{0.5 \text{ cm}}$; $M = -120$

$M = \frac{-q}{p} = -120$; $p = \frac{q}{120}$; $p = \frac{qf}{q-f}$; $\frac{q}{120} = \frac{qf}{q-f}$; $\frac{1}{120} = \frac{f}{q-f}$

$q - f = 120f$; $121f = q$; $f = \frac{q}{121} = \frac{600 \text{ cm}}{121}$; $\boxed{f = 4.96 \text{ cm}}$

$p = \frac{q}{120} = \frac{600 \text{ cm}}{120}$; $\boxed{p = 5.00 \text{ cm}}$

**36-39. A telescope has an objective lens of focal length 900 mm and an eyepiece of focal length 50 mm. The telescope is used to examine a rabbit 30 cm high at a distance of 60 m. What is the distance between the lenses if the final image is 25 cm in front of the eyepiece? What is the apparent height of the rabbit as seen through the telescope?

$p_1 = 6000$ cm, $f_1 = 90$ cm, $f_2 = 5$ cm;

(a) $q = \frac{(6000 \text{ cm})(90 \text{ cm})}{6000 \text{ cm} - 90 \text{ cm}} = 91.37$ cm

$p_2 = x - 91.37$ cm; $p_2 = \frac{q_2 f_2}{q_2 - f_2}$

$x - 91.3 \text{ cm} = \frac{(-25 \text{ cm})(5 \text{ cm})}{-25 \text{ cm} - 5 \text{ cm}}$; $x - 91.37 \text{ cm} = 4.167$; $\boxed{x = 95.54 \text{ cm}}$

The two lenses must be separated by a distance of 95.5 cm.

**36-39. (Cont.) (b) $p_2 = 95.54 \text{ cm} - 91.37 \text{ cm}$; $p_2 = 4.17 \text{ cm}$; $M = M_1 \times M_2$

$M = \frac{q_1 q_2}{p_1 p_2} = \frac{(91.37 \text{ cm})(-25 \text{ cm})}{(6000 \text{ cm})(4.17 \text{ cm})}$; $M = -0.0914$; $y' = My$

$y' = (-0.0914)(30 \text{ cm})$; $\boxed{y' = -2.74 \text{ cm, virtual, inverted, and diminished}}$

**36-40. The Galilean telescope consists of a diverging lens as the eyepiece and a converging lens as the objective. The focal length of the objective is 30 cm, and the focal length of the eyepiece is −2.5 cm. An object 40 m away from the objective has a final image located 25 cm in front of the diverging lens. What is the separation (x) of the lenses?

What is the total magnification (M)?

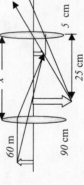

$q_1 = \frac{(4000 \text{ cm})(30 \text{ cm})}{4000 \text{ cm} - 30 \text{ cm}} = 30.23$ cm;

$p_2 = \frac{q_2 f_2}{q_2 - f_2} = \frac{(-25 \text{ cm})(-2.5 \text{ cm})}{-25 \text{ cm} - (-2.5 \text{ cm})}$; $p_2 = -2.78$ cm

$p_2 = x - 30.23$ cm; $x = 30.23 \text{ cm} + p_2 = 30.23 \text{ cm} + (-2.78 \text{ cm})$; $\boxed{x = 27.5 \text{ cm}}$

$M = \frac{q_1 q_2}{p_1 p_2} = \frac{(30.23 \text{ cm})(-25 \text{ cm})}{(4000 \text{ cm})(2.78 \text{ cm})}$; $\boxed{M = -0.068}$

**36-41. The focal length of the eyepiece of a particular microscope is 3.0 cm, and the focal length of the objective lens is 19 mm. The separation of the two lenses is 26.5 cm, and the final image formed by the eyepiece is at infinity. How far should the objective lens be placed from the specimen being studied?

$x = 256$ mm; $f_1 = 19$ mm; $f_2 = 30$ mm; $p_2 = f_2 = 30$ mm;

$q_1 = 265 \text{ mm} - 30 \text{ mm} = 235$ mm;

$p_1 = \frac{q_1 f_1}{q_1 - f_1} = \frac{(235 \text{ mm})(19 \text{ mm})}{235 \text{ mm} - 19 \text{ mm}}$; $\boxed{q = 20.7 \text{ mm}}$

Chapter 37. Interference, Diffraction, and Polarization

Young's Experiment; Interference

37-1. Light from a laser has a wavelength of 632 nm. Two rays from this source follow paths that differ in length. What is the minimum path difference required to cause (a) constructive interference, (b) destructive interference?

(a) Constructive: $\Delta p = n\lambda = (1)(632 \text{ nm})$; $\boxed{\Delta p = 632 \text{ nm.}}$

(b) Destructive: $\Delta p = n\lambda/2 = \frac{1}{2}(632 \text{ nm})$; $\boxed{\Delta p = 316 \text{ nm}}$

37-2. Find the difference in path length required in Problem 37-1 to provide the very next instances of constructive and destructive interference.

(a) 2nd Constructive: $\Delta p = n\lambda = (2)(632 \text{ nm})$; $\boxed{\Delta p = 1264 \text{ nm}}$

(b) 2nd Destructive: $\Delta p = n\lambda/2 = \frac{3\lambda}{2} = \frac{3(632 \text{ nm})}{2}$; $\boxed{\Delta p = 948 \text{ nm}}$

37-3. Monochromatic light illuminates two parallel slits 0.2 mm apart. On a screen 1.0 m from the slits, the first bright fringe is separated from the central fringe by 2.50 mm. What is the wavelength of the light?

$$\frac{yd}{x} = n\lambda; \quad \lambda = \frac{yd}{nx} = \frac{(2.5 \text{ mm})(0.2 \text{ mm})}{(1)(1000 \text{ mm})}; \quad \boxed{\lambda = 500 \text{ nm}}$$

37-4. Monochromatic light from a sodium flame illuminates two slits separated by 1.0 mm. A viewing screen is 1.0 m from the slits, and the distance from the central bright fringe to the bright fringe nearest it is 0.589 mm. What is the frequency of the light?

$$\frac{yd}{x} = (1)\lambda; \lambda = \frac{c}{f}; \quad f = \frac{cx}{yd} = \frac{(3 \times 10^8 \text{ m/s})(1 \text{ m})}{(5.89 \times 10^{-4} \text{ m})(0.001 \text{ mm})}; \quad \boxed{f = 5.09 \times 10^{14} \text{ Hz}}$$

37-5. Two slits 0.05 mm apart are illuminated by green ($\lambda = 520$ nm). A diffraction pattern is formed on a viewing screen 2.0 m away. What is the distance from the center of the screen to the first bright fringe? What is the distance to the third dark fringe?

The first bright fringe occurs when n = 1: $\quad \frac{yd}{x} = n\lambda \quad (n = 1, 2, 3, \ldots)$

$$y = \frac{(1)\lambda x}{d} = \frac{(5.2 \times 10^{-4} \text{ mm})(2000 \text{ mm})}{(0.05 \text{ mm})}; \quad \boxed{y = 20.8 \text{ mm}}$$

The third dark fringe occurs when n = 5: $\quad \frac{yd}{x} = n\frac{\lambda}{2} \quad (n = 1, 3, 5, \ldots)$

$$y = \frac{5\lambda x}{2d} = \frac{5(5.2 \times 10^{-4} \text{ mm})(2000 \text{ mm})}{(2)(0.05 \text{ mm})}; \quad \boxed{y = 52.0 \text{ mm}}$$

*37-6. For the situation described in Problem 37-5, what is the separation of the two first-order bright fringes located on each side of the central band?

$$y = \frac{(1)\lambda x}{d} = 20.8 \text{ mm}; \quad \Delta y = 2(20.8 \text{ mm}); \quad \Delta y = 41.6 \text{ mm}$$

*37-7. Young's experiment is performed using monochromatic light of wavelength 500 nm. The slit separation is 1.20 mm and the screen is 5.00 m away. How far apart are the bright fringes? *The separation of each fringe is same as for n = 1.*

$$y = \frac{(1)\lambda x}{d} = \frac{(5.00 \times 10^{-7} \text{ m})(5.00 \text{ m})}{(1.2 \times 10^{-3} \text{ m})}; \quad \boxed{y = 2.08 \text{ mm}}$$

*37-8. In Young's experiment it is noted that the second dark fringe appears at a distance of 2.5 cm from the central bright fringe. Assume that the slit separation is 60 μm and that the screen is 2.0 m away. What is the wavelength of the incident light? *(Note that n = 3)*

$$\frac{yd}{x} = (3)\frac{\lambda}{2}; \quad \lambda = \frac{2yd}{3x} = \frac{2(0.025 \text{ m})(60 \times 10^{-6} \text{ m})}{(3)(2.0 \text{ m})}; \quad \boxed{\lambda = 500 \text{ nm}}$$

The Diffraction Grating

37-9. A diffraction grating having 300 lines/mm is illuminated by light of wavelength 589 nm. What are the angles at which the first and second-order bright fringes are formed?

$$d = \frac{1}{300 \text{ lines/mm}} = 3.33 \times 10^{-3} \text{ mm} \quad or \quad d = 3.33 \times 10^{-6} \text{ m}$$

$$d\sin\theta = n\lambda; \quad \sin\theta = \frac{n\lambda}{d} = \frac{(1)(589 \times 10^{-9}\text{ m})}{3.33 \times 10^{-6}\text{ m}}; \quad \theta = 10.2^0$$

$$d\sin\theta = n\lambda; \quad \sin\theta = \frac{n\lambda}{d} = \frac{(2)(589 \times 10^{-9}\text{ m})}{3.33 \times 10^{-6}\text{ m}}; \quad \theta = 20.7^0$$

37-10. A diffraction grating has 250,000 lines/m. What is the wavelength of incident light if the second order bright fringe occurs at 12.6^0.

$$d = \frac{1}{2.50 \times 10^5 \text{ lines/m}} = 4.00 \times 10^{-6}\text{ m}; \quad d\sin\theta = n\lambda; \quad \lambda = \frac{d\sin\theta}{n}$$

$$\lambda = \frac{(4.00 \times 10^{-6}\text{ m})\sin 12.6^0}{2}; \quad \boxed{\lambda = 436 \text{ nm}}$$

37-11. A small sodium lamp emits light of wavelength 589 nm, which illuminates a grating marked with 6000 lines/cm. Calculate the angular deviation of the first and second order bright fringes?

$$d = \frac{1}{6000 \text{ lines/cm}} = 1.67 \times 10^{-4}\text{ cm} \quad or \quad d = 1.67 \times 10^{-6}\text{ m}$$

$$d\sin\theta = n\lambda; \quad \sin\theta = \frac{n\lambda}{d} = \frac{(1)(589 \times 10^{-9}\text{ m})}{1.67 \times 10^{-6}\text{ m}}; \quad \theta = 20.7^0$$

$$d\sin\theta = n\lambda; \quad \sin\theta = \frac{n\lambda}{d} = \frac{(2)(589 \times 10^{-9}\text{ m})}{1.67 \times 10^{-6}\text{ m}}; \quad \theta = 45.0^0$$

37-12. A parallel beam of light illuminates a diffraction grating with 6000 lines/cm. The second-order bright fringe is located 32.0 cm from the central image on a screen 50 cm from the grating. Calculate the wavelength of the light?

$$d = \frac{1}{6000 \text{ lines/cm}} = 1.67 \times 10^{-6}\text{ m}; \quad d\sin\theta = n\lambda \quad (n = 1, 2, 3, \ldots)$$

$$\tan\theta = \frac{32\text{ cm}}{50\text{ cm}}; \quad \theta = 32.6^0; \quad \lambda = \frac{d\sin\theta}{2} = \frac{(1.67 \times 10^{-6}\text{m})\sin 32.6^0}{2}; \quad \boxed{\lambda = 449 \text{ nm}}$$

*37-13. The visible light spectrum ranges in wavelength from 400 to 700 nm. find the angular width of the first-order spectrum produced by passing white light through a grating marked with 20,000 lines/in. *(Angular width = $\theta_{700} - \theta_{400}$)*

$$d = \frac{1}{20,000 \text{ lines/in.}} = 5.00 \times 10^{-5}\text{ in.}; \quad d = (5 \times 10^{-5}\text{ in.})\left(\frac{1\text{ m}}{39.37\text{ in.}}\right) = 1.27 \times 10^{-6}\text{ m}$$

$$d\sin\theta = n\lambda; \quad \sin\theta_4 = \frac{n\lambda_4}{d} = \frac{(1)(400 \times 10^{-9}\text{ m})}{1.27 \times 10^{-6}\text{ m}}; \quad \theta_4 = 18.4^0$$

$$d\sin\theta = n\lambda; \quad \sin\theta_7 = \frac{n\lambda_7}{d} = \frac{(1)(700 \times 10^{-9}\text{ m})}{1.27 \times 10^{-6}\text{ m}}; \quad \theta_7 = 33.4^0$$

$$\text{Angular width} = 33.4^0 - 18.4^0; \quad \boxed{\Delta\theta = 15.0^0}$$

*37-14. An infrared spectrophotometer uses gratings to disperse infrared light. One grating is ruled with 240 lines/mm. What is the maximum wavelength that can be studied with this grating? *(The maximum dispersion occurs when $\theta = 90^0$ and $\sin\theta = 1$)*

$$d = \frac{1}{240 \text{ lines/mm}} = 4.17 \times 10^{-3}\text{ mm} \quad or \quad d = 4.17 \times 10^{-6}\text{ m}$$

$$\lambda = \frac{d\sin\theta}{1} = \frac{(4.17 \times 10^{-6}\text{m})(1)}{1}; \quad \boxed{\lambda_{max} = 4.17 \text{ } \mu\text{m}}$$

Resolving Power of Instruments

37-15. Light of wavelength 600 nm falls on a circular opening of diameter 0.32 mm. A diffraction pattern forms on a screen 80 cm away. What is the distance from the center of the pattern to the first dark fringe?

$\theta_0 = \frac{R}{f} = \frac{1.22\lambda}{D}$; $R = \frac{1.22\lambda f}{D} = \frac{1.22(600 \times 10^{-9}\,\text{m})(0.80\text{ m})}{0.32 \times 10^{-3}\text{ m}}$; $\boxed{R = 1.83\text{ mm}}$

37-16. The limiting angle of resolution for an objective lens in an optical instrument is 3×10^{-4} rad for a 650 nm light source. What is the diameter of the circular opening?

$\theta_0 = \frac{1.22\lambda}{D}$; $D = \frac{1.22(650 \times 10^{-9}\,\text{m})}{3 \times 10^{-4}\,\text{rad}}$; $\boxed{D = 2.64\text{ mm}}$

37-17. A certain radio telescope has a parabolic reflector that is 70 m in diameter. Radio waves from outer space have a wavelength of 21 cm. Calculate the theoretical limit of resolution for this telescope?

$\theta_0 = \frac{1.22\lambda}{D} = \frac{1.22(0.21\text{ m})}{70\text{ m}}$; $\boxed{\theta_0 = 3.66 \times 10^{-3}\text{ rad}}$

37-18. Using a telescope whose objective lens has a diameter of 60 m, how far apart can two objects be resolved if they are located a distance in space equal to that from the earth to the sun (93 million miles)?

Assume that light is at the central wavelength of 500 nm

$\theta_0 = \frac{1.22\lambda}{D} = \frac{s_0}{p}$; $s_0 = \frac{1.22\lambda p}{D} = \frac{1.22(500 \times 10^{-9}\,\text{m})(9.3 \times 10^{7}\,\text{mi})}{60\text{ m}}$;

$s_0 = 0.946$ mi or $\boxed{4{,}990\text{ ft}}$

37-19. What is the angular limit of resolution of a person's eye when the diameter of the opening is 3 mm? Assume that the wavelength of the light is 500 nm.

$\theta_0 = \frac{1.22\lambda}{D} = \frac{1.22(500 \times 10^{-9}\,\text{m})}{3 \times 10^{-3}\,\text{m}}$; $\boxed{\theta_0 = 2.03 \times 10^{-4}\text{ rad}}$

37-20. At what distance could the eyes of Problem 37-19 resolve wires in a door screen that are separated by 2.5 mm?

$\theta_0 = \frac{s_0}{p}$; $p = \frac{s_0}{\theta_0} = \frac{2.5 \times 10^{-3}\,\text{m}}{2.03 \times 10^{-4}\,\text{rad}}$; $\boxed{p = 12.3\text{ m}}$

Supplementary Problems

37-21. In Young's experiment 600-nm light illuminates a slit located 2.0 m from a screen. The second bright fringe formed on the screen is 5 mm from the central maximum. What is the slit width?

$\frac{yd}{x} = n\lambda$; $d = \frac{n\lambda x}{y} = \frac{2(600 \times 10^{-9}\,\text{m})(2.0\text{ m})}{5 \times 10^{-3}\,\text{m}}$; $\boxed{d = 480\ \mu\text{m}}$

37-22. A transmission grating is ruled with 5000 lines/cm. For light of wavelength 550 nm, what is the angular deviation of the third order bright fringe?

$d = \frac{1}{5000\text{ lines/cm}} = 2.00 \times 10^{-4}$ cm or $d = 2.00 \times 10^{-6}$ m

$d\sin\theta = n\lambda$; $\sin\theta = \frac{n\lambda}{d} = \frac{(3)(550 \times 10^{-9}\,\text{m})}{2.00 \times 10^{-6}\,\text{m}}$; $\boxed{\theta = 55.6^{0}}$

*37-26. Light from a mercury-arc lamp is incident on a diffraction grating ruled with 7000 lines per inch. The spectrum consists of a yellow line (579 nm) and a blue line (436 nm).

Compute the angular separation (in radians) of these lines in the third-order spectrum.

$$d = \frac{1}{7000 \text{ lines/in.}} = 1.43 \times 10^{-4} \text{ in.}; \quad d = (1.43 \times 10^{-4} \text{in.})\left(\frac{1 \text{ m}}{39.37 \text{ in.}}\right) = 3.63 \times 10^{-6} \text{ m}$$

$$d \sin\theta = n\lambda; \quad \sin\theta_y = \frac{n\lambda_y}{d} = \frac{(3)(579 \times 10^{-9} \text{ m})}{3.63 \times 10^{-6} \text{ m}}; \quad \theta_4 = 28.6^0$$

$$d \sin\theta = n\lambda; \quad \sin\theta_b = \frac{n\lambda_b}{d} = \frac{(3)(436 \times 10^{-9} \text{ m})}{3.63 \times 10^{-6} \text{ m}}; \quad \theta_7 = 21.1^0$$

$$\Delta\theta = 28.6^0 - 21.1^0, \quad \boxed{\Delta\theta = 7.48^0}$$

*37-27. A telescope will be used to resolve two points on a mountain 160 km away. If the separation of the points is 2.0 m, what is the minimum diameter for the objective lens?

Assume that the light has an average wavelength of 500 nm.

$$\theta_0 = \frac{1.22\lambda}{D} = \frac{s_0}{p}; \quad D = \frac{1.22\lambda p}{s_0} = \frac{1.22(500 \times 10^{-9} \text{ m})(1.6 \times 10^5 \text{ m})}{2 \text{ m}}; \quad \boxed{D = 4.86 \text{ cm}}$$

37-23. Monochromatic light passes through two slits separated by 0.24 mm. In the pattern formed on a screen 50 cm away, the distance between the first bright fringe of the left of the central maximum and the first fringe on the right is 2.04 mm. What is the wavelength of the light? (*The deviation of the first bright fringe is half of 2.04 mm or 1.02 mm.*)

$$\frac{yd}{x} = n\lambda; \quad \lambda = \frac{yd}{nx} = \frac{(1.02 \times 10^{-3} \text{ m})(0.24 \times 10^{-3} \text{ m})}{(1)(0.50 \text{ m})}; \quad \boxed{\lambda = 490 \text{ nm}}$$

37-24. A transmission grating ruled with 6000 lines/cm forms a second-order bright fringe at an angle of 53° from the central fringe. What is the wavelength of the incident light?

$$d = \frac{1}{6000 \text{ lines/cm}} = 1.67 \times 10^{-4} \text{ cm} \quad or \quad d = 1.67 \times 10^{-6} \text{ m}$$

$$d \sin\theta = n\lambda; \quad \lambda = \frac{d \sin\theta}{n} = \frac{(1.67 \times 10^{-6} \text{ m}) \sin 53^0}{2}; \quad \boxed{\lambda = 667 \text{ nm}}$$

*37-25. If the separation of the two slits in Young's experiment is 0.10 mm and the distance to the screen is 50 cm, find the distance between the first dark fringe and the third bright fringe when the slits are illuminated with light of wavelength 600 nm.

$$Bright: \frac{yd}{x} = n\lambda \quad (n = 1, 2, 3, \ldots) \quad Dark: \frac{yd}{x} = n\frac{\lambda}{2} \quad (n = 1, 3, 5, \ldots)$$

$$\Delta y = y_{B3} - y_{D1} = \frac{(3)\lambda x}{d} - \frac{(1)\lambda x}{2d} = (2.5)\left(\frac{\lambda x}{d}\right);$$

$$\Delta y = \frac{2.5(600 \times 10^{-9} \text{ m})(0.5 \text{ m})}{0.10 \times 10^{-3} \text{ m}}; \quad \boxed{\Delta y = 7.50 \text{ mm}}$$

Critical Thinking Problems

37-28. A Michelson interferometer, as shown in Fig. 37-18, can be used to measure small distance. The beam splitter partially reflects and partially transmits monochromatic light of wavelength λ from the source S. One mirror M_1 is fixed and another M_2 is movable. The light rays reaching the eye from each mirror differ, causing constructive and destructive interference patterns to move across the scope as the mirror M_2 is moved a distance x. Show that this distance is given by

$$x = m\frac{\lambda}{2}$$

where m is the number of dark fringes that cross an indicator line on the scope as the mirror moves a distance x.

The difference in path lengths for each ray of light will be the distance x and back, or $2x$.

Thus, there is constructive interference when:

$$2x = m\lambda \quad m = 0, 1, 2, \ldots$$

$$m = 0, 1, 2, \ldots$$

Thus, $\boxed{x = m\dfrac{\lambda}{2}}$

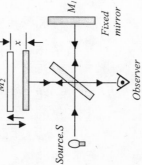

37-29. A Michelson interferometer (see previous problem) is used to measure the advance of a small screw. How far has the screw advanced if krypton-86 light ($\lambda = 606$ nm) is used and 4000 fringes move across the field of view as the screw advances?

$$x = \frac{m\lambda}{2} = \frac{(4000)(606 \times 10^{-9}\,\text{m})}{2}; \quad \boxed{x = 1.21\ \text{mm}}$$

---

*37-30. A diffraction grating has 500 lines/mm ruled on its glass surface. White light passes through the grating and forms several spectra on a screen 1.0 m away. Is the deviation of colors with a grating different than those experienced for prisms? On the screen, what is the distance between the first order blue line (400 nm) and the first order red line (680 nm). How many complete spectra (400-700 nm) are possible for these conditions?

(a) *When white light passes through a prism, the blue light bends more than the red light since the angle of refraction is less for longer wavelengths. (See Fig. 35-8 in text.) The reverse is true for gratings. The longer wavelengths are deviated more.*

(b) $d = \dfrac{1}{500\ \text{lines/mm}} = 2.00 \times 10^{-3}\ \text{mm}; \quad d = 2.00 \times 10^{-6}\ \text{m}$

$d\sin\theta = n\lambda; \quad \sin\theta_r = \dfrac{n\lambda_r}{d} = \dfrac{(1)(680 \times 10^{-9}\,\text{m})}{2.00 \times 10^{-6}\,\text{m}}; \quad \theta_r = 19.9^0$

$d\sin\theta = n\lambda; \quad \sin\theta_b = \dfrac{n\lambda_b}{d} = \dfrac{(1)(400 \times 10^{-9}\,\text{m})}{2.00 \times 10^{-6}\,\text{m}}; \quad \theta_7 = 11.5^0$

$\tan\theta = \dfrac{y}{x}; \quad y = x\tan\theta; \quad \Delta y = y_r - y_b = x\tan\theta_r - x\tan\theta_b$

$\Delta y = (1\,\text{m})\tan 19.9^0 - (1\,\text{m})\tan 11.5^0; \quad \boxed{\Delta y = 15.9\ \text{cm}}$

(c) *The maximum number of complete spectra is found by setting* $\theta = 90^0$ *for red line.*

$d\sin\theta = n\lambda; \quad n = \dfrac{d\sin 90^0}{\lambda} = \dfrac{2.00 \times 10^{-6}\,\text{m}}{700 \times 10^{-9}\,\text{m}}; \quad \boxed{n = 2.86}$

Therefore, only two complete spectra are possible for this grating.

Chapter 38. Modern Physics and the Atom

Relativity

38-1. A spaceship travels past an observer at a speed of 0.85c. A person aboard the space craft observes that it requires 6.0 s for him to walk the length of his cabin. What time would the observer record for the same event? [*Proper time* t_o = 6 s, *relative time t = ?*]

$$\alpha = \frac{v}{c} = \frac{0.85c}{c} = 0.850; \quad t = \frac{t_o}{\sqrt{1-\alpha^2}} = \frac{6.0 \text{ s}}{\sqrt{1-(0.85)^2}}; \quad \boxed{t = 11.4 \text{ s}}$$

38-2. A rocket A moves past a Lab B at a speed of 0.9c. A technician in the lab records 3.50 s for the time of an event which occurs on the rocket. What is the time as reckoned by a person aboard the rocket? [*Proper time* t_o = ?, *relative time t* = 3.50 s]

$$\alpha = \frac{v}{c} = \frac{0.9c}{c} = 0.90; \quad t = \frac{t_o}{\sqrt{1-\alpha^2}}; \quad t_o = t\sqrt{1-\alpha^2}$$

$$t_o = t\sqrt{1-(0.90)^2} = (3.5 \text{ s})\sqrt{1-0.81}; \quad \boxed{t_o = 1.52 \text{ s}}$$

38-3. A blinking light on a spacecraft moves past an observer at 0.75c. The observer records that the light blinks at a frequency of 2.0 Hz. What is the actual frequency of the blinking light? (*It's important to distinguish relative time from relative frequency.*)

Relative frequency is 2.0 blinks per second, which is relative time of 0.5 s/blink

Relative time t = 0.50 s; proper time t_o = ?; $\quad \alpha = \frac{v}{c} = \frac{0.75}{c} = 0.75$

$$t = \frac{t_o}{\sqrt{1-\alpha^2}}; \quad t_o = t\sqrt{1-(0.75)^2} = (0.50 \text{ s})\sqrt{1-0.563}; \quad t_o = 0.331 \text{ s/blink}$$

$$f_o = \frac{1}{t_o} = \frac{1}{0.331 \text{ s}}; \quad \boxed{f_o = 3.02 \text{ Hz}}$$

---

*37-31. The tail lights of an automobile are separated by 1.25 m. Assume that the pupil of a person's eye has a diameter of 5 mm and that the light has an average wavelength of 640 nm. At night, on a long straight highway, how far away can the two tail lights be resolved? Suppose you squint your eyes forming a slit where the limiting angle changes from $\theta_0 = 1.22 \lambda/D$ to $\theta_0 = \lambda/d$. What is the new distance for resolution of the images?

$$\theta_0 = \frac{1.22\lambda}{D} = \frac{s_0}{p}; \quad p = \frac{s_0 D}{1.22\lambda} = \frac{(1.25 \text{ m})(0.005 \text{ m})}{1.22(640 \times 10^{-9}\text{m})}; \quad \boxed{p = 8000 \text{ m}}$$

$$\theta_0 = \frac{\lambda}{d} = \frac{s_0}{p}; \quad p = \frac{s_0 D}{\lambda} = \frac{(1.25 \text{ m})(0.005 \text{ m})}{(640 \times 10^{-9}\text{m})}; \quad \boxed{p = 9765 \text{ m}}$$

**37-32. The intensity of unpolarized light is reduced by one-half when it passes through a polarizer. In the case of the plane-polarized light reaching the analyzer, the intensity I of the transmitted beam is given by

$$I = I_0 \cos^2 \theta$$

where I_0 is the maximum intensity transmitted and θ is the angle through which the analyzer has been rotated. Consider three Polaroid plates stacked so that the axis of each is turned 30^0 with respect to the spreading plate. By what percentage will the incident light be reduced in intensity when it passes through all three plates?

The first plate transmits ½ of the incident light intensity. Each succeeding plate transmits a vector resolution at angle 30^0 *and transmits a fraction,* $\cos 30^0 = 0.866$, *of the amplitude, or* $(\cos 30^0)^2$ *of the intensity. Since* $\cos 30^0 = 0.866$, $(\cos 30^0)^2 = 0.75$.

Thus the intensity of the stack is:

$$(0.5)(0.75)(0.75 = 0.281) \quad \text{or} \quad \boxed{28.1\%}$$

38-4. A particle on a table has a diameter of 2 mm when at rest. What must be the speed of an observer who measures the diameter as 1.69 mm? (*Proper length $L_0 = 2$ mm.*)

$$L = L_0\sqrt{1-\alpha^2}; \quad \frac{L^2}{L_0^2} = (1-\alpha^2); \quad \alpha^2 = 1 - \frac{L^2}{L_0^2} = 1 - \frac{(1.69\text{ mm})^2}{(2.00\text{ mm})^2}; \quad \boxed{v = 0.535c}$$

$$\alpha^2 = 0.286; \quad \alpha = \frac{v}{c} = \sqrt{0.286} = 0.535;$$

38-5. A blue meter stick is aboard ship A and a red meterstick is aboard ship B. If ship A moves past B at 0.85c, what will be the length of each meterstick as reckoned by a person aboard ship A? (*We must be careful to distinguish proper length from relative length.*)

Observer A sees blue stick as proper length L_o and red stick as relative length L.

$$\boxed{L_B = 1.00\text{ m};} \quad L_r = (1.00\text{ m})\sqrt{1-(0.85)^2}; \quad \boxed{L_r = 52.7\text{ cm};}$$

38-6. Three meter sticks travel past an observer at speeds of 0.1c, 0.6c, and 0.9c. What lengths would be recorded by the observer? (*Proper lengths L_o are each 1.00 m*)

$$\frac{0.1c}{c} = 0.1; \quad L_r = (1.00\text{ m})\sqrt{1-(0.1c)^2}; \quad \boxed{L_r = 99.5\text{ cm};}$$

$$\alpha = \frac{0.6c}{c} = 0.6; \quad L_r = (1.00\text{ m})\sqrt{1-(0.6)^2}; \quad \boxed{L_r = 80.0\text{ cm}}$$

$$\alpha = \frac{0.9c}{c} = 0.9; \quad L_r = (1.00\text{ m})\sqrt{1-(0.9)^2}; \quad \boxed{L_r = 43.6\text{ cm};}$$

38-7. What mass is required to run about 1 million 100-W light bulbs for 1 year?

$(1 \times 10^6)(100\text{ W})(86,400\text{ s/d})(356\text{ d/yr}) = 3.154 \times 10^{15}$ J/yr

$$E_o = m_o c^2 = \frac{E_o}{c^2} = \frac{3.154 \times 10^{15}\text{ J}}{(3 \times 10^8\text{ m/s})^2}; \quad \boxed{m_o = 35.0\text{ g}}$$

38-8. Elementary particles called mu-mesons rain down through the atmosphere at 2.97×10^8 m/s. At rest the mu-meson would decay on average 2 μs after it came into existence. What is the lifetime of these particles from the viewpoint of an observer on earth?

$$\alpha = \frac{2.97 \times 10^8\text{m/s}}{3.00 \times 10^8\text{m/s}} = 0.990; \quad t = \frac{t_o}{\sqrt{1-\alpha^2}} = \frac{2.0\ \mu s}{\sqrt{1-(0.99)^2}}; \quad t = 101\ \mu s$$

The Photoelectric Effect

38-9. The first photoelectrons are emitted from a copper surface when the wavelength of incident radiation is 282 nm. What is the threshold frequency for copper? What is the work function for a copper surface?

$$f_o = \frac{c}{\lambda_o} = \frac{(3 \times 10^8\text{m/s})}{282 \times 10^{-9}\text{m/s}}; \quad f_o = 1.06 \times 10^{15}\text{ Hz};$$

$$W = hf_o = (6.63 \times 10^{-34}\text{ J/Hz})(1.06 \times 10^{15}\text{ Hz}); \quad W = 7.028 \times 10^{-19}\text{ J}$$

$$W = 7.03 \times 10^{-19}\text{J}\left(\frac{1\text{ ev}}{1.6 \times 10^{-19}\text{ J}}\right); \quad \boxed{W = 4.40\text{ eV}}$$

38-10. If the photoelectric work function of a material is 4.0 eV, what is the minimum frequency of light required to eject photoelectrons? What is the threshold frequency?

$$W = 4.0\text{ eV}\left(\frac{1.6 \times 10^{-19}\text{ J}}{1\text{ eV}}\right) = 6.40 \times 10^{-19}\text{ J}; \quad W = hf_o$$

$$f_o = \frac{W}{h} = \frac{6.4 \times 10^{-19}\text{ J}}{6.63 \times 10^{-34}\text{ J/Hz}}; \quad \boxed{f_0 = 9.65 \times 10^{14}\text{ Hz}}$$

38-11. The energy E of a photon in joules is found from the product hf. Often we are given the wavelength of light and need to find its energy in electron volts. Show that

$$E = \frac{1240}{\lambda}$$

such that if λ is in nanometers, E will be the energy in electron volts.

$E = \frac{hc}{\lambda}$; $E\lambda = hc = (6.63 \times 10^{-34}\, J/Hz)(3 \times 10^8\, m/s) = 1.99 \times 10^{-25}\, J \cdot m$

$E\lambda = (1.99 \times 10^{-25}\, J \cdot m)\left(\frac{1\, ev}{1.6 \times 10^{-19}\, J}\right)\left(\frac{1\, nm}{1 \times 10^{-9}}\right)$; $E\lambda = 1240\ eV \cdot nm$

When λ is in nm, E will be in J: $\boxed{E = \frac{1240}{\lambda}}$

38-12. Use the equation derived in Problem 38-11 to verify that light of wavelength 490 nm has an energy of 2.53 eV. Also show that a photon whose energy is 2.10 eV has a wavelength of 590 nm.

$E = \frac{1240}{\lambda} = \frac{1240}{490\ nm}$; $\boxed{E = 2.53\ J}$; $\lambda = \frac{1240}{E} = \frac{1240}{2.10\ eV}$; $\boxed{\lambda = 590\ nm}$

*38-13. The threshold frequency for a certain metal is 2.5 x 10^{14} Hz. What is the work function? If light of wavelength 400 nm shines on this surface, what is the kinetic energy of ejected photoelectrons?

$W = hf_o = (6.63 \times 10^{-34}\, J/Hz)(2.5 \times 10^{14}\, Hz)\left(\frac{1\, ev}{1.6 \times 10^{-19}\, J}\right)$; $W = 1.66 \times 10^{-19}\, J$

$W = 1.66 \times 10^{-19}\, J\left(\frac{1\, ev}{1.6 \times 10^{-19}\, J}\right)$; $\boxed{W = 1.04\ eV}$

$E_k = \frac{hc}{\lambda} - W = \frac{(6.63 \times 10^{-34}\, J/Hz)(3 \times 10^8\, m/s)}{400 \times 10^{-9}\, m} - 1.66 \times 10^{-19}\, J$; $E_k = 3.31 \times 10^{-19}\, J$

$E = 3.31 \times 10^{-19}\, J\left(\frac{1\, ev}{1.6 \times 10^{-19}\, J}\right)$; $\boxed{E_k = 2.07\ eV}$

*38-14. When light of frequency 1.6 x 10^{15} Hz strikes a material surface, electrons just begin to leave the surface. What is the maximum kinetic energy of photoelectrons emitted from this surface when illuminated with light of frequency 2.0 x 10^{15} Hz?

$E_k = hf - hf_0 = h(f - f_0)$; $E_k = (6.63 \times 10^{-34}\, J/Hz)(2.0 \times 10^{15}\, Hz - 1.6 \times 10^{15}\, Hz)$;

$E_k = 2.65 \times 10^{-19}\, eV\left(\frac{1\, eV}{1.6 \times 10^{-19}\, J}\right)$; $\boxed{E_k = 1.66\ eV}$

*38-15. The work function of nickel surface is 5.01 eV. If a nickel surface is illuminated by light of wavelength 200 nm, what is the kinetic energy of the ejected electrons?

$E_k = \frac{hc}{\lambda} - W$; $\frac{hc}{\lambda} = \frac{(6.63 \times 10^{-34}\, J/Hz)(3 \times 10^8\, m/s)}{(200 \times 10^{-9}\, m)} = 9.945 \times 10^{-19}\, J = 6.22\ eV$

$E_k = \frac{hc}{\lambda} - W = 6.22\ eV - 5.01\ eV$; $\boxed{E_k = 1.21\ eV}$

*38-16. The stopping potential is a reverse voltage that just stops the electrons from being emitted in a photoelectric application. The stopping potential is therefore equal to the kinetic energy of ejected photoelectrons. Find the stopping potential for Problem 38-13.

The kinetic energy of the emitted electrons in Prob. 38-15 is 3.31 x 10^{-19} J (See above.)

$E_k = qV_s = (1e)V_s$; $V_s = \frac{E_k}{(1e)} = \frac{3.31 \times 10^{-19}\, J}{1.6 \times 10^{-19}\, C}$; $\boxed{V_s = 2.07\ V}$

Waves and Particles

38-17. What is the de Broglie wavelength of a proton (m = 1.67 x 10^{-27} kg) when it is moving with a speed of 2 x 10^7 m/s?

$\lambda = \frac{h}{mv} = \frac{(6.63 \times 10^{-34}\, J/Hz)}{(1.67 \times 10^{-27}\, kg)(2 \times 10^7\, m/s)}$; $\boxed{\lambda = 1.99 \times 10^{-14}\, m}$

38-18. The de Broglie wavelength of a particle is 3×10^{-14} m. What is its momentum?

$$mv = \frac{h}{\lambda} = \frac{6.63 \times 10^{-34} \text{ J/Hz}}{3 \times 10^{-14} \text{ m}}; \quad mv = p; \quad \boxed{p = 2.21 \times 10^{-20} \text{ kg m/s}}$$

38-19. Recalling formulas for kinetic energy and momentum, show that for non-relativistic speeds, the momentum of a particle can be found from

$$p = \sqrt{2mE_k}$$

where E_k is the kinetic energy and m is the mass of the particle.

$$p = mv; \quad v = \frac{p}{m}; \quad E_k = \frac{mv^2}{2} = \frac{m}{2}\left(\frac{p}{m}\right)^2 = \frac{p^2}{2m}; \quad \boxed{p = \sqrt{2mE_k}}$$

*38-20. Determine the kinetic energy of an electron if its de Broglie wavelength is 2×10^{-11} m.

$$\lambda = \frac{h}{mv}; \quad v = \frac{h}{m\lambda} = \frac{6.63 \times 10^{-34} \text{ J/Hz}}{(9.1 \times 10^{-31} \text{kg})(2 \times 10^{-11} \text{ m})}; \quad v = 3.64 \times 10^7 \text{ m/s}$$

Since $v \ll c$, we consider v to be nonrelativistic,

$$E_k = \tfrac{1}{2}mv^2 = \tfrac{1}{2}(9.1 \times 10^{-31} \text{ kg})(3.64 \times 10^7 \text{ m/s})^2; \quad \boxed{E_k = 6.03 \times 10^{-16} \text{ J}}$$

If we consider effects of relativity,

$$E_k = (m - m_o)c^2 = \left(\frac{m_o}{\sqrt{1-\alpha^2}} - m_o\right)c^2 = 6.10 \times 10^{-16} \text{ J}$$

So you can see that that the nonrelativistic value is not much off the mark.

*38-21. What is the de Broglie wavelength of the waves associated with an electron that has been accelerated through a potential difference of 160 V? *(See Prob. 38-21)*

$$p = \sqrt{2mE_k} = \sqrt{2m(qV)}; \quad p = \sqrt{2(9.1 \times 10^{-31} \text{kg})(1.6 \times 10^{-19} C)(160 \text{ V})}$$

$$p = 6.83 \times 10^{-24} \text{kg} \cdot \text{m/s}; \quad \lambda = \frac{h}{p} = \frac{6.63 \times 10^{-34} \text{J/Hz}}{6.83 \times 10^{-24} \text{kg} \cdot \text{m/s}}; \quad \boxed{\lambda = 9.71 \times 10^{-11} \text{ m}}$$

*38-22. The charge on a proton is $+1.6 \times 10^{-19}$ C and its rest mass is 1.67×10^{27} kg. What is the de Broglie wavelength of a proton if it is accelerated from rest through a potential difference of 500 V?

$$p = \sqrt{2mE_k} = \sqrt{2m(qV)}; \quad p = \sqrt{2(1.67 \times 10^{-27} \text{kg})(1.6 \times 10^{-19} C)(500 \text{ V})}$$

$$\lambda = \frac{h}{p} = \frac{6.63 \times 10^{-34} \text{J/Hz}}{5.17 \times 10^{-22} \text{kg} \cdot \text{m/s}}; \quad \boxed{\lambda = 1.28 \text{ pm}}$$

$$p = 5.17 \times 10^{-22} \text{kg} \cdot \text{m/s}$$

Atomic Spectra and Energy Levels

38-23. Determine the wavelength of the first three spectral lines of atomic hydrogen in the Balmer series. *(For the Balmer series, n = 2. The first three lines come for $n_i = 3$, 4, and 5.)*

$$\frac{1}{\lambda} = R\left(\frac{1}{2^2} - \frac{1}{n_i^2}\right); \quad (n_i = 3, 4, \text{ and } 5)$$

(a) $\frac{1}{\lambda} = (1.097 \times 10^7 \text{ m}^{-1})\left(\frac{1}{4} - \frac{1}{3^2}\right); \quad \lambda = 656.3 \text{ nm} \quad (n_i = 3)$

(b) $\frac{1}{\lambda} = (1.097 \times 10^7 \text{ m}^{-1})\left(\frac{1}{4} - \frac{1}{4^2}\right); \quad \lambda = 486.2 \text{ nm} \quad (n_i = 4)$

(c) $\frac{1}{\lambda} = (1.097 \times 10^7 \text{ m}^{-1})\left(\frac{1}{4} - \frac{1}{5^2}\right); \quad \lambda = 434.1 \text{ nm} \quad (n_i = 5)$

38-24. Find the wavelengths of the first three lines of atomic hydrogen in the Paschen series.

(a) $\frac{1}{\lambda} = (1.097 \times 10^7 \text{ m}^{-1})\left(\frac{1}{9} - \frac{1}{4^2}\right); \quad \lambda = 1887 \text{ nm} \quad (n_i = 4)$

(b) $\frac{1}{\lambda} = (1.097 \times 10^7 \text{ m}^{-1})\left(\frac{1}{9} - \frac{1}{5^2}\right); \quad \lambda = 1290 \text{ nm} \quad (n_i = 5)$

(c) $\frac{1}{\lambda} = (1.097 \times 10^7 \text{ m}^{-1})\left(\frac{1}{9} - \frac{1}{6^2}\right); \quad \lambda = 1101 \text{ nm} \quad (n_i = 6)$

38-25. Determine the radius of the n = 4 Bohr level of the classical Bohr hydrogen atom.

$$r = \frac{n^2 \varepsilon_0 h^2}{\pi m e^2} = \frac{(4)^2(8.85 \times 10^{-12} C^2/N \cdot m^2)(6.63 \times 10^{-34} J/Hz)^2}{\pi(9.1 \times 10^{-34} J/Hz)(1.6 \times 10^{-19}C)^2}; \quad \boxed{r = 847 \text{ pm}}$$

38-26. What is the classical radius of the first Bohr orbit in the hydrogen atom?

$$r = \frac{n^2 \varepsilon_0 h^2}{\pi m e^2} = \frac{(1)^2(8.85 \times 10^{-12} C^2/N \cdot m^2)(6.63 \times 10^{-34} J/Hz)^2}{\pi(9.1 \times 10^{-34} J/Hz)(1.6 \times 10^{-19}C)^2}; \quad \boxed{r = 53.2 \text{ pm}}$$

38-27. Determine the wavelength of the photon emitted from a hydrogen atom when the electron jumps from the n = 3 Bohr level to ground level.

$$\frac{1}{\lambda} = R\left(\frac{1}{2^2} - \frac{1}{n_i^2}\right) = (1.097 \times 10^7\, m^{-1})\left(\frac{1}{1^2} - \frac{1}{3^2}\right); \quad \boxed{\lambda = 102.6 \text{ nm}}$$

*38-28. What is the maximum wavelength of an incident photon if it can ionize a hydrogen atom originally in its second excited state (n = 3)?

Ionization Energy: $E_3 = \frac{-13.6 \text{ eV}}{n^2} = \frac{-13.6 \text{ eV}}{3^2}$; $\quad E_3 = 1.511 \text{ eV} = 2.42 \times 10^{-19} J$

$$\lambda = \frac{hc}{E_3} = \frac{(6.63 \times 10^{-34} J/Hz)(3 \times 10^8 m/s)}{2.42 \times 10^{-19} J}; \quad \boxed{\lambda = 823 \text{ nm}}$$

*38-29. What are the shortest and longest possible wavelengths in the Balmer series?

(Since E=hc/λ, the highest energy (greatest n level) is shortest wavelength and vice versa.)

Shortest λ, $n_i = \infty$: $\frac{1}{\lambda} = (1.097 \times 10^7\, m^{-1})\left(\frac{1}{2^2} - \frac{1}{\infty}\right)$; $\quad \boxed{\lambda = 365 \text{ nm}}$

Longest λ, $n_i = 3$: $\frac{1}{\lambda} = (1.097 \times 10^7\, m^{-1})\left(\frac{1}{2^2} - \frac{1}{3^2}\right)$;

Supplementary Problems

38-30. At a cost of 9 cents per kWh, what is the cost of the maximum energy to be released from a 1-kg mass?

$$E_o = m_o c^2 = (1 \text{ kg})(3 \times 10^8 m/s)^2; \quad E_o = 9 \times 10^{16} J$$

$$Cost = \frac{\$0.09}{kWh}\left(\frac{1 \text{ kWh}}{3.6 \times 10^6 J}\right)(9 \times 10^{16} J); \quad \boxed{Cost = 2.25 \times 10^9 \text{ dollars}}$$

38-31. An event that occurs on a spaceship traveling at 0.8c relative to the earth is observed by a person on the ship to last for 3 s. What time would be observed by a person on the earth? How far will the person on earth judge that the spaceship has traveled during this event?

Proper time is 3.0 s. $t = \frac{t_o}{\sqrt{1-\alpha^2}} = \frac{3.0 s}{\sqrt{1-(0.8)^2}}$; $\boxed{t = 5.00 \text{ s}}$

$$s = vt_o = (0.8c)t_o; \quad s = (0.8)(3 \times 10^8 m/s)(5.0 s); \quad \boxed{s = 1.20 \times 10^9 \text{ m}}$$

38-32. When monochromatic light of wavelength 450 nm strikes a cathode, photoelectrons are emitted with a velocity of 4.8 x 10⁵ m/s. What is the work function for the surface in electronvolts? What is the threshold frequency?

$$E_k = \tfrac{1}{2}mv^2 = \tfrac{1}{2}(9.1 \times 10^{-31} kg)(4.8 \times 10^5 m/s)^2; \quad E_k = 1.05 \times 10^{-19} J$$

$$W = \frac{hc}{\lambda} - E_k = \frac{(6.63 \times 10^{-34} J/Hz)(3 \times 10^8 m/s)}{450 \times 10^{-9} m} - 1.05 \times 10^{-19} J; \quad \boxed{W = 3.37 \times 10^{-19} J}$$

$$W = hf_0; \quad f_0 = \frac{W}{h} = \frac{3.37 \times 10^{-19} J}{(6.63 \times 10^{-34} J/Hz)}; \quad \boxed{f_0 = 5.09 \times 10^{14} \text{ Hz}}$$

In terms of electron-volts: $E_k = 0.656 \text{ eV}$; $W = 3.18 \text{ eV}$

38-33. In the hydrogen atom an electron falls from the n = 5 level to the n = 2 level and emits a photon in the Balmer series. What is the wavelength and energy of the emitted light?

$$\frac{1}{\lambda} = (1.097 \times 10^7\,m^{-1})\left(\frac{1}{2^2} - \frac{1}{5^2}\right); \qquad \boxed{\lambda = 434\,nm}$$

$$E = \frac{hc}{\lambda} = \frac{(6.63 \times 10^{-34}\,J/Hz)(3 \times 10^8\,m/s)}{434 \times 10^{-9}\,m}; \qquad \boxed{E = 4.58 \times 10^{-19}\,J\ \text{or}\ 2.86\,eV}$$

38-34. Calculate the frequency and the wavelength of the Hβ line of the Balmer series. The transition is from the n = 4 level of the Bohr atom.

$$\frac{1}{\lambda} = (1.097 \times 10^7\,m^{-1})\left(\frac{1}{2^2} - \frac{1}{4^2}\right); \qquad \boxed{\lambda = 486.2\,nm} \qquad (n_i = 4)$$

$$f = \frac{c}{\lambda} = \frac{(3 \times 10^8\,m/s)}{486 \times 10^{-9}\,m}; \qquad \boxed{f = 6.17 \times 10^{14}\,Hz}$$

38-35. A spaceship A travels past another ship B with a relative velocity of 0.2c. Observer B determines that it takes a person on ship A exactly 3.96 s to perform a task. What time will be measured for the same event by observer A? *(Event happens aboard A)*

Observer A records proper time t_o; Observer B records relative time t = 3.96 s.

$$t = \frac{t_o}{\sqrt{1-\alpha^2}}; \qquad t_o = t\sqrt{1-(0.20)^2} = (3.96\,s)\sqrt{1-0.04}; \qquad \boxed{t_o = 3.88\,s}$$

*38-36. The rest mass of an electron is 9.1×10^{-31} kg. What is the relativistic mass of an electron traveling at a speed of 2×10^8 m/s? What is the total energy of the electron? What is its relativistic kinetic energy?

$$\alpha = \frac{2 \times 10^8\,m/s}{3 \times 10^8\,m/s} = 0.667; \qquad m = \frac{m_0}{\sqrt{1-\alpha^2}} = \frac{1\,kg}{\sqrt{1-(0.667)^2}}; \qquad \boxed{m = 16.4 \times 10^{-31}\,kg}$$

---

*38-36. (Cont.) $E = mc^2 = (16.4 \times 10^{-31}\,kg)(3 \times 10^8\,m/s)^2$; $\boxed{E = 1.47 \times 10^{-13}\,J}$

$E_k = (m - m_0)c^2$; $E_k = (16.4 \times 10^{-31}\,kg - 9.1 \times 10^{-31}\,kg)(3 \times 10^8\,m/s)^2$;

$$\boxed{E_k = 6.57 \times 10^{-14}\,J}$$

*38-37. What is the de Broglie wavelength of an electron whose kinetic energy is 50 MeV?

$$E_k = 50\,MeV\left(\frac{1.6 \times 10^{-13}\,J}{1\,MeV}\right) = 8.00 \times 10^{-12}\,J; \quad E_k = \tfrac{1}{2}mv^2; \quad v = \frac{p}{m}$$

$$E_k = \tfrac{1}{2}m\left(\frac{p}{m}\right)^2; \quad p = \sqrt{2mE_k} = \sqrt{2(9.1 \times 10^{-31}\,kg)(8 \times 10^{-12}\,J)};$$

$$p = 3.82 \times 10^{-21}\,kg \cdot m/s; \quad \lambda = \frac{h}{p} = \frac{6.63 \times 10^{-34}\,J/Hz}{3.82 \times 10^{-21}\,kg \cdot m/s}; \quad \boxed{\lambda = 0.174\,pm}$$

*38-38. The rest mass of a proton is 1.67×10^{-27} kg. What is the total energy of a proton that has been accelerated to a velocity of 2.5×10^8 m/s? What is its relativistic kinetic energy?

$$\alpha = \frac{2 \times 10^8\,m/s}{3 \times 10^8\,m/s} = 0.667; \qquad \alpha = \frac{2 \times 10^8\,m/s}{3 \times 10^8\,m/s} = 0.833;$$

$$E = \frac{m_oc^2}{\sqrt{1-(0.833)^2}} = \frac{(1.67 \times 10^{-27}\,kg)(3 \times 10^8\,m/s)^2}{0.553}; \qquad E = 2.72 \times 10^{-10}\,J$$

$$E_k = E - m_oc^2; \qquad E_k = 2.72 \times 10^{-10}\,J - (1.67 \times 10^{-27}\,kg)(3 \times 10^8\,m/s)^2;$$

$$\boxed{E_k = 1.22 \times 10^{-10}\,J}$$

*38-39. Compute the mass and the speed of protons having a relativistic kinetic energy of 235 MeV. The rest mass of a proton is 1.67×10^{-27} kg.

$$E_k = 235\,MeV\left(\frac{1.6 \times 10^{-13}\,J}{1\,MeV}\right) = 3.76 \times 10^{-11}\,J; \qquad E_k = mc^2 - m_oc^2; \qquad m = \frac{E_k}{c^2} + m_0$$

$$m = \frac{3.76 \times 10^{-11}\,J}{(3 \times 10^8\,m/s)^2} + 1.67 \times 10^{-27}\,kg; \qquad \boxed{m = 2.09 \times 10^{-27}\,kg}$$

*38-41. A particle of mass m is traveling at 0.9c. By what factor is its relativistic kinetic energy greater than its Newtonian kinetic energy? (*First ignore effects of relativity*)

$$E_k = \tfrac{1}{2}m_0v^2 = \tfrac{1}{2}m_0(0.9c)^2; \quad E_k = 0.405m_0c^2 \quad \textit{Now with relativity:}$$

$$\alpha^2 = \left(\frac{0.9c}{c}\right)^2 = 0.81; \quad E_k = \frac{m_0c^2}{\sqrt{1-0.81}} - m_0c^2 = 2.294m_0c^2 - m_0c^2; \quad E_k = 1.294m_0c^2$$

$$ratio = \frac{E_{rel}}{E_0} = \frac{1.294m_0c^2}{0.405m_0c^2}; \quad \boxed{ratio = 3.20}$$

*38-42. What is the momentum of a 40-eV photon? What is the wavelength of an electron with the same momentum as this photon?

$$E = pc; \quad p = \frac{E}{c} = \frac{(40\text{ eV})(1.6 \times 10^{-19}\text{ J/eV})}{(3 \times 10^8\text{ m/s})}; \quad \boxed{p = 2.13 \times 10^{-26}\text{ kg}\cdot\text{m/s}}$$

$$\lambda = \frac{h}{p} = \frac{(6.63 \times 10^{-34}\text{ J/Hz})}{2.13 \times 10^{-26}\text{ kg}\cdot\text{m/s}}; \quad \boxed{\lambda = 31.1\text{ nm}}$$

*38-43. When monochromatic light of wavelength 410 nm strikes a cathode, photoelectrons are emitted with a velocity of 4.0×10^5 m/s. What is the work function for the surface and what is the threshold frequency?

$$E_k = \tfrac{1}{2}mv^2 = \tfrac{1}{2}(9.1 \times 10^{-31}\text{ kg})(4 \times 10^5\text{ m/s})^2; \quad E_k = 7.28 \times 10^{-20}\text{ J}$$

$$W = \frac{hc}{\lambda} - E_k = \frac{(6.63 \times 10^{-34}\text{ J/Hz})(3 \times 10^8\text{ m/s})}{410 \times 10^9\text{ m}} - 7.28 \times 10^{-20}\text{ J} = 4.12 \times 10^{-19}\text{ J};$$

$$W = 4.12 \times 10^{-19}\left(\frac{1\text{ eV}}{1.6 \times 10^{-19}\text{ J}}\right); \quad \boxed{W = 2.58\text{ eV}}$$

$$W = hf_0; \quad f_0 = \frac{W}{h} = \frac{4.12 \times 10^{-19}\text{ J}}{(6.63 \times 10^{-34}\text{ J/Hz})}; \quad \boxed{f_0 = 6.23 \times 10^{14}\text{ Hz}}$$

---

*38-39. (Cont.) $m = \frac{m_0}{\sqrt{1-\alpha^2}}$; $\sqrt{1-\alpha^2} = \frac{m_0}{m}$; $1-\alpha^2 = \left(\frac{m_0}{m}\right)^2$; $\alpha^2 = 1 - \left(\frac{m_0}{m}\right)^2$

$$\alpha^2 = 1 - \left(\frac{1.67 \times 10^{-27}\text{ kg}}{2.09 \times 10^{-27}\text{ kg}}\right)^2; \quad \alpha = \sqrt{0.362} = 0.601;$$

$$\alpha = \frac{v}{c}; \quad v = \alpha c = (0.601)(3 \times 10^8\text{ m/s}); \quad \boxed{v = 1.80 \times 10^8\text{ m/s}}$$

*38-40. How much work is required to accelerate a 1-kg mass from rest to a speed of 0.1c? How much work is required to accelerate this mass from an initial speed of 0.3c to a final speed of 0.9c? (Use the work-energy theorem.)

Recall that for nonrelativistic speeds: $Work = \tfrac{1}{2}mv_f^2 - \tfrac{1}{2}mv_0^2$

$$Work = \tfrac{1}{2}(1\text{ kg})(0.1c)^2 - 0; \quad \boxed{Work = 4.50 \times 10^{14}\text{ J}}$$

Now, consider the relativistic speeds and final and initial E_k's based on α's:

$$\alpha_f = \frac{v_f}{c}; \quad E_{kf} = \frac{m_0c^2}{\sqrt{1-\alpha_f^2}} - m_0c^2; \quad \alpha_0 = \frac{v_0}{c}; \quad E_{k0} = \frac{m_0c^2}{\sqrt{1-\alpha_0^2}} - m_0c^2;$$

$$Work = \Delta E_k = \left(\frac{m_0c^2}{\sqrt{1-\alpha_f^2}} - m_0c^2\right) - \left(\frac{m_0c^2}{\sqrt{1-\alpha_0^2}} - m_0c^2\right)$$

$$Work = E_f - E_0 \text{ eliminates } m_0c^2 \text{ terms: } \Delta E_k = \frac{m_0c^2}{\sqrt{1-\alpha_f^2}} - \frac{m_0c^2}{\sqrt{1-\alpha_0^2}}$$

$$\frac{v_f}{c} = \frac{0.9c}{c} = 0.9; \quad \alpha_f^2 = 0.81; \quad \frac{v_0}{c} = \frac{0.3c}{c} = 0.3; \quad \alpha_0^2 = 0.09$$

$$\Delta E_k = \frac{m_0c^2}{\sqrt{1-0.81}} - \frac{m_0c^2}{\sqrt{1-0.09}} = 2.294m_0c^2 - 1.05m_0c^2; \quad \Delta E_k = 1.25m_0c^2$$

$$\Delta E_k = 1.25m_0c^2 = 1.25(1\text{ kg})(3 \times 10^8\text{ m/s})^2; \quad \boxed{Work = \Delta E_k = 1.12 \times 10^{17}\text{ J}}$$

Critical Thinking Problems

38-47. A blue spacecraft is traveling at 0.8c relative to a red spacecraft. On the blue ship, a person moves a blue block a distance of 8 m in 3.0 s. On the red ship, a person moves a red block a distance of 4 m in 2.0 s. (a) What are the measurements of these four parameters from the viewpoint of the person on the blue ship? (b) What are the same measurements from the perspective of a person on the red ship? [$\alpha = 0.8c/c = 0.800$]

For person on blue craft, all blue measurements are proper and red values are relative:

$L_b = 8.00$ m; $\quad t_b = 3.00$s; $\quad L_r = L_{or}\sqrt{1-(0.8)^2} = (4 \text{ m})(0.6)$; $\quad \boxed{L_r = 2.40 \text{ m}}$

$t_r = \frac{t_{or}}{\sqrt{1-(0.8)^2}} = \frac{2.0 \text{ s}}{0.6}$; $\quad \boxed{t_r = 3.33 \text{ s}}$

For person on red craft, all red measurements are proper and blue values are relative:

$L_r = 4.00$ m; $\quad t_r = 2.00$s; $\quad L_b = L_{ob}\sqrt{1-(0.8)^2} = (8 \text{ m})(0.6)$; $\quad \boxed{L_b = 4.80 \text{ m}}$

$t_b = \frac{t_{ob}}{\sqrt{1-(0.8)^2}} = \frac{3.0 \text{ s}}{0.6}$; $\quad \boxed{t_b = 5.00 \text{ s}}$

*38-48. Use the work-energy theorem to compare the work required to change relativistic speeds with the values obtained from Newtonian physics. (a) The speed of a 1 kg mass changes from 0.1c to 0.2c? (b) The speed changes from 0.7c to 0.8c?

$Newtonian work = \Delta E_k = \frac{1}{2}mv_v^2 - \frac{1}{2}mv_0^2$ $\qquad$ (See Problem 38-40)

$Relativistic work = \Delta E_k = \frac{m_oc^2}{\sqrt{1-\alpha_f^2}} - \frac{m_oc^2}{\sqrt{1-\alpha_0^2}}$; $\qquad$ (See Problem 38-40)

(a) $Newtonian Work = \frac{1}{2}(1 \text{ kg})(0.2c)^2 - \frac{1}{2}(1 \text{ kg})(0.1c)^2$ $\quad \boxed{Newtonian Work = 1.35 \times 10^{15} \text{ J}}$

---

*38-44. What is the velocity of a neutron (m = 1.675 x 10^-27 kg) that has a de Broglie wavelength of 0.1 nm. What is its kinetic energy in electronvolts?

$\lambda = \frac{h}{mv}$; $\quad v = \frac{h}{m\lambda} = \frac{(6.63 \times 10^{-34} \text{ J/Hz})}{(1.675 \times 10^{-27} \text{ kg})(0.1 \times 10^{-9} \text{ m})}$; $\quad \boxed{v = 3960 \text{ m/s}}$

$E_k = \frac{1}{2}(1.675 \times 10^{-27} \text{ kg})(3960 \text{ m/s})^2$; $\quad \boxed{E_k = 1.31 \times 10^{-20} \text{ J}}$

**38-45. What is the velocity of a particle whose relativistic kinetic energy is twice its rest mass energy? [*Note: The conditions are that $E_k(rel.) = 2m_oc^2$*]

$(m - m_o)c^2 = 2m_oc^2$; $\quad mc^2 - m_oc^2 = 2m_oc^2$; $\quad mc^2 = 3m_oc^2$; $\quad m = 3m_o$

$\frac{m_o}{\sqrt{1-\alpha^2}} = 3m_0$; $\quad \sqrt{1-\alpha^2} = \frac{1}{3}$; $\quad 1-\alpha^2 = \frac{1}{9}$; $\quad \alpha^2 = 1-0.111$;

$\alpha = \frac{v}{c} = \sqrt{0.889}$; $\quad v = 0.943c$; $\quad \boxed{v = 2.83 \times 10^8 \text{ m/s}}$

**38-46. Compute the relativistic mass and the speed of electrons having a relativistic kinetic energy of 1.2 MeV.

$E_k = 1.20$ MeV $\left(\frac{1.6 \times 10^{-13} \text{ J}}{1 \text{ MeV}}\right) = 1.92 \times 10^{-13}$ J; $\quad E_k = mc^2 - m_oc^2$; $\quad m = \frac{E_k + m_o}{c^2}$

$m = \frac{1.92 \times 10^{-13} \text{ J}}{(3 \times 10^8 \text{ m/s})^2} + 9.1 \times 10^{-31} \text{ kg}$; $\quad \boxed{m = 3.04 \times 10^{-30} \text{ kg}}$

$m = \frac{m_0}{\sqrt{1-\alpha^2}}$; $\quad \sqrt{1-\alpha^2} = \frac{m_0}{m}$; $\quad 1-\alpha^2 = \left(\frac{m_0}{m}\right)^2$; $\quad \alpha^2 = 1-\left(\frac{m_0}{m}\right)^2$

$\alpha^2 = 1-\left(\frac{9.1 \times 10^{-31} \text{ kg}}{3.04 \times 10^{-30} \text{ kg}}\right)^2$; $\quad \alpha = \sqrt{0.910} = 0.954$;

$\alpha = \frac{v}{c}$; $\quad v = \alpha c = (0.954)(3 \times 10^8 \text{ m/s})$; $\quad \boxed{v = 2.86 \times 10^8 \text{ m/s}}$

*38-48. (Cont.) Relativistic work: $\alpha_f = \dfrac{v_f}{c} = \dfrac{0.2c}{c}$; $\alpha_f^2 = 0.04$; $\alpha_o = \dfrac{v_0}{c} = \dfrac{0.1c}{c}$; $\alpha_o^2 = 0.01$

$$\Delta E_k = \frac{m_0 c^2}{\sqrt{1-\alpha_f^2}} - \frac{m_0 c^2}{\sqrt{1-\alpha_o^2}} = \frac{m_0 c^2}{\sqrt{1-0.04}} - \frac{m_0 c^2}{\sqrt{1-0.01}}; \quad Work = 0.0156 m_0 c^2$$

$\boxed{\text{Relativistic Work} = 1.40 \times 10^{15} \text{ J}; \quad \text{Newtonian Work} = 1.35 \times 10^{15} \text{ J}}$

(b) Newtonian Work $= \frac{1}{2}(1 \text{ kg})(0.8c)^2 - \frac{1}{2}(1 \text{ kg})(0.7c)^2$ Newtonian Work $= 6.75 \times 10^{15}$ J

Relativistic work: $\alpha_f = \dfrac{v_f}{c} = \dfrac{0.8c}{c}$; $\alpha_f^2 = 0.64$; $\alpha_o = \dfrac{v_0}{c} = \dfrac{0.7c}{c}$; $\alpha_o^2 = 0.49$

$$\Delta E_k = \frac{m_0 c^2}{\sqrt{1-\alpha_f^2}} - \frac{m_0 c^2}{\sqrt{1-\alpha_o^2}} = \frac{m_0 c^2}{\sqrt{1-0.64}} - \frac{m_0 c^2}{\sqrt{1-0.49}}; \quad Work = 0.266 m_0 c^2$$

$\boxed{\text{Relativistic Work} = 24.0 \times 10^{15} \text{ J}; \quad \text{Newtonian Work} = 6.75 \times 10^{15} \text{ J}}$

*38-49. An electron in the hydrogen atom drops from the n = 5 level to the n = 1 level. What are the frequency, wavelength, and energy of the emitted photon. How much energy must be absorbed by the atom in order to kick the electron back up to the fifth level?

$$\frac{1}{\lambda} = (1.097 \times 10^7 \text{m}^{-1})\left(\frac{1}{1^2} - \frac{1}{5^2}\right); \quad \boxed{\lambda = 95.0 \text{ nm}}$$

$$f = \frac{c}{\lambda} = \frac{(3 \times 10^8 \text{m/s})}{95.0 \times 10^{-9} \text{ m}}; \quad \boxed{f = 3.16 \times 10^{15} \text{ Hz}}$$

$E = hf = (6.63 \times 10^{-34} \text{ J/Hz})(3.16 \times 10^{15} \text{Hz})$; $\boxed{E = 2.09 \times 10^{-18} \text{ J or } 13.1 \text{ eV}}$

$\boxed{\textit{The series that has } n = 1 \textit{ as its final level is: Lyman Series:}}$

The energy absorbed must be the same: $\boxed{E_{abs} = 2.09 \times 10^{-18} \text{ J or } 13.1 \text{ eV}}$

*38-50. In a photoelectric experiment shown as Fig. 38-15, a source of emf is connected in series with a galvanometer G. Light falling on the metal cathode produces photoelectrons. The source of emf is biased against the flow of electrons, retarding their motion. The potential difference V_0 just sufficient to stop the most energetic photoelectrons is called the stopping potential. Assume that a surface is illuminated with light of wavelength 450 nm. causing electrons to be ejected from the surface at a maximum speed of 6 x 10⁵ m/s.

What is the work function for the surface and what is the stopping potential?

(a) $E_k = \frac{1}{2}mv^2 = \frac{1}{2}(9.1 \times 10^{-31} \text{ kg})(6 \times 10^5 \text{ m/s})^2$; $E_k = 1.64 \times 10^{-19}$ J or 1.02 eV

$$W = \frac{hc}{\lambda} - E_k = \frac{(6.63 \times 10^{-34} \text{ J/Hz})(3 \times 10^8 \text{m/s})}{450 \times 10^{-9} \text{ m}} - 1.64 \times 10^{-19} \text{ J}; \quad W = 2.78 \times 10^{-19} \text{ J}$$

(b) The stopping potential must provide energy equal to $(1e)V_0 = E_k$:

$$V_0 = \frac{1.64 \times 10^{-19} \text{ J}}{1.6 \times 10^{-19} \text{ J/V}} = 1.02 \text{ V}; \quad \boxed{V_0 = 1.02 \text{ V}}$$

*38-51. In a photoelectric experiment, 400-nm light falls on a certain metal, and photoelectrons are emitted. The potential required to stop the flow of electrons is 0.20 V. What is the energy of the incident photons? What is the work function? What is the threshold frequency?

$Work = \Delta E_k = \frac{1}{2}mv^2$; $\Delta E_k = qV = (1e)V$ So that $E_k = eV_o$

$E_k = eV_o = hf - W$; where V_o is stopping potential

$$E = \frac{hc}{\lambda} = \frac{(6.63 \times 10^{-34} \text{ J/Hz})(3 \times 10^8 \text{m/s})}{400 \times 10^{-9} \text{ m}} = 4.97 \times 10^{-19} \text{ J}; \quad \boxed{E = 3.11 \text{ eV}}$$

$W = E - eV = 3.11 \text{ eV} - 0.20 \text{ eV}$; $\boxed{W = 2.91 \text{ eV}}$

$$f_0 = \frac{W}{h} = \frac{(2.91 \text{ eV})(1.6 \times 10^{-19} \text{J/eV})}{(6.63 \times 10^{-34} \text{J/Hz})}; \quad \boxed{f_o = 7.02 \times 10^{14} \text{ Hz}}$$

Chapter 39. Nuclear Physics and the Nucleus

The Elements

39-1. How many neutrons are in the nucleus of $^{208}_{82}$Pb? How many protons? What is the ratio N/Z? (*N is the number of neutrons and Z is the number of protons.*)

$A = N + Z$; $\boxed{N = A - Z = 126 \text{ neutrons}}$; $\boxed{Z = 82 \text{ protons}}$; $\boxed{\dfrac{A}{Z} = 1.54}$

39-2. The nucleus of a certain isotope contains 143 neutrons and 92 protons. Write the symbol for this nucleus.

$A = N + Z = 143 + 92 = 235$; $Z = 92$: $\boxed{^{235}_{92}U}$

39-3. From a stability curve it is determined that the ratio of neutrons to protons for a cesium nucleus is 1.49. What is the mass number for this isotope of cesium?

$Z = 55$; $\dfrac{N}{Z} = 1.49$; $N = 1.49(55) = 81.95$; $A = N + Z$; $\boxed{A = 137}$

39-4. Most nuclei are nearly spherical in shape and have a radius that may be approximated by

$$r = r_0 A^{\frac{1}{3}} \qquad r_0 = 1.2 \times 10^{-15} \text{ m}$$

What is the approximate radius of the nucleus of a gold atom $^{197}_{79}$Au?

$r = (1.2 \times 10^{-15} \text{ m})\sqrt[3]{197} = 6.98 \times 10^{-15} \text{ m}$; $\boxed{r = 6.98 \times 10^{-15} \text{ m}}$

39-5. Study Table 39-4 for information on the several nuclides. Determine the ratio of N/Z for the following nuclides: Beryllium-9, Copper-64, and Radium 224.

Beryllium: $A = 9$; $Z = 4$; $N = 9 - 4 = 5$; $\dfrac{N}{Z} = 1.25$

39-5. (Cont.) *Copper*: $A = 64$; $Z = 29$; $N = 64 - 29 = 35$; $\boxed{\dfrac{N}{Z} = 1.21}$

Radium: $A = 224$; $Z = 88$; $N = 224 - 88 = 136$; $\boxed{\dfrac{N}{Z} = 1.55}$

The Atomic Mass Unit

39-6. Find the mass in grams of a gold particle containing two million atomic mass units?

$m = 2 \times 10^6 \text{u} \left(\dfrac{1.66 \times 10^{-27} \text{kg}}{1.00 \text{ u}} \right)$; $\boxed{m = 3.32 \times 10^{-21} \text{ kg}}$

39-7. Find the mass of a 2-kg copper cylinder in atomic mass units? In MeV? In joules?

$m = 2 \text{ kg} \left(\dfrac{1 \text{ u}}{1.6606 \times 10^{-27} \text{kg}} \right)$; $\boxed{m = 1.20 \times 10^{27} \text{ u}}$

$m = 1.204 \times 10^{27} \text{ u} \left(\dfrac{931 \text{MeV}}{1 \text{ u}} \right)$; $\boxed{m = 1.12 \times 10^{30} \text{ MeV}}$

$m = 1.12 \times 10^{30} \text{ MeV} \left(\dfrac{1.6 \times 10^{-13} \text{J}}{1 \text{MeV}} \right)$; $\boxed{m = 1.79 \times 10^{17} \text{ J}}$

39-8. A certain nuclear reaction releases an energy of 5.5 MeV. How much mass (in atomic mass units) is required to produce this energy?

$m = 5.5 \text{ MeV} \left(\dfrac{1 \text{ u}}{931 \text{ MeV}} \right)$; $\boxed{m = 0.00591 \text{ u}}$

39-9. The periodic table gives the average mass of a silver atom as 107.842 u. What is the average mass of the silver nucleus? (*Recall that* $m_e = 0.00055$ u)

For silver, Z = 47. Thus, the nuclear mass is reduced by the mass of 47 electrons.

$m = 107.842 \text{ u} - 47(0.00055 \text{ u})$; $\boxed{m = 107.816 \text{ u}}$

*39-10. Consider the mass spectrometer as illustrated by Fig. 39-3. A uniform magnetic field of 0.6 T is placed across both upper and lower sections of the spectrometer., and the electric field in the velocity selector is 120 V/m. A singly charged neon atom (+1.6 x 10⁻¹⁹ C) of mass 19.992 u passes through the velocity selector and into the spectrometer. What is the velocity of the neon atom as it emerges from the velocity selector?

$v = \dfrac{E}{B} = \dfrac{120,000 \text{ V/m}}{0.6 \text{ T}}$; $\boxed{v = 2 \times 10^5 \text{ m/s}}$

*39-11. What is the radius of the circular path followed by the neon atom of Problem 39-10?

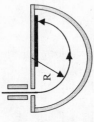

B = 0.6 T into paper

$m = 19.992 \text{ u} \left(\dfrac{1.66 \times 10^{-27} \text{ kg}}{1 \text{ u}}\right) = 3.32 \times 10^{-26} \text{ kg}$

$\dfrac{mv^2}{R} = qvB$; $R = \dfrac{mv}{qB}$; $R = \dfrac{(3.32 \times 10^{-27} \text{ kg})(2 \times 10^5 \text{ m/s})}{(1.6 \times 10^{-19} \text{ C})(0.600 \text{ T})}$; $\boxed{R = 6.92 \text{ cm}}$

Mass Defects and Binding Energy
(Refer to Table 39-4 for Nuclidic Masses.)

*39-12. Calculate the mass defect and binding energy for the neon-20 atom $^{20}_{10}$Ne.

$m_D = [(Zm_H + Nm_n)] - M = [10(1.007825 \text{ u}) + 10(1.008665 \text{ u})] - 19.99244 \text{ u}$

$m_D = 20.016490 \text{ u} - 19.99244 \text{ u}$; $\boxed{m_D = 0.17246 \text{ u}}$

$E = m_D c^2 = (0.17246 \text{ u})\left(\dfrac{931 \text{ MeV}}{1 \text{ u}}\right) = 160.6 \text{ MeV}$; $\boxed{E = 161 \text{ MeV}}$

*39-13. Calculate the binding energy and the binding energy per nucleon for tritium $^3_1$H. How much energy in joules is required to tear the nucleus apart into its constituent nucleons?

$m_D = [(Zm_H + Nm_n)] - M = [1(1.007825 \text{ u}) + 2(1.008665 \text{ u})] - 3.016049 \text{ u}$

39-13. (Cont.) $m_D = 0.009106$ u; $E = m_D c^2 = (0.009106 \text{ u})\left(\dfrac{931 \text{ MeV}}{1 \text{ u}}\right) = 8.48 \text{ MeV}$

$\boxed{E = 8.48 \text{ MeV}}$; $\dfrac{E_B}{A} = \dfrac{8.48 \text{ MeV}}{3}$; $\boxed{\dfrac{E_B}{A} = 2.83 \text{ MeV/nucleon}}$

Energy to tear apart: $E_B = 8.48 \text{ MeV}(1.6 \times 10^{-13} \text{ J/MeV}) = \boxed{1.36 \times 10^{-12} \text{ J}}$

*39-14. Calculate the mass defect of $^7_3$Li. What is the binding energy per nucleon?

$m_D = [(Zm_H + Nm_n)] - M = [3(1.007825 \text{ u}) + 4(1.008665 \text{ u})] - 7.016930 \text{ u}$

$m_D = 7.058135 - 7.016930 \text{ u}$; $\boxed{m_D = 0.041205 \text{ u}}$

$E = m_D c^2 = (0.041205 \text{ u})\left(\dfrac{931 \text{ MeV}}{1 \text{ u}}\right) = 38.4 \text{ MeV}$; $E = 38.4 \text{ MeV}$

$\dfrac{E_B}{A} = \dfrac{38.4 \text{ MeV}}{7}$; $\boxed{\dfrac{E_B}{A} = 5.48 \text{ MeV/nucleon}}$

*39-15. Determine the binding energy per nucleon for carbon-12 ($^{12}_6$C).

$m_D = [6(1.007825 \text{ u}) + 6(1.008665 \text{ u})] - 12.0000 \text{ u} = 0.09894 \text{ u}$

$E = m_D c^2 = (0.09894 \text{ u})\left(\dfrac{931 \text{ MeV}}{1 \text{ u}}\right)$; $\dfrac{E_B}{A} = \dfrac{92.1 \text{ MeV}}{12}$; $\boxed{7.68 \text{ MeV/nucleon}}$

*39-16. What is the mass defect and the binding energy for a gold atom $^{197}_{79}$Au ?

$m_D = [79(1.007825 \text{ u}) + 118(1.008665 \text{ u})] - 196.966541 \text{ u} = 1.674104 \text{ u}$

$E = m_D c^2 = (1.674104 \text{ u})\left(\dfrac{931 \text{ MeV}}{1 \text{ u}}\right) = 1.56 \text{ GeV};$

$\dfrac{E_B}{A} = \dfrac{1.56 \text{ GeV}}{197}$ = $\boxed{7.91 \text{ MeV/nucleon}}$

*39-17. Determine the binding energy per nucleon for tin-120 ($^{120}_{50}$Sn).

$$m_D = [50(1.007825 \text{ u}) + 70(1.008665 \text{ u})] - 119.902108 \text{ u} = 1.09569 \text{ u}$$

$$\frac{E_B}{A} = \left(\frac{(1.09569 \text{ u})(931 \text{ MeV/u})}{120}\right); \quad \boxed{\frac{E_B}{A} = 8.50 \text{ MeV/nucleon}}$$

Radioactivity and Nuclear Decay

39-18. The activity of a certain sample is rated as 2.8 Ci. How many nuclei will have disintegrated in a time of one minute?

$$Nuclei = 2.8 \text{ Ci}\left(\frac{3.7 \times 10^{10}\text{s}^{-1}}{1 \text{ Ci}}\right)(60 \text{ s}); \quad \boxed{nuclei = 6.22 \times 10^{12} \text{ nuclei}}$$

39-19. The cobalt nucleus $^{60}_{27}$Co emits gamma rays of approximately 1.2 MeV. How much mass is lost by the nucleus when it emits a gamma ray of this energy?

$$E = 1.2 \text{ MeV}\left(\frac{1 \text{ u}}{931 \text{ MeV}}\right); \quad \boxed{m = 0.00129 \text{ u}}$$

39-20. The half-life of the radioactive isotope indium-109 is 4.30 h. If the activity of a sample is 1 mCi at the start, how much activity remains after 4.30, 8.60, and 12.9 h?

$$R = R_0\left(\frac{1}{2}\right)^{t/T_{1/2}}; \quad \frac{t}{T_{1/2}} = \frac{4.3 \text{ h}}{4.3 \text{ h}} = 1; \quad R = (1 \text{ mCi})\left(\frac{1}{2}\right)^1; \quad \boxed{R = 0.5 \text{ mCi}}$$

$$R = R_0\left(\frac{1}{2}\right)^{t/T_{1/2}}; \quad \frac{t}{T_{1/2}} = \frac{8.6 \text{ h}}{4.3 \text{ h}} = 2; \quad R = (1 \text{ mCi})\left(\frac{1}{2}\right)^2; \quad \boxed{R = 0.25 \text{ mCi}}$$

$$R = R_0\left(\frac{1}{2}\right)^{t/T_{1/2}}; \quad \frac{t}{T_{1/2}} = \frac{12.9 \text{ h}}{4.3 \text{ h}} = 3; \quad R = (1 \text{ mCi})\left(\frac{1}{2}\right)^3; \quad \boxed{R = 0.125 \text{ mCi}}$$

39-21. The initial activity of a sample containing 7.7 × 10^{11} bismuth-212 nuclei is 4.0 mCi. The half-life of this isotope is 60 min. How many bismuth-212 nuclei remain after 30 min? What is the activity at the end of that time?

$$N = N_0\left(\frac{1}{2}\right)^{t/T_{1/2}}; \quad \frac{t}{T_{1/2}} = \frac{30 \text{ min}}{60 \text{ min}} = 0.5; \quad N = (7.7 \times 10^{11})\left(\frac{1}{2}\right)^{1/2} = \boxed{5.44 \times 10^{11} \text{ nucl.}}$$

$$R = R_0\left(\frac{1}{2}\right)^{t/T_{1/2}}; \quad R = (4 \text{ mCi})\left(\frac{1}{2}\right)^{1/2}; \quad \boxed{R = 2.83 \text{ mCi}}$$

*39-22. Strontium-90 is produced in appreciable quantities in the atmosphere during a nuclear explosion. If this isotope has a half-life of 28 years, how long will it take for the initial activity to drop to one-fourth of its original activity?

$$R = R_0\left(\frac{1}{2}\right)^n; \quad \frac{R}{R_0} = \left(\frac{1}{2}\right)^n = \frac{1}{4}; \quad n = 2$$

$$n = \frac{t}{T_{1/2}} = \frac{t}{28 \text{ yr}} = 2; \quad t = 2(28 \text{ yr}); \quad \boxed{t = 56 \text{ yr}}$$

*39-23. Consider a pure, 4.0-g sample of radioactive Gallium-67. If the half-life is 78 h, how much time is required for 2.8 g of this sample to decay?

When 2.8 g decay, that leaves 4 g − 2.8 g or 1.20 g remaining.

$$m = m_0\left(\frac{1}{2}\right)^n; \quad \frac{m}{m_0} = \frac{1.2 \text{ g}}{4 \text{ g}} = 0.300; \quad \left(\frac{1}{2}\right)^n = 0.300$$

The solution is accomplished by taking the common log of both sides:

$$n\log(0.5) = \log(0.300); \quad -0.301n = -0.523; \quad n = \frac{-0.523}{-0.301} = 1.74$$

$$n = \frac{t}{T_{1/2}} = \frac{t}{78 \text{ h}} = 1.74; \quad t = 1.74(78 \text{ h}); \quad \boxed{t = 135 \text{ h}}$$

*39-24. If one-fifth of a pure radioactive sample remains after 10 h, what is the half-life?

$$\frac{1}{5} = \left(\frac{1}{2}\right)^n; \quad 0.200 = (0.5)^n; \quad n\log(0.5) = \log(0.2); \quad -0.301n = -0.699$$

$$n = \frac{t}{T_{1/2}} = \frac{10\text{ h}}{T_{1/2}} = 2.32; \quad T_{1/2} = \frac{10\text{ h}}{2.32}; \quad \boxed{T_{1/2} = 4.31\text{ h}}$$

Nuclear Reactions

*39-25. Determine the minimum energy released in the nuclear reaction

$$_9^{19}\text{F} + {}_1^1\text{H} \rightarrow {}_2^4\text{He} + {}_8^{16}\text{O} + energy$$

The atomic mass of $_9^{19}\text{F}$ is 18.998403 u, $_2^4\text{He} = 4.002603$ u, $_1^1\text{H} = 1.007824$ u.

$$E = {}_9^{19}\text{F} + {}_1^1\text{H} - {}_2^4\text{He} - {}_8^{16}\text{O}; \quad (Energy\ comes\ from\ mass\ defect)$$

$$E = 18.998403\text{ u} + 1.007825\text{ u} - 4.002603 - 15.994915\text{ u} = 0.0087\text{ u}$$

$$E = (0.00871\text{ u})\left(\frac{931\text{ MeV}}{1\text{ u}}\right); \quad \boxed{E = 8.11\text{ MeV}}$$

*39-26. Determine the approximate kinetic energy imparted to the alpha particle when Radium-226 decays to form Radon-222. Neglect the energy imparted to the radon nucleus.

$$_{88}^{226}\text{Ra} \rightarrow {}_{86}^{222}\text{Rn} + {}_2^4\text{He} + \text{Energy}; \quad {}_{88}^{226}\text{Ra} = 226.02536$$

$$E = 226.02536\text{ u} - 222.017531\text{ u} - 4.002603\text{ u} = 0.00523\text{ u}\left(\frac{931\text{ MeV}}{1\text{ u}}\right) = \boxed{4.87\text{ MeV}}$$

*39-27. Find the energy involved in the production of two alpha particles in the reaction

$$_3^7\text{Li} + {}_1^1\text{H} \rightarrow {}_2^4\text{He} + {}_2^4\text{He} + energy$$

$$E = 7.016003\text{ u} + 1.007825\text{ u} - 2(4.002603\text{ u}) = 0.018622\text{ u}\left(\frac{931\text{ MeV}}{1\text{ u}}\right) = \boxed{17.3\text{ MeV}}$$

---

*39-28. Compute the kinetic energy released in the beta minus decay of thorium-233.

$$_{90}^{233}\text{Th} \rightarrow {}_{91}^{233}\text{Pa} + {}_{+1}^0\beta + \text{energy}; \quad {}_{90}^{233}\text{Th} = 233.041469 \text{ u}; \quad {}_{91}^{233}\text{Pa} = 233.040130$$

$$E = 233.041469\text{ u} - 233.040130\text{ u} - 0.00055\text{ u} = 0.000789\text{ u}$$

$$E = 0.000789\text{ u}\left(\frac{931\text{ MeV}}{1\text{ u}}\right); \quad E = 0.735\text{ MeV}$$

*39-29. What must be the energy of an alpha particle as it bombards a Nitrogen-14 nucleus producing $_8^{17}\text{O}$ and $_1^1\text{H}$? ($_8^{17}\text{O} = 16.999130$ u).

$$_2^4\text{He} + {}_7^{14}\text{N} + \text{Energy} \rightarrow {}_8^{17}\text{O} + {}_1^1\text{H}$$

$$E = 16.999130\text{ u} + 1.007825\text{ u} - 14.003074 - 4.002603\text{ u} = 0.001278\text{ u}\left(\frac{931\text{ MeV}}{1\text{ u}}\right)$$

$$\boxed{E = 1.19\text{ MeV}} \quad This\ is\ the\ Threshold\ Energy\ for\ the\ reaction$$

Supplementary Problems

*39-30. What is the average mass in kilograms of the nucleus of a boron-11 atom?

$$m = 11.009305\text{ u}\left(\frac{1.66 \times 10^{-27}\text{kg}}{1.00\text{ u}}\right); \quad \boxed{m = 1.83 \times 10^{-26}\text{ kg}}$$

*39-31. What are the mass defect and the binding energy per nucleon for boron-11?

$$m_D = [(Zm_H + Nm_n)] - M = [5(1.007825\text{ u}) + 6(1.008665\text{ u})] - 11.009305\text{ u}$$

$$m_D = 11.09112\text{ u} - 11.009305\text{ u} = 0.08181\text{ u}; \quad \boxed{m_D = 0.08181\text{ u}}$$

$$E = m_D c^2 = (0.08181\text{ u})\left(\frac{931\text{ MeV}}{1\text{ u}}\right) = 76.2\text{ MeV}; \quad E = 76.2\text{ MeV}$$

$$\frac{E_B}{A} = \frac{76.2\text{ MeV}}{11}; \quad \boxed{\frac{E_B}{A} = 6.92\text{ MeV/nucleon}}$$

*39-32. Find the binding energy per nucleon for Thallium-206.

$$m_D = [81(1.007825 \text{ u}) + 125(1.008665 \text{ u})] - 205.976104 \text{ u} = 1.740846 \text{ u}$$

$$E = m_D c^2 = (1.740846 \text{ u})\left(\frac{931 \text{ MeV}}{1 \text{ u}}\right); \quad \frac{E_B}{A} = \frac{1621 \text{ MeV}}{206} = \boxed{7.87 \text{ MeV/nucleon}}$$

*39-33. Calculate the energy required to separate the nucleons in mercury-204.

$$m_D = [80(1.007825 \text{ u}) + 124(1.008665 \text{ u})] - 203.973865 \text{ u} = 1.7266 \text{ u}$$

$$E = m_D c^2 = (1.7266 \text{ u})\left(\frac{931 \text{ MeV}}{1 \text{ u}}\right); \quad \boxed{E_B = 1610 \text{ MeV}}$$

*39-34. The half-life of a radioactive sample is 6.8 h. How much time passes before the activity drops to one-fifth of its initial value?

$$\frac{R}{R_0} = \frac{1}{5} = \left(\frac{1}{2}\right)^n; \quad 0.200 = (0.5)^n; \quad n\log(0.5) = \log(0.2); \quad -0.301 n = -0.699$$

$$n = \frac{0.699}{0.301} = 2.32; \quad n = \frac{t}{T_{1/2}} = \frac{6.8 \text{ h}}{T_{1/2}} = 2.32; \quad T_{1/2} = \frac{6.8 \text{ h}}{2.32}; \quad \boxed{T_{1/2} = 2.93 \text{ h}}$$

*39-35. How much energy is required to tear apart a deuterium atom? ($_1^2$H = 2.014102 u)

$$m_D = [1(1.007825 \text{ u}) + 1(1.008665 \text{ u})] - 2.014102 \text{ u} = 0.002388 \text{ u}$$

$$E = m_D c^2 = (0.002388 \text{ u})\left(\frac{931 \text{ MeV}}{1 \text{ u}}\right); \quad \boxed{E_B = 2.22 \text{ MeV}}$$

*39-36. Plutonium-232 decays by alpha emission with a half-life of 30 min. How much of this substance remains after 4 h if the original sample had a mass of 4.0 g? Write the equation for the decay?

$$m = m_0\left(\frac{1}{2}\right)^{1/T_{1/2}}; \quad \frac{t}{T_{1/2}} = \frac{4 \text{ h}}{0.5 \text{ h}} = 8.00; \quad m = (4 \text{ g})\left(\frac{1}{2}\right)^8; \quad \boxed{m = 15.6 \text{ mg}}$$

$$_{94}^{232}\text{Pu} \rightarrow {}_{92}^{228}\text{U} + {}_2^4\text{He} + energy$$

*39-37. If 32 x 10⁹ atoms of a radioactive isotope are reduced to only 2 x 10⁹ atoms in a time of 48 h, what is the half-life of this material?

$$\frac{N}{N_0} = \frac{2 \times 10^9}{32 \times 10^9} = \left(\frac{1}{2}\right)^n; \quad 0.0625 = (0.5)^n; \quad n\log(0.5) = \log(0.0625); \quad -0.301 n = -1.204$$

$$n = \frac{1.204}{0.301} = 4.00; \quad n = \frac{t}{T_{1/2}} = \frac{48 \text{ h}}{T_{1/2}} = 4.00; \quad T_{1/2} = \frac{48 \text{ h}}{4.00}; \quad \boxed{T_{1/2} = 12.0 \text{ h}}$$

*39-38. A certain radioactive isotope retains only 10 percent of its original activity after a time of 4 h. What is the half-life?

$$\frac{N}{N_0} = \frac{1}{10} = \left(\frac{1}{2}\right)^n; \quad 0.100 = (0.5)^n; \quad n\log(0.5) = \log(0.100); \quad -0.301 n = -1.00$$

$$n = \frac{1.00}{0.301} = 3.32; \quad n = \frac{t}{T_{1/2}} = \frac{4 \text{ h}}{T_{1/2}} = 3.32; \quad T_{1/2} = \frac{4 \text{ h}}{3.32}; \quad \boxed{T_{1/2} = 72.3 \text{ min}}$$

*39-39. When a $_3^6$Li nucleus is struck by a proton, an alpha particle and a produce nucleus are released. Write the equation for this reaction. What is the net energy transfer in this case?

$$_3^6\text{Li} + {}_1^1\text{H} \rightarrow {}_2^4\text{He} + {}_2^3\text{He} + energy$$

$$E = 6.015126 \text{ u} + 1.007825 \text{ u} - 4.002603 \text{ u} - 3.016030 = 0.00432 \text{ u}\left(\frac{931 \text{ MeV}}{1 \text{ u}}\right) = \boxed{4.02 \text{ MeV}}$$

*39-40. Uranium-238 undergoes alpha decay. Write the equation for the reaction and calculate the disintegration energy.

$$^{238}_{92}U \rightarrow ^{234}_{90}Th + ^4_2He + energy$$

$$E = 238.05079\ u - 234.04363\ u - 4.002603\ u = 0.00456\ u$$

$$E = 0.00456\ u\left(\frac{931\ MeV}{1\ u}\right); \quad \boxed{E = 4.24\ MeV}$$

*39-41. A 9-g sample of radioactive material has an initial activity of 5.0 Ci. Forty minutes later, the activity is only 3.0 Ci. What is the half-life? How much of the pure sample remains?

$$\frac{R}{R_0} = \frac{3\ Ci}{5\ Ci} = \left(\frac{1}{2}\right)^n; \quad 0.600 = (0.5)^n; \quad n\log(0.5) = \log(0.6); \quad -0.301n = -0.222$$

$$\frac{0.222}{0.301} = 0.737; \quad n = \frac{t}{T_{1/2}}; \quad \frac{40\ min}{T_{1/2}} = 0.737; \quad T_{1/2} = \frac{40\ min}{0.737}; \quad \boxed{T_{1/2} = 54.3\ min}$$

$$m = m_0\left(\frac{1}{2}\right)^n = (9\ g)\left(\frac{1}{2}\right)^{0.737} \quad \boxed{m = 5.40\ g}$$

Critical Thinking Problems

*39-42. Nuclear fusion is a process that can produce enormous energy without the harmful byproducts of nuclear fission. Calculate the energy released in the following nuclear fusion reaction:

$$^3_2H + ^3_2He \rightarrow ^4_2He + ^1_1H + ^1_1H + energy$$

$$E = 2(3.016030\ u) - 4.002603\ u - 2(1.007825\ u) = 0.013807\ u\left(\frac{931\ MeV}{1\ u}\right)$$

$$\boxed{E = 12.9\ MeV}$$

*39-43. Carbon-14 decays very slowly with a half-life of 5740 years. Carbon dating can be accomplished by seeing what fraction of carbon-14 remains, assuming the decay process began with the death of a living organism. What would be the age of a chunk of charcoal if it was determined that the radioactive C-14 remaining was only 40 percent of what would be expected in a living organism?

$$\frac{R}{R_0} = 0.40 = \left(\frac{1}{2}\right)^n; \quad 0.400 = (0.5)^n; \quad n\log(0.5) = \log(0.4); \quad -0.301n = -0.399$$

$$n = \frac{0.399}{0.301} = 0.737; \quad n = \frac{t}{T_{1/2}} = \frac{t}{5740\ yr} = 1.32; \quad t = 1.32(5740\ yr); \quad \boxed{t = 7590\ yr}$$

*39-44. The velocity selector in a mass spectrometer has a magnetic field of 0.2 T perpendicular to an electric field of 50 kV/m. The same magnetic field is across the lower region. What is the velocity of singly charged Lithium-7 atoms as they leave the selector? If the radius of the path in the spectrometer is 9.10 cm, find the atomic mass of the lithium atom?

$$v = \frac{E}{B} = \frac{50,000\ V/m}{0.2\ T}; \quad \boxed{v = 2.5 \times 10^5\ m/s}$$

$$\frac{mv^2}{R} = qvB; \quad m = \frac{qBR}{v}; \quad m = \frac{(1.6 \times 10^{-19}C)(0.2\ T)(0.091\ m)}{(2.5 \times 10^5\ m/s)};$$

$$m = 1.165 \times 10^{-26}kg\left(\frac{1\ u}{1.66 \times 10^{-27}kg}\right); \quad \boxed{m = 7.014\ u}$$

B = 0.2 T into paper

R

*39-45. A nuclear reactor operates at a power level of 2.0 MW. Assuming that approximately 200 MeV of energy is released for a single fission of U-235, how many fission processes are occurring each second in the reactor?

$$P = \frac{2 \times 10^6\ J/s}{1.6 \times 10^{-19}\ J/MeV} = 1.25 \times 10^{19}\ MeV/s; \quad \frac{1.25 \times 10^{19}\ MeV/s}{200\ MeV/fission} = \boxed{6.25 \times 10^{16}\ fissions/s}$$

Transistors and Applications

40-1. Given an NPN transistor with a common-base connection and $α = 0.98$, determine the base current and the collector current when the emitter current is 40 mA.

$I_b = I_e(1 - α) = (40 \text{ mA})(1 - 0.98)$; $\boxed{I_b = 0.800 \text{ mA}}$

$I_c = I_e - I_b = 40 \text{ mA} - 0.800 \text{ mA}$; $\boxed{I_c = 39.2 \text{ mA}}$

40-2. If the base current of a transistor with a common-base connection is 1.6 mA and the emitter current is 60 mA, what is $α$?

$I_b = 1.6 \text{ mA}$; $I_e = 60 \text{ mA}$; $I_c = 60 \text{ mA} - 1.6 \text{ mA} = 58.4 \text{ mA}$

$α = \dfrac{I_c}{I_e} = \dfrac{58.4 \text{ mA}}{60 \text{ mA}}$; $\boxed{α = 0.973}$

40-3. For a common-base amplifier, the input resistance is 800 Ω and the output resistance is 600 kΩ. (a) Determine the voltage gain if the emitter current is 12 mA and $α = 0.97$.

(b) What is the power gain?

(a) $V_{in} = I_e R_{in} = (12 × 10^{-3} \text{ A})(800 \text{ Ω})$; $V_{in} = 9.60 \text{ V}$ *To find V_{out} we need I_c;*

$I_c = α I_e = 0.97(12 × 10^{-3} \text{ A}) = 0.0116 \text{ A}$; $V_{out} = I_c R_{out} = (0.0116 \text{ A})(600,000 \text{ Ω})$

$V_{out} = 6980 \text{ V}$; $A = \dfrac{V_{out}}{V_{in}} = \dfrac{6980 \text{ V}}{9.6 \text{ V}}$; $\boxed{A_v = 727}$

(b) $G = α A_v = 0.97(727)$; $\boxed{G = 705}$

40-4. The power gain is 800 for a common-base amplifier, and the voltage amplification factor is 840. Determine the collector current when the base current is 1.2 mA.

$α = \dfrac{G}{A_v} = \dfrac{800}{840} = 0.952$; $I_c = α I_e = (0.952)(1.2 \text{ mA})$; $\boxed{I_c = 1.14 \text{ mA}}$

---

*39-46. Consider an experiment which bombards $^{14}_{7}N$ with an alpha particle. One of the two product nuclides is $^{1}_{1}H$.   The reaction is

$$^{4}_{2}He + ^{14}_{7}N → ^{A}_{Z}X + ^{1}_{1}H$$

What is the product nuclide indicated by the symbol X?   How much kinetic energy must the alpha particle have in order to produce the reaction?

Conservation of nucleons means: $^{4}_{2}He + ^{14}_{7}N + enery → ^{17}_{8}O + ^{1}_{1}H$

$E = 16.99913 \text{ u} + 1.007825 \text{ u} - 4.002603 \text{ u} - 14.003074 \text{ u} = 0.001282 \text{ u}$

$E = 0.001282 \text{ u} \left(\dfrac{931 \text{ MeV}}{1 \text{ u}}\right)$; $\boxed{E = 1.19 \text{ MeV}}$

*39-47. When passing a stream of ionized lithium atoms through a mass spectrometer, the radius of the path followed by $^{7}_{3}Li$ (7.0169 u) is 14.00 cm. A lighter line is formed by the $^{6}_{3}Li$ (6.0151 u). What is the radius of the path followed by the $^{6}_{3}Li$ isotopes?

$\dfrac{mv^2}{R} = qvB$; $R = \dfrac{mv}{qB}$;   *(See Problems 39-10 and 39-11)*

$\dfrac{m_1}{m_2} = \dfrac{R_1}{R_2}$; $R_2 = \dfrac{m_2 R_1}{m_1} = \dfrac{(6.0151 \text{ u})(14 \text{ cm})}{7.0169 \text{ u}}$; $\boxed{R_2 = 6.92 \text{ cm}}$

277

40-5. Determine the current gain in a common-emitter amplifier circuit when α = 0.98.

$$\beta = \frac{\alpha}{1-\alpha} = \frac{0.98}{1-0.98}; \quad \boxed{\beta = 49}$$

Supplementary Problems

40-6. In the previous problem, what is the collector current if the emitter current is 20 µA? What is the base current?

$$\alpha = \frac{I_c}{I_e}; \quad I_c = 0.98(20 \text{ µA}); \quad \boxed{I_c = 19.6 \text{ µA}}$$

40-7. A transistor with an effective input resistance of 400 Ω, an effective output resistance of 900 kΩ, and α = 0.96 is connected in a common-base circuit. (a) What is the voltage gain when the input current I_e is 8 µA? (b) What is the power gain?

$$V_{in} = I_e R_{in} = (8 \text{ µA})(400 \text{ Ω}) = 3.2 \text{ mV}; \quad I_c = (0.96)(8 \text{ µA}) = 7.68 \text{ µA}$$

$$V_{out} = I_c R_{out} = (7.68 \text{ µA})(900{,}000 \text{ Ω}) = 6.912 \text{ V}; \quad A_v = \frac{6.912 \text{ V}}{3.2 \times 10^{-3}\text{V}}; \quad \boxed{A_v = 2160}$$

$$G = \alpha A_v = (0.96)(2160); \quad \boxed{G = 2074}$$

40-8. Calculate I_c and I_b for the conditions described in Problem 40-7.

$$I_c = \alpha I_e = 0.96(8 \text{ µA}) = \boxed{7.68 \text{ mA}}; \quad I_b = 8 \text{ µA} - 7.68 \text{ µA} = \boxed{0.320 \text{ µA}}$$

40-9. For a transistor with $I_e = 8$ µA and α = 0.97 connected with a common emitter, calculate β, I_{in}, and I_{out}.

$$\beta = \frac{\alpha}{1-\alpha} = \frac{0.97}{1-0.97}; \quad I_b = \boxed{7.76 \text{ µA}}; \quad \boxed{\beta = 32.3}$$

$$I_c = 0.97(8 \text{ µA}) = \boxed{7.76 \text{ µA}}; \quad I_b = (8 \text{ µA} - 7.76 \text{ µA}) = \boxed{0.240 \text{ µA}}$$

40-10. For a transistor with α = 0.99 connected with a common collector, calculate the current gain A_i.

$$A_i = \frac{I_{out}}{I_{in}} = \frac{I_c}{I_c(1-\alpha)} = \frac{1}{1-\alpha}; \quad A_i = \frac{1}{1-0.99} = \boxed{100}$$

40-11. A transistor has β = 99; what is the value of α?

$$\beta = \frac{\alpha}{1-\alpha}; \quad \beta - \beta\alpha = \alpha; \quad \alpha + \alpha\beta = \beta$$

$$\alpha = \frac{\beta}{1+\beta} = \frac{99}{1+99} = 0.99; \quad \boxed{\alpha = 0.99}$$

40-12. For the transistor of Problem 40-11, if $I_b = 0.10$ mA, what are the values of I_e and I_c?

$$I_b = I_e(1 - \alpha); \quad I_b = 0.10 \text{ mA}; \quad I_e - I_e\alpha = 0.10 \text{ mA};$$

$$I_e = \frac{I_b}{1-\alpha} = \frac{0.10 \text{ mA}}{1-0.99}; \quad \boxed{I_e = 10 \text{ mA}}$$

$$\alpha = \frac{I_c}{I_e}; \quad I_c = \alpha I_e = 0.99(10 \text{ mA}); \quad \boxed{I_c = 9.9 \text{ mA}}$$

Critical Thinking Problems

40-13. It is known that zener breakdown and avalanche breakdown are affected oppositely by temperature. From this fact, can you determine a good voltage rating for a zener diode when temperature stability is important?

There is a transition region between 5 and 6 volts where the breakdown mechanism is a combination of both zener and avalanche. This voltage range is best for temperature stability since the temperature effects are opposite and tend to cancel.

40-17. Write an equation that describes the current gain from base to emitter in terms of B and identify the amplifier configuration where it would be most useful.

$$\beta + 1 = \frac{I_e}{I_b}$$

The common collector configuration.

40-18. Suppose there is an application where the common-emitter amplifier would serve best but the phase reversal would not be acceptable. Can you think of a solution?

A second common-emitter amplifier will invert the phase again and the overall result is no phase change.

40-14. A lab worker is directed to build the circuit shown in Fig. 40-2, but connects the diode as shown in Fig. 40-38. Can you predict how the circuit will work?

This configuration is often used for voltage clipping or bilateral voltage regulation. Properly connected, the configuration will turn on at the zener voltage plus 0.7 volts. Thus, with two 10 volt zeners, we would have turn-on voltages of +10.7 volts and -10.7 volts. If one diode is reversed, then the symmetry is lost. Using the same zeners, the turn-on thresholds would be 20 volts and 1.4 volts.

40-15. Incandescent lamps have a large current flow when first turned on and then the current drops as they heat up. Thus, they often burn out at the moment they are turned on. Is there a solution based on the information covered in this chapter?

Conductors have a positive temperature coefficient and semiconductors have a negative temperature coefficient. Thus, one solution is to place a semiconductor in series with the lamp. At turn-on, the semiconductor will be cool, have a higher resistance, and limit the surge current. After a time, the temperature of the semiconductor will go up, its resistance will drop and allow normal lamp operation.

40-16. Incandescent lamps produce a lot of heat and are thus rather inefficient. Why can't they be replaced with LEDs that are more efficient?

LEDs are monochromatic (they emit one color). Incandescent lamps produce mostly white light which is a mixture of all the visible colors of the spectrum. It might be feasible (economically) to combine red, green and blue LED light to make white light at some time in the future.

Instructor Notes for Laboratory Experiments

UNIT
B

Contents for Unit B

Reading Assignments in *Physics,* Sixth Edition

Experiment number and title	Chapters referenced	Sections assigned
1. Vernier and Micrometer Calipers	3. Technical Measurements and Vectors	3-5 and 3-6
2. Addition of Force Vectors	3. Technical Measurements and Vectors	3-7 to 3-13
3. Friction	4. Translational Equilibrium and Friction	4-6
4. Accelerated Motion	6. Uniform Acceleration	6-1 to 6-6
5. Acceleration Due to Gravity	6. Uniform Acceleration	6-7
6. Range of a Projectile	6. Uniform Acceleration 7. Newton's Second Law	6-7 to 6-9 7-1 and 7-2
7. Newton's Second Law	7. Newton's Second Law	7-1 to 7-3
8. Conservation of Energy	8. Work, Energy, and Power	8-5 to 8-7
9. Conservation of Momentum	9. Impulse and Momentum	9-1 and 9-2
10. Kepler's Laws	10. Uniform Circular Motion	10-7 to 10-10
11. Pulleys	12. Simple Machines	12-4 and 12-5
12. Hooke's Law and Simple Harmonic Motion	14. Simple Harmonic Motion 15. Fluids	13-1 and 13-3 14-1 and 14-4
13. Archimedes' Principle	15. Fluids	15-6
14. Specific Heat	17. Quantity of Heat	17-1 to 17-4
15. Standing Waves in a Vibrating String	21. Mechanical Waves	21-7 and 21-8
16. Investigating Static Electricity	23. The Electric Force	23-1 to 23-5
17. The Capacitor	26. Capacitance	26-1 to 26-4
18. Ohm's Law	27. Current and Resistance	27-1 and 27-4
19. Series Resistance	28. Direct-Current Circuits	28-1
20. Parallel Resistance	28. Direct-Current Circuits	28-2
21. Principles of Electromagnetism	29. Magnetism and the Magnetic Field	29-3 and 29-8
22. Electromagnetic Induction	29. Magnetism and the Magnetic Field	29-8 to 29-10
23. Planck's Constant	33. Light and Illumination	33-3 and 33-4
24. Reflection of Light	34. Reflection and Mirrors	34-1 and 34-2
25. Concave and Convex Mirrors	34. Reflection and Mirrors	34-3 and 34-7
26. Snell's Law	35. Refraction	35-1 to 35-3
27. Convex and Concave Lenses	36. Lenses and Optical Instruments	36-1 to 36-5
28. Double-Slit Interference	37. Interference, Diffraction, and Polarization	37-1 to 37-4
29. Semiconductor Properties	40. Electronics	40-1, 40-5 to 40-7

Vernier and Micrometer Calipers

Process Skills

Observing, measuring, using significant digits, interpreting data, inferring, and computing.

Troubleshooting

Micrometer and vernier calipers that have been in use for a length of time frequently need adjusting to assure that they work properly. If a student notices a zero reading on the micrometer caliper that is off by as much as ±0.05 mm, it will be extremely difficult to make accurate readings. Read the instructions that came with the instrument and make the adjustments.

Teaching Suggestions

1. Before the lab begins, make sure that all the necessary materials are available. It is not essential that everyone has the same kind of wooden block or metal cylinder, but each object must have dimensions that do not exceed the capacity of the measuring instrument.
2. Even if students have received previous instruction on significant figures, a quick review is helpful. Encourage the use of scientific notation; it provides an excellent method for indicating only those digits that are significant.
3. A discussion of the uncertainty of a measurement is important. Students must recognize that the last digits assigned to measurements are estimated. The meter stick reads to the nearest millimeter with the estimated digit between two millimeter marks on the meter stick. Address similar concerns for vernier and micrometer calipers.
4. Some students may ask about the uncertainty of the calculated values of area and volume. Point out that they do not have instruments that directly measure area or volume, and, therefore, the uncertainty in those quantities must be calculated based on the proportional errors of the measured lengths. The procedure is quite complicated, but very important, and you may wish to expand the lab to include such an analysis.

Observations and Data

Table 1 The Meter Stick
(Sample data are given.)

Laboratory Manual	Measurement	Number of Significant Digits	Uncertainty (±)
Length (mm)	280.5 mm	4	±1 mm
Width (mm)	231.3 mm	4	±1 mm
Area (mm^2)	64880 mm^2	4	

Table 2 The Vernier Caliper
(The data shown are for a particular block.)

Wooden Block	Measurement	Number of Significant Digits	Uncertainty (±)
Length (cm)	2.65 cm	3	±0.01 cm
Width (cm)	1.03 cm	3	±0.01 cm
Height (cm)	0.980 cm	3	±0.01 cm
Volume (cm^3)	2.67 cm^3	3	

Table 3 The Micrometer Caliper
(Again the data will vary.)

Metal Cylinder	Measurement	Number of Significant Digits	Uncertainty (±)
Length (mm)	23.020 mm	5	±0.01 mm
Diameter (mm)	8.925 mm	4	±0.01 mm
Volume (mm^3)	1440 mm^3	4	

Analysis

1. The vernier caliper allows a *precise* reading to ±0.01 cm. The last digit, which would otherwise be "estimated," is accurately provided by the moving scale. The micrometer caliper, on the other hand, allows for an extra estimated digit between two marks on the circular scale.
2. The zero correction is made by subtracting the zero reading (algebraically) from the indicated value. Thus, measurement (a) is 20.000 mm and measurement (b) is 22.000 mm.
3. The answers are given in the following table:

Measurement	Instrument of choice	Uncertainty of measurement
Depth of a small cup	Vernier caliper	±0.01 cm
Height of a table	Meter stick	±0.01 cm
Diameter of a wire	Micrometer caliper	±0.001 cm

2 Addition of Force Vectors

INSTRUCTOR NOTES

Process Skills

observing, using numbers, formulating models, classifying, communicating, interpreting data, measuring, predicting, questioning, defining operationally

Troubleshooting

Make sure students check that the scales register zero at no load. Explain how to make zero corrections if the scales are off.

Teaching Suggestions

1. The activity and data collection are easily and quickly performed. Even with a limited number of equipment set-ups, all students should be able to obtain data in a class period if they have previously read and prepared for the experiment.
2. Remind students that the lengths of the vectors are proportional to the forces, not to the lengths of the strings or the spring scales.

Observations and Data

Students drawing will vary, but should be similar to what is shown in Figure 2.

Analysis

1. Student answers will vary.
2. Student answers will vary. Students should have good results, but they will not be perfect. The resultant of $A + B$ should be nearly equal to and opposite C. Relative error should be less than 15%.
3. Student diagrams will vary.
4. The sum of $A + B + C$ is a closed triangle indicating equilibrium. (No net force is exerted on point **P**.)
5. If B is added to C, the resultant should be the negative of the value of A.
6. If C is added to A, the resultant should be the negative of the value of B.
7. The addition of $C + B + A$ should give the same result as the addition of $B + C + A$. The resultant is zero. It might be helpful at this time to remind students that, in vector addition, the order of addition does not affect the final result (commutative law). Also, in the case of two or more vectors, the grouping of vectors as they are added does not affect the final result (associative law).

Application

When a body falls through a fluid such as air, a frictional or drag force acts on it, slowing its downward velocity. As it first begins to fall through the air, its velocity increases, but so does the frictional force acting on it. When the upward frictional force equals the downward force due to gravity, the net force acting on the body becomes zero. At this point, equilibrium is reached, and the body falls at its constant terminal velocity. The frictional force of the air that acts on the skydiver's body, or the body and the parachute, depends on the configuration of the body. When the total surface area of the falling body exposed to the frictional force is increased, the terminal velocity is decreased.

Extension

The results should be the same as those obtained earlier. The sum of $A + B + C$ is zero.

INSTRUCTOR NOTES

3 Friction

Process Skills

observing, measuring, using numbers, communicating, interpreting data, predicting, questioning, controlling variables

Teaching Suggestions

1. The large wood blocks used for storage of mass sets are the correct size and weight to use for objects. Chalkboard erasers work well for objects of small mass.
2. Demonstrate another method for determining the coefficient of static friction without using a protractor. The tangent of θ is the ratio of the height of the plane above the horizontal (at which sliding begins) to the length of the plane. Thus

$$\frac{h}{l} = \tan \theta = \mu.$$

Observations and Data
Table 1 (Sample data are given.)

	Description
Object	chalkboard eraser
Surface	cardboard

Table 2 (Sample data are given.)

Weight of object (N)				1.86
	1	2	3	Average
Force of sliding friction (N)				0.39

Table 3 (Sample data are given.)

Motion	Angle (degrees)	$\mu = \tan\theta$
Static	20	0.36
Sliding	13	0.23

Analysis

1. $\mu_{static} = \tan 20° = 0.36$
   $\mu_{sliding} = \tan 13° = 0.23$
2. The coefficient of static friction should be greater. The force needed to overcome the frictional force of an object at rest (static frictional force) is greater than the force needed to keep an object in motion (kinetic frictional force).
3. $\mu = F_\parallel/F_\perp = 0.39/1.86 = 0.21$
4. They should be the same (or nearly identical). Student explanations for differences will vary.
5. The angles at which the brick begins sliding should be the same regardless of the area of the surfaces in contact. The weight of the brick, $F_\perp$, perpendicular to the surface influences the force of friction; the coefficient of static friction is independent of the area of contact.
6. An unwrapped brick begins to slide at an angle greater than that required by a waxed paper-wrapped brick. The waxed paper changes the nature of the surfaces in contact, essentially acting as a lubricant to reduce the coefficient of static friction, and, thus, the force of friction.
7. The type of surface and the force normal to the surface (perpendicular component of weight) influence the force of friction.

Application

Brand *Y* will give better service since it will have greater traction in wet weather than brand X. Both tires have nearly the same coefficient of friction on a dry pavement and, thus, the same amount of traction in dry weather.

Extension

The predicted angle should be very close to the angle at which sliding begins (at a constant speed).

4 Accelerated Motion

Process Skills

observing, using numbers, communicating, interpreting data, measuring, questioning, defining operationally

Troubleshooting

The recording timer must make accurate marks. If distinguishable marks do not show up, try replacing the carbon disc.

Alternative Materials

In place of the recording timer, an electronic blinky can be attached to the cart, and the moving cart can be photographed by using an instant developing camera. The dots can be measured on the developed film.

Teaching Suggestions

1. Prior to the experiment, review with students the three basic graphs of motion (displacement vs. time, velocity vs. time, acceleration vs. time).
2. This experiment is easily accomplished because the period of the recording timer is not required. If the period is known, the actual times may be substituted for each interval.
3. The sequence of dots (left to right or right to left) varies with the set-up. Students should make sure they count and mark the intervals in the direction of the movement.

Observations and Data

Table 1 (Sample data are given.)

Time (interval)	Displacement (cm)	Total displacement (cm)
1	1.80	1.80
2	3.50	5.30
3	5.55	10.85
4	6.90	17.75
5	8.95	26.70
6	10.55	37.25
7	12.30	49.55
8		
9		
10		
11		
12		

Table 2 (Sample data are given.)

Time (interval)	Average velocity (cm/interval)	Acceleration ($\Delta v/\Delta t$)
1	1.80	1.80
2	3.50	1.75
3	5.55	1.85
4	6.90	1.73
5	8.95	1.79
6	10.55	1.76
7	12.30	1.76
8		
9		
10		
11		
12		

Analysis

1.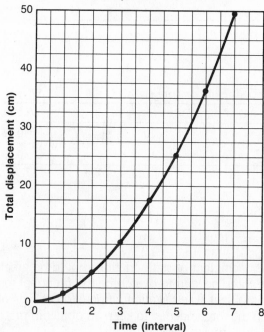
Total Displacement vs Time

2.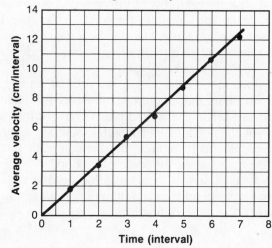
Average Velocity vs Time

3. The slope of the curve is a parabola. The constantly increasing slope indicates that the cart was traveling greater distances during successive intervals of time.

4. The graph is a straight line passing through the origin. It indicates that the velocity of the cart is increasing at a constant rate.

5. Student answers will vary. The unit for the slope should be cm/interval^2.

6. The graph is a straight line parallel to the *x*-axis. Acceleration is uniform.

Acceleration vs Time

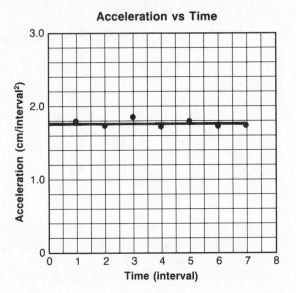

Application

Passengers would experience the same acceleration that exists on Earth. A greater rate of acceleration might cause physical discomfort. If the spacecraft were able to accelerate at that rate for a year, it would be traveling at close to the velocity of light, 3×10^8 m/s.

Extension

1. Student answers will vary. The slopes should be close to the values for average velocity.
2. Student answers will vary. The acceleration of the cart will be less than the acceleration due to gravity since the falling mass is accelerating itself and the cart.

INSTRUCTOR NOTES

5 Acceleration Due to Gravity

Process Skills

observing, measuring, communicating, using numbers, interpreting data, questioning, controlling variables

Alternative Materials

For Part B, a less expensive and simpler method is to use a PASCO Digital Free Fall apparatus, #ME-9202B, instead of the Apple or IBM computer, game port interface, computer software, and Free Fall Adapter. It is a simple electronic timing device that accurately measures the time required for a steel ball to fall.

Teaching Suggestions

Part A
1. It is important that the mass be stationary before it is dropped to ensure that the initial velocity of the falling mass is zero.
2. Students must not exert any force on the mass by tossing or throwing it to the floor; it must simply be dropped.
3. If student results in Part A have a large relative error, explain that, since the mass falls 1 m or less and the velocity is computed in m/s, even a small error in measurement or technique can have a significant effect.

Observations and Data

Table 1 (Sample data are given.)

Period of recording timer ___0.0167___ s

Interval	Time (s)	Displacement (m)	Total displacement (m)	Average velocity (m/s)
1	0.017	0.0030	0.0030	0.18
2	0.033	0.0065	0.0095	0.39
3	0.050	0.0090	0.0185	0.54
4	0.067	0.0120	0.0305	0.72
5	0.083	0.0145	0.0450	0.87
6	0.100	0.0170	0.0620	1.02
7	0.117	0.0195	0.0815	1.17
8	0.133	0.0220	0.1035	1.32
9	0.150	0.0250	0.1285	1.50
10	0.167	0.0280	0.1565	1.68
11	0.183	0.0300	0.1865	1.80
12	0.200	0.0330	0.2195	1.98
13	0.217	0.0360	0.2555	2.16
14	0.233	0.0380	0.2935	2.28
15	0.250	0.0410	0.3345	2.46
16	0.267	0.0435	0.3780	2.61
17	0.283	0.0460	0.4240	2.76

Interval	Time (s)	Displacement (m)	Total displacement (m)	Average velocity (m/s)
18	0.300	0.0490	0.4730	2.94
19	0.317	0.0510	0.5240	3.06
20	0.333	0.0540	0.5780	3.24

Table 2 (Sample data are given.)

Free fall distance  0.905 m

Trial	Time (s)
1	0.4285
2	0.4290
3	0.4288
4	0.4282
5	0.4291
Average	0.4287

$g = $ 9.849 m/s^2

Table 3 (Sample data are given.)

Free fall distance 1.900 m

Trial	Time (s)
1	0.6226
2	0.6227
3	0.6231
4	0.6222
5	0.6230
Average	0.6227

$g = $ 9.799 m/s^2

Analysis

Part A

1.

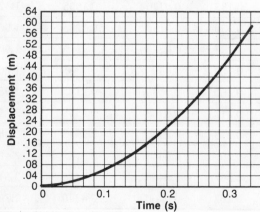

Displacement vs Time

2.

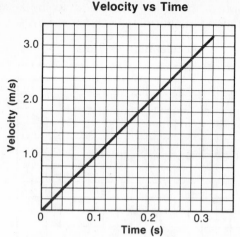

Velocity vs Time

3. The shape of the curve is parabolic. The constantly increasing slope indicates that the mass was traveling greater distances during each successive time interval.

4. The graph is a straight line passing through the origin. It indicates that the velocity of a falling mass increases at a constant rate.

5. $\quad$ slope $= \dfrac{3.24 \text{ m/s} - 0}{0.333 \text{ s} - 0} = 9.82 \text{ m/s}^2$

$\dfrac{\text{relative}}{\text{error}} = \dfrac{9.82 \text{ m/s}^2 - 9.80 \text{ m/s}^2}{9.80 \text{ m/s}^2} \times 100$

$= 0.2\%$

Part B

1. a. $\dfrac{\text{relative}}{\text{error}} = \dfrac{9.849 \text{ m/s}^2 - 9.80 \text{ m/s}^2}{9.80 \text{ m/s}^2} \times 100\%$

$= 0.5\%$

b. $\dfrac{\text{relative}}{\text{error}} = \dfrac{9.80 \text{ m/s}^2 - 9.799 \text{ m/s}^2}{9.80 \text{ m/s}^2} \times 100\%$

$= 0.01\%$

Student results should have an error of less than 5% for the measurement of g.

2. The uncertainty in measuring the free fall distance is a smaller percent of the larger distance, so the results for 2 m may be slightly better.

3. Free fall distance was constant. Time was responding.

Application

At higher elevations, the acceleration due to gravity is usually somewhat diminished. A smaller acceleration due to gravity would permit an object, such as the hammer or javelin in the track and field events, to remain in the air slightly longer, yielding a better distance.

6 Range of a Projectile

INSTRUCTOR NOTES

Process Skills

observing, measuring, predicting, interpreting data, communicating, questioning, defining operationally

Alternative Materials

Shelving brackets, grooved rulers, or curtain rods can be substituted for the U-channel.

Teaching Suggestions

1. If your laboratory tables are not level, students should use a level to adjust the horizontal sections of track. The leveling assures that there is no initial vertical component of motion.
2. If the steel ball just misses the cup, have students recheck all their measurements and calculations. If the cups are too tall, the ball may hit the edge of the cup. Predictions by students should be within 5% to 10% of the actual distances.

Observations and Data

Table 1 (Sample data are given.)

Trial	Distance (m)	Time (s)
1	0.20	0.153
2	0.20	0.153
3	0.20	0.153
Average	0.20	0.153

Vertical distance, y, = 0.96 m

Analysis

1. $v_x = \Delta d/\Delta t = 0.20 \text{ m}/0.153 \text{ s} = 1.3 \text{ m/s}$
2. $t = [(2)(0.96 \text{ m})/(9.80 \text{ m/s}^2)]^{1/2} = 0.44 \text{ s}$
3. $x = v_x t = (1.3 \text{ m/s})(0.44 \text{ s}) = 0.57 \text{ m}$
4. The ball lands in the cup.
5. Yes. The equations used to calculate the horizontal and vertical positions of the ball were based on the premise that the components of motion are independent of each other.
6. The results would probably be different. The displacement of the sponge ball or ping-pong ball will be affected by the significantly large frictional resistance of the air.

Application

$t_{air} = [(2)(6 \text{ m})/(9.80 \text{ m/s}^2)]^{1/2} = 1.1 \text{ s}$

$x = v_x t = (3.75 \text{ m/s})(1.1 \text{ s}) = 4.1 \text{ m}$

The diver will land in the water at a point 4.1 m from the edge of the platform.

Extension

1. If $\theta_i = 45°$, $2\theta_i = 90°$ and $\sin 90° = 1$. For all other values of θ_i, $\sin 2\theta_i$ will be less than 1. Student examples will vary. Some possible answers: If $\theta_i = 60°$, $\sin 2\theta_i = 0.8660$; if $\theta_i = 53°$, $\sin 2\theta_i = .9612$; if $\theta_i = 75°$, $\sin 2\theta_i = 0.4999$; and if $\theta_i = 32°$, $\sin 2\theta_i = 0.8829$.

2.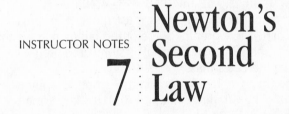
$$v_i = \frac{160\ 000 \text{ m/h}}{3600 \text{ s/h}} = 44.4 \text{ m/s}$$

$$x = \frac{(44.4 \text{ m/s})^2}{9.8 \text{ m/s}^2} \times 2(0.8910 \times 0.4540)$$

$$x = 162.7 \text{ m}$$

7 Newton's Second Law

INSTRUCTOR NOTES

Process Skills

observing, using numbers, measuring, communicating, interpreting data, questioning, controlling variables

Teaching Suggestions

1. A large-capacity electronic balance (4 kg) will speed the process of determining the mass of the carts and attached tape and string.
2. Be sure that students begin measuring the zero dot as close as possible to the beginning cluster of dots so that the initial velocity is zero.

Observations and Data

Table 1 (Sample data are given.)

	Value
Period of timer (s)	1/60
Mass of laboratory cart (kg)	1.292
Mass needed to equalize friction of cart (kg)	0.015

Copyright © by Glencoe/McGraw-Hill.

Table 2 (Sample data are given.)

Trial	Accelerating force (N)	Distance (m)	Number of dots	Time (s)
1	9.80	0.610	33	0.55
2	9.80	0.493	30	0.50
3	9.80	0.550	30	0.50

Table 3 (Sample data are given.)

Trial	Acceleration (m/s^2)	Total mass (kg)	(m)(a) (N)
1	4.03	2.308	9.30
2	3.94	2.308	9.09
3	4.40	2.308	10.2

Analysis

1. See Table 2.
2. Trial 1: $a = 2(0.610 \text{ m})/(0.55 \text{ s})^2 = 4.03 \text{ m/s}^2$
   Trial 2: $a = 2(0.493 \text{ m})/(0.50 \text{ s})^2 = 3.94 \text{ m/s}^2$
   Trial 3: $a = 2(0.55 \text{ m})/(0.50 \text{ s})^2 = 4.40 \text{ m/s}^2$
3. less than. The falling mass must move itself plus the cart. Therefore, the force of the falling mass is diminished by that amount of force required to move the cart's mass.
4. total mass = 1.293 kg (cart + string + tape) + 1.000 kg (falling mass) + 0.015 kg (small masses) = 2.308 kg
5. Trial 1: $(2.308 \text{ kg})(4.03 \text{ m/s}^2) = 9.30 \text{ N}$
   Trial 2: $(2.308 \text{ kg})(3.94 \text{ m/s}^2) = 9.09 \text{ N}$
   Trial 3: $(2.308 \text{ kg})(4.40 \text{ m/s}^2) = 10.2 \text{ N}$
6. Error should be less than 20% and, with careful technique, it can be less than 10%. Using the sample data from the three trials, the values for relative error were 5%, 7%, and 4%.
7. $F = mg = (0.015 \text{ kg})(9.8 \text{ m/s}^2) = 0.15 \text{ N}$
8. Frictional forces oppose the force (weight) of the falling mass; the net force is thus reduced by this friction.

Application

The frictional forces acting on an automobile include sliding friction between tires and the road and air resistance to automobile movement. When the frictional forces are equal to the force produced by the engine, the net force is zero. Therefore, there will be no acceleration, and the automobile will travel at a constant velocity.

8 Conservation of Energy

Processing Skills

observing, measuring, using numbers, communicating, interpreting data, questioning, defining operationally

Alternative Materials

A non-stick cooking spray can be substituted for the silicone spray.

Teaching Suggestions

1. Emphasize the importance of moving the block up and down the incline at constant speed. If the block is accelerated, the scale reading will be wrong.
2. The quantity $F_{\parallel}d$ is the work done going up the frictionless inclined plane. $F_{up}d$ represents the work input including the work done against friction.

Observations and Data

Weight of the block = 6.0 N

Table 1 (Sample data are given.)

Trial	Length, d (m)	Height, h (m)	F_{up} (N)	F_{down} (N)
1	0.96	0.46	5.0	1.0
2	0.73	0.46	5.5	2.0
3				

Table 2 (Sample data are given.)

Trial	$F_{\parallel}$ (N)	Work done without friction, $F_{\parallel}d$ (J)	Potential energy mgh (J)	Work input $F_{up}d$ (J)
1	3.0	2.9	2.8	4.8
2	3.8	2.8	2.8	4.0
3				

Analysis

1.
$$F_{up} = F_{\parallel} + F_f$$
$$F_{down} = F_{\parallel} - F_f$$
$$\overline{F_{up} + F_{down} = 2F_{\parallel}}$$
$$F_{\parallel} = (F_{up} + F_{down})/2$$

2. Trial 1: $F_{\parallel}$ = (5.0 N + 1.0 N)/2 = 3.0 N
   Trial 2: $F_{\parallel}$ = (5.5 N + 2.0 N)/2 = 3.8 N
3. Trial 1: W = (3.0 N)(0.96 m) = 2.9 J
   Trial 2: W = (3.8 N)(0.73 m) = 2.8 J
4. PE = (6.0 N)(0.46 m) = 2.8 J
5. In the absence of friction, the energy within the system is conserved. Students should have nearly the same values for work and potential energy.

Application

Since the hill is frictionless, the gravitational force converts the stored potential energy of the skier at the top of the hill to kinetic energy.

$$mgh = \tfrac{1}{2}mv^2$$
$$(60.0 \text{ kg})(9.80 \text{ m/s}^2)(10.0 \text{ m}) = \tfrac{1}{2}(60.0 \text{ kg})v^2$$
$$v^2 = 196 \text{ m}^2$$
$$v = 14 \text{ m/s}$$

Extension

Trial 1: $F_{\parallel} = W \sin \theta$ = (6 N)(0.46/0.96) = 2.9 N
Trial 2: $F_{\parallel} = W \sin \theta$ = (6 N)(0.46/0.73) = 3.7 N

Student answers for differences will vary, but most students will suggest that they may have pulled too hard, causing some acceleration of the block, or they pulled at an angle to the direction parallel to the plane, thus increasing the force reading.

INSTRUCTOR NOTES

9 Conserva- tion of Momentum

Process Skills

observing, formulating models, interpreting, defining operationally, using numbers, questioning, communicating, measuring

Troubleshooting

If students have trouble making the steel balls land on their paper sheets, lower the starting position of the ball on the incline so that it has a smaller initial velocity.

Teaching Suggestions

1. Use this laboratory investigation only after students are comfortable with the concept of conservation of momentum for a collision in one direction.
2. Remind students that their results may not be perfect, as evidenced by a clustering of the points where the steel balls land. Students will have and should expect some discrepancy between the magnitude and direction of the momentum vector after the collision and those of the momentum vector before the collision.

Observations and Data

Table 1 (Sample data are given.)

Magnitude of Vectors		
$p_{initial}$ (cm)	p_{target} (cm)	$p_{incident}$ (cm)
29.4	23.1	13.4

Analysis

1. $p_{target} + p_{incident}$ = 23.1 cm + 13.4 cm. The sum, 36.5 cm, does not equal $p_{initial}$. These are vector quantities; their sum is the resultant, not the numerical sum of their magnitudes.
2. p_{final} is represented by 27.7 cm.
3. The magnitude of the initial momentum is represented by 29.4 cm while that of the final momentum is represented by 27.7 cm. These values are close. Students should have values that are within 20% of each other.

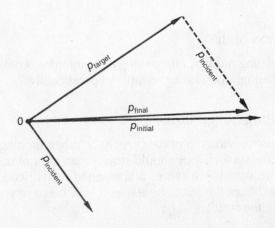

4. The directions of the initial and final momentum vectors are nearly the same. Ideally, the resultant should be equal in magnitude and identical in direction to the initial momentum vector of the incident ball before the collision. Students should realize that their experimental results may not be perfect.

Application

Assuming that the ball is thrown with the same velocity each time, the momentum will be the same. If you let your hands move backwards as you catch the ball, the transfer of momentum will occur over a longer period of time. This extension will relieve the sting your hands feel.

Extension

1. The final momentum of the incident ball and the two target balls will be equal to the initial momentum of the incident ball. The total momentum of a closed, isolated system always remains constant no matter how many objects there are in the system. This relationship is shown by the following:

$$p_a = p'_a + p_b + p_c.$$

2. Mass can be canceled out, and the equation can be recognized as a form of the Pythagorean theorem, $v_a^2 = v_a'^2 + v_b^2$, for a right triangle. Therefore, if this equality holds, the angle between the velocity vectors after the collision must be a right angle.

INSTRUCTOR NOTES

10 Kepler's Laws

Process Skills

formulating models, interpreting data, inferring, communicating, questioning, defining operationally

Teaching Suggestions

1. Students should plot data precisely. When plotting radius vectors, they should strive for an error of no more than the width of a sharpened pencil lead. The better the plot, the easier it will be to interpret the result.

2. The eccentricity of an orbit is a measure of the roundness of an orbit. The closer the eccentricity is to zero, the more circular the orbit becomes. The closer the eccentricity is to one, the more oval the ellipse becomes as it approaches a straight line. The eccentricity of an orbit is computed with the following:

$$e = \frac{(\text{longest radius} - \text{shortest radius})}{\text{length of the major axis}}$$

The eccentricity of Mercury's orbit is 0.206 and of Earth's orbit is 0.0167.

Observations and Data

Table 1 is found in the student edition.

Analysis

1. Yes. Mercury's orbit is an ellipse, with the center of the sun at one focus.

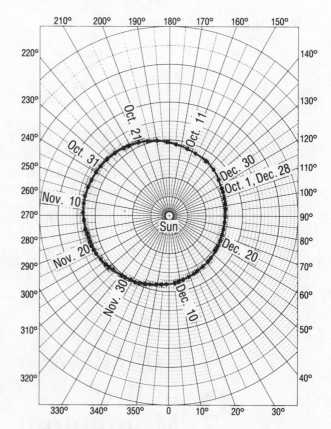

The orbit of Mercury.

2. The area for the section of Mercury's orbit between December 20 and December 30 is found with

$$\text{area} = (61°/360°)(\pi)(0.318 \text{ AU})^2$$
$$= 0.054 \text{ AU}^2/10 \text{ days}.$$

3. Student choices for areas may vary. Two choices are the following:

Oct. 11–21,
  area = (38°/360°)(π)(0.396 AU)²
       = 0.052 AU²/10 days
Nov. 10–20,
  area = (29°/360°)(π)(0.457 AU)²
       = 0.053 AU²/10 days

4. The average area should be about 0.053 AU²/10 days. Students should have errors of less than 5% if their graphs are carefully plotted. Yes, the orbit supports Kepler's law of areas.

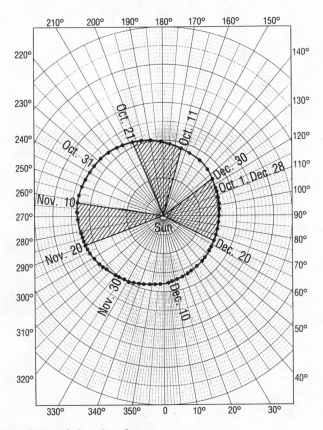

Three areas of the orbit of Mercury.

5. Average radius = (0.307 AU + 0.467 AU)/2
                  = 0.387 AU

$$\frac{T_M^2}{T_E^2} = \frac{r_M^3}{r_E^3},$$

$$T_M^2 = \frac{(0.387\ AU)^3(365.25\ days)^2}{(1.0\ AU)^3}$$

$$T_M = 88\ days$$

6. From the graph, the period = 30 days + 30 days + 28 days = 88 days. The values from Questions 5 and 6 for the period of Mercury are the same (88 days). Thus, the results from the graph are consistent with Kepler's law of periods.

Application

$$T_x^2 = \frac{(1.0\ AU)^3(1.0\ yr)^2}{(1.0\ AU)^3} = (1.0\ yr)^2$$

$$T_x = 1.0\ yr$$

Extension

The orbit of Mars and three different areas of the orbit of Mars are shown in the figures below. The area per day = 0.01 AU²/day. The orbit is an ellipse. Yes, Kepler's law of areas applies.

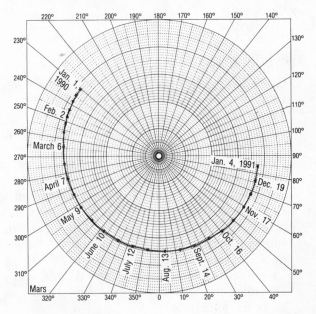

The orbit of Mars.

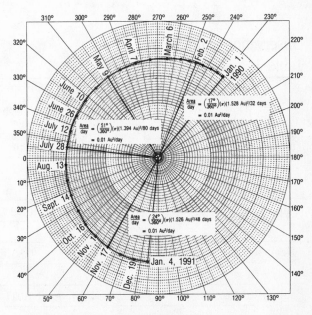

Three areas of the orbit of Mars.

11 Pulleys

Process Skills

observing, using numbers, communicating, interpreting data, measuring, inferring, questioning, defining operationally, designing experiments

Teaching Suggestions

1. Grade the results reasonably. Although this investigation should work out well, there are several sources of error in doing the laboratory activity, mostly in getting accurate spring scale readings. Consequently, results usually do not show very close agreement. Demonstrate the proper use of the spring scale in each arrangement. Emphasize the necessity for using the least pull required to keep the mass moving upward at a slow and steady rate. Tell students to consider other potential sources of error and to take precautions that will minimize their effect on results.
2. Demonstrate the measurement of W, h, F, and d. Students often have difficulty measuring d, the distance the force moves.
3. If time and equipment permit, you may want to let students experiment with the pulley systems they have designed in response to the Application suggestion.

Observations and Data

Table 1 (Sample data are given.)

Pulley arrange-ment	Mass raised (kg)	Weight (W) of mass (N)	Height (h) mass is raised (m)	Force (F) of spring scale (N)	Distance (d) through which force acts (m)
(a)	0.50	4.9	0.25	5.0	0.27
(b)	0.50	4.9	0.25	2.8	0.50
(c)	1.0	9.8	0.25	5.0	0.53
(d)	1.0	9.8	0.25	2.7	1.02

Table 2 (Sample data are given.)

Pulley arrange-ment	Work output (Wh) (J)	Work input (Fd) (J)	IMA (d_e/d_e)	MA Number of lifting strands	Efficiency %
(a)	1.2	1.4	1	1	86
(b)	1.2	1.4	2	2	86
(c)	2.5	2.7	2	2	93
(d)	2.5	2.8	4	4	89

Analysis

1. Inaccuracies in reading the spring scale, accuracy of the spring scale, and friction are the largest causes of error.
2. The force gets smaller as the mechanical advantage gets larger.
3. The IMA and the efficiency should be the same.
4. As the number of pulleys increases, the IMA increases. The efficiency may or may not decrease.
5. The values for IMA and MA should be the same.
6. The amount of work is not reduced, but the force that must be applied is reduced. Considering the losses of energy due to friction, more, not less, work usually must be done.

Application

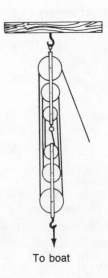

To boat

Hooke's Law and Simple Harmonic Motion

12

Observations and Data

Table 1

Mass added to the weight hanger (kg)	Applied force due to added mass (N)	Scale reading (cm)	Displacement x of mass (m)
		zero reading =	
0	0	15.12	0
0.100 kg	0.980 N	24.92 cm	0.098 m
0.200 kg	1.96 N	35.12 cm	0.200 m
0.300 kg	2.94 N	45.22 cm	0.301 m
0.400 kg	3.92 N	55.22 cm	0.401 m
0.500 kg	4.90 N	65.42 cm	0.503 m

GRAPH (The following graph represents the sample data given above.)

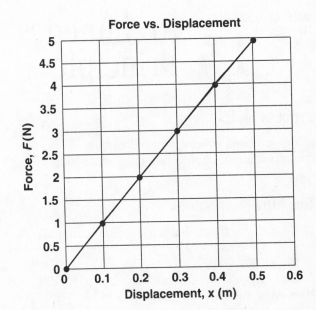

Force vs. Displacement

The slope from your graph $\dfrac{\Delta F}{\Delta x} = 9.72$ N/m.

The spring constant $k = 9.72$ N/m.

Process Skills

Observing, measuring, using significant digits, interpreting data, inferring, computing, and comparing.

Troubleshooting

Conversion of units is often the source of problems with this experiment. Make sure that the units of force are *newtons* and the units of displacement are *meters*. Additionally, you might caution the students to be careful that the vibrating spring oscillates vertically with no possibility of striking the support.

Teaching Suggestions

1. Take a little time before the exercise to review the correct procedures for plotting data on a graph. Make sure that they use a straight edge to draw the best straight line fitting the data and that they determine the slope independent of any specific data points.
2. Emphasize that the spring constant k is the ratio of the *change* in force to the *change* in displacement. It is not necessary to consider what weight might be already attached to the hanger; consider only how *additional* mass causes *additional* displacements.
3. Explain that the spring itself is a part of the vibrating system, and its mass must also be considered in a theoretical determination of the period of vibration.

Table 2 (In this example, the mass of the spring was 171.72 g.)

Total mass m suspended from the spring (kg)	Effective mass $m' = m + m_s/3$ (kg)	Time for 50 vibrations (s)	Period T (s) Experimental	Period T (s) Calculated	Percent error
0.200 kg	0.257 kg	48.50 s	0.970 s	1.02 s	4.9%
0.400 kg	0.457 kg	66.10 s	1.32 s	1.36 s	2.9%

Analysis

1. The spring constant is determined by the change in applied force, and, therefore does not depend on the initial force that may already be present. At any time you can determine the spring constant by simply adding mass and recording the corresponding increase in the stretch of the spring.
2. If you had ignored the mass of the spring, the additional correction factor would not be present. In our example, this means that $m' = m$. We would have used 0.200 kg instead of 0.257 kg. The theoretical period would have been 0.90 s instead of 1.02 s. This represents a value that is about 12% less than the value which accounts for spring mass.

INSTRUCTOR NOTES

13 Archimedes' Principle

Process Skills

using numbers, observing, predicting, communicating, interpreting data, measuring, questioning

Teaching Suggestions

1. Be sure that the spring scales are functioning properly. If they stick, a large error is introduced into the results.
2. Each laboratory group could be given different masses, such as 200 g, 400 g, and 1000 g. To prevent damage to the equipment, be sure that the spring scale has the capacity to measure the larger masses.
3. Review with students the equation for buoyant force, $F_b = \rho V g$. This will help them understand that the buoyant force is related to the weight of the volume of fluid displaced, not the weight of the submerged object.

Observations and Data

Table 1 (Sample data are given.)

Weight of 500-g mass in air	4.9 N
Weight of 500-g mass immersed in water	4.2 N
Volume of water in beaker	300 mL
Volume of water in beaker with 500-g mass immersed	375 mL

Table 2 (Sample data are given.)

Volume of water in beaker	300 mL
Volume of water with 100-g mass immersed	320 mL
Volume of water with 100-g mass in polystyrene cup	400 mL

Analysis

1. $F_{buoyant} = 4.9 \text{ N} - 4.2 \text{ N} = 0.70 \text{ N}$
2. Volume displaced = 375 mL − 300 mL
   = 75 mL;
   75 mL of water is equivalent to 75 g of water.

   $$F = (0.075 \text{ kg})(9.8 \text{ m/s}^2) = 0.73 \text{ N}.$$

   Student explanations will vary, but may include errors in measuring volume and force. Students might also note the effect of air bubbles that adhere to the surface of the mass.
3. It rose. The 100-g mass in the boat has an average density less than that of water, and the boat (with mass) floats. But the weight of the fluid it displaces is now greater than the weight of the water displaced by the mass alone. Whereas the volume of water displaced by the weight of the mass alone was 20 mL, now the 100-g mass displaces 100 g of water when it is placed in the boat. Since 100 g of water is equivalent to 100 mL of water, this is the difference between the observed volumes.

Application

The water level in the pool drops because Tim and Sally are heavier than the weight of the water they displace while submerged. When they fall into the water, they displace a volume of water that is less than their weight; the volume of water displaced is equal to the buoyant force acting on them. Since they displace less water while submerged than when floating, the pool water level drops when they fall off the raft.

INSTRUCTOR NOTES

14 Specific Heat

Process Skills

observing, communicating, interpreting data, measuring, using numbers, questioning

Teaching Suggestions

1. Mercury thermometers are dangerous and should be removed from school laboratory supply stock. Use only alcohol thermometers to avoid the risk of a mercury spill.
2. The old-style calorimetry cups (typically aluminum) can be used. However, if this type is used, then the heat lost by the hot metal equals the heat gained by the water, plus the heat gained by the calorimeter.
3. If lead is used, the mass must be large enough (300–400 g) to cause a measurable temperature change.
4. Review with students the values for specific heat of common substances found in Appendix B. They may note that the value for water is very high. Explain that this property of water makes it a particularly good coolant for car engines.

Observations and Data

Table 1 (Sample data are given.)

	Trial 1	Trial 2
Type of metal	brass	aluminum
Mass of calorimeter cup (kg)	0.0016	0.0016
Mass of calorimeter cup and water (kg)	0.1203	0.1251
Mass of metal (kg)	0.2741	0.0905
Initial temperature of room temperature water (°C)	22	23
Temperature of hot metal (°C)	100	100
Final temperature of metal and water (°C)	35	33.5

Table 2 (Sample data are given.)

	Trial 1	Trial 2
Mass of room temperature water (kg)	0.1187	0.1235
ΔT metal (°C)	65	66.5
ΔT room temperature water (°C)	13	10.5

Analysis

1. See Table 2.
2. Trial 1
$$Q_{\text{gained by water}} = (0.1187 \text{ kg})(13°C)(4180 \text{ J/kg} \cdot °C)$$
$$= 6450 \text{ J}$$

Trial 2
$$Q_{\text{gained by water}} = (0.1235 \text{ kg})(10.5°C)(4180 \text{ J/kg} \cdot °C)$$
$$= 5420 \text{ J}$$

3. Trial 1
$$C_{\text{brass}} = 6450 \text{ J}/(0.2741 \text{ kg})(65°C)$$
$$= 362 \text{ J/kg} \cdot °C = 362 \text{ J/kg} \cdot K$$

Trial 2
$$C_{\text{aluminum}} = 5420 \text{ J}/(0.0905 \text{ kg})(66.5°C)$$
$$= 901 \text{ J/kg} \cdot °C = 901 \text{ J/kg} \cdot K$$

4. Trial 1
$$\text{relative error} = [(376 - 362) \times 100\%]/376$$
$$= 4\%$$

Trial 2
$$\text{relative error} = [(903 - 901) \times 100\%]/903$$
$$= 0.2\%$$

Student errors should be less than 15%. If samples are of lead or of very small mass, errors will be larger because the temperature changes in these situations will not be great enough to measure.

5. The thermometer may not be reading accurately (however, the difference in temperature should be accurate). Heat may have been lost to the environment from radiation out of the top of the cup. Some hot water from the sample may have dripped into the calorimeter.

Application

$$C_{\text{substance}} = \frac{(m_{\text{water}})(\Delta T_{\text{water}})(4180 \text{ J/kg} \cdot K)}{(m_{\text{substance}})(\Delta T_{\text{substance}})}$$
$$= 656 \text{ J/kg} \cdot K$$

From Appendix B, this value for specific heat is closest to that of glass.

Extension

As demonstrated in the application, students should be able to identify the substance by its specific heat. Be sure that the unknown has a large enough mass or the temperature change will be insignificant, and a large error will result.

15 Standing Waves in a Vibrating String

Process Skills

Observing, inferring, communicating, interpreting data, and questioning.

Teaching Suggestions

1. The electromagnetic vibrator exhibits a frequency of 120 Hz rather than the actual ac line frequency of 60 Hz. This is due to the fact that the metal vibrating strip is not magnetized, and it is attracted to the magnetic pole no matter which way the current flows. The strip is lifted as the current rises in either positive or negative direction and it springs back as the current falls. This results in twice the frequency that might be expected.
2. Once again the use of consistent units is of paramount importance. Common errors result from improper conversions. The mass must be in *kilograms,* the length in *meters,* and the force in *newtons.*
3. If desired, you can obtain slightly greater accuracy by having the students measure the internodal distances directly. The procedure chosen here is to divide the entire length of the string by the number of loops. However, the hole in the vibrating strip is obviously not a true nodal point. Thus, the first loop is not truly a half-wavelength. The error is small enough that it shouldn't affect the results very much.
4. Because the tension required to reach a single or a double loop is so great, you may wish to have students record data for 7, 6, 5, 4, and 3 loops. It will make for a better graph and probably a more accurate slope calculation.

Observations and Data

Mass of string m = 0.136 g = 0.000136 kg

Length of string L = 100 cm = 1.00 m

Linear density of string μ = 0.00014 kg/m

Number of loops	5	4	3	2	1
Length of vibrating string in meters (m)	1.00 m	1.00 m	1.00 m	1.00 m	1.00 m
Average length of one loop (m)	0.200 m	0.250 m	0.333 m	0.500 m	1.00 m
Wavelength λ (m)	0.400 m	0.500 m	0.666 m	1.00 m	2.00 m
Wavelength squared λ^2 (m²)	0.160 m²	0.250 m²	0.444 m²	1.00 m²	4.00 m²
Mass suspended from string (kg)	0.0330 kg	0.0510 kg	0.0910 kg	0.220 kg	0.840 kg
Tension in string T (N)	0.323 N	0.500 N	0.892 N	2.16 N	8.23 N

Slope of your graph T/λ^2 (include units)   2.07 N/m²

Calculated frequency of the vibrator   122 Hz

Relative error   1.7%

16 Investigating Static Electricity

Process Skills

observing, classifying, communicating, interpreting data, inferring, hypothesizing, questioning

Troubleshooting

On a humid day, it may not be possible to produce a positive charge with the glass rods. In these weather conditions, you will find that many of the lucite or acrylic materials produce adequate positive charges. The strength of the positive charge produced by these materials can be verified by comparison with the negative charge produced by a hard rubber rod.

Alternative Materials

Nylon or cotton scraps can also be used for rubbing pads.

Teaching Suggestions

1. Encourage students to make detailed observations. Often students rush through this experiment and are unsure of what they saw.
2. On a dry day, the vane type of electroscope should perform well. This type requires more charge to cause a deflection than does the leaf electroscope. On more humid days, it is better to use a leaf electroscope; it responds better with a smaller charge.

Observations and Data

Table 1

A. Negatively Charging a Pith Ball

Observations of pith ball with nearby charged rod:

The pith ball is attracted toward the charged rod.

Observations of pith ball after it has been touched with a charged rod:

The pith ball is attracted toward the rod but, after it has been touched, it is repelled.

Table 2

B. Positively Charging a Pith Ball

Observations of pith ball with nearby charged rod:

The pith ball is attracted toward the charged rod.

Observations of pith ball after it has been touched with a charged rod:

The pith ball is attracted toward the rod but, after it has been touched, it is repelled.

Table 3

C. Charging an Electroscope by Conduction

Observations of uncharged electroscope when negatively-charged rod touches it:

The vane deflects (or the leaves separate).

Observations of negatively-charged electroscope when negatively-charged rod is brought near:

The electroscope vane is (or leaves are) further deflected while the rod is nearby; the original charged position is assumed when the rod is removed.

Observations of negatively-charged electroscope when a positively-charged rod is brought near:

The vane moves back toward zero (or the leaves collapse). When the rod is removed, the electroscope again indicates the presence of charge.

Observations of deflection of leaves or vane when plastic material charges the electroscope and a negatively-charged rod is brought near:

The rubber rod causes the electroscope to move back toward zero, indicating that it has a charge opposite that of the rod. The electroscope is positively charged.

Table 4

D. Charging an Electroscope by Induction

Observations of electroscope when charged rod is brought near:

The electroscope vane or leaves move, indicating the presence of charge, but when the rod is removed, the vane returns to zero or the leaves fall.

Observations of electroscope after touching with finger:

The electroscope indicates the presence of charge when the charged rod is brought near, but drops to zero when it is touched by a finger. After the finger and then the charged rod are removed from the electroscope top, the electroscope again indicates the presence of charge.

Observations to determine the type of charge:

The electroscope has a charge opposite that of the charged rod that was originally brought near. The leaves converge or the vane returns to zero, indicating that the original charged rod is attracting the charge of the electroscope.

Table 5

E. Charging a Leyden Jar

Observations of charging a Leyden jar-electroscope combination:

The electroscope charges easily by itself, but does not (apparently) charge when the Leyden jar is attached. The charge travels through the wire to the Leyden jar, which stores charge.

Analysis

1. The ball touches the charged rod, becomes charged, and then is repelled.
2. The ball touches the charged rod, becomes charged, and then is repelled.
3. The process is the same for either type of charge.
4. When the charged rod touches the electroscope ball, the vane deflects (leaves diverge). The vane or leaves return to normal when the electroscope ball is touched by a finger.
5. Electrons were transferred to the electroscope, the vane (leaves) became negatively charged and deflected (repelled each other).
6. The leaves were still negatively charged.
7. The charge was positive. Student results may vary depending on the type of material available. The charge type can be confirmed by testing it with a known negatively-charged rod.
8. The finger provided a path to ground for the charge that was the same type as that of the charged rod brought near the electroscope. The net charge remaining on the electroscope, after the finger and rod were removed from the electroscope top, was opposite that of the charged rod.
9. It was the charge opposite that of the rod.
10. It acted as a ground, removing some of the charges.

11. Conduction produces the same charge; induction produces the opposite charge.
12. The charge was transferred to the Leyden jar (it stores static charges) from the electroscope. The electroscope does not retain the charge, as shown by the action of the leaves (they come together) or the vane (it returns to zero).

Application

When the record is slid out of its plastic cover, static electricity is produced as a result of the rubbing together of these two materials. These static charges can damage the needle if, when it comes down onto the record, a discharge (electrical spark) occurs. Record cleaners serve two purposes—to remove dust and to eliminate static electricity. Dust may accumulate on or be attracted to a record, which is easily charged with static electricity. The fluid or water causes static charge to dissipate quickly.

2. The initial value of the current will rise very quickly, and then begin dropping off. In analog meters, there will be a slight delay while the meter reaches the initial reading, so students probably will not have an accurate recorded value for time = 0. At time = 0, the capacitor acts like a short, so the actual value of current is $I = V/R$, where V is the potential difference of the power source and R is the value of the circuit resistor. When the graph is plotted, the initial reading will not make a significant difference in the curve.
3. Show students how the unit of RC (seconds) can be traced from the derived SI units of resistance (ohms) and capacitance (farads).

Observations and Data

Table 1 (Sample data are given.)

Battery voltage	15.0 VDC
Capacitance	1000 μF

INSTRUCTOR NOTES

17 The Capacitor

Process Skills

observing, measuring, communicating, predicting, hypothesizing, questioning, controlling variables

Alternative Materials

Larger capacitors may be substituted for the 1000 μF value; however, if smaller capacitors are used, the time constant, RC, will be small. The capacitor will charge too quickly, making measurements difficult.

Teaching Suggestions

1. Discuss polarity for meters, batteries, and capacitors prior to the experiment. This preparation will minimize the chances that students will wire the circuit incorrectly. Before they close the switch, have students trace the circuit path with a finger while looking at the circuit diagram. Review with students the "Rules for Using Meters" in Appendix C.

Table 2 (Sample data are given.)

Time (s)	27 kΩ Current (mA)	10 kΩ Current (mA)
0	1.100	0.510
5	0.900	0.450
10	0.640	0.400
15	0.450	0.340
20	0.320	0.300
25	0.230	0.250
30	0.170	0.210
35	0.130	0.190
40	0.100	0.160
45	0.080	0.140
50	0.060	0.120
55	0.050	0.100
60	0.046	0.095
65	0.039	0.083
70	0.035	0.075
75	0.032	0.064
80	0.030	0.058
85	0.028	0.052
90	0.025	0.048

Analysis

1. With no current on the capacitor plates, the current begins as a maximum. As the capacitor becomes charged, the current flow gradually becomes smaller until it approaches zero as the capacitor becomes fully charged.

2. The resistor controls the amount of current flowing to the capacitor; thus, it regulates the charging rate. The larger the value of resistance, the longer it will take to charge the capacitor.

3.

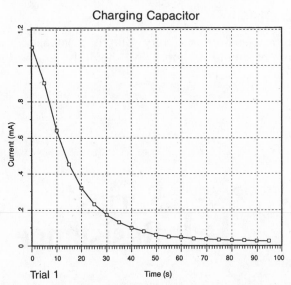

Trial 1

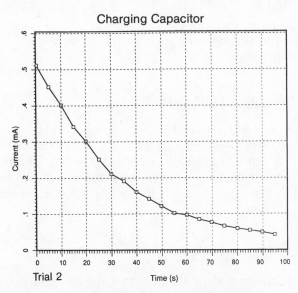

Trial 2

These graphs of current versus time for a charging capacitor were produced using the Lab Partner™ graphing program.

4. Charge $= $Area$_{27\ k\Omega} = \frac{1}{2}bh$
$= \frac{1}{2}(35\text{ s})(1.1 \times 10^{-3}\text{ A})$
$= 1.9 \times 10^{-2}\text{ C}$
Charge $= $Area$_{10\ k\Omega} = \frac{1}{2}bh$
$= \frac{1}{2}(90\text{ s})(0.4 \times 10^{-3}\text{ A})$
$= 1.8 \times 10^{-2}\text{ C}$

5. Trial 1: $C = q/V = (1.9 \times 10^{-2}\text{ C})/15.0\text{ V} =$
$1.3 \times 10^{-3}\text{ F} = 1300\ \mu F$
Trial 2: $C = q/V = (1.8 \times 10^{-2}\text{ C})/15.0\text{ V} =$
$1.2 \times 10^{-3}\text{ F} = 1200\ \mu F$

6. Trial 1: relative error $= (1300 - 1000)(100\%)/$
$1000 = 30\%$
Trial 2: relative error $= (1200 - 1000)(100\%)/$
$1000 = 20\%$

7. Without a resistor, the capacitor would become charged almost instantly; the current would as quickly drop to zero.

8. The capacitor value and the power source voltage remained constant while the resistance was manipulated. The current in the circuit varies inversely with time.

Application

Since a capacitor requires a specific time to charge through a resistor, the RC combination can be used for timing applications, such as for a burglar alarm or a timer to turn on or off a light. For a short time of charging or discharging, the RC circuit can be used to produce musical notes for an electronic instrument or keyboard.

Extension

Answers will vary depending on the capacitor used. The exponential decay of current shown on the graph will drop more slowly as the capacitance increases.

INSTRUCTOR NOTES

18 Ohm's Law

Process Skills

observing, measuring, using numbers, interpreting data, communicating, predicting, inferring, questioning, controlling variables, defining operationally

Alternative Materials

An excellent source for an inexpensive, high quality voltmeter is Radio Shack. The versatile multitester unit provides several voltage ranges and current ranges from the same meter. The multitester can measure resistance if it is powered by a battery which, of course, you would not include if students are expected to find the values of unknown resistors.

Teaching Suggestions

1. Variable power supplies work well for this experiment. Remind students not to exceed the values each meter is designed to measure.
2. The recommended resistors are readily available and inexpensive, particularly if they are purchased from an electrical supply house or ordered from Radio Shack. Use of milliammeters and these resistors reduces the circuit currents; however, the resistors can still become warm. Caution students not to touch resistors when current flows in the circuit.
3. Unknown resistors can be made by covering other known resistors with heat-shrink tubing. To prevent current readings from being small and difficult to measure, try not to exceed values of more than about 470 Ω for unknowns. A couple of resistors can be placed in parallel or in series to create various resistance values. When resistors are sealed in heat-shrink tubing, the color bands are not visible. The use of unknowns encourages students to do their own work.
4. Tell students to open the switch immediately if the meter "pegs" or travels all the way to the far side of the meter.

Observations and Data

Table 1 (Sample data are given.)

Resistor	Printed value of resistor (Ω)	Tolerance range (+/− %)	Voltage (V)	Current (mA)	Current (A)	Resistance (Ω)
R_1	100	20	1.5	14	0.014	110
	100	20	5.0	49	0.049	100
R_2	150	20	1.5	10	0.010	150
	150	20	5.0	30	0.030	170
R_3	220	20	1.5	7.0	0.0070	210
	220	20	5.0	24	0.024	210

Analysis

1. See Resistance column of Table 1.
2. R_1 error: $(105 - 100)(100\%)/100 = 5\%$
   R_2 error: $(160 - 150)(100\%)/150 = 7\%$
   R_3 error: $(220 - 210)(100\%)/220 = 5\%$
   These sample values agree fairly well; however, student answers (values) may be more divergent.
3. The resistors may have overheated, causing the values to change. The voltmeter may introduce some error in the circuit, since it requires some current to cause deflection of the needle.
4. The ammeter must be placed in series with the circuit element.

5. The voltmeter must be placed in parallel with the circuit element to be measured.
6. The current in a circuit is equal to the voltage divided by the resistance.

Application

$$R = \frac{V}{I} = \frac{120 \text{ V}}{0.5 \text{ A}} = 240 \ \Omega$$

Extension

Student answers will vary. Graphs of voltage versus current should be linear and should have a positive slope.

INSTRUCTOR NOTES

19 Series Resistance

Process Skills

observing, measuring, using numbers, communicating, interpreting data, predicting, questioning

Alternative Materials

Resistors of 5, 10, or 15 Ω can be used, but they are more expensive and difficult to obtain and must have 10-W ratings to prevent overheating in Part A (use of a single resistor). In this case, an ammeter with a range of 0–1 A must be used instead of the smaller milliammeter.

Teaching Suggestions

1. Caution students that, even though the resistors are small, they can still become hot if too large a voltage is applied. Do not exceed the recommended voltage and do not handle the resistors while the current is flowing through the circuit.
2. Remind students to check the polarity of their meters before activating the circuit to prevent damage to the meters.
3. Remind students to convert milliamps to amps before applying Ohm's law.

Observations and Data

Table 1 (Sample data are given.)

	R_1 (Ω)	Ammeter reading (mA)	Voltmeter reading (V)
	100	50	5.0
Tolerance (%)	10		

Table 2 (Sample data are given.)

	R_1 (Ω)	R_2 (Ω)	Ammeter reading (mA)	Voltmeter reading (V)
	100	82	28	5.0
Tolerance (%)	10	10		

Table 3 (Sample data are given.)

	R_1 (Ω)	R_2 (Ω)	R_3 (Ω)	Ammeter reading (mA)	Voltmeter reading (V)			
					$V_{1,2,3}$	V_1	V_2	V_3
	100	82	68	20.0	5.0	2.0	1.6	1.4
Tolerance (%)	10	10	5					

Analysis

1. Measured value of resistance $= \dfrac{V}{I}$

   $= \dfrac{(5.0 \text{ V})}{(0.05 \text{ A})} = 100 \ \Omega$. The two values agree.

2. Measured value of the equivalent resistance $= \dfrac{V}{I} = \dfrac{(5.0 \text{ V})}{(0.028 \text{ A})} = 180 \ \Omega$. The equivalent resistance $= 100 \ \Omega + 82 \ \Omega = 182 \ \Omega$. 180 Ω is within the 20% tolerance range. Student answers will vary, but should be within the tolerance range.

3. Measured equivalent resistance $= \dfrac{V}{I}$

   $= \dfrac{(5.0 \text{ V})}{(0.02 \text{ A})} = 250 \ \Omega$. The calculated equivalent resistance $= R_1 + R_2 + R_3 = 100 + 82 + 68 = 250 \ \Omega$. The two values agree. Student answers should fall within the sum of the tolerances for the resistors.

4. The equivalent resistance is determined by adding the individual resistances together.

5. The sum of the individual voltages $= 2.0 \text{ V} + 1.6 \text{ V} + 1.4 \text{ V} = 5.0 \text{ V}$. The sum of the voltage drops across individual resistances is equal to the total voltage drop around the circuit.

6. The amount of (equivalent) resistance determines the current in the circuit as long as the voltage remains constant.

Application

The equivalent resistance is found by

$$R = \frac{V}{I} = \frac{120 \text{ V}}{1.0 \text{ A}} = 120 \ \Omega.$$

Since there are 50 lights of equal resistance, the resistance of an individual light is 120 Ω/50 = 2.4 Ω. The voltage drop per light is $V = IR = (1.0 \text{ A})(2.4 \ \Omega) = 2.4 \text{ V}$.

INSTRUCTOR NOTES

20 Parallel Resistance

Process Skills

observing, predicting, measuring, using numbers, interpreting data, communicating, inferring

Teaching Suggestions

1. Remind students to convert milliamps to amps before applying Ohm's law.
2. Caution students to use care when touching the resistors and to leave switches closed no more than a few seconds at a time.
3. Depending on the internal resistance of the ammeters, student data may not match perfectly. Remind them to take careful measurements.
4. Be sure to allow sufficient time for students to complete this experiment. It takes time to move the meters about and obtain circuit measurements.

Observations and Data

Table 1 (Sample data are given.)

	R_1 (Ω)	Ammeter reading (mA)	Voltmeter reading (V)
	180	17	3.0
Tolerance (%)	10		

Table 2 (Sample data are given.)

	R_1 (Ω)	R_2 (Ω)	Ammeter reading (mA)			Voltmeter reading (V)		
			I	I_1	I_2	V	V_1	V_2
	180	220	30	17	14	3	3	3
Tolerance (%)	10	10						

Table 3 (Sample data are given.)

	R_1 (Ω)	R_2 (Ω)	R_3 (Ω)	Ammeter reading (mA)				Voltmeter reading (V)			
				I	I_1	I_2	I_3	V	V_1	V_2	V_3
	180	220	330	39	17	14	10	3	3	3	3
Tolerance (%)	10	10	10								

Analysis

1. $R_1 = \dfrac{3.0\,V}{0.017\,A} = 176\ \Omega.$

   Student answers will vary; the sample data yield a result within the tolerance range.

2. a. $R = \dfrac{V}{I} = \dfrac{3.0\,V}{0.03\,A} = 100\ \Omega$

   b. $I = 17\,mA + 14\,mA = 31\,mA$

   c. $R_1 = \dfrac{3.0\,V}{0.017\,A} = 176\ \Omega$

   d. $R_2 = \dfrac{3.0\,V}{0.014\,A} = 214\ \Omega$

   e. $R = 99\ \Omega$

3. Student values may have a greater difference, depending on the quality of the ammeters used.

   a. The measured current should equal the sum of the currents (or very nearly).

   b. Using the sample readings, the calculated equivalent resistance (99 Ω) equals the measured equivalent resistance (97 Ω) within the tolerance of the resistors.

4. a. $R = \dfrac{3.0\,V}{0.039\,A} = 77\ \Omega$

   b. $I = 17\,mA + 14\,mA + 10\,mA = 41\,mA$

   c. $R_1 = \dfrac{3.0\,V}{0.017\,A} = 176\ \Omega$

   d. $R_2 = \dfrac{3.0\,V}{0.014\,A} = 214\ \Omega$

   e. $R_3 = \dfrac{3.0\,V}{0.010\,A} = 300\ \Omega$

   f. $R = 76\ \Omega$

5. Student values may have a greater difference, depending on the quality of the ammeters used.

   a. The two currents are very nearly equal (they should be equal).

b. Using the sample readings, the calculated equivalent resistance (76 Ω) equals the measured equivalent resistance (73 Ω) within the tolerance of the resistors.

6. The sum of the current in the branches of a parallel circuit equals the total current in the circuit.

7. The voltage drop across each branch of a parallel circuit is the same as the voltage drop across the entire circuit.

8. The total current increases.

Application

Since the equivalent resistance is 0.5000 Ω and the meter resistance is 500.0 Ω, the shunt resistance is found from

$$\frac{1}{R} = \frac{1}{R_1} + \frac{1}{R_2}, \text{ or } \frac{1}{0.5000\ \Omega} = \frac{1}{500.0\ \Omega} + \frac{1}{R_s}.$$

Solving for $\dfrac{1}{R_s}$,

$$\frac{1}{R_s} = 2.0\ \Omega - 0.002\ \Omega = 1.998\ \Omega.$$

Therefore, $R_s = \dfrac{1}{1.998} = 0.5005\ \Omega.$

Extension

There are many ways to solve this problem. In one solution, the circuit can be reduced to two parallel sets, each having four 100-Ω resistors in parallel connected in series with a pair of 100-Ω resistors in parallel. This reduces to two 75-Ω resistors in parallel, which is equivalent to one 37.5-Ω resistor in series with the 1.0-V battery.

The current = $I = \dfrac{V}{R} = \dfrac{1.0\,V}{37.5\ \Omega} = 27\,mA.$

INSTRUCTOR NOTES

21 Principles of Electro-magnetism

Process Skills

observing, communicating, formulating models, classifying, interpreting data, predicting, questioning

Teaching Suggestions

1. Review the right-hand rule with students before beginning the lab.
2. Remind students to leave the switches closed only long enough to make observations.

Observations and Data

A. The Field Around a Long, Straight Wire

With current flowing upward, the north pole points counter-clockwise about the wire.

With current flowing downward, the north pole points clockwise about the wire.

B. Strength of the Field

The filings are oriented in circular patterns about the wire. The smaller the current, the less distinct the patterns. With 0.5 A of current, almost no pattern is observed.

C. The Field Around a Coil

The compass needle lines up as indicated by the labels in the figure.

D. An Electromagnet

1. Sample electromagnet picks up six clips.
2. Sample electromagnet picks up ten clips; increasing the number of loops increases the magnet's strength.
3. Sample electromagnet picks up 16 clips; increasing the current increases the magnet's strength.

Analysis

1. The direction of the magnetic field follows the direction of the fingers of the right hand when the right thumb points in the direction of the conventional current (from positive to negative).
2. It increases electromagnetic strength.
3.

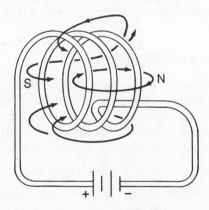

4. The number of turns, the current strength, and the type of core determine the strength of an electromagnet.

5. A bar magnet maintains its magnetism for a long time, while an electromagnet is a temporary magnet, which loses its magnetism as soon as the current flow is stopped.

Application

Continuously applied current: strong electromagnets—such as in junk yards, magnetic-resonance-imaging equipment

Intermittently applied current: telephone ringers, door bells, buzzers, door locks, electric switches (relays)

INSTRUCTOR NOTES

22 Electro-magnetic Induction

Process Skills

observing, communicating, interpreting data, measuring, hypothesizing, predicting, questioning

Alternative Materials

Students can wind the coils around cardboard tubes, such as toilet-paper tubes or paper-towel tubes, using 20- or 22-gauge copper wire. A few pieces of masking or electrical tape keep the coils together. Commercially made coils are available or use a galvanoscope block with wound coils.

Teaching Suggestions

1. Help students understand that while the conversion of electrical energy to mechanical energy in a magnetic field is the principle of the electric motor, the conversion of mechanical energy to electrical energy in a magnetic field is the principle of the electric generator. Emphasize that this correspondence of opposites prevails in many areas of science and provides guidance and structure to researchers and students alike.
2. Remind students to keep magnets away from their wrist watches.

Observations and Data

1. The galvanometer just barely moves. Student answers will vary, depending on the strength of the magnet and the sensitivity of the galvanometer.

2. Students should see movement of the galvanometer needle, indicating that a current was produced.

3. Students should find that a much stronger current is produced, compared to that produced by the 25-turn coil.

4. The galvanometer needle deflects in one direction when the magnet is thrust into the coil and in the opposite direction when the magnet is pulled out. The needle deflects in opposite directions when the north or south pole is thrust into the coil, due to the different directions of the magnetic fields.

5. The stronger magnet produces the stronger current. The greater the speed of the magnets' motion, the stronger the current.

6. No current is induced when the magnets are stationary. A current is produced when the coil moves over the magnets.

Analysis

1. The end of the coil into which the north pole of the magnet is thrust becomes a south pole, and then reverses when the magnet is pulled out. An induced current acts in such a direction that its magnetic properties oppose the change by which the current is induced.

2. The *EMF,* measured in volts, depends on the strength of the magnetic field, the number of loops in the coil, and the speed at which the wire cuts through the magnetic flux. If the moving wire is part of a closed circuit, the induced current is equal to the voltage divided by the resistance of the circuit.

3. From Ohm's law, $V = IR$. If resistance is constant, the voltage *(EMF)* is proportional to the current. This experiment showed that the strength of the magnetic field, B, affected the magnitude of the current; the number of turns, I, affected the current; and the rate of movement, v, of the wire through the magnetic field affected the current. Therefore $EMF \propto B$, $EMF \propto I$, and $EMF \propto v$, and the equation, $EMF = BIv$, is substantiated.

4. No current flows in the wire. An electric current is produced only when the wire cuts the magnetic field lines.

5. No matter what its source, each field exerts a force, $q'E$, on a test charge, q'.

Application

A changing magnetic field appears in the iron core due to the alternating current in the primary coil. Through the iron core, the field moves over the loops of the secondary coil, causing an induced current, and an induced *EMF,* to appear in that coil. The transformer does not work with direct current since no changing magnetic field is produced; thus, no current can be induced.

Extension

1. $EMF = Blv \sin \theta$
   $= (0.75 \times 10^{-2} \text{ T})(0.40 \text{ m})(5.0 \text{ m/s})(\sin 45°)$
   $= 1.1 \times 10^{-2} \text{ V}$

2. *EMF* is greatest when $\theta = 90°$ and diminishes to zero as θ approaches $0°$.

3. The output is an alternating current that varies sinusoidally over a period of time; the amplitude of the current changes with the sine of the angle between v and B. In the U.S., the frequency of alternating current is 60 cycles per second; the current changes direction (alternates) 120 times per second.

INSTRUCTOR NOTES

23 Planck's Constant

Process Skills

observing, measuring, using numbers, communicating, interpreting data, predicting, questioning

Alternative Materials

A variable power supply can be used instead of the battery; however, it should provide well-filtered, clean DC power. Most new variable power supplies meet these criteria. Using a variable power supply permits elimination of the battery and potentiometer.

Teaching Suggestions

1. The packing material of many LEDs displays the wavelength of their emitted radiation. However, if you have some LEDs that are not identified, the following table will help in approximating the wavelengths of light for typical LEDs.

Color	Wavelength (nm)
red	635, 650, 660, 675, 690 (standard red is 650 or 660)
yellow	590, 610
green	550, 563, 570

2. The purpose of the 22-Ω resistor is to limit current to the LED, thus preventing instantaneous destruction of the LED if students accidentally apply too large a voltage. Resistance could be increased to as much as 33 Ω, if desired, or eliminated. If it is eliminated and a potential difference of 3 V is applied to the LED, excess current will flow through the junction and destroy it.

Observations and Data
Table 1

LED	LED Color	Wavelength (nm)
1	red	650
2	yellow	590
3	green	563

Table 2 (Sample data are given.)

LED 1		LED 2		LED 3	
Voltage (V)	Current (mA)	Voltage (V)	Current (mA)	Voltage (V)	Current (mA)
1.50	0	1.50	0	1.50	0
1.55	0	1.55	0	1.55	0
1.60	0	1.60	0	1.60	0
1.65	1	1.65	0	1.65	0
1.70	2	1.70	0	1.70	0
1.75	3.7	1.75	0	1.75	0
1.80	5.0	1.80	1	1.80	0
1.85	7.5	1.85	1.7	1.85	1
1.90	11.0	1.90	3.1	1.90	1.8
1.95	13.5	1.95	5.5	1.95	3.2
2.00	17.5	2.00	7.0	2.00	5.1
2.05	22.0	2.05	13.5	2.05	9.0
2.10	25.0	2.10	17.0	2.10	13.0
2.15		2.15	21.0	2.15	15.0
2.20		2.20		2.20	18.0
2.25		2.25		2.25	21.0
2.30		2.30		2.30	23.0
2.35		2.35		2.35	

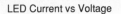
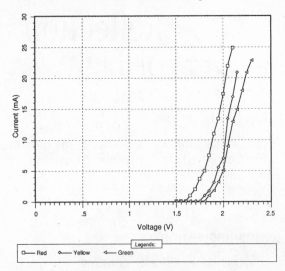

This graph of LED current versus voltage was produced with the Lab Partner™ graphing program.

Analysis

1. a. red voltage: 1.75 V
   b. yellow voltage: 1.95 V
   c. green voltage: 2.05 V
2. red LED, $h = qV\lambda/c = (1.6 \times 10^{-19}\ \text{C})$ $(1.75\ \text{V})(650\ \text{nm})/(3.0 \times 10^8\ \text{m/s})$ $= 6.1 \times 10^{-34}\ \text{J} \cdot \text{s}$
   yellow LED, $h = qV\lambda/c = (1.6 \times 10^{-19}\ \text{C})$ $(1.95\ \text{V})(590\ \text{nm})/(3.0 \times 10^8\ \text{m/s})$ $= 6.14 \times 10^{-34}\ \text{J} \cdot \text{s}$
   green LED, $h = qV\lambda/c = (1.6 \times 10^{-19}\ \text{C})$ $(2.05\ \text{V})(563\ \text{nm})/(3.0 \times 10^8\ \text{m/s})$ $= 6.2 \times 10^{-34}\ \text{J} \cdot \text{s}$
3. red error $= (6.6 \times 10^{-34} - 6.1 \times 10^{-34})$ $(100\%)/6.6 \times 10^{-34} = 8\%$
   yellow error $= 7\%$
   green error $= 6\%$
   Student answers will vary but should be within 10–15% of h.
4. A blue LED should have a voltage greater than that of the green LED, which may be approximately 2.4–2.6 V. The infrared LED will have a voltage less than that of the red LED, or less than 1.6 V, possibly 1.2–1.4 V.

Application

The light-emitting diode is more durable because it has no fragile filament. Light from an incandescent light bulb comprises the entire visible spectrum, while light from the LED has only one wavelength (monochromatic light). The wavelength of an LED is a very narrow band around its computed value, with a band width of about 25–30 nm. When wavelength is closely controlled and the light is produced in a cavity at the junction, a laser diode results.

24 Reflection of Light

Process Skills

observing, measuring, using numbers, interpreting data, inferring, predicting, hypothesizing, defining operationally

Teaching Suggestions

1. If students have difficulty constructing their triangles in Part B, tell them to repeat the procedure, but emphasize that they must sight very carefully along the lines to the image of the pin in the mirror.
2. One set-up for Part C can be used for all students. As they work on Parts A and B, each lab group can take a turn with the laser. In this way, the laser remains in a separate, protected area of the room.

Observations and Data

Table 1 (Sample data are given.)

Object distance	4.1 cm
Image distance	3.8 cm
Angle of incidence, i_1, **PXN**	13°
Angle of reflection, r_1, **AXN**	13.5°
Angle of incidence, i_2, **PYN'**	24°
Angle of reflection, r_2, **BYN'**	25°

Table 2 (Sample data are given.)

Points	Distance to mirror line (cm)
A	1.7
B	5.4
C	1.8
A'	1.8
B'	5.2
C'	1.9

Table 3

Drawing of reflected laser light from a thin plane mirror:
A single large spot should appear.

Drawing of reflected laser light from a thick plane mirror:

● ● ● ● ● ·

The second spot is brightest; this is the reflection from the mirrored surface.

Observation of reflected laser beams:
Students should note a series of reflected beams, becoming progressively narrower as they are more distant from the incident beam.

Analysis

1. They are equal (or should be nearly so).
2. The image is the same distance behind the mirror as the object is in front of the mirror.
3. The image should be the same size as the object. Students may have some small errors due to sighting inaccuracies.
4. Images formed by plane mirrors are as far behind the mirror as the object is in front of the mirror. The image is reversed right to left and is the same size as the object.
5. The image appears where the light rays apparently cross, not where they actually cross. This image does not exist behind the mirror, where it appears to be.
6. The second spot is brightest, because this beam is the reflection from the mirrored surface. The first spot is the reflection from the glass.
7. The thin mirror reflects light from the glass and mirrored surface, but the reflected spots are nearly in the same location. The thick mirror has multiple reflections, spaced farther apart, from the glass at the top and the silver at the bottom of the mirror, as shown below.

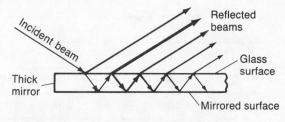

Partial reflection occurs at the mirror-air interface.

Application

Students should state that some of the light is transmitted while most light is reflected. One-way mirrors generally reflect a large portion of the incident light,

such as 50%–60%, while allowing a smaller portion, such as 5%–15%, to pass through. Since a smaller portion of the light is transmitted, the viewing area is usually darker than the observed area.

Extension

The distances should be equal.

25 Concave and Convex Mirrors

Process Skills

observing, measuring, interpreting data, communicating, questioning, designing experiments

Troubleshooting

If students have difficulty locating sharp images, check the mirror. The mirror must be clean and of good quality to produce clear, sharp images. To check the quality of the mirrors, take clean mirrors and focus sunlight onto a screen. Those mirrors that are of good quality will produce a small image of the sun while those of poorer quality will not focus the sunlight.

Alternative Materials

1. Object markers may be used with the light sources. However, students usually have no trouble identifying the orientations of the images. Light bulbs generally have flat bases or glowing filaments, which indicate upright or inverted positions.
2. Candles can be substituted for light sources. If candles are used, caution should be observed around the flames.

Teaching Suggestions

1. Allow ample time to complete this investigation. A prelab discussion of the types of images formed by mirrors and a demonstration of how to find focal lengths may be helpful.

2. Use a concave mirror to project an outdoor scene from outside a window onto a screen. This demonstration will familiarize students with mirrors and real images. They should also be fascinated by the color image.

Observations and Data

Table 1 (Sample data are given.)

Focal length of mirror, f	33 cm
Center of curvature of mirror, C	66 cm
Height of light source, h_o	1 cm

Table 2 (Sample data are given.)

Position of object	Beyond C	At C	Between C and F	At F	Between F and A
d_o	1.0 m	66 cm	48 cm	33 cm	16 cm
d_i	49 cm	66 cm	98 cm	—	—
h_i	0.8 cm	1.0 cm	6 cm	—	larger than object
Type of image: real, none or virtual	real	real	real	none	virtual
Direction of image: inverted or erect	inverted	inverted	inverted	no image	erect

Table 3 (Sample data are given.)

Trial	Position of object	Position of image	Type of image: real or virtual	Image size compared to object size	Direction of image: inverted or erect
1	for all positions	behind mirror	virtual	smaller	erect
2					
3					

Analysis

1. a. The image is between **C** and **F**, inverted, real, and smaller than the object.
   b. The image is at **C**, real, inverted, and the same size as the object.
   c. The image is beyond **C**, inverted, real, and larger than the object.
   d. No image is formed.
   e. The image is behind the mirror, erect, and larger than the object.

2. The images are virtual, smaller and erect, and located behind the mirror.
3. For beyond **C**, $f = 33$ cm; at **C**, $f = 33$ cm; between **C** and **F**, $f = 32$ cm. Student values should be in good agreement.
4. The average is 33 cm, relative error = 0%. Students should have an error of no more than 10%–15% if they have made careful observations and have reasonably good mirrors.

Application

The top edge of the box should be along the principal axis, while the light bulb socket should be located at **C** to produce an image equal in size to the object and inverted.

26 Snell's Law

Process Skills

observing, using numbers, measuring, inferring, interpreting data, questioning, communicating

Teaching Suggestions

1. This activity should be easy to understand and complete, even for students who have not studied trigonometry. However, review the relationships of triangles prior to the lab and introduce Snell's law as a relationship between the opposite side and the hypotenuse of a triangle. The results should be apparent, even if the math is not.
2. A dish of water or oil could be substituted for the glass plate to provide a different index of refraction. The activity is conducted in the same manner. However, the oil is messy if it is spilled.

Observations and Data

Table 1 (Sample data are given.)

θ_i	θ_r	$\sin \theta_i$	$\sin \theta_r$	$\theta_{r'}$	Index of refraction, n
30°	19°	0.5	0.326	30°	1.53
45°					

Analysis

1. They should be equal or nearly equal. Students might have as much as 10% error if they are not careful while sighting along their rulers.
2. As the light rays pass at an angle from a less dense to a more dense medium, they bend toward the normal.
3. As the light rays pass at an angle from a more dense to a less dense medium, they bend away from the normal.
4. The two angles are equal. According to Snell's law, as the light ray passes back to the optically less dense medium, it should resume its original speed and bend away from the normal.
5. $v_s = c/n_s = (3.00 \times 10^8 \text{ m/s})/1.53$
   $= 1.96 \times 10^8$ m/s
   Light travels 3.00×10^8 m/s $- 1.96 \times 10^8$ m/s
   $= 1.04 \times 10^8$ m/s faster in a vacuum.
   % increase $= 1.04 \times 10^8/1.96 \times 10^8 = 53\%$ faster in a vacuum.

Application

Light will bend more traveling from air into water than from water into glass. Using the general form of Snell's law, $n_i \sin \theta_i = n_r \sin \theta_r$, light traveling from air into water yields an effective $n = 1.34$, while light traveling from water into glass yields an effective $n = 1.14$, determined from $(1.34)(\sin \theta_i) = (1.53)(\sin \theta_r)$. The greater the index of refraction, the greater the amount of refraction.

Extension

The sample materials should be easy to identify. The samples will take on a ghostlike appearance and be just barely visible in the liquid with nearly the same index of refraction. Glass normally has an index of refraction of about 1.5. You probably will not have any glass with $n = 1.7$.

27 Convex and Concave Lenses

Process Skills

observing, measuring, interpreting data, communicating, questioning, predicting, designing experiments

Troubleshooting

When using sunlight to determine the focal length of the concave lens, the contrast between the circle of light projected on the screen and the ambient light can be increased by placing a piece of paper around the lens so that sunlight is blocked from falling directly on the screen.

Teaching Suggestion

To find the focal length of the convex lens, arrange your lens, meter stick, and screen, as shown in Figure 3. When sunlight is used, the focal length can be determined by projecting a focused image of the sun onto a screen and measuring the distance from the lens to the focused spot on the screen. Measure the distance quickly, since a focused spot can become hot and cause the screen to burn. Supervise students and be sure to caution them to avoid looking directly at the sun.

Observations and Data

Table 1 (Sample data are given.)

Focal length	18 cm
2F	36 cm
Height of light source, h_o	1.2 cm

Table 2 (Sample data are given.)

Position of object	Beyond 2F (cm)	At 2F (cm)	Between 2F and F (cm)	At F (cm)	Between F and lens (cm)
d_o	50	37	25	17.5	10
d_i	29.2	37.2	66.5	—	—
h_i	1.0	1.2	1.8	—	appears larger as viewed through lens
Type of image: real, none, or virtual	real	real	real	none	none
Direction of image: inverted or erect	inverted	inverted	inverted	—	erect

Table 3

Distance from lens (m)	Diameter of screen image (cm)
0.0	0.15
0.5	0.5
1.0	0.75
1.5	1.1
2.0	1.4
2.5	1.8
3.0	2.0

Analysis

1. a. The image is between F and 2F, real, about the same size, and inverted.
   b. The image is at 2F, the same size as the object, real, and inverted.
   c. The image is beyond 2F, larger, real, and inverted.
   d. No image was readily apparent.
   e. The image is virtual, larger, erect, and on the same side of the lens as the object.
2. a. $f = 18.4$ cm; b. $f = 18.5$ cm; c. $f = 18.2$ cm. There should be good agreement for all measurements.
3. Average $f = 18.4$ cm; relative error = $(18.4 - 18)(100\%)/18 = 2\%$. Students should have a relative error of less than 10%.
4. The intersection provides a focal length of −0.25 m. The accepted value is −0.20 m, therefore the relative error = $(0.25 - 0.20)(100\%)/0.20 = 25\%$. Student error may vary greatly, since the observed diameters are usually not clearly defined at the edges.

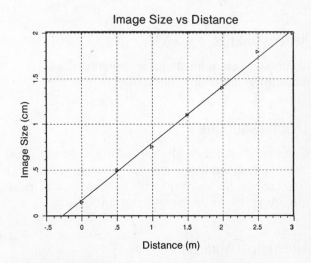

This graph of image size versus distance from the lens was produced using the Lab Partner™ graphing program. The x-intercept is −0.26 m.

Application

If the direction of the reflected laser pattern is opposite to that of the observer's head, then this person is nearsighted. If the direction of the reflected laser pattern is the same as that of the observer's head, then this person is farsighted. If the observer does not perceive any relative motion, then his or her eyesight is normal. To simulate near- or farsightedness, students could hold various lenses in front of their eyes and observe the laser light spot.

Extension

The object appears about normal when viewed through a convex or a concave air lens in air. However, the object appears smaller when viewed through the convex air lens immersed in water and larger when viewed through the concave air lens immersed in water. Note the reversal of the usual effects of glass lenses on these shapes. In water, light rays are traveling from the object through a more dense medium (water) to a less dense medium (air in the lenses). This reversal of media accounts for the opposite effects of the lenses.

INSTRUCTOR NOTES

28 Double-Slit Interfer-ence

Process Skills

observing, communicating, interpreting data, measuring, predicting, questioning

Troubleshooting

If students have difficulty measuring x for the violet filter, suggest that they move farther away (increase L). This color is the most difficult to observe and measure, especially if the room lights are on.

Alternative Materials

Double slits can be purchased or constructed. If you wish to have students construct their own double slits, tape a pair of razor blades together and lightly pull

the unit across a microscope slide covered with dried graphite emulsion. An alternative to graphite emulsion is aluminum foil, placed over a microscope slide and cut with the razor-blades unit.

Teaching Suggestions

1. Suggest that students use the red filter material first, since it provides the best observations of diffraction and interference.
2. If students have difficulty when the filter material is placed on the light bulbs, they can try holding the filter material in front of their slits.
3. If a variety of color filter material is available, give each lab partnership a red piece and two other colors, so that the variety of other colors is different for different lab partners. This individualizes the lab, and partners are less inclined to copy data.

Observations and Data

Table 1 (Sample data are given.)

	Observations of Light
Close	The bright bands of red are close together.
Far away	The bright bands of red move farther apart and are easier to see.

Table 2 (Sample data are given.)

Color	d (mm)	x (m)	L (m)
Red	0.15	0.017	4.0
Yellow	0.15	0.015	4.0
Violet	0.15	0.012	4.0

Analysis

1. The pattern spreads out, so the first-order, second-order, etc., lines are farther apart.
2. $\lambda_{red} = xd/L$
   $= (0.017\ m)(0.15 \times 10^{-3}\ m)/4.0\ m$
   $= 640\ nm$
   $\lambda_{yellow} = xd/L$
   $= (0.015\ m)(0.15 \times 10^{-3}\ m)/4.0\ m$
   $= 560\ nm$
   $\lambda_{violet} = xd/L$
   $= (0.012\ m)(0.15 \times 10^{-3}\ m)/4.0\ m$
   $= 450\ nm$

Student answers will vary and will be dependent on how carefully they measure x. Answers should be within the visible spectrum (in the range of 400–700 nm).

3. Red light is diffracted most. Using the same values for L and d, the angle will be larger, since x is greater for the larger wavelength, $x = \lambda L/d$.
4. Student answers will vary. However, the distance should be greater than the measured distance of x for the red light. The infrared light will be diffracted more than visible red light, since it has a larger wavelength.
5. Student answers will vary. However, the distance should be less than the measured distance for x for the violet light. The ultraviolet light will be diffracted less than visible violet light, since it has a smaller wavelength.

Applications

1. Since $\tan \theta = x/L$ and $\theta = 0.8°$, $\lambda = xd/L = d(\tan \theta) = (0.05 \times 10^{-3}$ m$)(\tan 0.8) = 700$ nm, which is the wavelength of red light.
2. $L = xd/\lambda$

   $= \dfrac{(14.7 \times 10^{-3}\text{ m})(1.50 \times 10^{-5}\text{ m})}{5.00 \times 10^{-7}\text{ m}}$

   $= 0.441$ m
3. $x = L\lambda/d$

   $= \dfrac{(4.41 \times 10^{-1}\text{ m})(5.89 \times 10^{-7}\text{ m})}{1.5 \times 10^{-5}}$

   $= 0.0173$ mm

Extension

The solutions will vary, depending on the values for L and x. However, when students substitute their values into $d = \lambda L/x$, the resulting value for d should be very close to the actual value.

INSTRUCTOR NOTES

29 Semi-conductor Properties

Process Skills

observing, measuring, using numbers, communicating, interpreting data, predicting, questioning

Alternative Materials

Any diode or rectifier can be substituted for the 1N4004 series diode as long as the diode working voltage is greater than the voltage you are using.

Teaching Suggestions

1. The 10-Ω resistor serves as a current-limiting device to prevent damage to the ammeter in case students accidentally turn the potentiometer control and apply the full battery or power-supply voltage to the meter. If the power-supply voltage is over 3 V, such as 6 V, the resistance can be increased to 33–47 Ω.
2. You can use any of the laboratory power supplies with an AC power output. The small transformer adapters with an AC output can be substituted. Use only a low-voltage AC power supply, not the 120-VAC line current.

Observations and Data

Table 1 (Sample data are given.)

Forward-Biased Diode								
Voltage (V)	0.00	0.10	0.20	0.30	0.40	0.50	0.60	0.70	0.80
Current (mA)	0	0	0	0	0	0	2	17.5	180

Table 2 (Sample data are given.)

Reverse-Biased Diode								
Voltage (V)	0.00	0.10	0.20	0.30	0.40	0.50	0.60	0.70	0.80
Current (mA)	0	0	0	0	0	0	0	0	0

Table 3

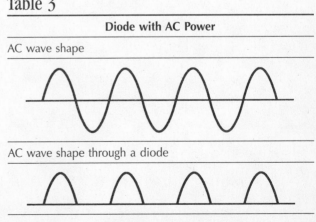

Diode with AC Power

AC wave shape

AC wave shape through a diode

Analysis

1.

Current versus Voltage for Forward and Reverse Biasing of a Diode

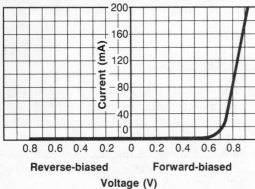

Reverse-biased   Forward-biased

Voltage (V)

2. With a resistor in the circuit, a linear relationship between current and voltage exists for both negative and positive values of voltage. With a diode in the circuit, no current flows when it is reverse biased (for negative voltages), but the current increases exponentially when the diode is forward biased and the voltage is increased.
3. The diode conducts current in only one direction.

4. The diode is made of silicon because it begins to conduct current with a forward bias at a voltage of about 0.6 V.
5. An alternating current source has a sinusoidal wave shape. The wave shape of a current across the resistor that passes through the diode is only the positive portion of the alternating current. The negative portion of the alternating current is blocked.
6. The shape is the opposite half (negative portion) of the AC wave shape that was drawn in Table 3 (AC wave shape through a diode).

Application

The figure shows full-wave rectification. Each diode alternately conducts current for one-half of the time.

Extension

The wave shape observed should be the same as the one predicted in the application.

A Technical Overview of the Internet

UNIT
C

The Internet—reachable by computer—is a great place to find technical and career information. There you will find no shortage of topics to discuss with your students! In teaching students how to research physics topics on the Internet, you will be providing them with the means by which they can stay current in their future careers. Even if students do not have computers at home, most public libraries allow Internet research on their computers. This manual contains several Internet activities you might try out with your class. The following information is meant to help you to instruct students in how to gain access to the Internet.

GETTING LOGGED ON TO THE INTERNET

Begin by showing students how to connect to your school's Internet service provider (ISP—or large, online service provider) in order to get on to the Internet. We suggest that you provide written instructions for the students to keep on hand, so that they can log on later on their own. Some students will already have online experience; still, start at the basics for those students who don't know how yet (or don't want to "let on" that they don't know). Your school's computers will have software installed that works together with the ISP to allow the students to step on to the Internet. A popular browser software program, for instance, is Netscape Navigator. Examples of popular online services are the companies America Online or CompuServe. So, although no one "owns" the Internet, students will need the ISP connection and the software to help get them *easily* logged on.

In most cases, the logon procedure begins with hitting the On button on the drive box and the On button that is on or just under the terminal's screen. Next, the screen asks for passwords or the user's name. After these are filled in, the screen may show a series of options in the form of icons. With the mouse, click the picture representing the ISP or the browser software. You may once again be asked for an identifying name or password. Once that is taken care of, you are on the Internet.

As mentioned, most public libraries have Internet access. A user can sign up for a computer at the librarian's desk and then go to a terminal. With the mouse, the user clicks on any picture on the screen that indicates the Internet. For example, if you are at a library that is using Netscape Navigator software, you will see on the screen a picture of a boat wheel or large N.

CAUTIONS ABOUT THE INTERNET

Some ISPs are paid for based on how much time the user has been logged on (if so, let students know their time limit); other accounts are for unlimited time, paid for as a flat fee per month or year.

You will probably want students, while they are using class time to be online, to seek out only materials related to class work and not go too far afield. Be aware that if adherence to this policy becomes a problem, there are filtering software packages that you can use to restrict inappropriate content.

Content and time-monitoring software packages, if you want to use them, are listed at the end of this unit.

Remind students that Internet sites, unlike a published book, can change daily. What's up today can be gone tomorrow. Therefore, if you see a good informational site, print out a master paper copy or save the site to disk, in case the site is taken down or altered substantially at some point in the future.

Materials on the Internet are protected by copyright. So, when making instructional materials from text, photos, and art that you find on the Internet, give credit to the source. (Credit can be in the form of a footnote on the appropriate page or pages.) If you intend to distribute many copies of something you've found on the Internet, contact the source to ask permission. Remind students who are about to write research papers that although material found on the Internet can be saved to disk and printed out to "look" original, instructors throughout the ages have taken a dim view of plagiarism.

A lot of advertising appears on the Internet. Although we're grateful that the Internet has become so easy to use, in part this has happened because of the human drive to make money. Ask students to avoid exploring ads unless they pertain to the topic at hand.

Last but not least: Anyone can post a letter, article, or Web site on the Internet. Not all of these people know what they are talking about. Just because the material is in print on the screen does not mean that it is true. Information on the Internet does not have to pass an accuracy test! Therefore, warn students to use common sense about what to believe and to use credible sources.

CHOOSING A SEARCH ENGINE

Once students are on the Internet and trying to research a topic, let them know that there are many free search engines to choose from. Encourage students to try out the same topic on various search engines, to see what the differences are between them. Here are just a few of the popular free search engines: Infoseek, Yahoo, Excite, Lycos, Alta Vista, and HotBot. Complicated research may be aided by the use of fee-required search engines; however, most topics can be adequately examined via free search engines. Each search engine can be brought up on screen by keying in its unique address.

KEYING AN ADDRESS (URL)

Internet addresses are formally called *URLs*. These addresses usually begin with

http://www

and end with

.com/

Most search engines have URLs similar to their names. For example, Infoseek's address is

http://www.infoseek.com/

The address is to be keyed in, usually on the top left of the screen, in a long open box sometimes labeled *Location*. The computer goes to that location after the Enter key is hit.

KEYBOARDING TIPS

Internet addresses must be typed in free of errors. The symptom of a wrongly typed-in address is a screen that says that it cannot find the site you are looking for. Many addresses use punctuation marks or other keyboard signs that are not familiar, such as ~ (tilde). Caution students to check their typing before hitting the Enter key.

Computer keyboards can be fussy when conditions are not clean. Thin plastic covers that fit over keyboards and allow the keyboards to be used while the cover protects the keys can be purchased. Such covers are a big help if a person is using a keyboard in the vicinity of a repair or maintenance area, where it is hard to keep hands clean.

DIRECTING THE SEARCH ENGINE

Students should know that they often can direct search engines to look in various places for their topic. For instance, the engine can look in newsgroups (where people have conversations), Web page articles, the news, or business. Once the student has found something of interest, it can be saved to disk or printed out if it's not lengthy. (Some public libraries have printers available at a per-page fee.)

Newsgroups. As we mentioned, your school probably hooks up to the Internet using an ISP. Some of these companies offer their own newsgroups and chat rooms. Some search engines have their own newsgroups, too. In newsgroups, people post messages on an on-screen bulletin board, for everyone to read. In chat rooms, people can talk back and forth, sometimes with only a few seconds' delay. For the student looking for very specific answers to questions, newsgroups and chat rooms can be helpful. It is a way for people who have information to share it with someone else.

Web page articles. For general information about a topic, Web page articles are an excellent choice. These pages can have text, art, and photos. Most software will allow the user to easily add any Web site to a list of favorites (sometimes called *bookmarks*), so that the page's address need not be typed in by the user each time. Some Web pages show *links,* which are the names of other Web pages on the same topic. Some pages have sound or movies.

Going forward and backward. Users who follow links may forget what site they began with. Fortunately, most software has an instant record of where you have been searching recently so that you can get back easily to places you've recently visited. This record is sometimes accessed by the toolbar, by clicking on Go, or by an arrow at the end of the address box. Sometimes a toolbar item with a name such as Window will have an option called *History,* which lists where you've just been. Going backward and forward are accomplished on the toolbar or by buttons on the mouse.

INTERNET RESEARCH

Here is a step-by-step example of doing an Internet search in which the student keys in a few words relating to the topic. For this exercise, we will use the word *automobile.* This example leads onto the Internet, to a Web page, and then to a link to a newsgroup.

1. Log on to the school's ISP.
2. Type in the address of a search engine, in the upper long box, likely labeled *Location.* Of the search engines mentioned earlier, let us use Infoseek, whose address is http://www.infoseek.com/.
3. Press Enter.
4. You will see a long box that asks you what you want to search for. Type in the key word *automobile.*
5. Infoseek says that you can narrow your search to the Web, news, companies, or newgroups. Select the circle next to the word *Web* to begin your search there.
6. Select Seek.
7. The screen says that it has found over 100,000 Web pages using the word *automobile.* Type in another word to narrow your search, check the box that says *within these pages,* and hit *Seek.*
8. The screen says that it has found a few hundred Web pages using the additional words. Using the scroll arrows on the right, run through several of them. Most describe school programs teaching the topic. Select and click on the topic of your choice.
9. The screen has several pages and illustrations that conclude your search. E-mail and mailing addresses and toll-free numbers may also be provided on the Web pages.
10. You can now download the item by saving it to disk or by printing out a copy.
11. If you want to add this site to your list of favorites, follow your software's directions to do so. For example, some software programs call items on this list *bookmarks.* Other programs have a heart picture that you can click on to make the site become a list item. Items you put on the list can be easily accessed next time without having to type in the address again.

SAVING AN ITEM TO DISK

Locate File on the toolbar and open it. Click on Save as to reveal a save box. Place a disk into the disk drive, black part in first, metal circle underneath. Hit Save in the save box on the screen.

Explain to students that saving a Web page as an HTML file on disk is not always going to save the accompanying illustrations. To also save the art and photos, place the mouse over each piece. With many computers, the mouse buttons can click over the art; the screen will then give a number of options, including Save image as.

MAKING A PRINTED COPY

Likewise, a Web page can be printed out. Go to File on the toolbar. Open it and select Print. Web pages with extensive illustrations can take time to print. Also, complex pages may not print completely if the printer has insufficient memory.

At times, your computer may tell you that there are no pages to print. Try a couple of times before you take that statement as the truth.

Your browser may have a print preview option under File. This feature shows the length and layout of the Web page before printing and is useful when students want to print only a portion of the Web page.

DOWNLOAD- ING TIPS

Explain to students that some computer programmers whose motives are destructive develop computer viruses. Computer viruses can be very harmful to your system.

Most software programs will warn students about viruses whenever they download materials from the Internet. It is best, when downloading, to download to a disk rather than to the computer itself. There are many excellent antivirus programs available on the Internet and from software vendors. Many are free or available for a nominal cost. Some programs offer users regular virus update information. These programs keep computers "aware" of the latest viruses that have been detected.

Make students aware that large amounts of material can take a very long time to download! Some large program files, illustrations, or movies require an "unzip" feature or a "plug-in" to be viewed or downloaded. If you encounter material that tells you that you need such a feature to go further, know that these features can be found on the Internet, often free, for your use. At that point, you temporarily stop your search, retrieve the feature from the Internet, install it on your computer, and then go back to your search. Acquiring these special features, if it is your first time, takes twenty minutes or so. Examples of popular plug-ins are Quicktime and Acrobat.

INTERNET SERVICES

A wealth of services are available on the Internet, some of which have already been mentioned, like newgroups, e-mail, and Web pages. Other places to visit are FTPs, gophers, and chat rooms.

FTP. One of the earliest Internet services was File Transfer Protocol (FTP), which allows users to transfer files from one computer to another, like dipping into an open file storage cabinet. The school may have FTP capability, to send or receive, or both. By using FTP software on your machine, you can connect to another computer on the Internet, browse through the files available for transfer, and download them to your computer. To log on to computer A, you usually must have an account on that computer A. Depending on the type of account you have, you can also send files from your machine to computer A. If you don't have an account on computer A, know that many FTP computers on the Internet are *anonymous* FTP computers. This means that users *without* accounts can log on using the logon name Anonymous and any password, and browse through files available to the public. You can use FTP to transfer any type of file, even illustrations and photos.

Gophers. Gophers locate and retrieve information on the Internet. Like FTP, gophers let you download files. They also let you search for information. They give you access to online phone books, online library catalogs, databases, and e-mail directories, as well as the text of actual files. Information on a given topic is presented in an easy-to-use form. For instance, parts lists can be accessed for the mechanic.

Chat rooms. Another aspect of the Internet is interactive communications. Simply put, this means that people can use the Internet to communicate with each other in "real time" (with only a few seconds' delay), like a written telephone conversation. People carry on conversations with one another by typing back and forth, with each person's words appearing on the other person's computer screen. Conversations can be held privately between two individuals or in groups, as with a telephone party line. These group discussions are often referred to as *chat rooms*. Like newsgroups, chat rooms provide people from all parts of the world with the opportunity to discuss solutions to specific mechanical problems.

ADDRESS CLUES

You can guess a lot by looking at an Internet address. Here are some lettering groupings often seen in Internet addresses, and what clues they give to you.

http	a Web site
ftp	a file transfer archive
gopher	a gopher archive and search
com	a business
edu	a school
gov	the government
mil	the military
net	an ISP (an Internet service provider)
org	a nonprofit group, trade association, or other organization
html	the program language that creates Web pages

IDEAS FOR STUDENT ACTIVITIES ON THE INTERNET

We suggest that instructors and students work together to create Internet assignments that allow individuals to establish their career goals.

Instructors may ask students to simply search a topic and report on what they found. The following are a few ideas for activities that stimulate critical thinking:

1. Ask students to look for information regarding possible technical careers. What kinds of positions are available? What salaries are possible in these jobs? What educational requirements and experience are needed to get these jobs?

2. Have students visit various Web pages about a topic. If an e-mail address is listed, have the student e-mail the Web author with a question about the topic.

3. Visualize a possible technical problem in which the technician must obtain current service data or locate the source of replacement parts.

4. Determine the sources of parts and equipment from multiple suppliers.

5. Write a report or create a presentation about a new technology. Use specific facts from the Web.

6. Write a report or create a presentation to send to a manufacturing company about a new piece of equipment designed and developed by students.

7. Create a bookmark listing of favorite Web page articles about new equipment.

SOFTWARE TO MANAGE TIME AND CONTENT

Here are some examples of software that monitors content and time:

Net-Monitor   Logs all pages the student has visited.

WatchDog   An internal clock that allows a student to stay on only so long or logs the student's time.

CyberPatrol, Net Nanny, CYBERsitter   Blocks adult-rated content, but the manufacturers may not tell you what will be blocked.

Tech Prep

UNIT **D**

The Tech Prep initiative is directed toward establishing a constructive bridge between high school and postsecondary education to provide better direction for students in terms of their future careers. Some high schools have changed from general education programs to Tech Prep/Associate Degree (TPAD) applied-academics programs to parallel the college prep and vocational education programs. TPAD programs are directed toward the middle range of occupations that require some postsecondary education and training for which students receive certificates or associate degrees. They are carefully structured and coordinated programs in which high school and community college or technical institute teachers, instructors, and administrators work closely with the area business community.*

A goal of TPAD programs is to reduce the high school dropout rate. Most dropouts leave school between the tenth and eleventh grade. The Tech Prep program represents a viable alternative for students who are contemplating an end to their high school years. Students can select the TPAD major in their junior year and continue for two years of postsecondary education and training. This common form results in these programs being referred to as 2 + 2 Tech Prep programs.

Studies and reports support the need for improving the school-to-work transition.**

- Of the high school graduates who go directly to the workforce, more than 60% do so without training in specific skills.

- Approximately 50% of high school graduates go to a four-year postsecondary institution, and only 50% of those students graduate within a ten-year period.

- Nearly 80% of all future jobs will require education beyond high school.

The need for qualitative and quantitative technical knowledge is increasing exponentially. The nation's economic transformation from an industrial-labor base to an information-technology-service base has created two dramatic changes within the workplace:

- Employers are demanding higher performance in the workplace that requires advanced technical skills and an ability to understand complex theories and ideas.

- Businesses are requiring increased skills in problem solving, computer applications, critical thinking, teamwork, and higher-level skills in math, the sciences, and communications.

Research suggests the following statistics to the workforce and education:

- Graduates from a technical college have higher employment rates, higher average pay, and a greater likelihood of success in life-long learning than those from other educational institutions.

- Approximately 11% of the students attending technical/community colleges do so directly from high school. This low figure suggests a "floundering" period during which the majority of youth are likely to find themselves in minimum-wage, dead-end, high-turnover jobs.

- Relevant education and training in high school will enable students to make an easier transition to advanced training in postsecondary institutions.

Many students today are not being prepared for a current and rapidly expanding technological, global economy. Youth need access to a full range of education-based, future-oriented life-choice options, *College prep, tech prep,* and *work prep* are three

*Portions of the information contained in this article have appeared in other Glencoe/McGraw-Hill publications, including, *Strategies for Implementing Tech Prep,* © 1995, by Loock and Voiers; *Strategies for Implementing Tech Prep into Communication,* © 1994, by Loock and Voiers; and *Tech Prep Strategies in Accounting,* © 1995, by Ross, Swinehart, Hogan, Morrison, Hoyt and Haber. Although footnotes are used sparingly, a complete list of references does appear at the end of this Tech Prep segment.
**See items 2, 10, and 17 of the References and Suggested Readings listing.

terms used to describe postsecondary choices students can make. School districts and community/technical college systems must work together to enable students to make a successful transition from high school to postsecondary education or work.

Federal Provision

The federal government has devoted significant funds to support Tech Prep. Increased expectations for integration of occupational and academic learning accompany this support. The Carl Perkins Vocational and Applied Technology Education Act Amendments of 1990 devoted an entire part to Tech Prep (Title III, PART E—TECH-PREP EDUCATION, Sections 342–347, September 25, 1990).

Criteria

The Tech Prep part of the Perkins Act includes these criteria:

- The program provides planning and demonstration grants to consortia of local education agencies and postsecondary education institutions that will develop and operate four-year Tech Prep education programs. Strong links will exist between secondary and postsecondary educational institutions.

- Programs will consist of two years of secondary and two years of postsecondary education or two years of apprenticeship. The program leads to a two-year associate degree or a two-year certificate.

- Programs will combine nontraditional school-to-work technical education, will use state-of-the-art equipment, and will use appropriate technologies.

- Programs have a common core of required proficiency in mathematics, science, communication, and technologies.

- Programs must include strong teacher and counselor in-service and training programs to effectively implement Tech Prep education curricula, and must also recruit students and ensure that students not only successfully complete such programs but also are placed in appropriate employment.

For long-term success, however, states and local school districts must continue to support the restructuring established by Tech Prep. Thus, many states and local school districts have passed legislation and allocated funds to supplement federal monies and continue this endeavor.

Objectives

The long-term objectives for Tech Prep in many states are as follows:

- An increase in the percentage of students entering a community/technical college program within one semester after high school graduation.

- An increase in the percentage of students successfully completing a community/technical college program within three years of initial entry.

- An increase in the percentage of students qualifying for advanced standing in a community/technical college program after high school graduation.

- A reduction in the percentage of recent high school graduates needing remedial course work to be admitted to, or to receive a diploma/degree from, the community/technical college.

- A reduction in the percentage of recent high school graduates who seek entrance to a community/technical college uncertain about what program they want to pursue.

What Is Tech Prep?

Tech Prep is a competency-based program of combined secondary and postsecondary educational and occupational experience that includes a common core of required proficiency in mathematics, science, communication, and technologies designed to lead to an associate degree or certificate in specific career fields. The Tech Prep process is intended to help students select a sequence of courses and experiences that will enable them to achieve the academic and technical competence they will need to successfully pursue a specific associate degree program in a community/technical college after high school graduation.

Student Goals

Avoiding overlap and duplication between secondary and postsecondary experiences is a major feature of Tech Prep. Tech Prep emphasizes the advanced skills rather than time-shortened education. Students who have successfully completed Tech Prep will

- Identify and capitalize on their interests, aptitudes, abilities, values, and preferences.
- Recognize the broad range of postsecondary options that capitalize on their identified strengths.
- Establish tentative postsecondary education or employment goals and plans to achieve these goals.
- Select learning experiences designed to help them achieve their postsecondary educational or employment goals.
- Earn advanced standing, dual credit, and the like in a technical/community college for high school courses that result in the same student competencies.

Common Denominators of Tech Prep

All Tech Prep programs have five things in common:

- Continuity in learning
- Content-based teaching (applied academics)
- Competency-based teaching
- Communication between learning institutions (high school and postsecondary technical institutes and community colleges and the local business community)
- Completion of the program with an associate degree (or certificate)

The Tech Prep/Associate Degree (TPAD) approach assists students in developing broad-based competencies in a career field of their choice and in identifying long-term education and training goals. It provides a chance for many students who might otherwise leave high school with few opportunities to reach for promising long-term, higher-paying employment fields. By having the business community involved with TPAD programs, both students and future employers have a greater sense of the skills and talents these students bring to the workplace.

Developing Core Personal Abilities

Based upon the SCANS (Secretary's Commission on Achieving Necessary Skills, United States Department of Labor), the underlying Tech Prep goals include "soft" general competencies and "hard" occupationally specific competencies. These general competencies are valued assets for all managers and employees. Two national reports, "Workplace Basics: The Skills Employers Want" and "What Work Requires of Schools," A SCANS Report for America 2000," identify the skills, competencies, and abilities students need to live full lives. Every Tech Prep program should incorporate these skills, competencies, and abilities. A discussion of these two reports follows.

Workplace Basics: The Skills Employers Want
Although Workplace Basics focuses primarily on skills needed for productive employment, it does not diminish the importance of skills people need to participate in their communities, to raise families, and to enjoy their leisure time. In fact, these new "basics" are the keys to greater opportunity and a better quality of life.

Under a grant from the Employment and Training Administration, a two-year research project was conducted by the American Society for Training and Development and the U.S. Department of Labor. The portion of research that summarized findings on workplace skills found that employers want good basic academic skills. Specifically, the summary identified these seven skill groups:

1. **Learning to learn.** The most basic of all skills is knowing how to learn. The skill is the key to all other skills for learning and is now a fact of life in the workplace.

Employers are putting a premium on the ability to absorb, process, and apply new information quickly and effectively.

2. **Reading, writing, and computation.** Today's workforce is called on to use these basic skills in ways totally different from the ways workers have been traditionally taught. Traditionally students have been taught reading in isolation, writing for creativity, and mathematics in concept only. Educators know now, through their research and through implementation of applied academics, that these basics are learned more effectively when taught in context, using or adapting materials, and using concepts that are job-based.

   Students must learn the process of reading to locate information and of using higher-level thinking strategies to solve problems. Writing should rely on analysis, conceptualization, synthesis, and dissemination of information in a clear, concise, and correct manner. Building on the learner's prior math knowledge and emphasizing problem identification, reasoning, estimation, and problem solving, the instruction can simulate specific job tasks bringing computation into a "real world" context.

3. **Communication: Listening and oral communication.** Students need listening and speaking skills to ensure good communication in the workplace.

4. **Creative thinking and problem solving.** Creative thinking should focus on expanding the thinking process of students. Students need to escape from logical and sequential thought patterns and solve problems creatively.

5. **Self-esteem, goal setting/motivation, personal/career development.** This skill area can be accomplished by assisting students in
   a. Recognizing their current skills and knowledge
   b. Being aware of their impact on others
   c. Understanding their personal emotional set points to cope with varying situations

6. **Interpersonal skills, negotiation, and teamwork.** This ongoing self-development requires first an awareness and then an ability to deal effectively with inappropriate behavior to provide inspiration to others, to share responsibility, and to interact confidently.

7. **Organizational effectiveness and leadership.** Students must first understand structures of organizations in general: what they are, why they exist, and how an individual moves within the structure.

What Work Requires of Schools, A SCANS Report for America 2000

To examine the changes for learning, the Secretary of Labor organized the Secretary's Commission on Achieving Necessary Skills (SCANS). The Commission spent 12 months talking to the working public, union officials, and workers at all levels. Their consensus was that all workers need to be able to put knowledge to work and to be creative and responsible problem solvers with the skills and attitudes on which employers can build.

The SCANS report listed three findings:

1. All American high school students must develop a new set of competencies and foundation skills if they are to enjoy a productive, full, and satisfying life.

2. The qualities of high performance that today characterize our most competitive companies must become the standard for the vast majority of our companies, large and small, local and global.

3. The nation's schools must be transformed into high-performance organizations in their own right.

Although these conclusions may appear abstract in isolation, the Commission asks that they be considered, instead, in the context of traditional education, current business needs, and the standards of our schools. The SCANS report then addresses what these convictions mean in practice on the job, and in the school.

The report identifies five competencies that, in conjunction with a three-part foundation of skills and personal qualities, lie at the heart of job performance today. The eight areas identified are not only consistent with the purposes of a Tech Prep program but also complement and add credence to the efforts of Tech Prep proponents. These eight areas represent essential preparation for all students, both those going directly to work and those planning further education. The Commission maintains that all eight areas must be an integral part of each student's education and should be taught and understood in a way that reflects the workplace contexts in which they are applied.

The five competencies differ from a person's technical knowledge. An effective workers should be able to productively use resources, interpersonal skills, information, systems, and technology.

WORKPLACE KNOW-HOW

According to SCANS, workplace know-how consists of the five competencies and a three-part foundation of skills and personal qualities. The five competencies necessary for effective job performance are the following:

1. **Resources:** allocating time, money, materials, space, and staff
2. **Interpersonal skills:** working on teams, teaching others, serving customers, leading, negotiating, and working well with people from culturally diverse backgrounds
3. **Information:** acquiring and evaluating data, organizing and maintaining files, interpreting and communicating, and using computers to process information
4. **Systems:** understanding social, organizational, and technological systems, monitoring and correcting performance, and designing or improving systems
5. **Technology:** selecting equipment and tools, applying technology to specific tasks, and maintaining and troubleshooting technologies

The three-part foundation includes:
- **Basic skills:** reading, writing, arithmetic and mathematics, speaking, and listening
- **Thinking skills:** thinking creatively, making decisions, solving problems, seeing things in the mind's eye, knowing how to learn, and reasoning
- **Personal qualities:** individual responsibility, self-esteem, sociability, self-management, and integrity

---

The Commission defines each of these competencies as generic across industries and at many steps of the career ladder. The five competencies and the resulting behaviors are defined as follows:

1. **Resources:** Identifies, organizes, plans, and allocates resources
   a. *Time*—selects goal-relevant activities, ranks them, allocates time, and prepares and follows schedules

b. *Money*—uses or prepares budgets, makes forecasts, keeps records, and makes adjustments to meet objectives

   c. *Materials and facilities*—acquires, stores, allocates, and uses materials or space efficiently

   d. *Human resources*—assesses skills and distributes work accordingly, evaluates performance and provides feedback

2. **Interpersonal skills:** Works with others
   a. *Participates as a member of a team*—contributes to group effort
   b. *Teaches others new skills*
   c. *Serves clients/customers*—works to satisfy customers' expectations
   d. *Exercises leadership*—communicates ideas to justify position, persuades and convinces others, assumes responsibility, challenges existing procedures and policies
   e. *Negotiates*—works toward agreements involving exchanges of resources, resolves divergent interests
   f. *Works with diversity*—works well with people from diverse backgrounds

3. **Information:** Acquires and uses information
   a. *Acquires and evaluates information*
   b. *Organizes and maintains information*
   c. *Interprets and communicates information*
   d. *Uses computers to process information*

4. **Systems:** Understands complex interrelationships
   a. *Understands systems*—knows how social, organizational, and technical systems work and operates effectively with them
   b. *Monitors and corrects performance*—distinguishes trends, predicts impacts on system operations, diagnoses deviations in system's performance and corrects malfunctions
   c. *Improves or designs systems*—suggests modifications in existing systems and develops a new or alternative design to improve performance

5. **Technology:** Works with a variety of technologies
   a. *Selects technology*—chooses procedures, tools, or equipment including computers and related technologies
   b. *Applies technology to task*—understands overall intent and proper procedures for setup and operation of equipment
   c. *Maintains and troubleshoots equipment*—prevents, identifies, or solves problems with equipment, including computers and other technologies

The Commission's work represents a further evolution of the recommendations in *America's Choice.** More important, it develops a framework for a skills structure that schools and employers can use.

Incorporating the findings from both reports can serve as the core of personal abilities from which further content integration can occur in the redesign of curriculum and the restructure of education. However, for any curriculum to be as effective as possible, it needs the support and acceptance from more than just the educational community. A redesign of curriculum, such as that suggested by Tech Prep, needs the support of students, parents, business and industry, and the community at large. The first step in gaining this support is through knowledge and understanding, which can be achieved through marketing of the program.

*See items 2 and 19 in References and Suggested Readings.

Developing Learning Strategies

To dramatically change all schools—from elementary through high school, technical training or community college, and four-year colleges and universities—educators must begin by placing learning objectives within real environments so that students no longer first learn in the abstract what they will then be expected to apply. When instructors teach skills in the context of competencies, students will learn the skill more rapidly and will be more likely to apply that skill to real situations.

Any teacher or instructor can support the goals of the Tech Prep program, which are to help students learn the subject, as well as to achieve these skills:

- Think logically
- Write well
- Read critically
- Listen perceptively
- Speak clearly
- Use imagination creatively
- Develop interpersonal skills

Many vocational educators have, by the nature of their subject matter, traditionally taught skills in context of real situations but have not emphasized the inherent "academic skills" used in their application. In contrast, instructors in the academic wing have taught "the basics" in isolation without demonstrating the link to the real world. Though both of these statements are generalities, neither group can maintain its status quo. Academic and vocational instructors will have to collaborate in the transformation needed for a Tech Prep program to be one of cooperation, quality, equity, and learning.

Tech Prep Sequence of Courses

No single sequence of courses exists that all Tech Prep students will pursue. To the contrary, students will select a sequence of elective courses depending on their tentative postsecondary educational or employment goals. In some instances, a student planning to pursue a specific bachelor's degree program will choose the same course work as a student planning a related associate degree major in a technical college. One student may choose to "prep," or prepare for a four-year college (College Prep), whereas another student may plan to pursue a technical college degree (Tech Prep).

Tech Prep Components

- **Common core outcomes (for K–12).** Each student must demonstrate an ability to perform complex tasks—the use of mathematics, languages, and artistic expression in everyday application.

- **Specialty courses and experiences (primarily in grades 11 and 12).** Some specialty courses will be academically based whereas others will be vocationally based; still others will be based in the arts, foreign languages, or other areas of special interest. In some instances, these specialty courses may be formally articulated to offer advanced placement opportunities in two-year or four-year institutions.

Applied Academics

Applied academics combines thinking and doing. Applied academics is the integration of a particular academic discipline (such as mathematics, science, or English) with personal workforce applications (hands-on laboratories dealing with practical equipment and devices). It is imperative that applied academics be understood as a competency-oriented curriculum with high expectations rather than a traditional curriculum with lower expectations. Applied learning can motivate students who currently fail to make the connection between classroom study and real-life application. Applied academic programs provide mathematics, science, communication, and social science courses which offer activities that are relevant to experiences students will have as adults. The courses are developed in a competency-based curriculum that provides concepts and skills related to real-world applications.

Tech Prep in Middle/Junior High Schools

Tech Prep also has a significant role in the middle/junior high school. More applied curriculum and instruction needs to take place in middle/junior high schools, along with greater opportunities to explore future options. The competencies identified in the SCANS report, such as learning to learn, critical thinking, and problem solving, need to be integrated components of the middle school curriculum.

Designing the Curriculum

Curriculum Clusters Many states have chosen to cluster student competencies and curriculum topics into five major occupational areas:

- Health and medical services
- Business and marketing
- Agribusiness/agriscience
- Family/consumer services
- Technical/industrial

Curriculum Models The basic design of most Tech Prep curriculum models is focused on applied academics. The integration of applied math, applied science, applied communication, and the principles of technology is the foundation for each cluster and its specific career paths. The actual outcomes from these models encompass a broad range of competencies that prepare Tech Prep students to be productive workers and good citizens. Following is a curriculum model in the area of physics.

COMPETENCIES FOR ENGINEERING TECHNOLOGY: PHYSICS

1. *Resources:* Identifies, organizes, plans, and allocates resources. This includes time, money, human resources, materials and facilities.

2. *Interpersonal skills:* Includes skills for working with others. This includes participating as a member of a team, teaching, serving clients, exhibiting leadership, negotiation, and working with people from diverse backgrounds.

3. *Information:* Acquires and uses information. This includes evaluation, organization, maintenance, interpretation, communication, and using computers to process information.

4. *Systems:* Understands complex interrelationships. This includes design or redesign and monitoring or correcting performance.

5. *Technology:* Works with technologies, including selection, application to tasks, maintenance, and troubleshooting equipment.

FEATURES THAT MEET COMPETENCIES

Laboratory assignments require allocation of resources within specified time periods with expensive equipment.

Students should be assigned team projects, such as laboratory experiments where they prepare team reports that they present to the class. Student demonstrations of technical applications to textbook theory is encouraged.

Students should be encouraged to use their home or school computers to process classroom and laboratory assignments and to write algorithms to solve homework problems.

Household heating and air conditioning systems, or a common refrigerator-freezer, offer excellent examples of systems. These systems can be presented in more detail via student projects and demonstrations.

Students can be encouraged to look at the advances in heating–air conditioning systems and can envision what advances will take place in the future. These systems offer excellent opportunities to look at troubleshooting. Other areas where students enjoy discussing troubleshooting concepts include electronic systems, e.g., their stereo equipment or computer systems.

6. *Measurement and Graphic Methods:* Has an awareness of precision measurement, vectors, statistics, and graphic methods.

Students will be shown metric and English systems of measurement, measuring instruments, significant digits, and addition of vectors by both graphical and analytical methods.

7. *Mechanics:* Understands the concept of force, motion, work, energy, momentum, power, friction, torque, and rotational dynamics.

Students will cover Newton's laws, statics and dynamics, friction, linear and angular motion, torque, work, energy, power, impulse, and momentum.

8. *Mechanical Properties:* Knows the structure of matter, properties of solids, liquids, and gases.

Students will examine solids (Young's modulus, shear modulus, hardness, ductility), fluids (density, pressure, hydraulic presses, measuring pressure, Archimedes' principle, fluid flow, Bernoulli's equation), and gases (Boyle's law, ideal gas laws, vapor pressure, phase change, humidity).

9. *Thermodynamics:* Understands temperature, heat, heat transfer, engines, refrigeration, and air conditioning.

Students will explore temperature and energy, specific heat, change of phase, heat transfer, conduction, convection, insulation, and radiation, laws of thermodynamics, heat engines, and refrigeration.

10. *Wave Motion and Sound:* Understands acoustics, vibratory and sound waves.

Students will survey types of waves, periodic motion, standing waves, superposition, sound, pitch, quality, and Doppler effect.

11. *Light and Optics:* Is familiar with the nature, reflection, refraction, dispersion, and polarization of light, and optical instruments.

Students will explore quantum theory, speed of light, luminous flux and intensity, reflection, refraction, mirrors, focal length, lenses, interference, diffraction, and polarization.

12. *Electricity and Magnetism:* Understands basic circuits, source and effect of current, magnetism, electromagnetism, induction, generators, motors, AC, and energy distribution.

Students will observe charge, insulators, conductors, Coulomb's law, fields, Gauss's law, electrical and field potential, capacitance, simple circuits, ac circuits, emf, resistance, magnetic fields, motors, generators, and transformers.

13. *Modern Physics:* Understands electronics; atomic and nuclear physics.

Students will examine the theory of relativity, Rutherford atom, atomic spectra, Bohr atom, nuclear physics, radioactivity, nuclear reactors, semiconductors, and integrated circuits.

Physics, Sixth Edition, by Paul E. Tippens could be used for a Tech Prep physics course. Postsecondary students who were in Tech Prep high school programs will enjoy having opportunities for critical thinking and group problem-solving activities. *Physics* includes a good, thorough treatment of metric and English units. It also contains a sufficient number of practice problems, and each chapter concludes with a short summary. The book offers an appropriate level of mathematics for most students. Physics principles are sometimes illustrated by the use of real-world mechanisms such as gears. These mechanisms are shown in drawings rather than photographs.

REFERENCES AND SUGGESTED READINGS

1. *America 2000: An Education Strategy Sourcebook* (April 1991). Washington, D.C.: United States Department of Education.

2. *America's Choice: High Skills or Low Wages* (June 1990). National Center on Education and the Economy, P.O. Box 10670, Rochester, New York 14610.

3. *The AVA Guide to the Carl Perkins Vocational and Applied Technology Education Act of 1990*, AVA, 1410 King Street, Alexandria, Virginia 22314.

4. Bureau for Vocational Education, Wisconsin Department of Public Instruction, 125 South Webster Street, Madison, Wisconsin 53702.

5. Center on Education and Training for Employment, The Ohio State University, 1900 Kenny Road, Columbus, Ohio 43210.

6. Center for Occupational Research and Development, 601 Lake Air Drive, Waco, Texas 76710.

7. Dutton, Maurice (January 1996). "Tech Prep/School to Work: Career Paths for All." *The Education Digest.*

8. Edgar, Elaine D., and Parnell, Dale. "Technical Colleges Are Powerful Partners in Developing Tech Prep Associate Degree Programs." *Community College Journal* (Feb./March 1996).

9. ERIC® Clearinghouse, Adult Career Vocational Education. http://www.coe.ohio-state.edu/cete/ericave/

10. *The Forgotten Half: Non-College Youth in America*, Washington, D.C.: Youth and America's Future: The William T. Grant Foundation Commission on Work, Family and Citizenship (1988).

11. Grubb, N. W., Davis, G., Lum, J., Phihal, J., and Morgaine, C. (July 1991). "The Cunning Hand, The Cultured Mind": Models for Integrating Vocational and Academic Education. Berkeley: National Center for Research in Vocational Education, University of California.

12. Hull, D., and Parnell, D. "Tech-Prep Associate Degree: A Win Win Experience" (1991). Center for Occupational Research and Development, 601 Lake Air Drive, Waco, Texas 76710.

13. Loock, J. W., and Voiers, J. S.: *Strategies for Implementing Tech Prep* (1995), Columbus, Ohio: Glencoe/McGraw-Hill.

14. Loock, J. W., and Voiers, J. S.: *Strategies for Implementing Tech Prep into Communication* (1994), Columbus, Ohio: Glencoe/McGraw-Hill.

15. *A Nation at Risk.* Washington, D.C.: United States Department of Education (1983).

16. *National Tech-Prep Network Newsletter.* Membership available from Center for Occupational Research and Development, 601 Lake Air Drive, Waco, Texas 76710.

17. Parnell, D., *The Neglected Majority* (1985). Center for Occupational Research and Development, 601 Lake Air Drive, Waco, Texas 76710.

18. Ross, Maryanne, Swinehart, Carole P., Hogan, Diane, Morrison, Connie, Hoyt, Bill, and Haber, Barry. *Tech Prep Strategies in Accounting.* 1995, Columbus, Ohio: Glencoe/McGraw-Hill.

19. *SCANS: Secretary's Commission on Achieving Necessary Skills.* United States Department of Labor, SCANS Office, Room C-2318, 200 Constitution Avenue N.W., Washington, D.C. 20210.

20. *Training Strategies: Preparing Non-College Youth for Employment in U.S. and Foreign Countries* (1990). United States General Accounting Office, P.O. Box 6015, Gaithersburg, Maryland 20877.

21. United States Statutes at Large, 1990 and Proclamations, Volume 104 in Six Parts, Public Law 101–392, September 25, 1990, "Carl D. Perkins Vocational and Applied Technology Education Act Amendments of 1990," United States Government Printing Office, Washington, D.C.

22. *Workplace Basics: The Essential Skills Employers Want* (October 1988). American Society for Training and Development, 1630 Duke Street, Box 1443, Alexandria, Virginia 22313.

Transparency Masters

UNIT E

Chapter	Transparency Number and Title	Section Reference
1	None	
2	**1.** Scales for Time and Mass	3-3
3	**2.** Indicating Directions for Vectors	3-7
3	**3.** Forces on Inclined Plane	3-9
4	**4.** The Component Method of Vector Addition	3-12
4	**5.** Action and Reaction Forces	4-2
4	**6.** Newton's Third Law	4-2
4	**7.** A Free-Body Diagram	4-3
4	**8.** Friction on the Inclined Plane	4-5
5	**9.** Calculating Torque	5-3
6	**10.** Graphs of Position as a Function of Time	6-1
6	**11.** Graphs of Velocity as a Function of Time	6-2
6	**12.** Gravity and Freely-Falling Bodies	6-7
6	**13.** The Motion of a Ball Thrown Horizontally	6-7
6	**14.** A Projectile Launched at an Angle	6-8
7	**15.** Acceleration Is Proportional to an Applied Force	7-1
7	**16.** Acceleration Is Inversely Proportional to the Mass	7-1
8	None	
9	**17.** Impulse and Momentum	9-1
9	**18.** Impulse and Momentum for a Glancing Collision	9-3
9	**19.** Conservation of Momentum	9-3
10	**20.** Newton's Law of Gravitation	10-7
10	**21.** Kepler's Second Law	10-10
11	**22.** Moments of Inertia	11-5
12	**23.** Simple Machines	12-3 and 12-6
13	None	
14	**24.** Velocity and the Reference Circle	14-3
14	**25.** Acceleration and the Reference Circle	14-4
15	None	
16	**26.** The Celsius and Fahrenheit Temperature Scales	16-2
16	**27.** Representative Kelvin Temperatures	16-4
16	**28.** Absolute Temperature Scales	16-4
17	**29.** Specific Heat Capacity	17-3
17	**30.** Change of Phase for Water	17-5
18	None	
19	None	
20	**31.** Thermodynamics	20-5
20	**32.** Thermodynamic Processes	20-6 to 20-8
20	**33.** Heat Pumps	20-13
21	**34.** Wave Properties	21-2
21	**35.** Standing Waves in a Vibrating String	21-8
22	**36.** Standing Waves in Air Columns	22-3

SCALES FOR TIME AND MASS

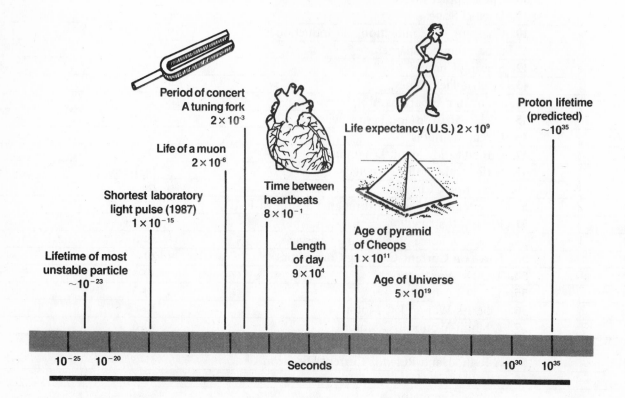

Period of concert
A tuning fork
2×10^{-3}

Life of a muon
2×10^{-6}

Shortest laboratory
light pulse (1987)
1×10^{-15}

Life expectancy (U.S.) 2×10^{9}

Proton lifetime
(predicted)
$\sim 10^{35}$

Time between
heartbeats
8×10^{-1}

Length
of day
9×10^{4}

Age of pyramid
of Cheops
1×10^{11}

Lifetime of most
unstable particle
$\sim 10^{-23}$

Age of Universe
5×10^{19}

10^{-25}	10^{-20}					Seconds						10^{30}	10^{35}

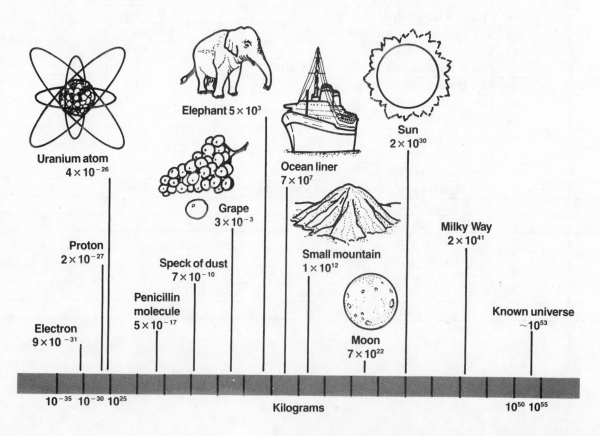

Uranium atom
4×10^{-26}

Elephant 5×10^{3}

Ocean liner
7×10^{7}

Sun
2×10^{30}

Grape
3×10^{-3}

Proton
2×10^{-27}

Speck of dust
7×10^{-10}

Small mountain
1×10^{12}

Milky Way
2×10^{41}

Penicillin
molecule
5×10^{-17}

Electron
9×10^{-31}

Known universe
$\sim 10^{53}$

Moon
7×10^{22}

10^{-35}	10^{-30}	10^{25}				Kilograms					10^{50}	10^{55}

TRANSPARENCY 1 (Use with 3-3)

INDICATING DIRECTIONS FOR VECTORS

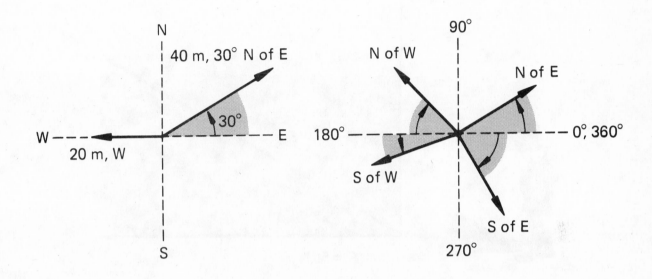

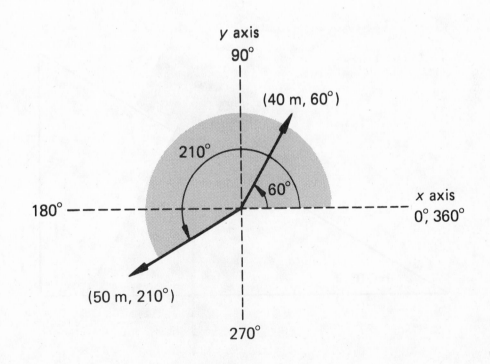

TRANSPARENCY 2 (Use with 3-7)

339

FORCES ON INCLINED PLANE

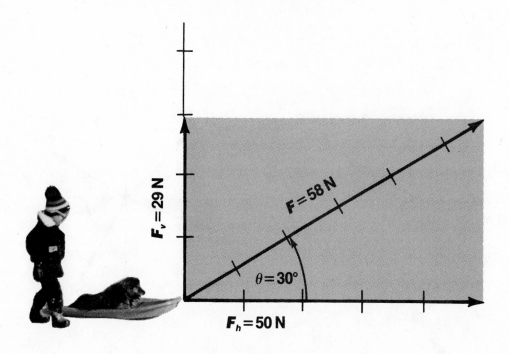

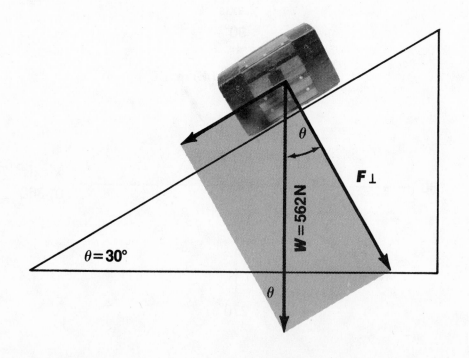

TRANSPARENCY 3   (Use with 3-9)

THE COMPONENT METHOD OF VECTOR ADDITION

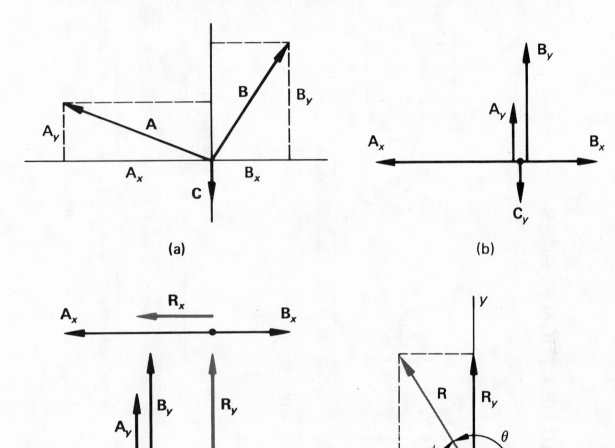

(a)　　　　　　　　(b)

(c)　　　　　　　　(d)

1. Resolve each vector into its *x* and *y* components.

Example: $A_x = \pm \, |A \cos \varphi| \qquad A_y = \pm \, |A \sin \varphi|$

2. Add components of each vector to find (R_x, R_y).

$$R_x = A_x + B_x + C_x; \qquad R_y = A_y + B_y + C_y$$

3. Find magnitude *R* and direction θ for resultant vector.

$$R = \sqrt{R_x^2 + R_y^2}; \qquad \tan\theta = \frac{R_y}{R_x}$$

TRANSPARENCY 4　(Use with 3-12)

ACTION AND REACTION FORCES

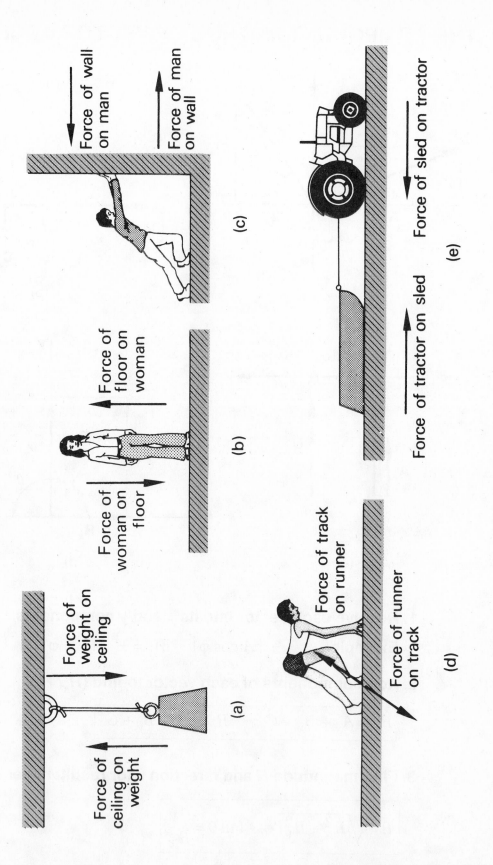

(a)
Force of weight on ceiling
Force of ceiling on weight

(b)
Force of floor on woman
Force of woman on floor

(c)
Force of wall on man
Force of man on wall

(d)
Force of track on runner
Force of runner on track

(e)
Force of sled on tractor
Force of tractor on sled

TRANSPARENCY 5 (Use with 4-2)

NEWTON'S THIRD LAW

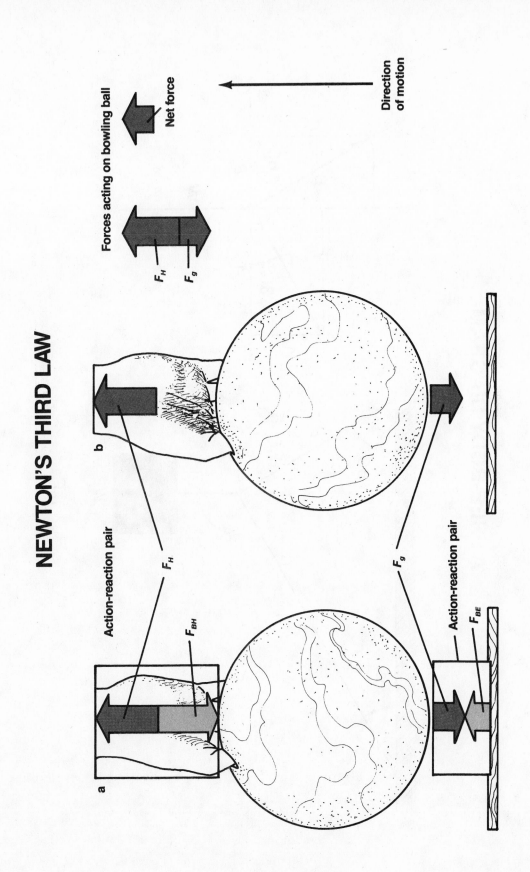

Forces acting on bowling ball

Net force

Direction of motion

F_H

F_g

Action-reaction pair

F_H

F_{BH}

Action-reaction pair

F_g

F_{BE}

a

b

Copyright © by Glencoe/McGraw-Hill.

A FREE-BODY DIAGRAM

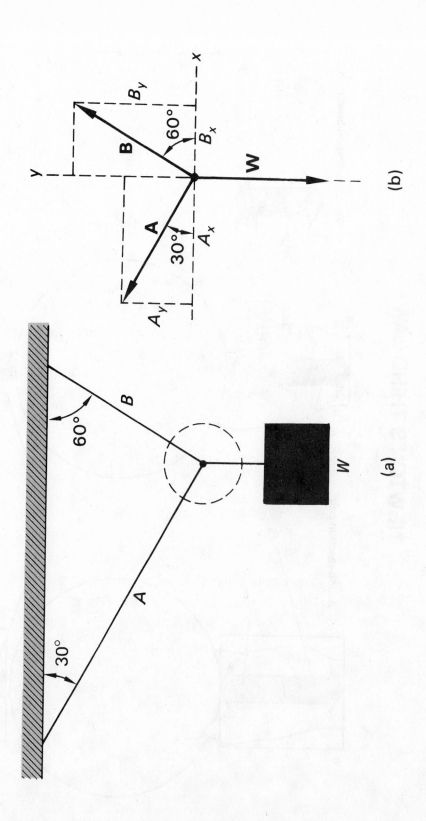

(a)

(b)

FRICTION ON THE INCLINED PLANE

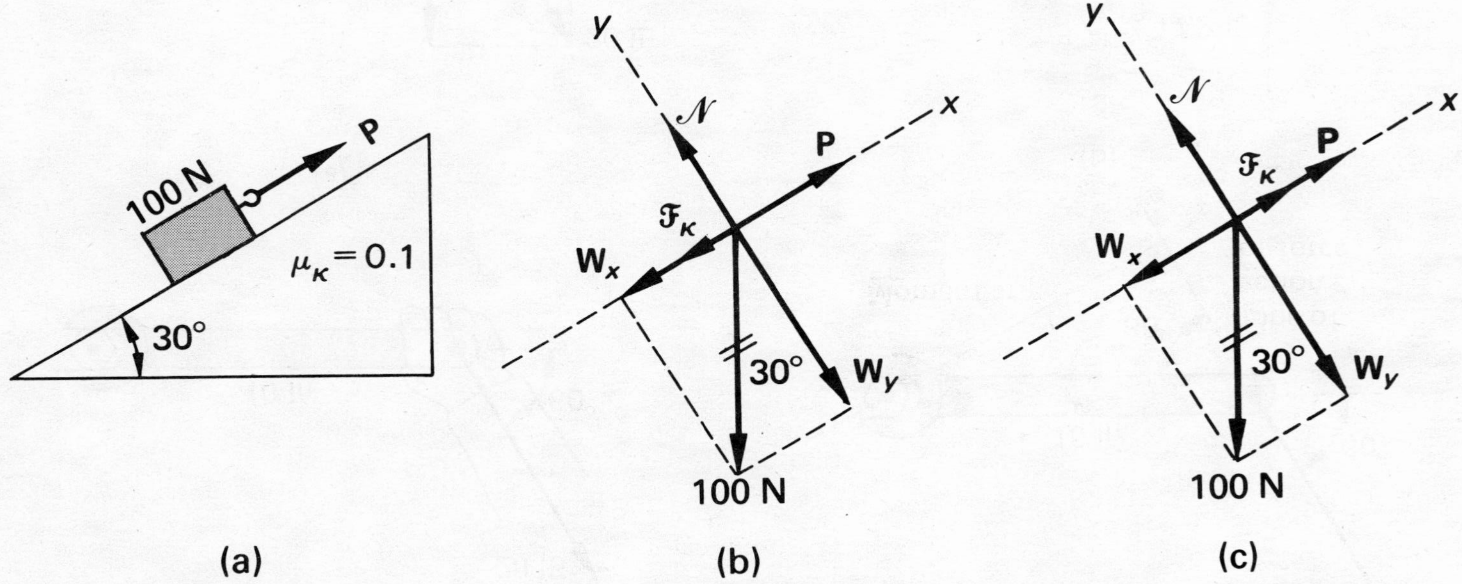

(a)

$\mu_K = 0.1$

100 N

P

30°

(b)

y

P

$\mathcal{F}_K$

$\mathcal{N}$

W_x

30°

W_y

100 N

x

(c)

y

$\mathcal{N}$

$\mathcal{F}_K$

P

W_x

30°

W_y

100 N

x

CALCULATING TORQUE

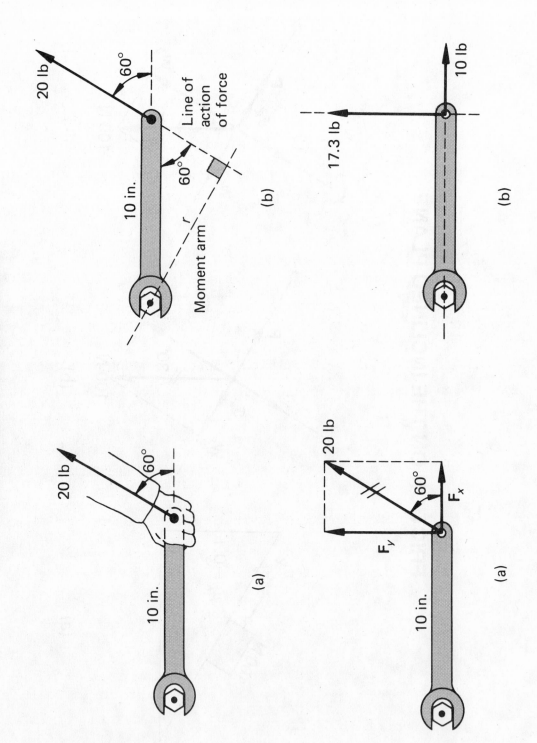

20 lb

60°

Line of action of force

10 in.

60°

r

Moment arm

(b)

10 lb

17.3 lb

(b)

20 lb

60°

10 in.

(a)

20 lb

60°

F_x

F_y

10 in.

(a)

TRANSPARENCY 9 (Use with 5-3)

GRAPHS OF POSITION AS A FUNCTION OF TIME

CONSTANT VELOCITY

Position versus Time

Time (s)	Position (m)
0	0
1	20
2	40
3	60
4	80
5	100

CONSTANT ACCELERATION

Position versus Time

Time (s)	Position (m)
0	+0
1	+10
2	+40
3	+90
4	+160
5	+250

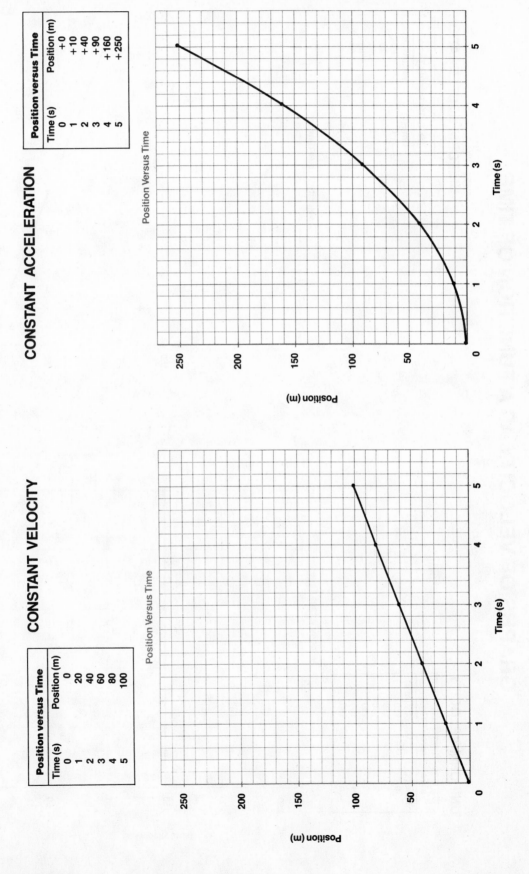

Position Versus Time

GRAPHS OF VELOCITY AS A FUNCTION OF TIME

UNIFORM VELOCITY

Velocity versus Time

Time (s)	Velocity (m/s)
0	150
1	150
2	150
3	150
4	150
5	150

UNIFORM ACCELERATION

Velocity versus Time

Time (s)	Velocity (m/s)
0	+0
1	+20
2	+40
3	+60
4	+80
5	+100

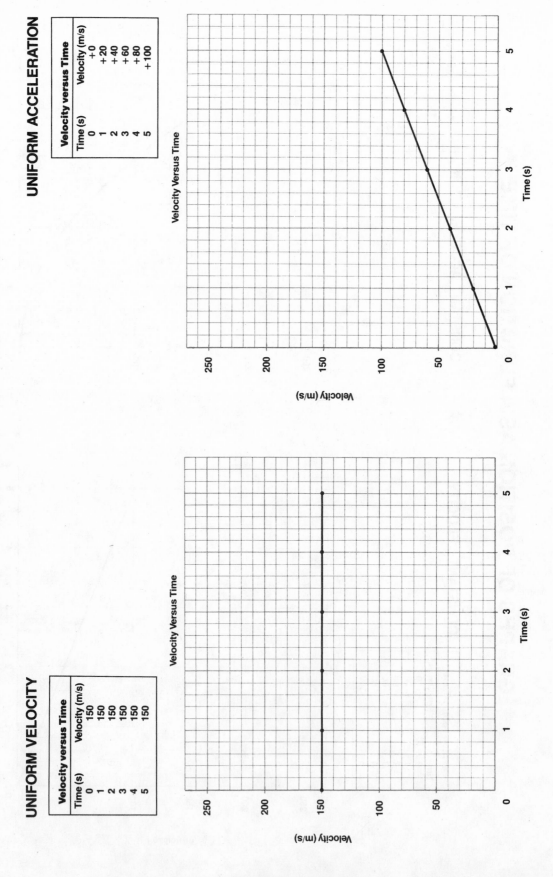

TRANSPARENCY 11   (Use with 6-2)

348

GRAVITY AND FREELY-FALLING BODIES

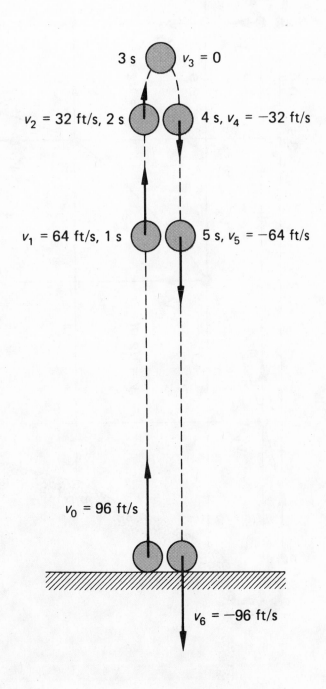

THE MOTION OF A BALL THROWN HORIZONTALLY

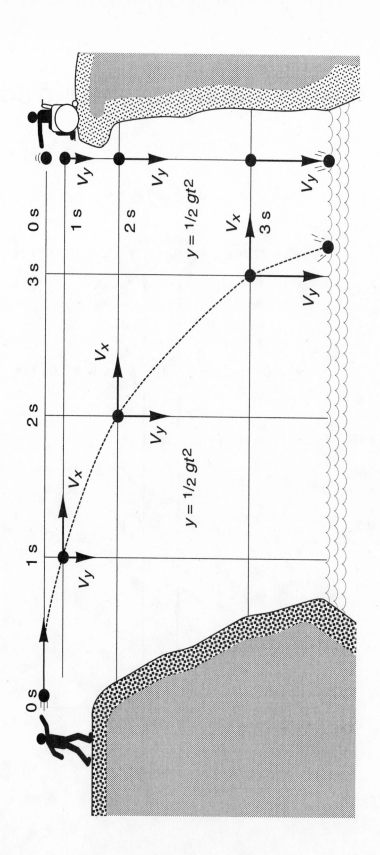

TRANSPARENCY 13 (Use with 6-7)

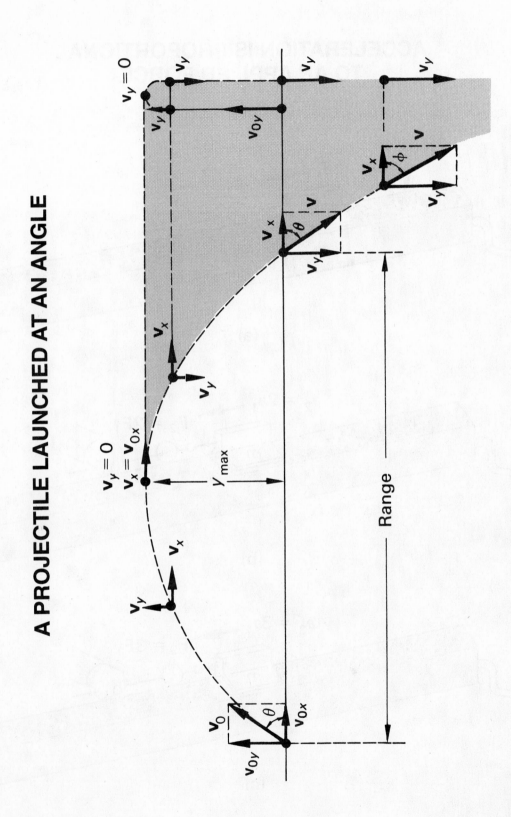

A PROJECTILE LAUNCHED AT AN ANGLE

ACCELERATION IS PROPORTIONAL
TO AN APPLIED FORCE

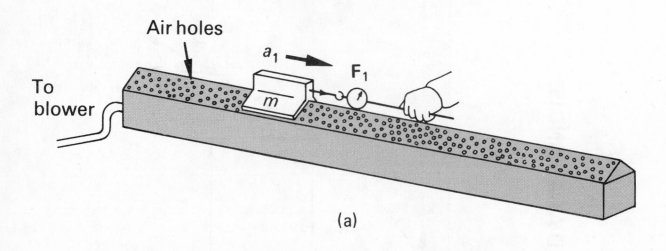

(a)

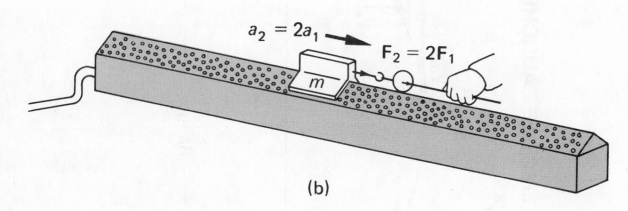

(b)

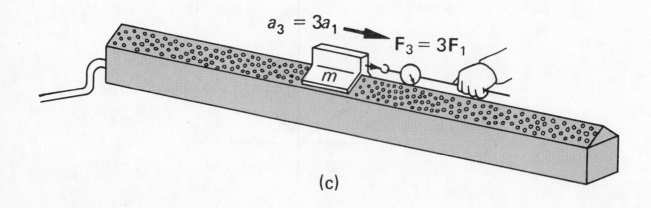

(c)

TRANSPARENCY 15 (Use with 7-1)

ACCELERATION IS INVERSELY PROPORTIONAL TO THE MASS

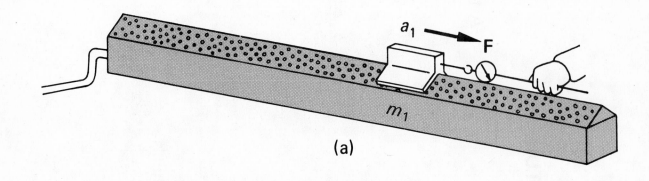

(a)

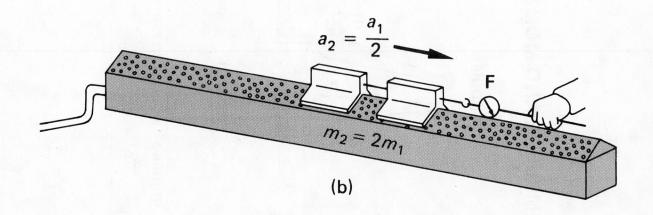

(b)

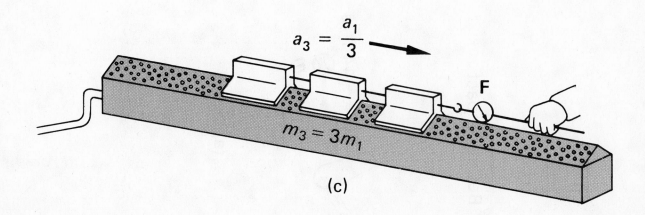

(c)

TRANSPARENCY 16   (Use with 7-1)

IMPULSE AND MOMENTUM

Before impact

$v_0 = -44$ ft/s

m

(a)

Impulse

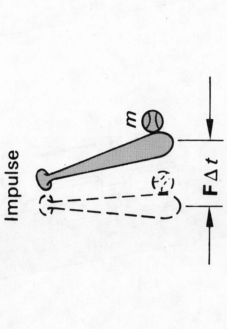

m

$\mathbf{F}\Delta t$

(b)

Impulse = change in momentum
$\mathbf{F}\Delta t = mv_f - mv_0$

After impact

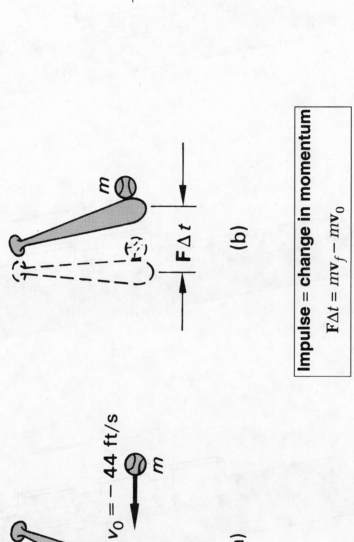

mv_f

88 ft/s

(c)

TRANSPARENCY 17   (Use with 9-1)

IMPULSE AND MOMENTUM FOR A GLANCING COLLISION

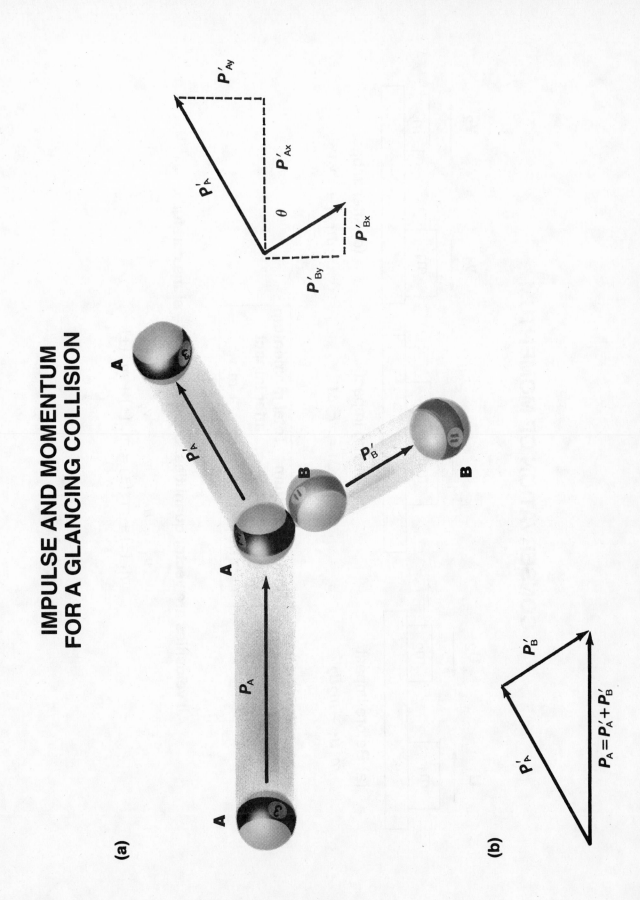

(a)

(b)

CONSERVATION OF MOMENTUM

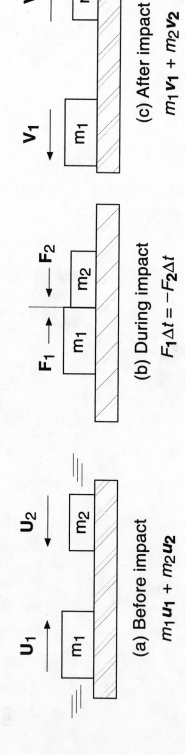

(a) Before impact

$m_1\boldsymbol{u_1} + m_2\boldsymbol{u_2}$

(b) During impact

$F_1\Delta t = -F_2\Delta t$

(c) After impact

$m_1\boldsymbol{v_1} + m_2\boldsymbol{v_2}$

Total momentum before impact	=	Total momentum after impact

$$m_1u_1 + m_2u_2 = m_1v_1 + m_2v_2$$

All velocities are vector quantities. Substitute + or – signs carefully.

$$u_1 \quad u_2 \quad v_1 \quad v_2$$
$$m_1\,(\pm) + m_2\,(\pm) = m_1\,(\pm) + m_2\,(\pm)$$

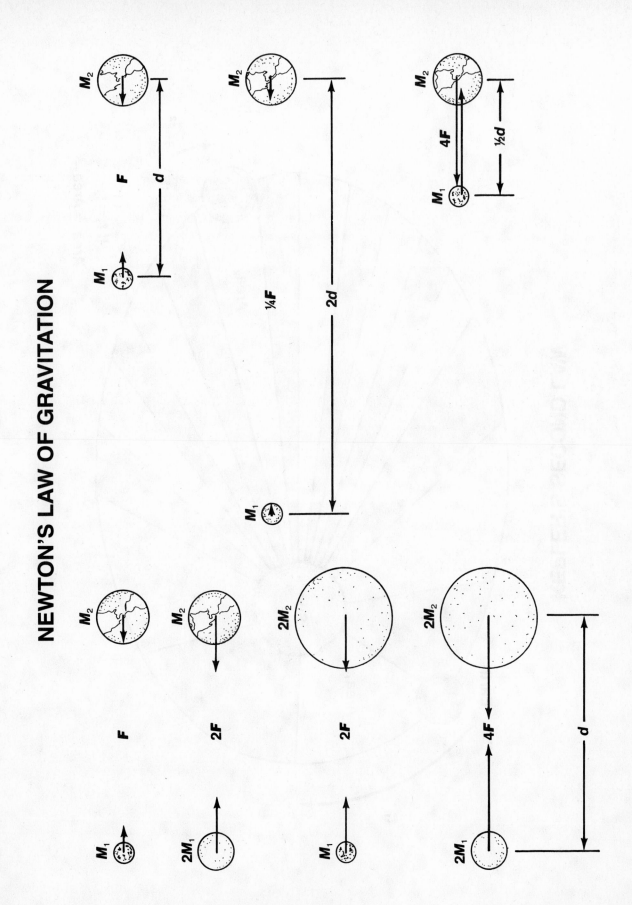

NEWTON'S LAW OF GRAVITATION

Copyright © by Glencoe/McGraw-Hill.

KEPLER'S SECOND LAW

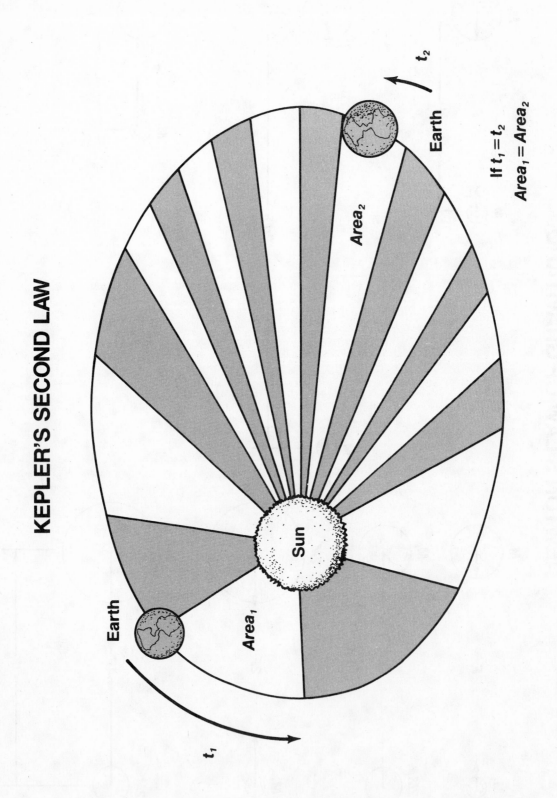

Sun

Earth

Earth

Area₁

Area₂

t_1

t_2

If $t_1 = t_2$
Area₁ = Area₂

TRANSPARENCY 21 (Use with 10-10)

MOMENTS OF INERTIA

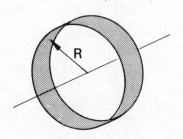

(a) Thin hoop

$I = mR^2$

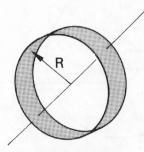

(b) Thin hoop about a diameter

$I = \frac{1}{2}mR^2$

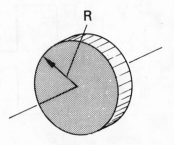

(c) Solid disk

$I = \frac{1}{2}mR^2$

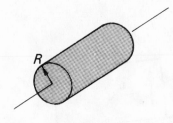

(d) Solid cylinder

$I = \frac{1}{2}mR^2$

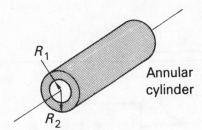

Annular cylinder

(e) Hollow cylinder

$I = \frac{1}{2}m(R_1^2 + R_2^2)$

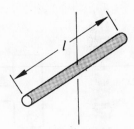

(f) Thin rod, axis through center

$I = \frac{1}{12}m\ell^2$

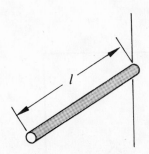

(g) Thin rod, axis about end point

$I = \frac{1}{3}m\ell^2$

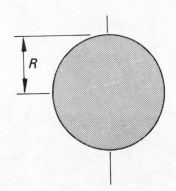

(h) Solid sphere, axis along diameter

$I = \frac{2}{5}mR^2$

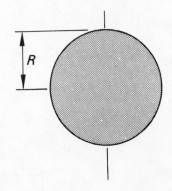

(i) Hollow sphere with thin wall

$I = \frac{2}{3}mR^2$

SIMPLE MACHINES

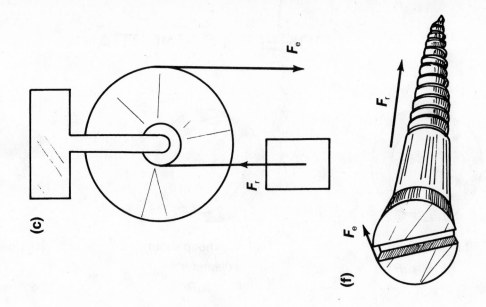

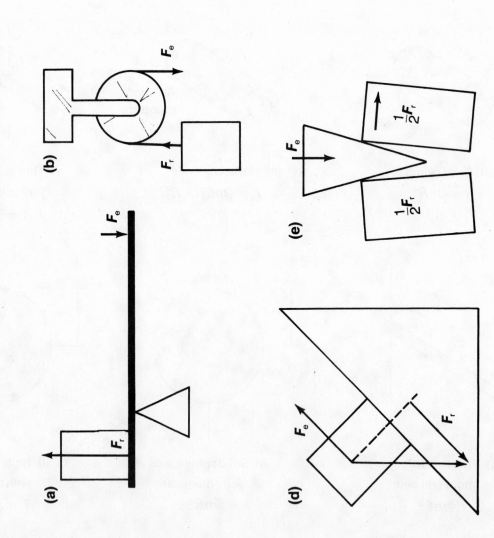

(a)

(b)

(c)

(d)

(e)

(f)

F_e

F_r

$\frac{1}{2}F_r$

$\frac{1}{2}F_r$

TRANSPARENCY 23   (Use with 12-3 and 12-6)

360

VELOCITY AND THE REFERENCE CIRCLE

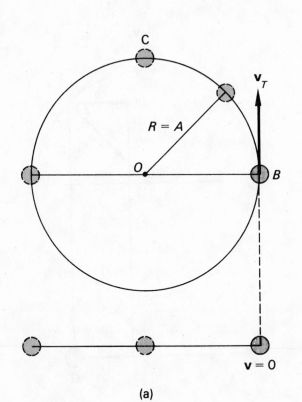

$R = A$

$\mathbf{v}_T$

O

B

$\mathbf{v} = 0$

(a)

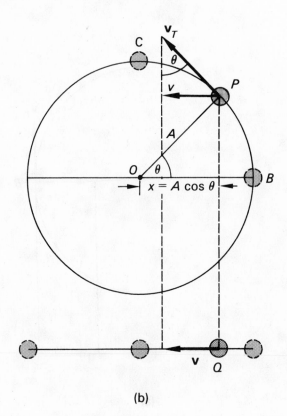

$\mathbf{v}_T$

θ

C

$\mathbf{v}$

P

A

O

θ

B

$x = A \cos \theta$

$\mathbf{v}$

Q

(b)

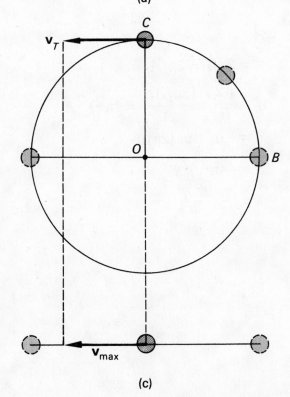

C

$\mathbf{v}_T$

O

B

$\mathbf{v}_{max}$

(c)

$x = A \cos \theta$

$x = 2\pi f A \cos(2\pi f t)$

$v = -2\pi f A \sin(2\pi f t)$

ACCELERATION AND THE REFERENCE CIRCLE

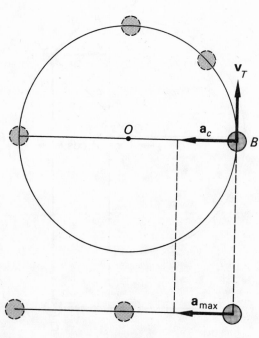

(a)

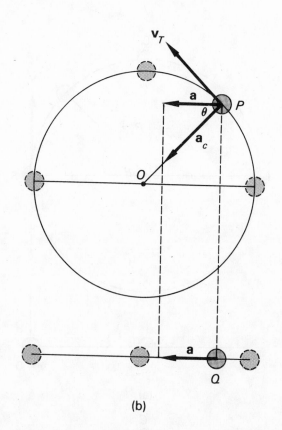

(b)

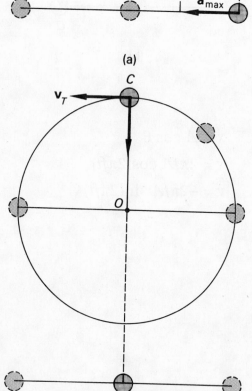

(c)

$$v = 2\pi f R = 2\pi f A$$

$$a_C = \frac{v^2}{R} = \frac{(2\pi f A)^2}{A} = 4\pi^2 f^2 A$$

$$a = -a_C \cos(2\pi f t)$$

$$a = -4\pi^2 f^2 x$$

$$f = \frac{1}{2\pi}\sqrt{\frac{-a}{x}}$$

TRANSPARENCY 25   (Use with 14-4)

THE CELSIUS AND FAHRENHEIT
TEMPERATURE SCALES

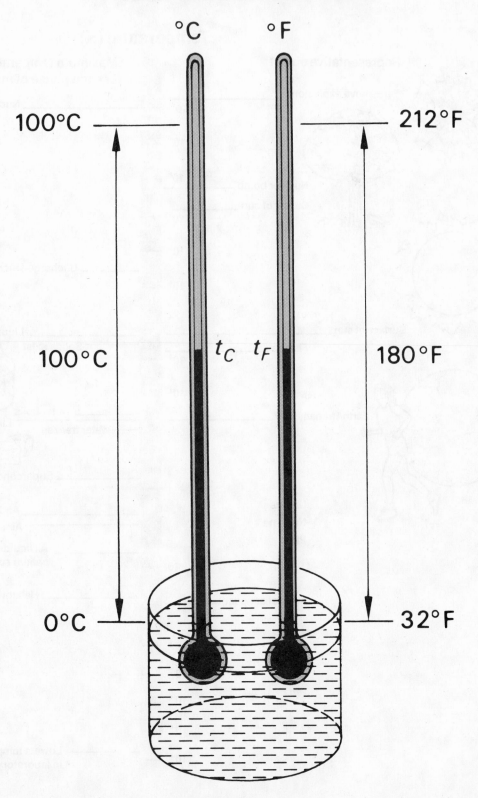

°C   °F

100°C ————   ———— 212°F

100°C t_C t_F 180°F

0°C ————   ———— 32°F

REPRESENTATIVE KELVIN TEMPERATURES

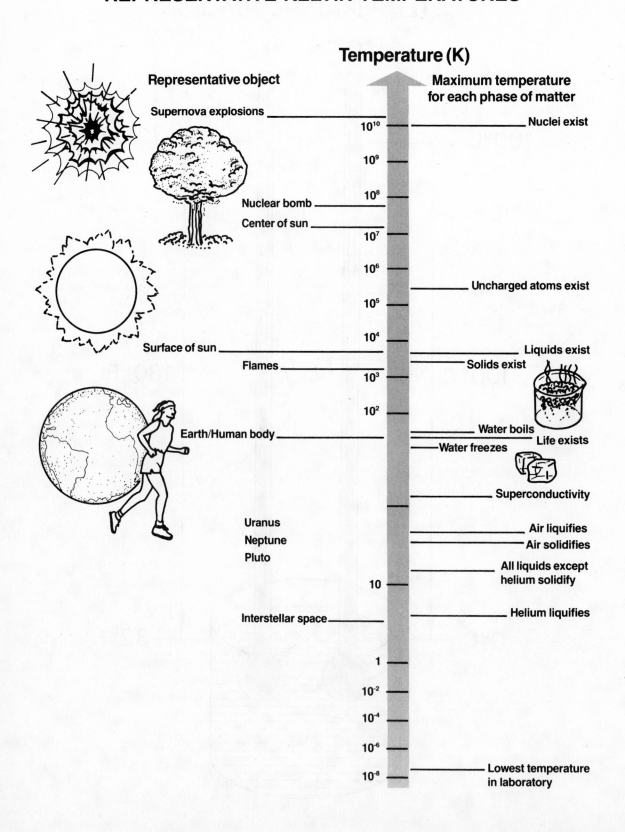

Temperature (K)

Representative object

Supernova explosions _____ 10^{10}

10^9

Nuclear bomb _____ 10^8

Center of sun _____ 10^7

10^6

10^5

10^4

Surface of sun _____ 10^3

Flames _____

10^2

Earth/Human body _____

Uranus

Neptune

Pluto

10

Interstellar space _____

1

10^{-2}

10^{-4}

10^{-6}

10^{-8}

Maximum temperature for each phase of matter

Nuclei exist

Uncharged atoms exist

Liquids exist

Solids exist

Water boils

Life exists

Water freezes

Superconductivity

Air liquifies

Air solidifies

All liquids except helium solidify

Helium liquifies

Lowest temperature in laboratory

TRANSPARENCY 27 (Use with 16-4)

ABSOLUTE TEMPERATURE SCALES

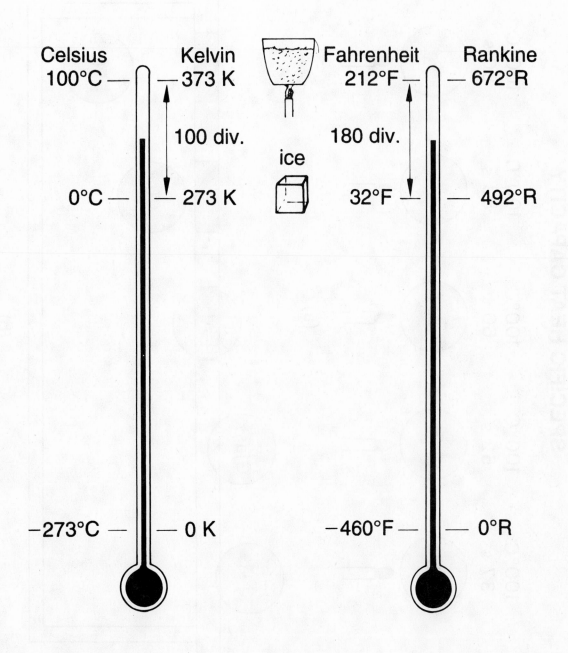

SPECIFIC HEAT CAPACITY

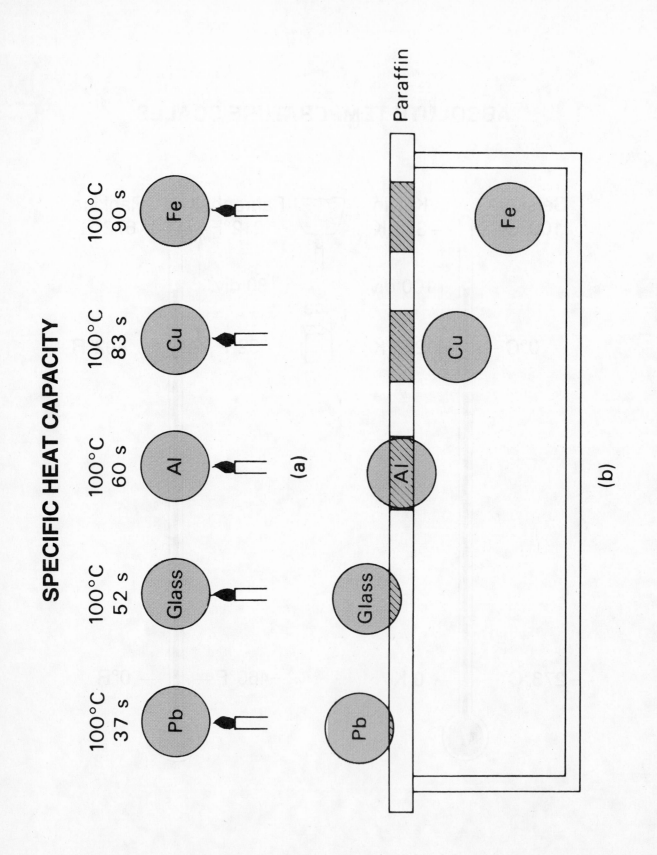

Paraffin

100°C	100°C	100°C	100°C	100°C
37 s	52 s	60 s	83 s	90 s
Pb	Glass	Al	Cu	Fe

(a)

(b)

TRANSPARENCY 29   (Use with 17-3)

CHANGE OF PHASE FOR WATER

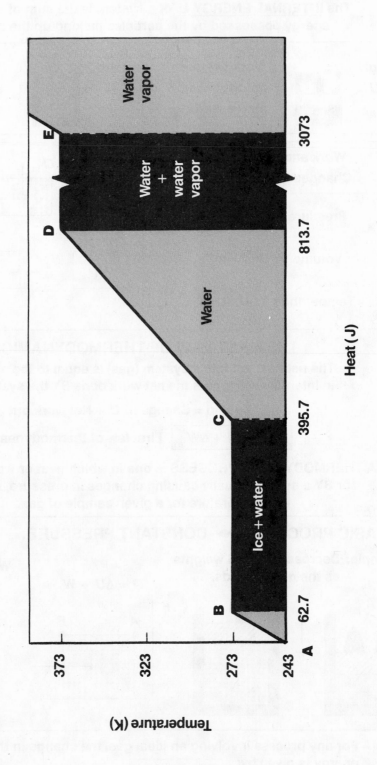

THERMODYNAMICS

The <u>INTERNAL ENERGY U</u> of a system is the sum of all kinds of energy possessed by the particles making up the system.

High
U
Work <u>ON</u> gas or input heat <u>increases</u> U.

Low
U
Work done <u>BY</u> expanding gas <u>decreases</u> U.

Work and Heat Cause Changes in P, V, and T:

Pressure P: Unit = Pa

Volume V: Unit = m^3

Temperature T: Unit = K

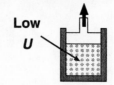

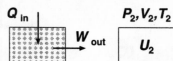
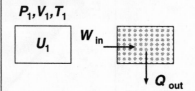

P_1, V_1, T_1 Q_{in} W_{out} P_2, V_2, T_2

U_1 U_2

P_1, V_1, T_1 W_{in} P_2, V_2, T_2

U_1 U_2

Q_{out}

THE FIRST LAW OF THERMODYNAMICS:

The net heat put into a system (gas) is equal to the net change in internal energy plus the net work done BY the system (gas).

Net heat in = Change in U + Net work out

$$\Delta Q = \Delta U + \Delta W$$ First law of thermodynamics

A THERMODYNAMIC PROCESS is one in which heat or work is done ON or BY a system usually causing changes in pressure, volume, or temperature for a given sample of gas.

ISOBARIC PROCESS → CONSTANT PRESSURE: $\Delta P = 0$; $P_A = P_B$

Example: Decrease in lifted weights as the gas expands.

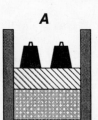

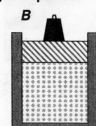

A B

F

$Q = \Delta U + W$

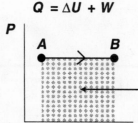

P

A ——→ B

V

Work = $P\,\Delta V$ = Area

$$\frac{V_A}{T_A} = \frac{V_B}{T_B}$$

Work = Area under PV curve

$$W = \int P\,dV$$

For any process involving an ideal gas, the change in the internal energy is given by: $\Delta U = nc_v \Delta T$

TRANSPARENCY 31   (Use with 20-5)

THERMODYNAMIC PROCESSES

ISOTHERMAL PROCESS → CONSTANT TEMPERATURE: $\Delta T = 0$; $\Delta U = 0$

$Q = \Delta U + W \qquad \Delta U = 0$

Heat In = Work Out

Work In = Heat Out

$\boxed{Q = W}$

Q_{in}

W_{out}

W_{in}

Q_{out}

(Reversible Process)

Example: Slow isothermal compression.

$T_A = T_B$

A B

F

$P_A V_A$ $P_B V_B$

P

B

$T_A = T_B$

A

V

Boyle's Law Applies:

$\boxed{P_A V_A = P_B V_B}$

$\text{Work} = nRT \; \ln \dfrac{V_B}{V_A}$

ADIABATIC PROCESS → NO HEAT EXCHANGE: $\Delta Q = 0$

$\boxed{\gamma = \dfrac{c_p}{c_v}}$

$Q = \Delta U + W = 0 \qquad \boxed{W = -\Delta U = -nc_v \, \Delta T}$

Work out decreases $U\,(-\Delta U)$

Input work increases $U\,(+\Delta U)$

$-\Delta U$

W_{out}

W_{in}

$+\Delta U$

Example: Adiabatic expansion. $\Delta Q = 0$

A B

F

P

A

B

V

For adiabatic processes:

$$\dfrac{P_A V_A}{T_A} = \dfrac{P_B V_B}{T_B}$$

$$P_A V_A{}^{\gamma} = P_B V_B{}^{\gamma}$$

$$V_A \, T_A{}^{\gamma-1} = V_B \, T_B{}^{\gamma-1}$$

ISOCHORIC PROCESS → CONSTANT VOLUME: $\Delta V = 0$; Work = 0

$Q = \Delta U + W$

$Q = \Delta U = nc_v \, \Delta T$

$\boxed{Q = \Delta U}$

Q_{in}

$+\Delta U$

Q_{out}

$-\Delta U$

$\text{Work} = P\,\Delta V = 0$

Heat input increases P with constant V

P

A

B

V

For an isochoric process:

$$\boxed{\dfrac{P_A}{T_A} = \dfrac{P_B}{T_B}}$$

TRANSPARENCY 32   (Use with 20-6 to 20-8)

369

HEAT PUMPS

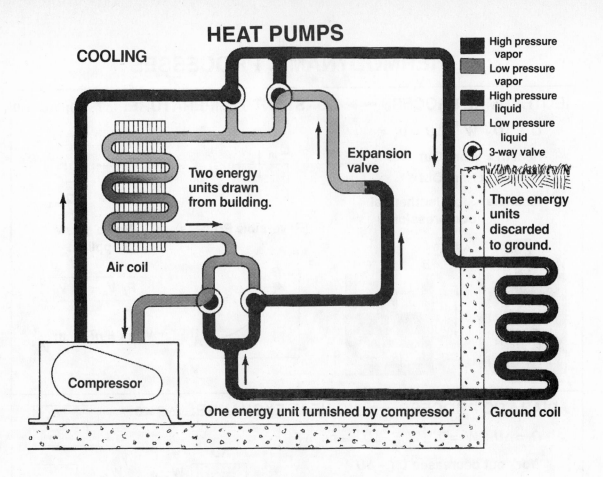

COOLING

Two energy units drawn from building.

Expansion valve

Air coil

Compressor

One energy unit furnished by compressor

Three energy units discarded to ground.

Ground coil

High pressure vapor
Low pressure vapor
High pressure liquid
Low pressure liquid
3-way valve

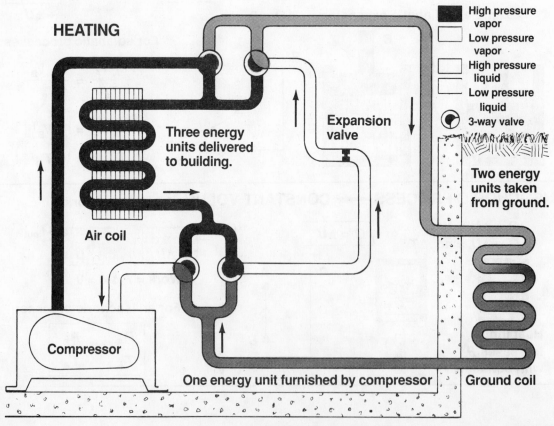

HEATING

Three energy units delivered to building.

Expansion valve

Air coil

Compressor

One energy unit furnished by compressor

Two energy units taken from ground.

Ground coil

High pressure vapor
Low pressure vapor
High pressure liquid
Low pressure liquid
3-way valve

TRANSPARENCY 33 (Use with 20-13)

WAVE PROPERTIES

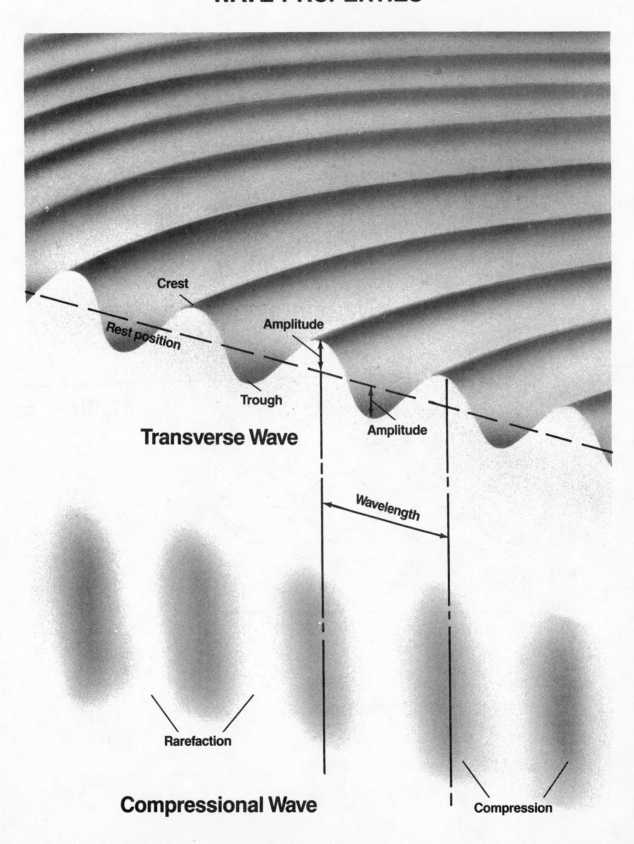

Crest

Rest position

Amplitude

Trough

Amplitude

Transverse Wave

Wavelength

Rarefaction

Compressional Wave

Compression

TRANSPARENCY 34   (Use with 21-2)

STANDING WAVES IN A VIBRATING STRING

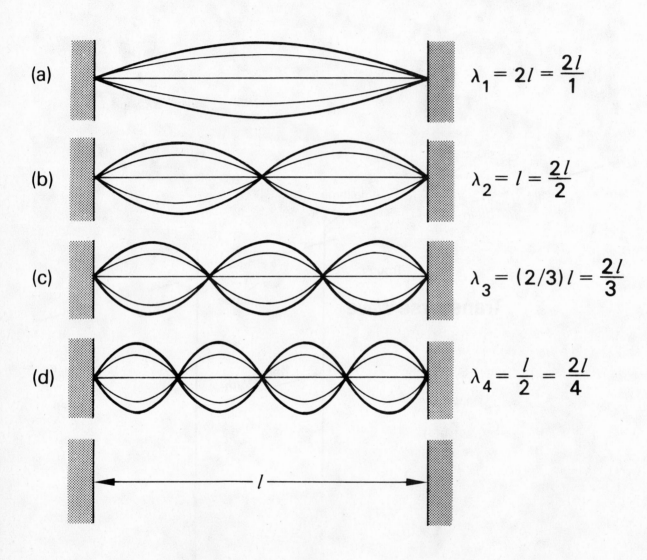

(a) $\lambda_1 = 2l = \dfrac{2l}{1}$

(b) $\lambda_2 = l = \dfrac{2l}{2}$

(c) $\lambda_3 = (2/3)\,l = \dfrac{2l}{3}$

(d) $\lambda_4 = \dfrac{l}{2} = \dfrac{2l}{4}$

l

Characteristic Frequencies: $f_n = \dfrac{nv}{2l}$ $n = 1, 2, 3, \ldots$

STANDING WAVES IN AIR COLUMNS

$\lambda_1 = \dfrac{2l}{1}$ Fundamental

$\lambda_2 = \dfrac{2l}{2}$ First overtone

$\lambda_3 = \dfrac{2l}{3}$ Second overtone

$\lambda_4 = \dfrac{2l}{4}$ Third overtone

(a) Open pipes

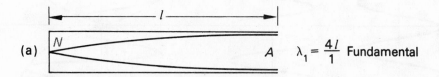

(a) $\lambda_1 = \dfrac{4l}{1}$ Fundamental

(b) $\lambda_3 = \dfrac{4l}{3}$ First overtone

(c) $\lambda_5 = \dfrac{4l}{5}$ Second overtone

(d) $\lambda_7 = \dfrac{4l}{7}$ Third overtone

(b) Closed pipes

TRANSPARENCY 36   **(Use with 22-3)**

THE ORIGIN OF BEATS

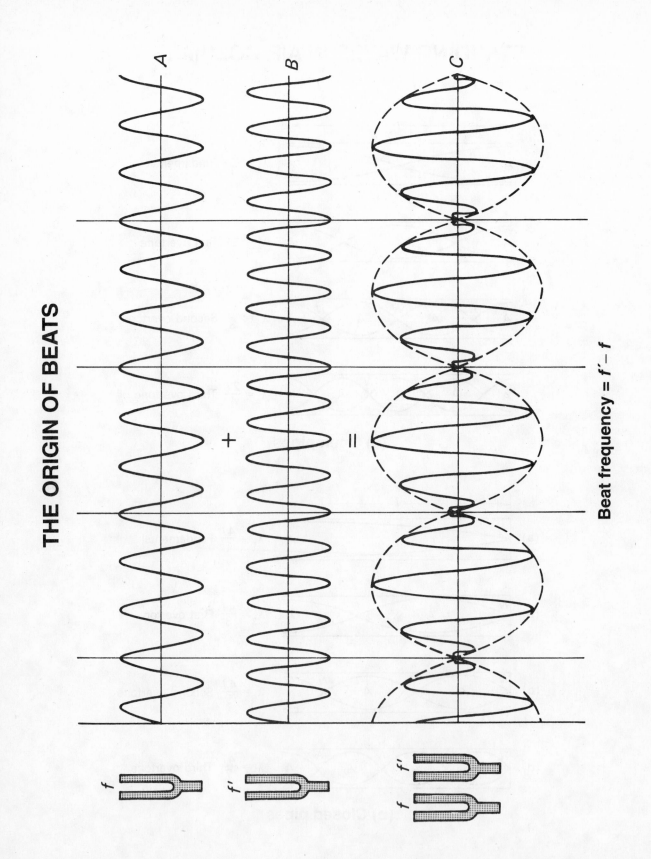

Beat frequency = $f' - f$

TRANSPARENCY 37 (Use with 22-7)

THE DOPPLER EFFECT

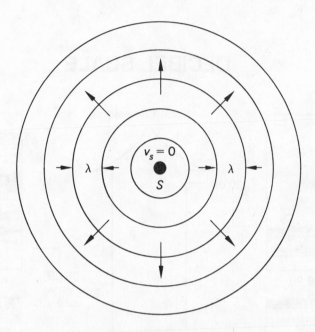

Sound from a stationary source

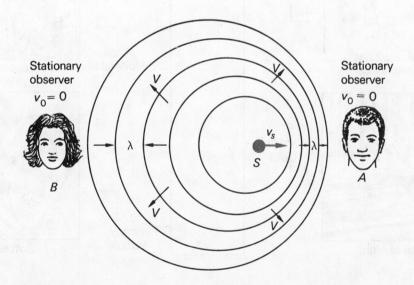

Illustration of the Doppler Effect: waves in front of a moving source are closer together; those behind are farther apart.

DECIBEL SCALE

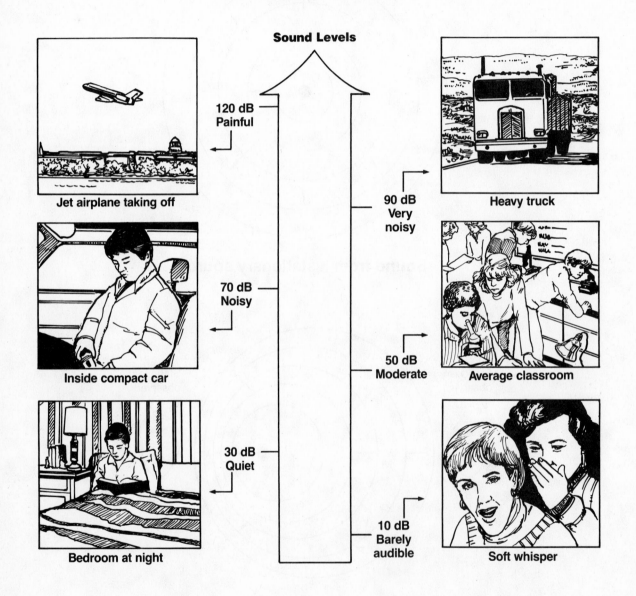

Sound Levels

120 dB
Painful

Jet airplane taking off

70 dB
Noisy

Inside compact car

30 dB
Quiet

Bedroom at night

90 dB
Very
noisy

Heavy truck

50 dB
Moderate

Average classroom

10 dB
Barely
audible

Soft whisper

TRANSPARENCY 39   (Use with 22-5)

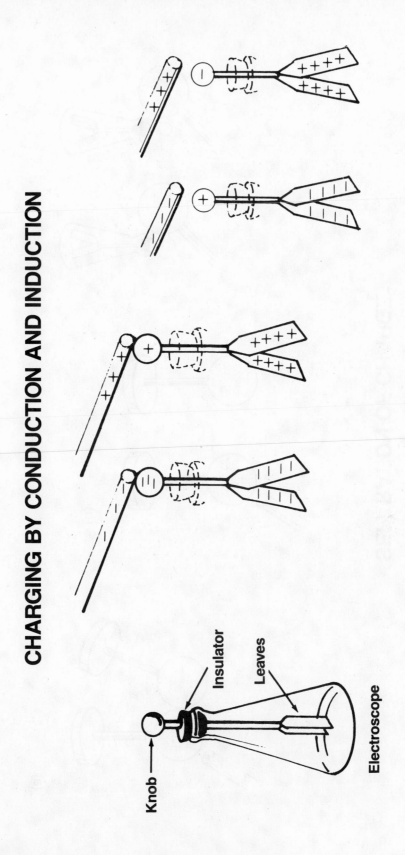

CHARGING BY CONDUCTION AND INDUCTION

Knob

Insulator

Leaves

Electroscope

SEPARATION OF CHARGE

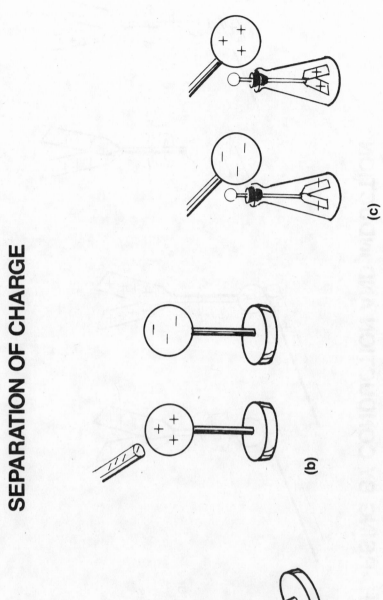

(c)

(b)

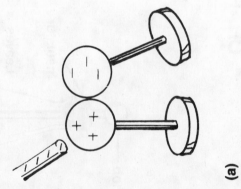

(a)

TRANSPARENCY 41 (Use with 23-6)

SHARING CHARGES

Metal spheres of equal size

Charged sphere

Neutral sphere

a b

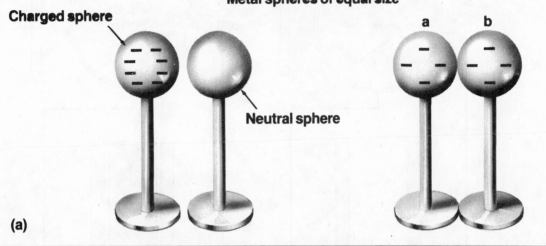

(a)

Metal spheres of unequal size

Low **V**   High **V**

High **q**   Low **q**

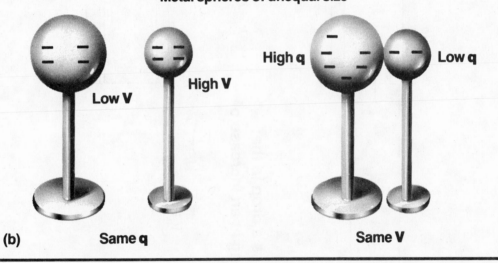

(b)   Same **q**   Same **V**

---

a b c

ELECTRIC FIELD LINES

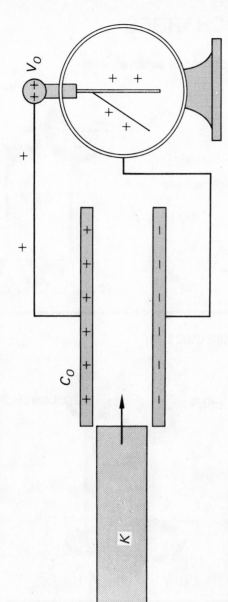

$$K = C/C_0 = V_0/V$$

Insertion of a dielectric causes a drop in the potential difference V resulting in an increase of capacitance C.

$$K = \frac{C}{C_0} \qquad C = KC_0 \qquad V = \frac{V_0}{K}$$

TRANSPARENCY 43   (Use with 24-3)

MILLIKAN'S APPARATUS

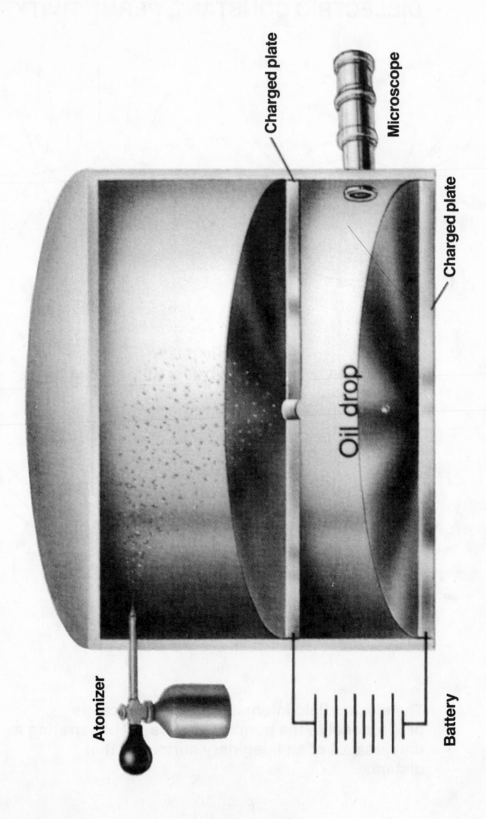

Charged plate

Microscope

Charged plate

Oil drop

Atomizer

Battery

DIELECTRIC CONSTANT; PERMITTIVITY

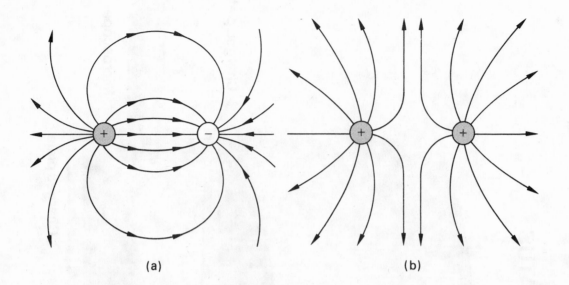

(a)

(b)

**Electric Field Lines
(a) Between two unlike charges; (b) Between two like charges.**

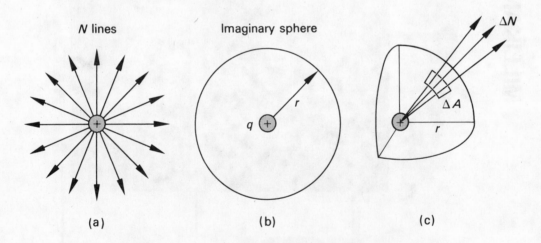

N lines

Imaginary sphere

ΔN

(a)

(b)

(c)

The electric field intensity *E* at a distance *r* is proportional to the number of lines ΔN penetrating a unit area ΔA of an imaginary surface at that distance.

$$E \propto \frac{\Delta N}{\Delta A}$$

CIRCUIT SYMBOLS

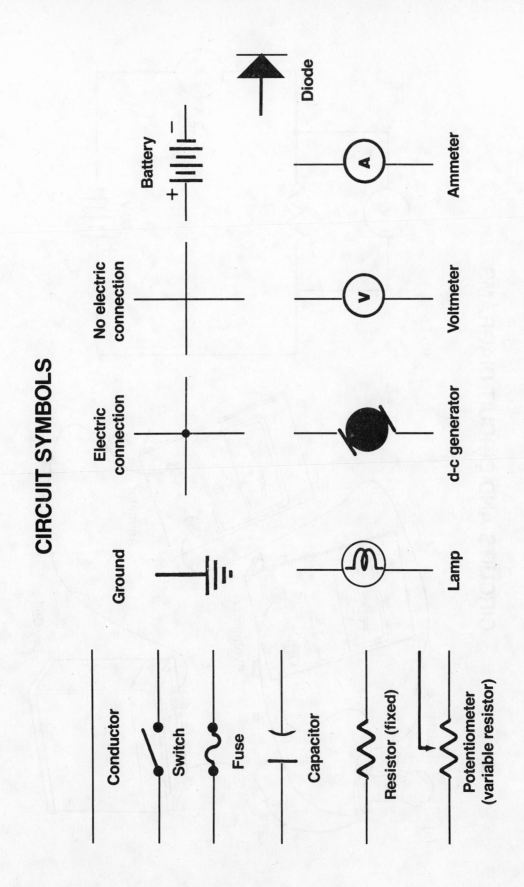

Diode

Battery

No electric connection

Electric connection

Ground

Conductor

Switch

Fuse

Capacitor

Resistor (fixed)

Potentiometer (variable resistor)

Ammeter

Voltmeter

d-c generator

Lamp

CIRCUITS AND CIRCUIT DIAGRAMS

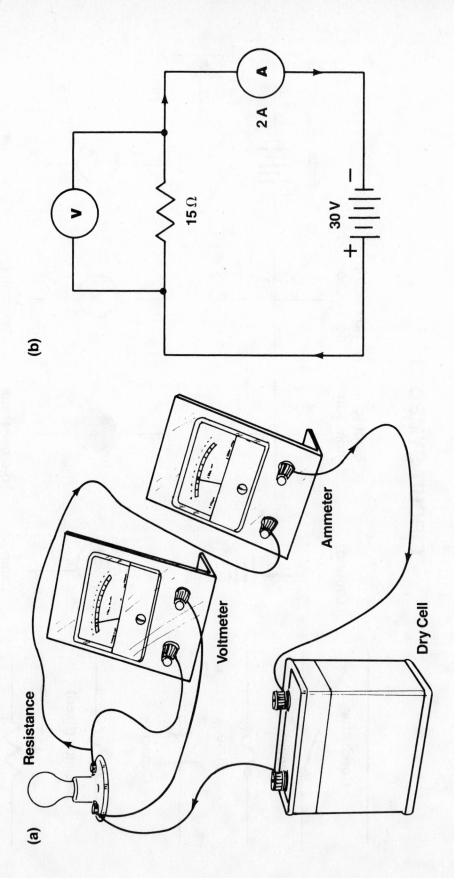

(a)

Resistance

Voltmeter

Ammeter

Dry Cell

(b)

V

15 Ω

A

2 A

30 v

TRANSPARENCY 47   (Use with 28-4)

SERIES AND PARALLEL CIRCUITS

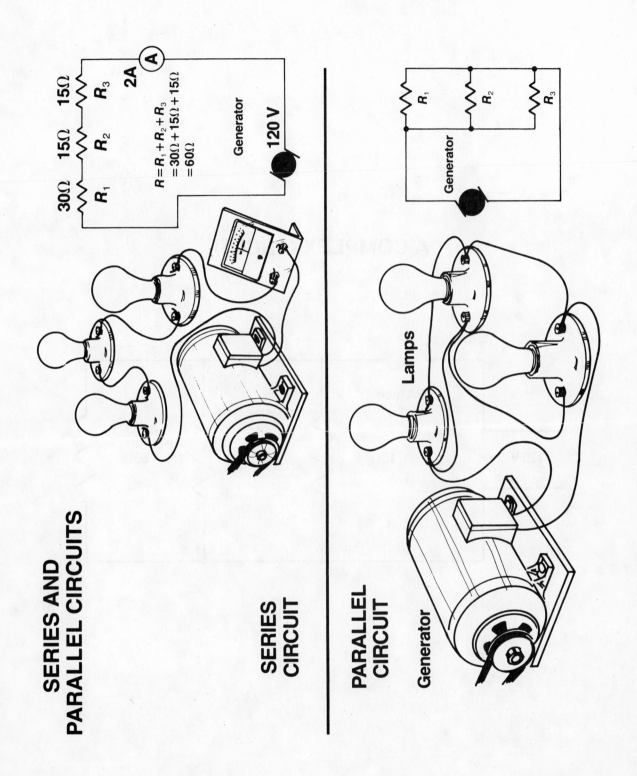

SERIES CIRCUIT

R_1 30Ω R_2 15Ω R_3 15Ω

$$R = R_1 + R_2 + R_3$$
$$= 30\Omega + 15\Omega + 15\Omega$$
$$= 60\Omega$$

2A (A)

Generator

120 V

PARALLEL CIRCUIT

R_1 R_2 R_3

Generator

Lamps

Generator

A COMPLEX CIRCUIT

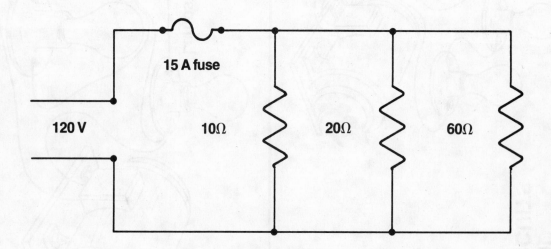

120 V

15 A fuse

10Ω   20Ω   60Ω

TRANSPARENCY 49   (Use with 28-2)
Copyright © by Glencoe/McGraw-Hill.

REVERSING THE CURRENT
THROUGH A SOURCE OF EMF

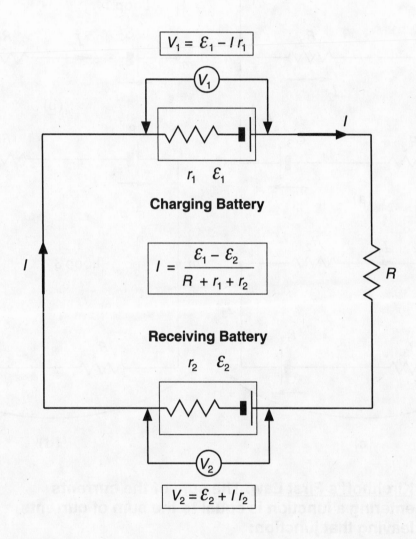

$$V_1 = \mathcal{E}_1 - I\,r_1$$

V_1

$r_1 \quad \mathcal{E}_1$

Charging Battery

$$I = \frac{\mathcal{E}_1 - \mathcal{E}_2}{R + r_1 + r_2}$$

R

Receiving Battery

$r_2 \quad \mathcal{E}_2$

V_2

$$V_2 = \mathcal{E}_2 + I\,r_2$$

I

Reversing the current through a source of emf. The terminal voltage V_1 across the charging source is less than the emf ε_1; but the terminal voltage V_2 is grater than ε_2.

TRANSPARENCY 50   (Use with 28-5)

KIRCHHOFF'S LAWS

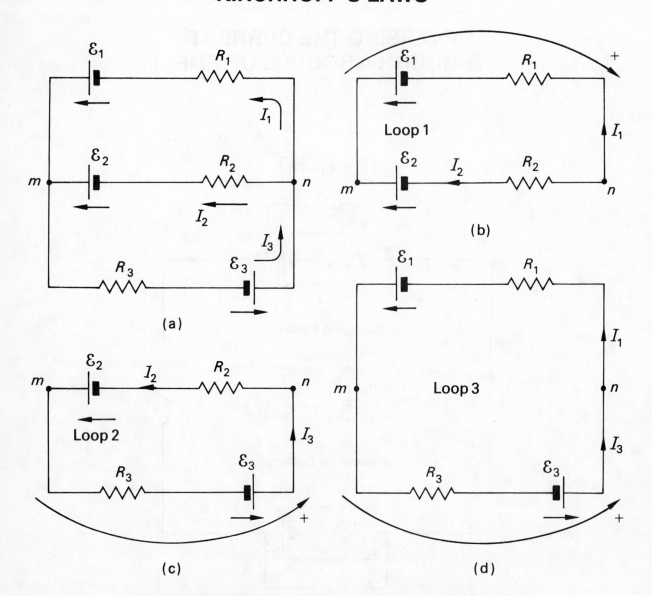

Kirchhoff's First Law: The sum of the currents entering a junction is equal to the sum of currents leaving that junction:

$$\Sigma I_{\text{entering}} = \Sigma I_{\text{leaving}}$$

Kirchhoff's Second Law: The sum of emfs around any closed loop is equal to the sum of all the *IR* drops around that loop:

$$\Sigma \varepsilon = \Sigma IR$$

TRANSPARENCY 51   (Use with 28-6)

MAGNETIC FORCE ON A MOVING CHARGE

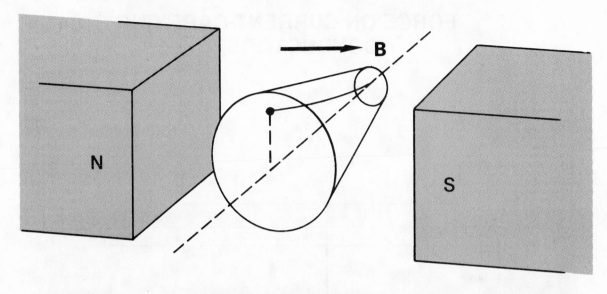

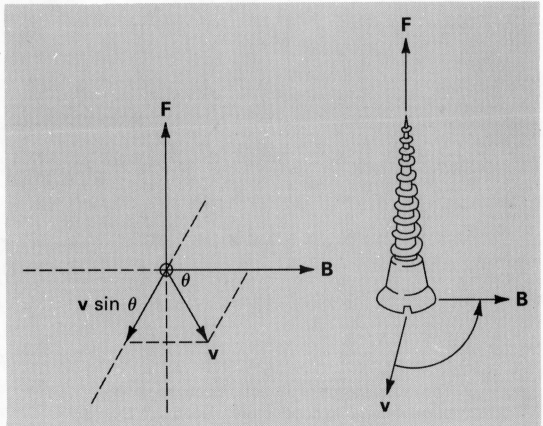

The right-hand screw rule for determining the direction of force *F* on a moving charge *q*.

$$F = qvB \sin \theta$$

FORCE ON CURRENT-CARRYING CONDUCTORS

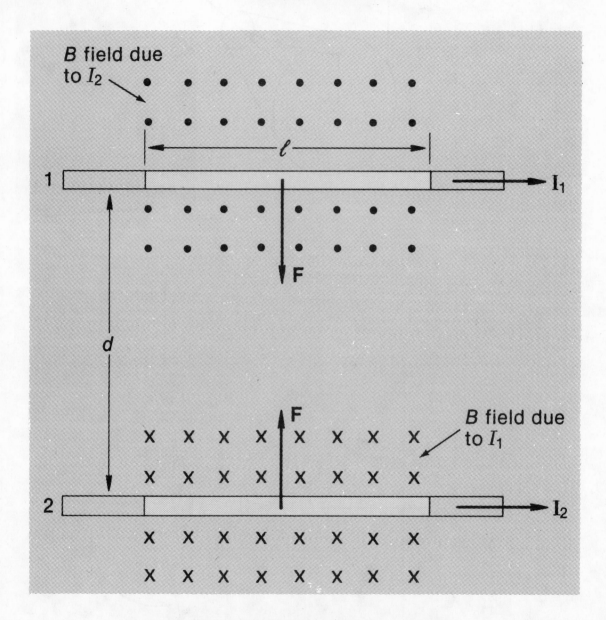

The mutual force of attraction between two current-carrying conductors placed in a *B* field.

$$\frac{F}{l} = \frac{\mu I_1 I_2}{2\pi d}$$

TRANSPARENCY 53 (Use with 29-7)

THE DC VOLTMETER

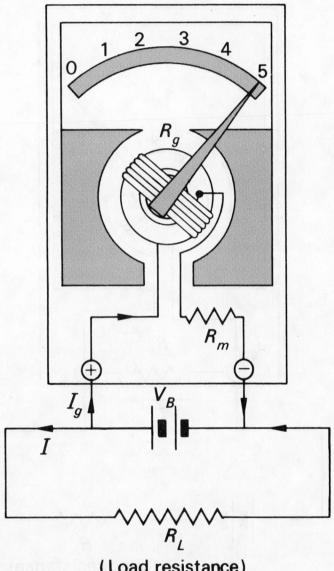

(Load resistance)

A galvanometer used as a voltmeter. It is connected in parallel with the battery. The multiplier resistance is R_m.

$$V_B = IR_L = I_gR_g + I_gR_m$$

$$R_m = \frac{V_B - I_gR_g}{I_g}$$

THE DC AMMETER

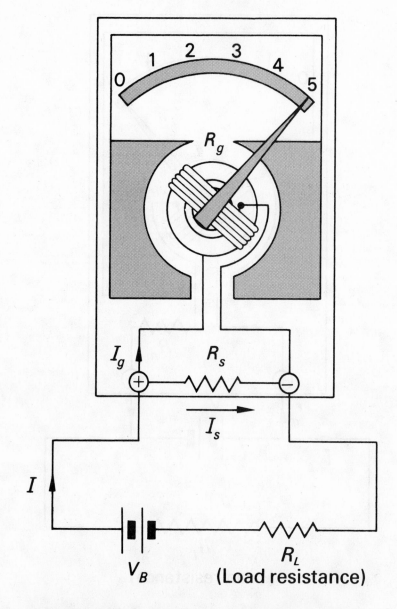

A galvanometer used as an ammeter. It is connected in series with the battery. The parallel shunt resistance is R_s.

$$I_g R_g + I_g R_s \qquad I_s = I - I_g$$
$$R_s = \frac{I_g R_g}{I - I_g}$$

A SERIES-WOUND DC MOTOR

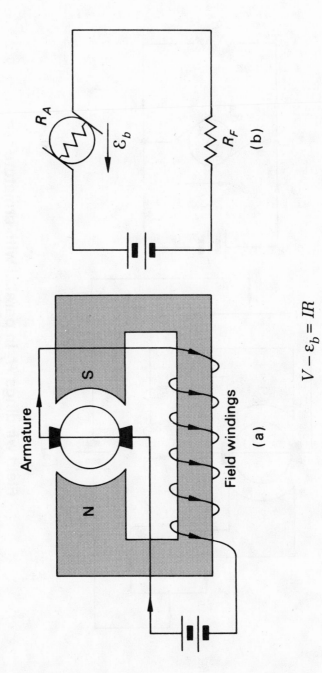

Armature

S

N

Field windings

(a)

R_A

ε_b

R_F

(b)

$V - \varepsilon_b = IR$

A SHUNT-WOUND DC MOTOR

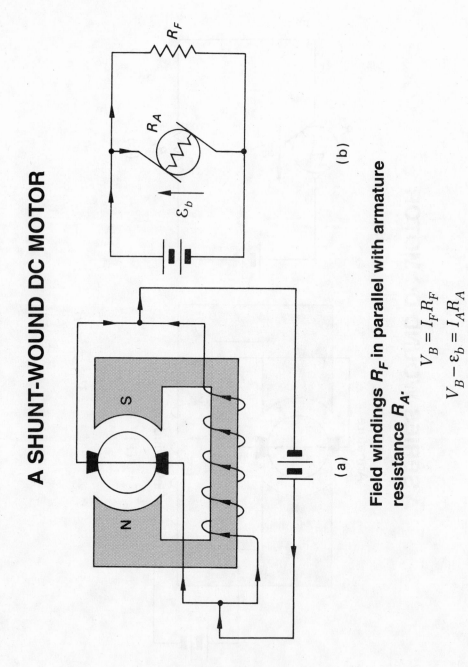

(a)

(b)

Field windings R_F in parallel with armature resistance R_A.

$$V_B = I_F R_F$$
$$V_B - \varepsilon_b = I_A R_A$$

TRANSPARENCY 57 (Use with 30-6)

LENZ'S LAW

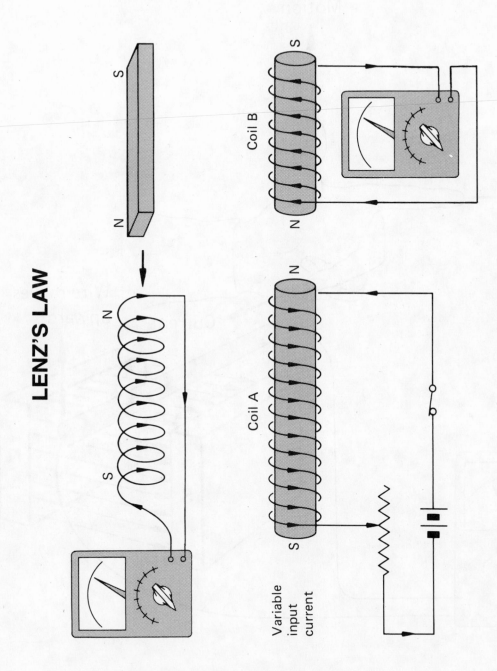

An induced current will flow in such a direction that it will oppose by its magnetic field the motion of the magnetic field that is producing the current.

A RIGHT-HAND RULE FOR CURRENT DIRECTION

Motion

Flux

Current

Wire moves upward

S

N

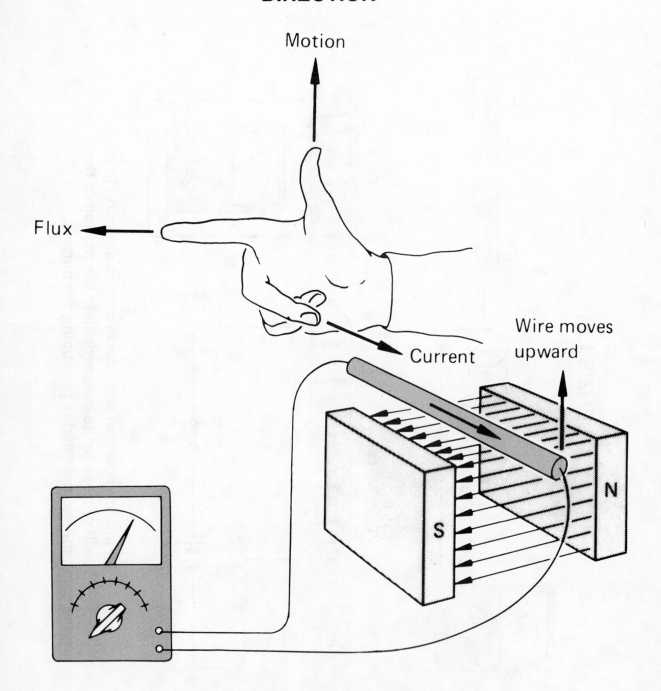

Right-hand rule for determining the direction of induced current.

$$\varepsilon = Blv \sin \theta$$

TRANSPARENCY 59   (Use with 31-3)

THE ELECTRIC MOTOR

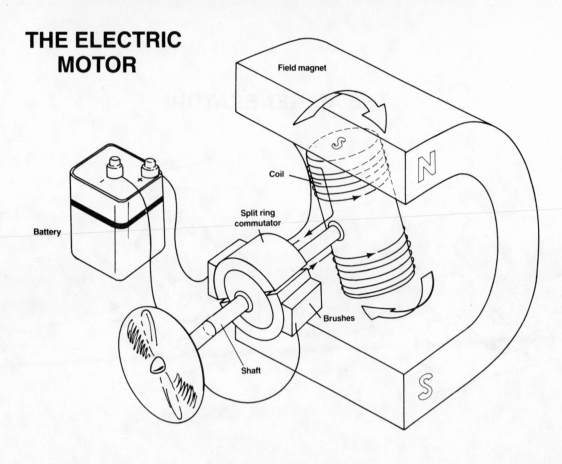

Field magnet

Battery

Coil

Split ring commutator

S

N

Brushes

Shaft

S

DC GENERATOR

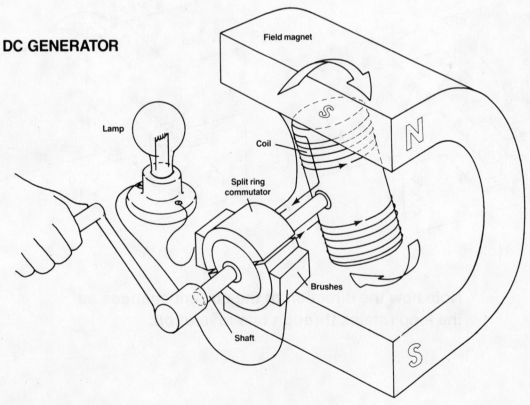

Field magnet

Lamp

Coil

Split ring commutator

S

N

Brushes

Shaft

S

THE AC GENERATOR

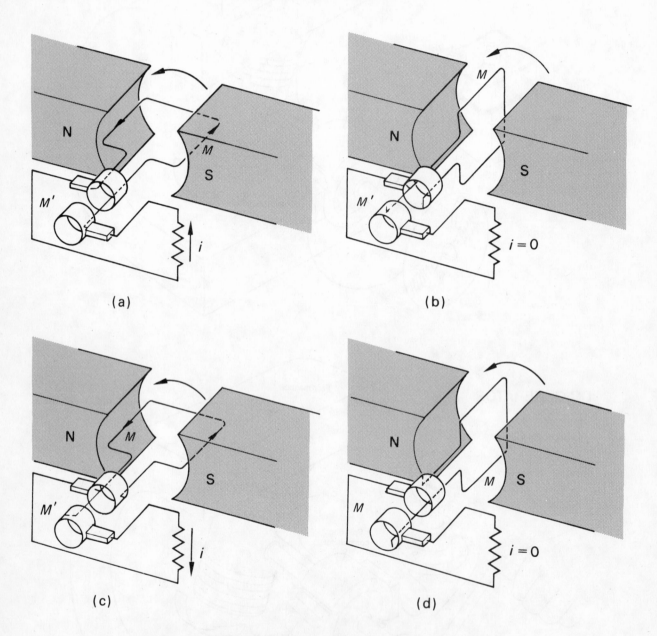

(a)

(b)

(c)

(d)

Note how the direction of the current changes as the loop rotates through one revolution.

PHASE RELATION IN AC CIRCUITS

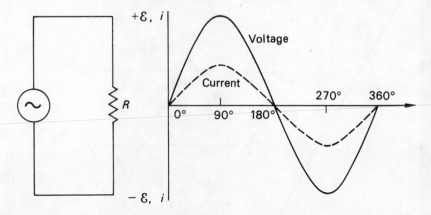

(a) Pure resistance: Current and voltage are in phase.

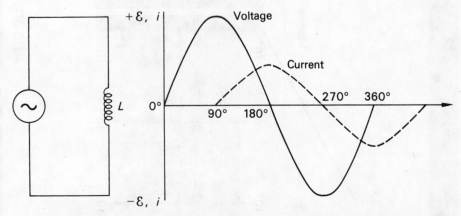

(b) Pure inductance: Voltage LEADS the current by 90°.

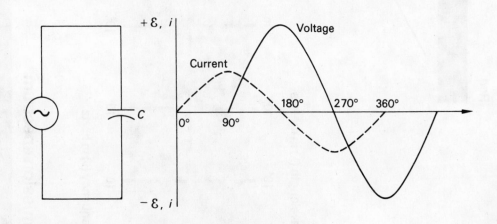

TRANSPARENCY 62   (Use with 32-4)

THE ELECTROMAGNETIC SPECTRUM

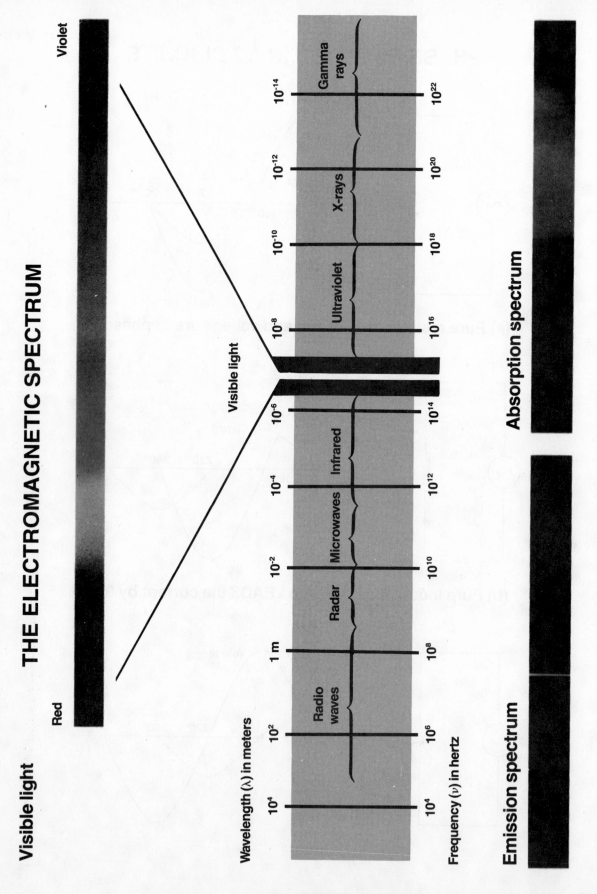

Visible light

Violet

Red

Gamma rays

X-rays

Ultraviolet

Visible light

Infrared

Microwaves

Radar

Radio waves

Wavelength (λ) in meters

10^{-14} 10^{-12} 10^{-10} 10^{-8} 10^{-6} 10^{-4} 10^{-2} 1 m 10^{2} 10^{4}

Frequency (ν) in hertz

10^{22} 10^{20} 10^{18} 10^{16} 10^{14} 10^{12} 10^{10} 10^{8} 10^{6} 10^{4}

Absorption spectrum

Emission spectrum

LIGHT RAYS AND SHADOWS

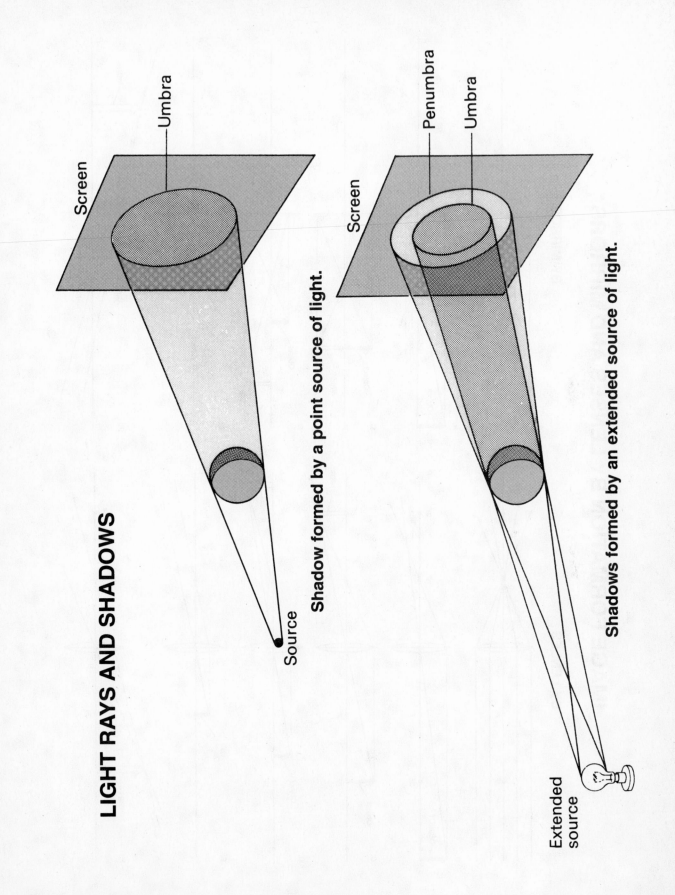

Screen

Umbra

Source

Shadow formed by a point source of light.

Penumbra

Umbra

Screen

Extended source

Shadows formed by an extended source of light.

TRANSPARENCY 64   (Use with 33-6)

401

IMAGE FORMATION BY LENSES AND MIRRORS

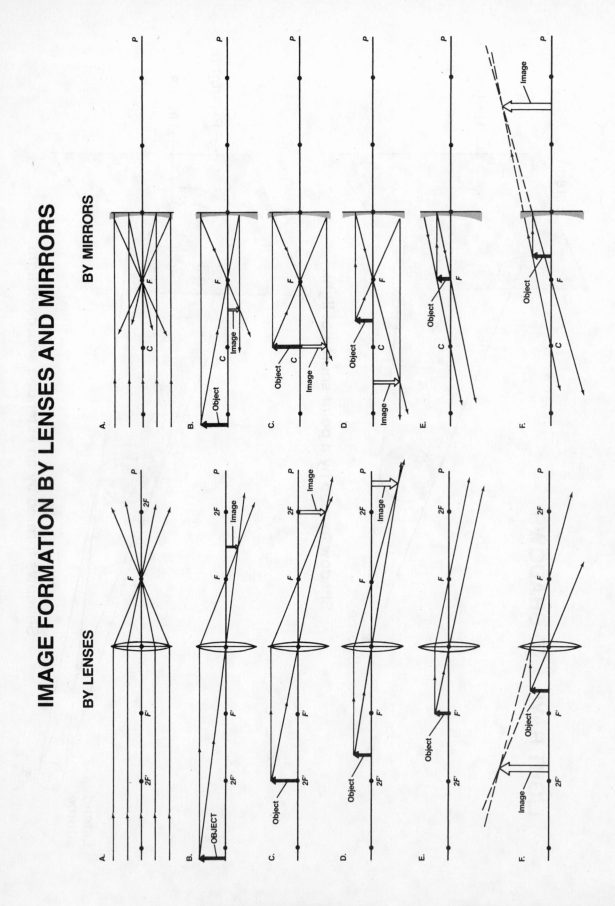

TRANSPARENCY 65   (Use with 34-4 and 36-3)

402

RAY TRACING FOR MIRRORS

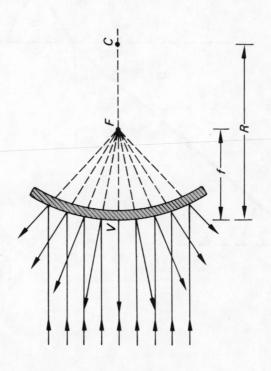

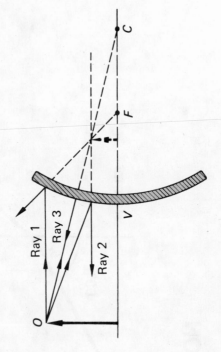

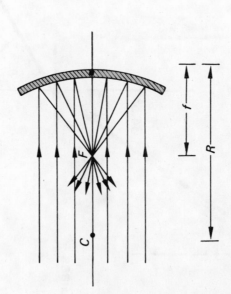

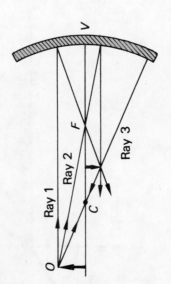

INDEX OF REFRACTION

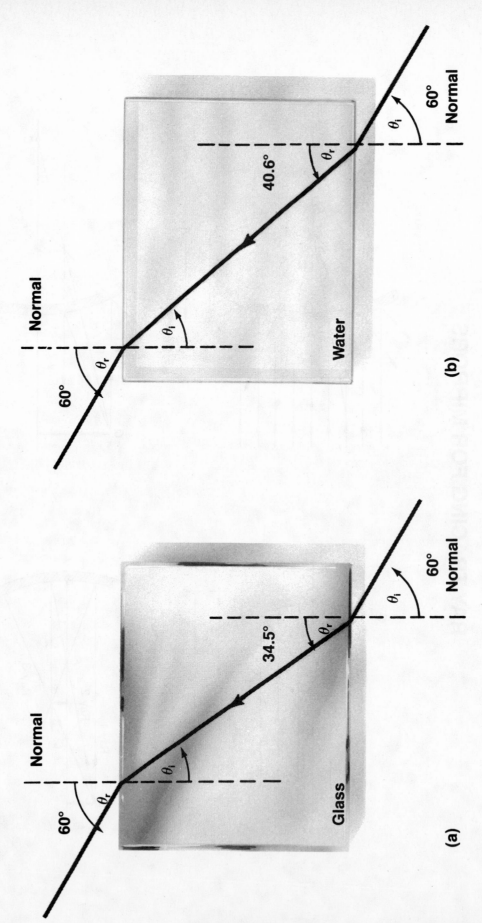

(a) Glass

(b) Water

TRANSPARENCY 67 (Use with 35-1)

SIMPLE LENSES

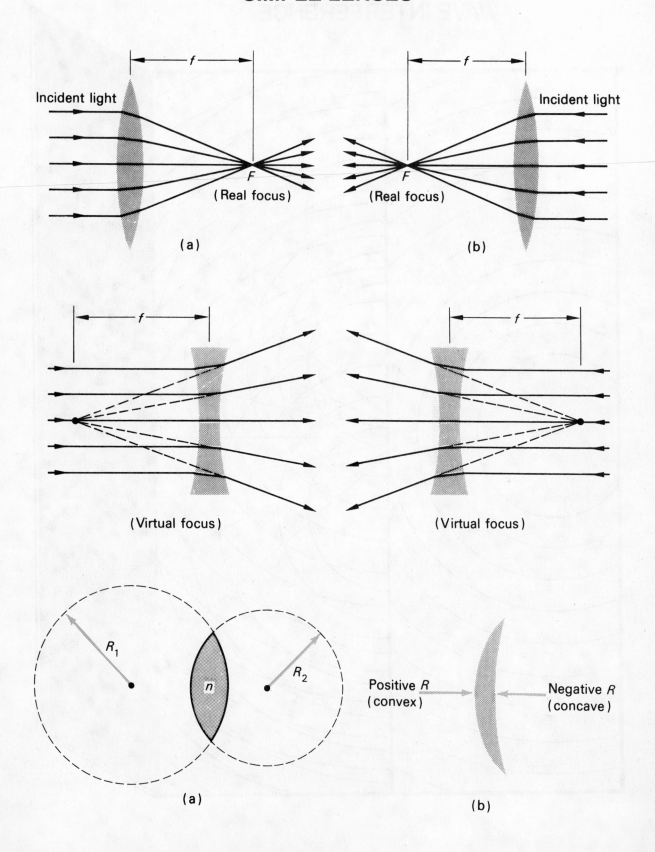

Incident light

f

F
(Real focus)

(a)

Incident light

f

F
(Real focus)

(b)

f

(Virtual focus)

f

(Virtual focus)

R_1

n

R_2

(a)

Positive R
(convex)

Negative R
(concave)

(b)

WAVE INTERFERENCE

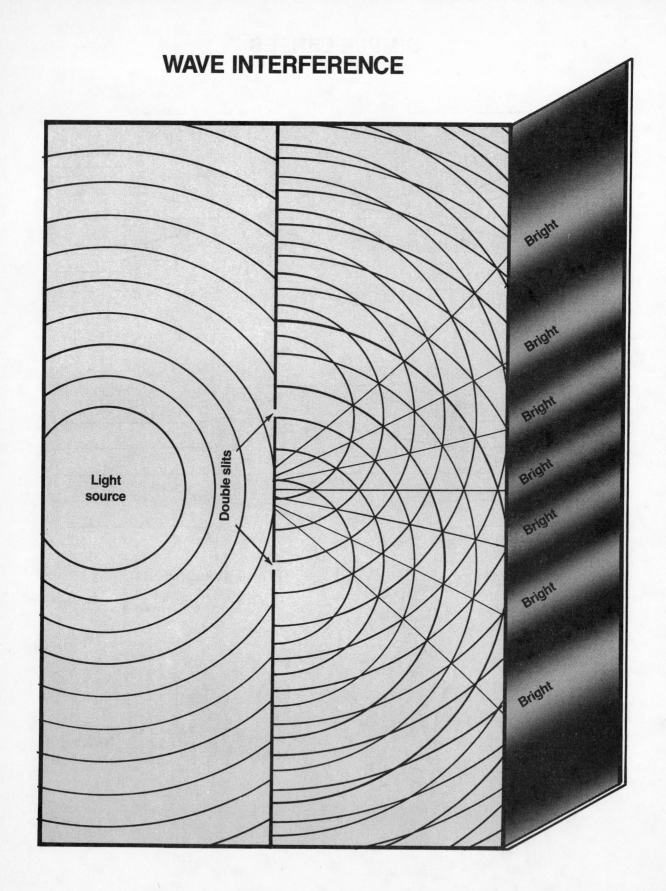

TRANSPARENCY 69   (Use with 37-2)

LIGHT INTERFERENCE IN SLITS

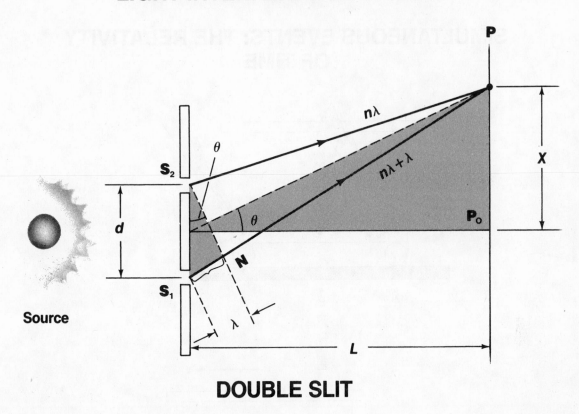

DOUBLE SLIT

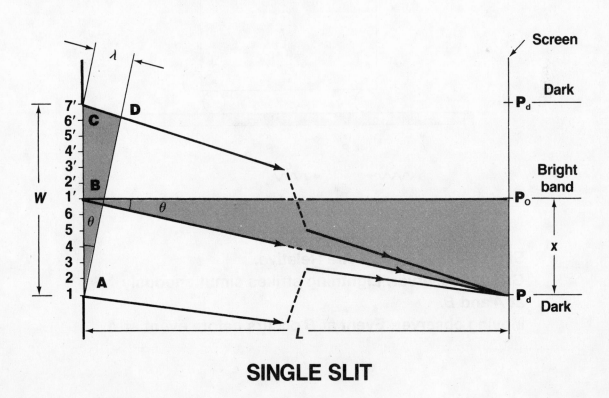

SINGLE SLIT

SIMULTANEOUS EVENTS: THE RELATIVITY OF TIME

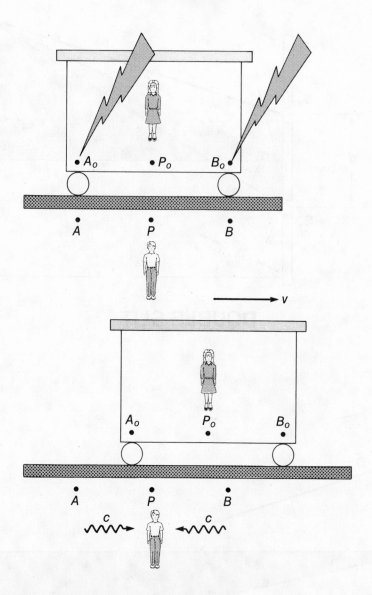

Simultaneous Events Are Relative.
Ground observer: Lightning strikes simultaneously at _A_ and _B_.
Moving observer: Event at _B_ occurs before event at _A_.

TRANSPARENCY 71   (Use with 38-2)

THE RELATIVITY OF LENGTH, MASS, AND TIME

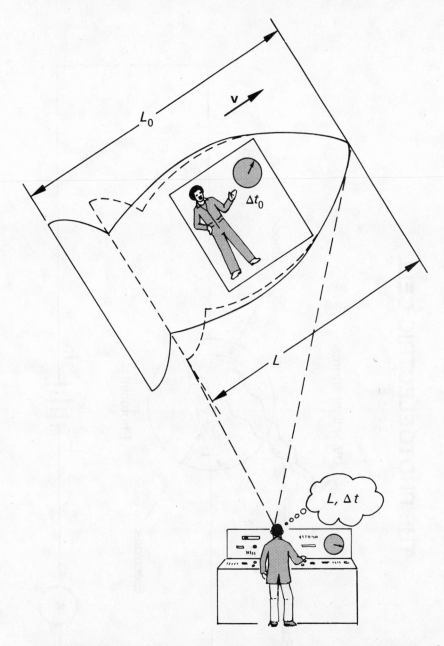

Observers in *relative* motion will measure *time t* and *length L* differently. Here the PROPER frame of reference (L_0 and Δt_0) is aboard the space ship. This is where the actual events take place. The relative measurements are *L* and Δt.

$$\Delta t = \frac{\Delta t_0}{\sqrt{1 - \dfrac{v^2}{c^2}}} \qquad L = L_0 \sqrt{1 - \frac{v^2}{c^2}}$$

TRANSPARENCY 72 (Use with 38-3)

THE PHOTOELECTRIC CELL

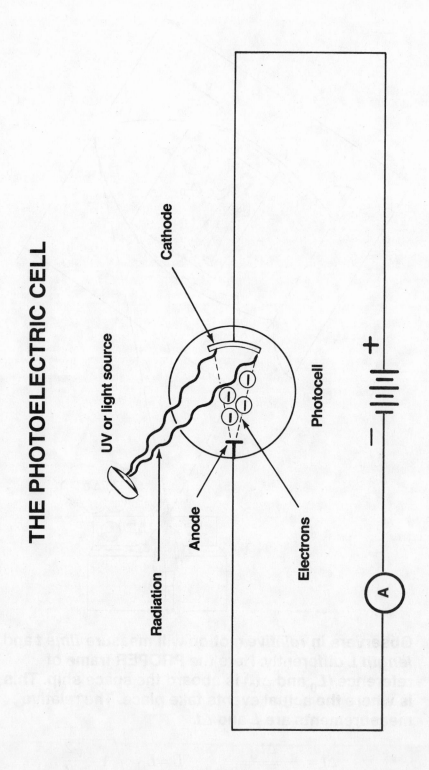

UV or light source

Radiation

Cathode

Anode

Electrons

Photocell

+

−

A

TRANSPARENCY 73   (Use with 38-5)

THE GOLD FOIL EXPERIMENT

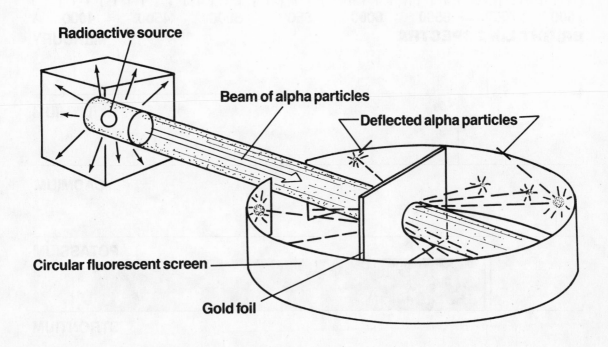

Radioactive source

Beam of alpha particles

Deflected alpha particles

Circular fluorescent screen

Gold foil

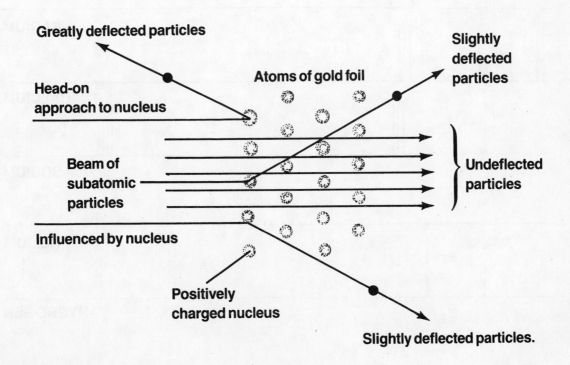

Greatly deflected particles

Slightly deflected particles

Head-on approach to nucleus

Atoms of gold foil

Beam of subatomic particles

Undeflected particles

Influenced by nucleus

Positively charged nucleus

Slightly deflected particles.

EMISSION SPECTRA

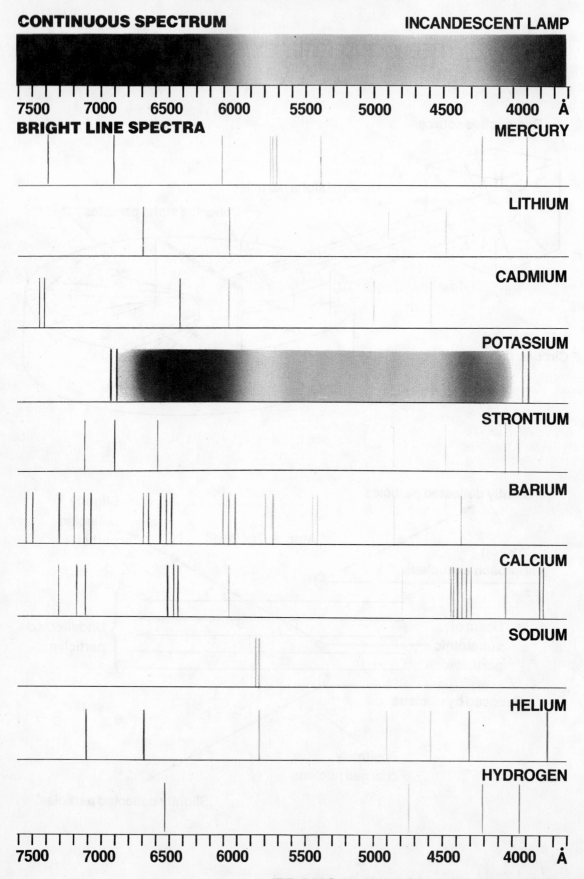

CONTINUOUS SPECTRUM

INCANDESCENT LAMP

7500 7000 6500 6000 5500 5000 4500 4000 Å

BRIGHT LINE SPECTRA

MERCURY

LITHIUM

CADMIUM

POTASSIUM

STRONTIUM

BARIUM

CALCIUM

SODIUM

HELIUM

HYDROGEN

7500 7000 6500 6000 5500 5000 4500 4000 Å

TRANSPARENCY 75   (Use with 39-9)

412

THE ELECTROMAGNETIC SPECTRUM

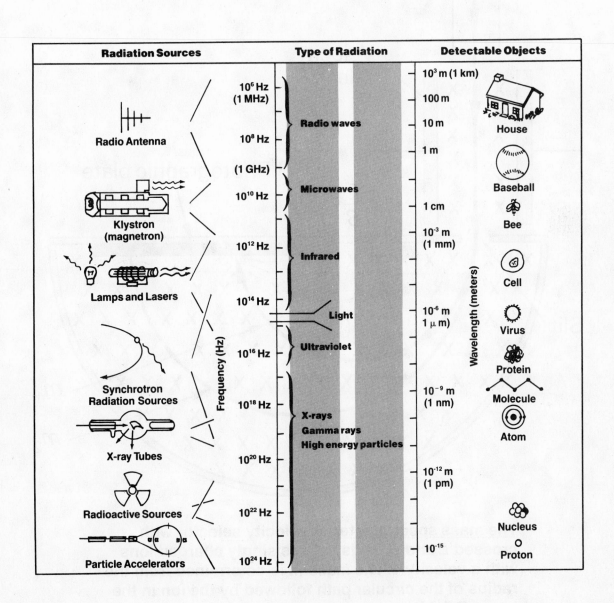

Radiation Sources	Type of Radiation	Detectable Objects

Radio Antenna

10^6 Hz (1 MHz)

10^8 Hz

Radio waves

10^3 m (1 km)

100 m

10 m — House

1 m

Klystron (magnetron)

(1 GHz)

10^{10} Hz

Microwaves

Baseball

1 cm

Bee

Lamps and Lasers

10^{12} Hz

Infrared

10^{-3} m (1 mm)

Cell

10^{14} Hz

Light

10^{-6} m (1 μm)

Virus

Synchrotron Radiation Sources

10^{16} Hz

Ultraviolet

Protein

10^{18} Hz

X-rays

10^{-9} m (1 nm)

Molecule

X-ray Tubes

Gamma rays

High energy particles

Atom

10^{20} Hz

10^{-12} m (1 pm)

Radioactive Sources

10^{22} Hz

Nucleus

Particle Accelerators

10^{24} Hz

10^{-15}

Proton

Frequency (Hz)

Wavelength (meters)

THE MASS SPECTROMETER

Source of positive
ions of various speeds

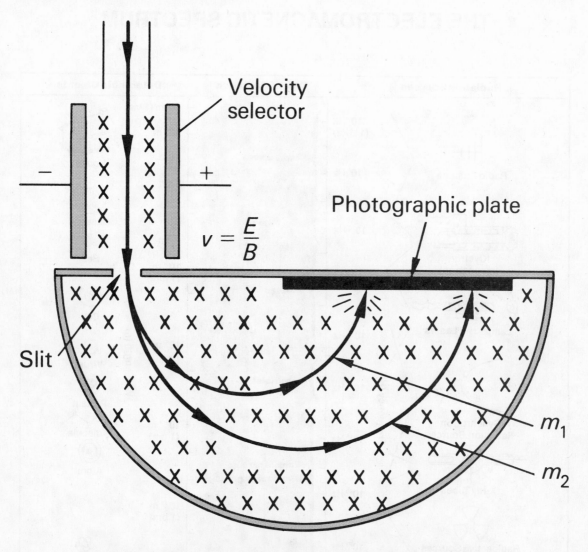

Velocity
selector

Photographic plate

$$v = \frac{E}{B}$$

Slit

m_1

m_2

The mass spectrometer: A velocity selector with
crossed *E* and *B* fields selects singly charged ions
with a velocity *v*. The mass *m* is determined from the
radius of the circular path followed by the ion in the
lower *B* field.

$$\frac{mv^2}{R} = qvB \qquad m = \frac{qBR}{v}$$

TRANSPARENCY 77   (Use with 40-4)

ALPHA, BETA AND GAMMA PARTICLES

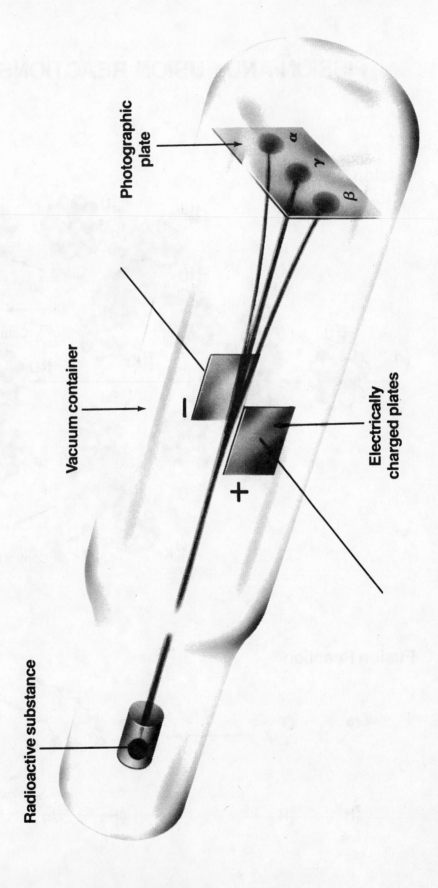

Photographic plate

α

γ

β

Vacuum container

−

+

Electrically charged plates

Radioactive substance

FISSION AND FUSION REACTIONS

Fission Reaction

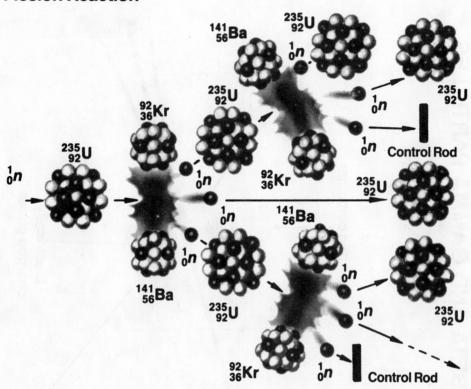

Fusion Reaction

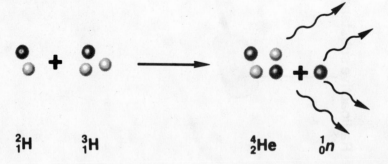

$$^{2}_{1}H \quad ^{3}_{1}H \quad\quad\quad ^{4}_{2}He \quad ^{1}_{0}n$$

TRANSPARENCY 79 (Use with 40-9)